Spectrometric Identification of Organic Compounds

SECOND EDITION

ROBERT M. SILVERSTEIN

RESEARCH FELLOW, STANFORD RESEARCH INSTITUTE

G. CLAYTON BASSLER

SENIOR ORGANIC CHEMIST, STANFORD RESEARCH INSTITUTE

John Wiley & Sons, Inc., New York · London · Sydney

10 9 8 7 6 5

Library of Congress Catalog Card Number: 66-28255
Printed in the United States of America

Preface

We undertake a complete rewriting of the first edition for the following reasons: (1) The numerous deficiencies of the first edition became painfully apparent on further teaching and on using the book for reference in the laboratory. (2) The spectacular recent advances in mass and NMR spectrometry made Chapters 2 and 4 obsolete. (3) We are frankly delighted by the reception accorded our initial effort.

This book is still a teaching manual at the introductory level. However, it also appears to be useful to the practicing chemist as a quick reference source.

In this second edition we have expanded the coverage of each of the four areas of spectrometry, added much new reference material, and added a number of new problems.

The extensive rewriting was made possible by a generous grant from Consolidated Electrodynamics Corporation.

We are indebted to our colleagues at Stanford Research Institute: Mr. W. R. Anderson, Jr. who ran many of the NMR spectra and is responsible for much of the Appendix to the NMR chapter; Miss J. S. Whittick and Mr. F. M. Church who ran many of the mass spectra; and Dr. R. F. Muraca, Director of Analysis and Instrumentation.

The mass spectrometry chapter was read by Dr. W. H. McFadden of the Western Regional Laboratories USDA, the IR chapter by Dr. J. P. Collman of the University of North Carolina, the NMR chapter by Dr. L. J. Durham of Stanford University, and the UV chapter by Dr. R. H. Eastman of Stanford University. Their many helpful comments are deeply appreciated.

We gratefully acknowledge the following sources for permission to use the material indicated.

Consolidated Electrodynamics Corporation: Chapter 2, Fig. 1.

J. H. Beynon, *Mass Spectrometry and its Application to Organic Chemistry*, Elsevier, Amsterdam, 1960: Chapter 2, Appendix A.

Sadtler Research Laboratories, 3314–20 Spring Garden St., Philadelphia, Pa.: The Infrared Spectra Used as Illustrations in the Discussion of Characteristic Group Frequencies.

Varian Associates: Chapter 4, Figs. 19, 20, 21, 22, 23, and 26.

E. A. Becher, *J. Chem. Ed.*, **42,** 591 (1965): Chapter 4, Fig. 27, with permission of the *Journal of Chemical Education*.

J. A. L. Anet, *Can. J. Chem.*, **39,** 2262 (1961): Chapter 4, Fig. 28b, with permission of the *Canadian Journal of Chemistry*.

Perkin-Elmer Corporation: Chapter 3, Fig. 2; Chapter 5, Fig. 5.

A. E. Gillam and E. S. Stern, *An Introduction to Electronic Absorption Spectroscopy in Organic Chemistry*, Edward Arnold, London, 2nd ed., 1957: Chapter 5, Table III.

A. I. Scott, *Interpretation of the Ultraviolet Spectra of Natural Products*, Pergamon Press Ltd., Oxford, England, 1964: Chapter 5, Tables VI and XI.

R. P. Bauman, *Absorption Spectroscopy*, John Wiley and Sons, New York, 1962, and R. A. Friedel and Milton Orchin, *Ultraviolet Spectra of Aromatic Compounds*, John Wiley and Sons, New York, 1951: Chapter 5, Fig. 7.

R. A. Friedel and Milton Orchin, *Ultraviolet Spectra of Aromatic Compounds*, John Wiley and Sons, New York, 1951: Chapter 5, Fig. 8.

As are most authors, we are acutely aware of the burden carried by our wives during manuscript preparation.

Menlo Park, California
January 1967

R. M. Silverstein
G. C. Bassler

Preface to First Edition

During the past several years, we have been engaged in isolating small amounts of organic compounds from complex mixtures and identifying these compounds spectrometrically.

At the suggestion of Dr. A. J. Castro of San Jose State College, we developed a one unit course entitled "Spectrometric Identification of Organic Compounds," and presented it to a class of graduate students and industrial chemists during the 1962 spring semester. This book has evolved largely from the material gathered for the course and bears the same title as the course.

We should first like to acknowledge the financial support we received from two sources: The Perkin-Elmer Corporation and Stanford Research Institute.

A large debt of gratitude is owed to our colleagues at Stanford Research Institute. We have taken advantage of the generosity of too many of them to list them individually, but we should like to thank Dr. S. A. Fuqua, in particular, for many helpful discussions of NMR spectrometry. We wish to acknowledge also the cooperation at the management level, of Dr. C. M. Himel, chairman of the Organic Research Department, and Dr. D. M. Coulson, chairman of the Analytical Research Department.

Varian Associates contributed the time and talents of its NMR Applications Laboratory. We are indebted to Mr. N. S. Bhacca, Mr. L. F. Johnson, and Dr. J. N. Shoolery for the NMR spectra and for their generous help with points of interpretation.

The invitation to teach at San Jose State College was extended by Dr. Bert. M. Morris, head of the Department of Chemistry, who kindly arranged the administrative details.

The bulk of the manuscript was read by Dr. R. H. Eastman of Stanford University whose comments were most helpful and are deeply appreciated.

Finally, we want to thank our wives. As a test of a wife's patience, there are few things to compare with an author in the throes of composition. Our wives not only endured, they also encouraged, assisted, and inspired.

Menlo Park, California
April 1963

R. M. Silverstein
G. C. Bassler

Contents

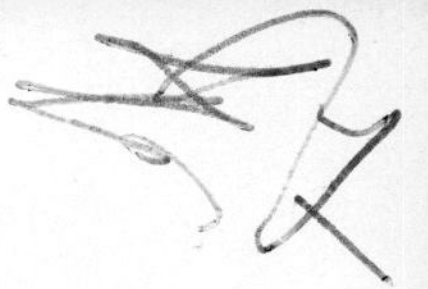

CHAPTER 1

Introduction

Our sole purpose in writing this book is to teach the organic chemist how to identify organic compounds from the complementary information afforded by four spectra: mass, infrared, nuclear magnetic resonance, and ultraviolet. Essentially, the molecule in question is subjected to four energy probes, and the molecule's responses are recorded as spectra.

The small amounts of pure compounds that can be isolated from complex mixtures by gas chromatography or thin-layer chromatography present a challenge to the chemist concerned with identification and structure elucidation of organic compounds. These techniques have two characteristics: they are rapid, and they are most effective in milligram and microgram quantities. There is neither enough time nor enough material to accommodate the classical manipulations involving sodium fusion, boiling point, refractive index, solubility tests, functional group tests, derivative preparation, mixture melting points, combustion analysis, molecular weight, and degradation with similar manipulations of the degradation products.

Our goal in this book is a rather modest level of sophistication and expertise in each of the four areas of spectrometry. Even this level will permit solution of a gratifying number of identification problems with *no history and no other chemical or physical data.* Of course, in practice other information is usually available: the sample source, details of isolation, a synthesis sequence, or information on analogous material. Often complex molecules can be identified because partial structures are known and specific questions can be formulated; the process is more confirmation than identification. In practice, however, difficulties arise in physical handling of minute amounts of compound: trapping, elution from adsorbents, solvent removal, prevention of contamination, and decomposition of unstable compounds. Water, air, stopcock greases, solvent impurities, and plasticizers have frustrated many investigations. The quality of spectra obtained in practice is usually inferior to that presented here.

For pedagogical reasons, we deal only with pure organic compounds. *Pure* in this context is a relative term, and all we can say is: the purer, the better. Probably the ultimate practical criterion of purity (for a sufficiently volatile compound) is gas chromatographic homogeneity on two capillary columns, one containing a nonpolar substrate, the other a polar. Various forms of liquid-phase chromatography (adsorption and liquid–liquid columns, paper, thin layer) are applicable to relatively nonvolatile compounds. The spectra presented in this book were obtained on samples that were purified by recrystallization to constant melting point, or by gas chromatography.

In many cases, identification can be made on a fraction of a milligram, or even on several micrograms, of sample. Identification on the milligram scale is routine. Of course, not all molecules yield so easily. Chemical manipulations may be necessary. But the information obtained from the four spectra will permit intelligent selection of chemical treatment, and the energy probe methodology can be applied to the resulting products.

There are limitations to the methodology we espouse. A mass spectrum is dependent on a degree of volatility and thermal stability. However, mass spectra have been obtained on many high molecular weight compounds—steroids, terpenoids, peptides, polysaccharides, and alkaloids—by inserting the sample very close to the ionizing beam. Solubility is a limiting factor in nuclear magnetic resonance spectrometry. However, the availability of many deuterated solvents and the development of the CAT make it possible to obtain adequate spectra in dilute solutions.

The problem of cost of necessary instrumentation is raised, and answered by pointing to the amazing evolution of commercial instruments. The time saved, the smaller samples required, and the information made available far overbalance the cost. Identifications are frequently made on the basis of several hours of a technician's and analyst's time. Under a classical regime, much larger samples and several days or even weeks of a skilled analyst's time would probably be necessary. Infrared and ultraviolet spectrometers have been developed beyond the stage of reliable instruments in the hands of a trained technician. They are now cheap, rugged, and simple enough to be used as a bench tool by the organic chemist. A nuclear magnetic resonance spectrometer is still a fairly expensive, complicated instrument that requires the services of a trained technician; but even here, the trend is toward use by relatively unskilled personnel (even by organic chemists) backed by a network of factory-trained servicemen.

Almost from its inception, the utility of nuclear magnetic resonance spectrometry to the organic chemist has been evident. Mass spectrometry, however, has had a somewhat different history. Developed by the physicist and utilized extensively by the petroleum chemist, it has been ignored almost completely by the organic chemist concerned with identification and structure determination. Until a few years ago, there were only a few laboratories in which the application of mass spectrometry to these problems was appreciated. And yet, as we show, it is an extremely powerful tool. It is still an expensive, complex instrument that requires considerable skill in its use and maintenance. An inexpensive rugged instrument would find a ready market.

We spend very little time on instrumentation per se for three reasons: It is not requisite to our goal; we are not qualified; and excellent treatises are available. The four chapters on spectrometry are designed to give the analyst an appreciation of the potentialities of each technique as applied to the identification of organic compounds. The rest of the book consists of selected spectra. These mass, infrared, nuclear magnetic resonance, and ultraviolet spectra are presented as sets, each set representing a compound. These are translated, as exercises, into the chemical structure they represent in twenty cases. Ten sets of spectra are identified only by a Beilstein reference. Twenty-one additional sets are presented without identification. Aside from practical applications, the considerations involved in translating spectra into organic compounds lead to an appreciation of modern concepts of structural organic chemistry.

If we have been judicious in our selection of spectra, they should serve as useful reference material for teachers and for chemists in industry. In one form or another, such material should become part of the training of every organic chemist.

References

The following books deal, at the introductory level, with the utilization of several aspects of spectrometry for the organic chemist. Additional references are cited in each chapter.

Flett, M. St. C., *Physical Aids to the Organic Chemist*, Elsevier, Amsterdam, 1962.

Schwarz, J. C. P., Ed., *Physical Methods in Organic Chemistry*, Oliver and Boyd, Edinburgh, 1964.

Brand, J. C. D., and G. Eglinton, *Applications of Spectroscopy to Organic Chemistry*, Oldbourne Press, London, 1965.

Dyer, John R., *Applications of Absorption Spectroscopy of Organic Compounds*, Prentice-Hall, Englewood Cliffs, N.J., 1965.

Cairns, T., *Spectroscopic Problems in Organic Chemistry*, Heyden and Sons, London, 1964.

Baker, A. J., and T. Cairns, *Spectroscopic Techniques in Organic Chemistry*, Heyden and Sons, London, 1965.

Freeman, S. K., Ed., *Interpretive Spectroscopy*, Reinhold, New York, 1965.

Mathieson, D. W., *Interpretation of Organic Spectra*, Academic Press, New York, 1965.

Nachod, F. C., and W. D. Phillips, Eds., *Determination of Organic Structures by Physical Methods*, Vol. 2, Academic Press, New York, 1962.

Bentley, K. W., Ed., *Elucidation of Structure by Physical and Chemical Methods*, Vol. XI, Part 1, Interscience Publishers, New York, 1963.

CHAPTER 2

Mass Spectrometry

I. INTRODUCTION

A mass spectrometer bombards a substance under investigation with an electron beam and quantitatively records the result as a spectrum of positive ion fragments. This record is a mass spectrum. Separation of the positive ion fragments is on the basis of mass (strictly, mass/charge, but the majority of ions are singly charged). How this is accomplished will be sketched in just sufficient detail to impart some appreciation to the organic chemist for the potentialities of mass spectrometry as applied to compound identification.

To supplement the material in this chapter, the reader is urged to read Biemann's text[1] first, then the text by Budzikiewicz, Djerassi, and Williams.[2] For a more thorough coverage of the broad field of mass spectrometry, the monumental treatise by Beynon[3] is recommended. Several other useful general texts, and chapters published since 1959 are listed.[4–10,10a,10b]

The most extensive catalog of mass spectra is that available from the American Petroleum Institute.[11] This catalog and the spectra in the files of ASTM Committee E-14, and of the Manufacturing Chemists Association have been indexed.[12]

Despite their long history of development, mass spectrometers are hardly commonplace pieces of laboratory equipment. They are still characterized by high cost and the need for highly skilled technicians for operation and maintenance. Despite these characteristics, their routine use in the petroleum industry is well established, and their applications in many other areas are increasing; the organic chemist, in particular, is rapidly becoming aware of their possibilities. The following quotation,[2] written in 1963, is notable:

"Three years ago one had to search far and wide in the organic chemical literature to find examples of its use in structural problems. Three years hence it will be difficult to open a journal dealing with organic chemistry without encountering multiple applications of mass spectrometry. No physical tool in organic chemistry—not even infrared spectrometry—is so easily appreciated by the average organic chemist and, once used, none is so difficult to do without."

II. INSTRUMENTATION

A brief discussion of commercially available instruments has been given by Kiser.[10]

The minimum instrumental requirement for the organic chemist is the ability to record the molecular weight of the compound under examination to the nearest whole number. Thus the recording should show a peak at, say, mass 400 which is distinguishable from a peak at mass 399, and at mass 401. In order to select possible molecular formulas by measuring isotope peak intensities (see Section IV), adjacent peaks must be quite cleanly separated. Arbitrarily, a valley between two adjacent peaks should not be more than about 10% of the height of the larger peak. This latter degree of resolution is termed "unit" resolution, and can be obtained up to about mass 500 on several single-focusing (magnetic-focusing) instruments.*

The introduction of an electrostatic field ahead of the magnetic field (double-focusing) permits resolution such that a molecular weight can be obtained to three or four decimal places.[1,3–7] However, the cost (about $120,000) and complexity make this instrument available to relatively few laboratories at this time. Use of other types of spectrometers such as the time-of-flight, or the quadrupole, is limited at this time to obtaining the molecular weight and fragmentation pattern of compounds of moderate molecular weight; however, new developments continue to upgrade these instruments. Varian Associates has recently announced the development of a "double-focusing cycloidal" spectrometer.

* Consolidated Electrodynamics Corporation, Pasadena, Calif., U.S.A. Nuclide Corporation, State College, Pa., U.S.A. Associated Electrical Industries, Ltd., Manchester, England. Atlas Mess-und Analysen Technik, G.m.b.H., Bremen, Germany (distributor: Applied Physics Corp., Monrovia, Calif., U.S.A.). Hitachi Ltd., Tokyo, Japan (distributor: Perkin-Elmer Corp., Norwalk, Conn., U.S.A.).

A schematic diagram of a typical 180° single-focusing mass spectrometer is shown in Figure 1. There are five component parts.

1. Sample handling system. This consists of a device for introducing the sample, a micromanometer for determining the amount of sample introduced, a device (molecular leak) for metering the sample to the ionization chamber, and a pumping system. Introduction of gases is usually a simple matter of transfer from a gas bulb into the metering volume, thence to the ionizing chamber. Liquids are introduced with various break-off devices, by touching a micropipette to a sintered glass disc or an orifice under mercury or gallium, or simply by hypodermic needle injection through a silicone rubber dam or serum cap. A bulb containing the sample may be pumped out under Dry Ice, then warmed to vaporize the sample into the inlet system. Heated inlet systems are used for less volatile liquids and for solids. Insertion of the sample directly into the ionization chamber further extends the limitations imposed by lack of volatility and of thermal stability. Reproducible breakdown patterns have been obtained on high molecular weight terpenoids, steroids, polysaccharides, peptides, and alkaloids. Even with these special techniques, a compound must be stable at a temperature at which its vapor pressure is of the order of 10^{-7} to 10^{-6} Torr. For routine work, using a molecular leak, a vapor pressure of about 10^{-1} to 10^{-3} Torr. is desired. Sample sizes for liquids and solids range from several milligrams to less than a microgram, depending on the method of introduction and the detector.

2. Ionization and accelerating chambers. The gas stream from the molecular leak enters the ionization chamber (operated at a pressure of about 10^{-6} to 10^{-5} Torr.) in which it is bombarded at right angles by an electron beam emitted from a hot filament. The positive ions, produced by interaction with the electron beam, are forced through the first accelerating slit by a small electrostatic field between the repellers and the first accelerating slit. A strong electrostatic field between the first and second accelerating slits accelerates the ions to their final velocities. Additional focusing of the ion beam is provided between the accelerating slits. To obtain a spectrum, either the magnetic field applied to the analyzer tube (Figure 1) or the accelerating voltage between the first and second ion slits is varied. Thus, the ions are successively focused at the collector slit as a function of mass (strictly mass/charge). In modern instruments, a scan from mass 12 to mass 500 may be performed in 1 to 4 minutes. However, scan speeds of a few seconds have been used to obtain spectra of gas chromatography fractions.

3. Analyzer tube and magnet. The analyzer tube is an evacuated (10^{-7} to 10^{-8} Torr.), curved (in Figure 1,

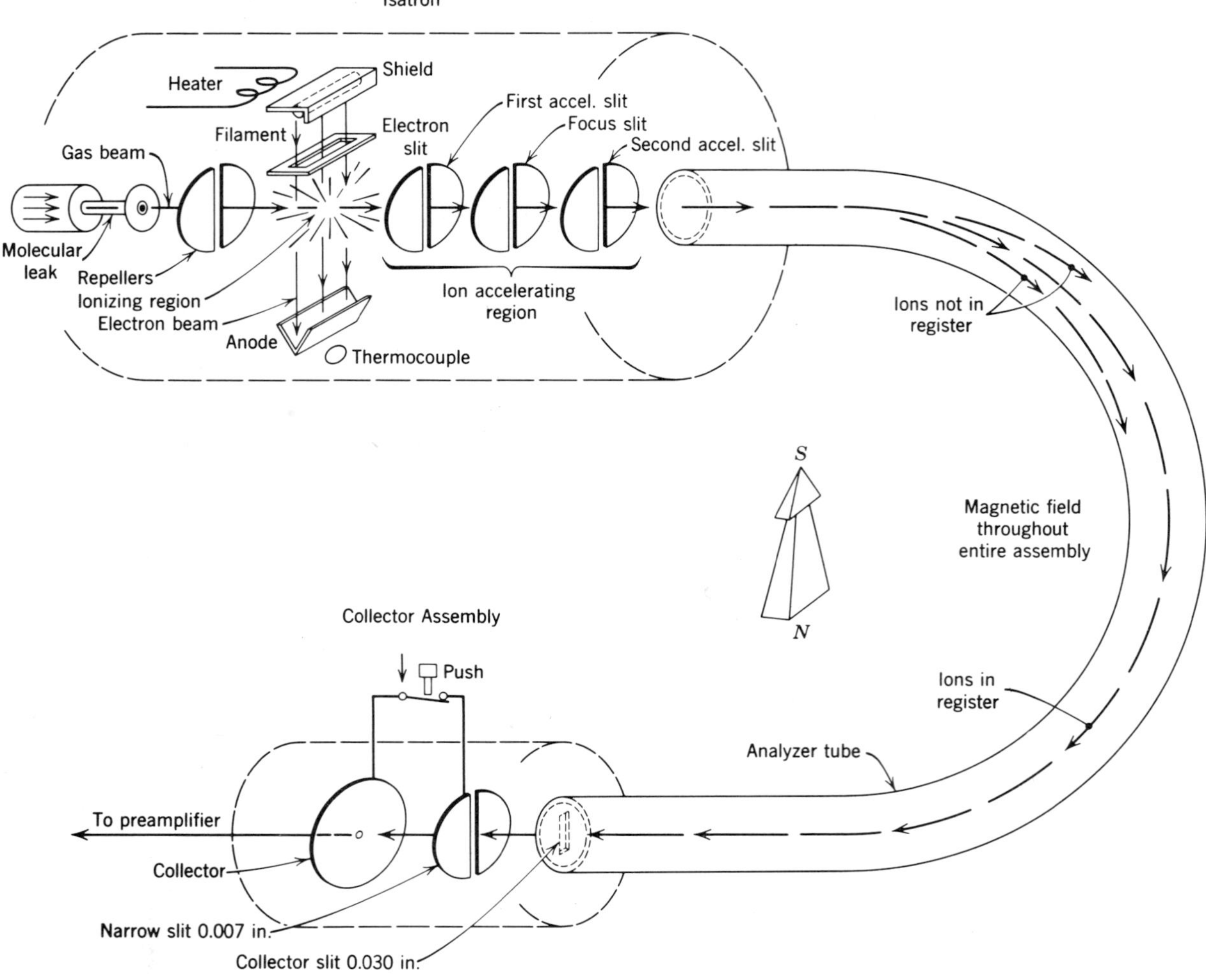

Fig. 1. Schematic diagram of CEC model 21-103 Mass Spectrometer. The magnetic field is perpendicular to the page.

a 180° curve), metal tube through which the ion beam passes from ion source to collector. The magnetic pole pieces (electromagnets are usually used for the larger instruments) are mounted perpendicular to the plane of the diagram (Figure 1). The main requirement is a uniform, stable magnetic field.

4. *Ion collector and amplifier*. A typical ion collector consists of one or more collimating slits and a Faraday cylinder; the ion beam impinges axially into the collector, and the signal is amplified by a vacuum-tube electrometer or an electron multiplier.

5. *Recorder*. A widely used recorder employs five separate galvanometers that record simultaneously on photographic paper (ultraviolet recording paper, which does not require wet development, is also common). Figure 2a presents a spectrum traced by a five-element galvanometer system at sensitivity levels decreasing from top to bottom in the ratios of 1:3:10:30:100. Peak heights from the base line are read on the most sensitive trace remaining on scale and are multiplied by the appropriate sensitivity factor. Peak heights are proportional to the number of ions of each mass. The recorder trace can be presented as a table or a graph (Figures 2b and c). Note several half-mass peaks in the tracing; these represent odd-numbered masses that carry a double charge. A broad, weak, "metastable" peak can be seen between m/e 90 and 91 (see p. 9).

Assignment of mass to the peaks of the recorder tracing can be a problem at the high mass end of the scan. The common practice is to start at the low mass end of the scan, which can be accurately set, and count the peaks to the last recorded peak. This is generally feasible because the most sensitive galvanometer will record a slight ion current at each mass unit. Sometimes the peaks at the high end of the spectrum may be widely spaced, and the background trace indistinct; in this case, a calibration compound may be added to the sample. Some instruments are equipped with automatic mass markers, but the usual experience is that these are not reliable where they are most needed—at the high mass

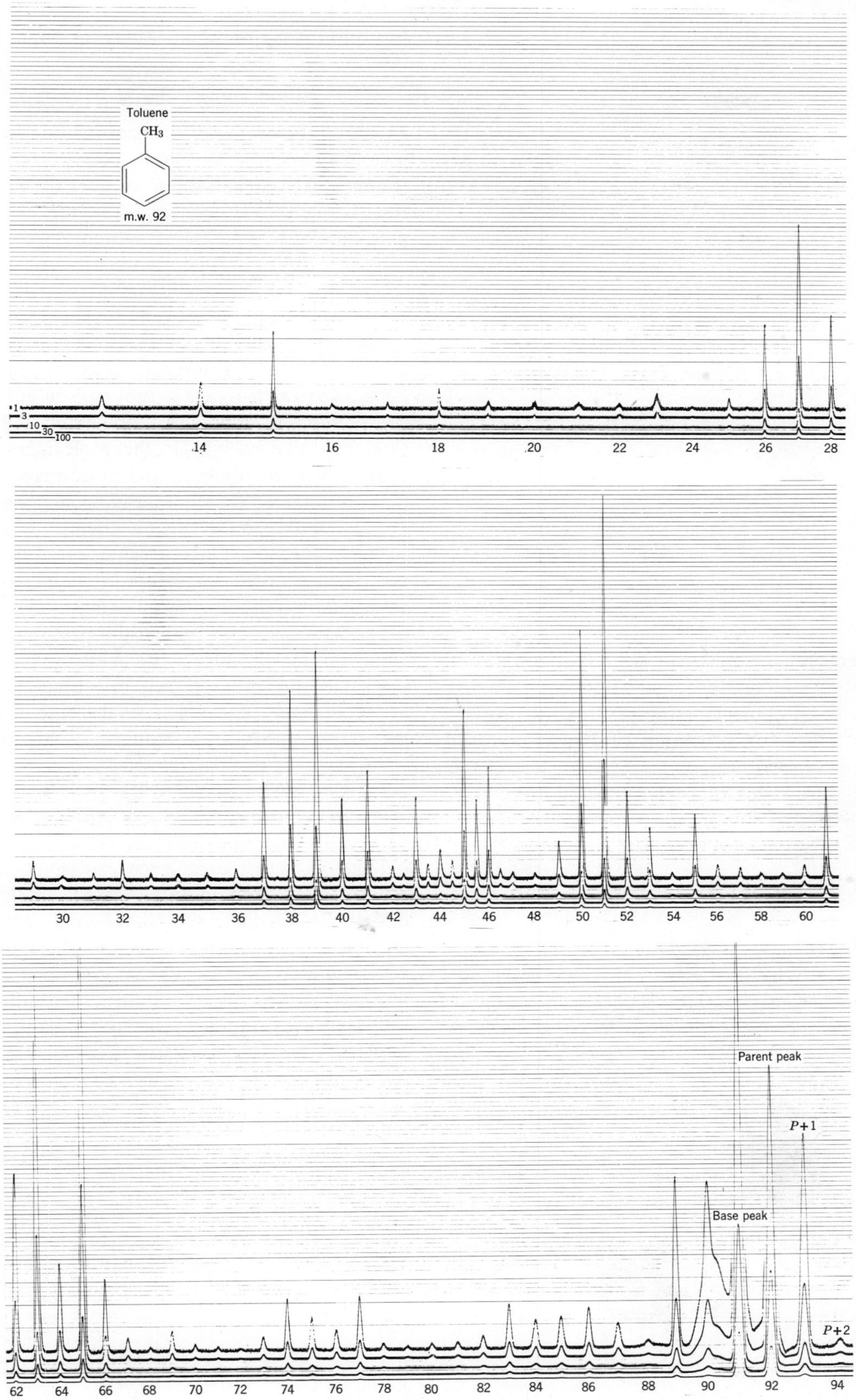

Fig. 2a. Mass spectrum traced by a five-element galvanometer.

Toluene

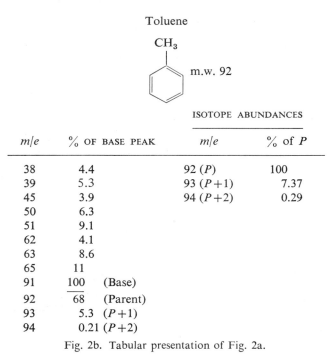

CH_3

m.w. 92

m/e	% OF BASE PEAK		ISOTOPE ABUNDANCES m/e	% of P
38	4.4		92 (P)	100
39	5.3		93 ($P+1$)	7.37
45	3.9		94 ($P+2$)	0.29
50	6.3			
51	9.1			
62	4.1			
63	8.6			
65	11			
91	100	(Base)		
92	68	(Parent)		
93	5.3	($P+1$)		
94	0.21	($P+2$)		

Fig. 2b. Tabular presentation of Fig. 2a.

end of the spectrum. A mass digitizer that prints out the mass number and relative intensities is a valuable auxiliary piece of equipment. However, a slight maladjustment may result in loss or gain of a full mass unit in a scan; this can be disastrous. At the present state of the art, it is well to check the digitizer print-out against the galvanometer trace.

III. THE MASS SPECTRUM

Mass spectra are routinely obtained at an electron beam energy of 70 electron volts. The simplest event that occurs is removal of a single electron from the molecule in the gas phase by an electron of the electron beam to form a molecular (parent) ion. This is a radical ion.

$$R{:}R' \xrightarrow{e} R\overset{+}{\cdot}R' + 2e$$

Many of these parent ions disintegrate in 10^{-10} to 10^{-8} second to give, in the simplest case, a positively charged fragment and a radical. A number of fragment ions are thus formed, and each of these can cleave in turn to give smaller fragments.

$$R\overset{+}{\cdot}R' \rightarrow \overset{+}{R} + \cdot R'$$

If some of the parent ions remain intact long enough (about 10^{-6} seconds) to reach the detector, we see a parent peak. It is important to recognize the parent peak because this gives the molecular weight of the compound. It should be emphasized at this point that this molecular weight is the molecular weight to the nearest whole number, and not merely the approximation obtained by all other molecular weight determinations familiar to the organic chemist.

A mass spectrum is a presentation of the masses of the positively charged fragments (including the parent ion) versus their relative concentrations. The most intense peak in the spectrum, called the base peak, is assigned a value of 100%, and the intensities (height × sensitivity factor) of the other peaks, including the parent peak, are reported as percentages of the base peak. Of course, the parent peak may sometimes be the base peak. In Figure 2a, the parent peak is m/e 92, and the base peak is m/e 91.

A tabular or graphic presentation of a spectrum may be used. A graph has the advantage of presenting patterns that, with experience, can be quickly recognized. However, a graph must be drawn so that there is no difficulty in distinguishing mass units. Mistaking a peak at, say, m/e 79 for m/e 80 can result in total confusion. Unfortunately, many of the graphs presented in the journals consist of an almost solid ink smudge surmounted by a number of spikes. In the first edition of

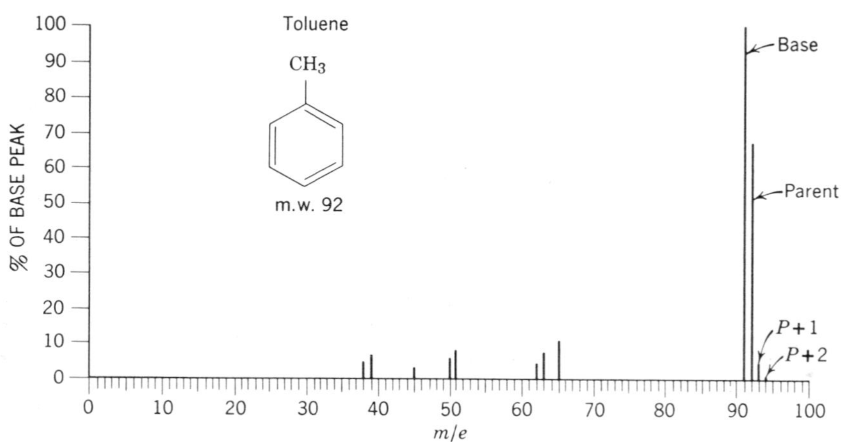

Fig. 2c. Graphical presentation of Fig. 2a.

this book, we used the tabular presentation. We are satisfied now that the grid used in this edition permits ready recognition of individual mass units as well as patterns. Except for isotope peaks, peaks of less than 3% intensity are not shown unless they have special significance.

The parent peak is the peak of highest mass number except for the isotope peaks. These isotope peaks are present because a certain number of molecules contain heavier isotopes than the common isotopes. We shall show how the intensities of the isotope peaks relative to the parent peak can lead to the determination of a molecular formula. In a separate table accompanying the mass spectral graphs in the problems in Chapters 6 to 8, the parent peak is given an intensity of 100%, and the isotope peak intensities are given relative to the parent peak intensity.

If an ion (m_1) fragments in the accelerator section of the mass spectrometer near the exit slit, it will have been accelerated as mass m_1, but dispersed in the magnetic field as m_2. The resulting ion current will be recorded as a low-intensity, broad peak at apparent mass m^*. The numerical value of m^* is given by

$$m^* = \frac{(m_2)^2}{m_1}$$

The peak caused by the ion current corresponding to mass m^* is called a metastable peak. Measurement of the mass of the metastable peak affords information that m_2 is derived directly from m_1 by loss of a neutral fragment. Although this technique is useful in interpretations of spectra, it will not be used in this book. Its use is discussed in Reference 1, pp. 153–157, and in Reference 3, pp. 251–262.

IV. DETERMINATION OF A MOLECULAR FORMULA

A unique molecular formula can often be derived from a sufficiently accurate mass measurement alone (high resolution mass spectrometry). It is no longer a startling experience to see the molecular formula of a natural product of molecular weight 600 or more derived from a molecular weight reported to three decimal places. This is possible because the atomic masses are not whole numbers. For example, we can distinguish at a nominal mass of 28 among CO, N_2, CH_2N, and C_2H_4.

^{12}C	12.0000	$^{14}N_2$	28.0062	^{12}C	12.0000	$^{12}C_2$	24.0000
^{16}O	15.9949			$^{1}H_2$	2.0156	$^{1}H_4$	4.0312
	27.9949			^{14}N	14.0031		28.0312
					28.0187		

It is a tedious task to find a molecular formula by arithmetic trial and error from the output of a high-resolution mass spectrometer. Tables, algorithms, and computer programs have been assembled for this purpose.[13–18]

Because the required instrumentation is not nearly so available as "unit resolution" spectrometers, we rely on the intensities of isotope peaks to arrive at several possible formulas, and we make the final selection on the basis of other evidence. Bear in mind that these are exact formulas; they are not the approximations obtained by combustion analysis. Determination of a molecular formula from the isotope peak intensities is limited to those cases in which the parent peak is relatively intense so that the isotope peaks are large enough to be measured accurately. The high-resolution instrument permits selection of an unequivocal molecular formula even for a compound that gives a relatively weak parent peak. Within a few years, high-resolution mass spectrometry will be commonplace.

Table I lists the principal stable isotopes of the common elements and their relative abundance as percentages of the isotope of lowest mass which is set at 100%. Note that this presentation differs from the usual isotope abundance tables in which the sum of all the isotopes of an element add up to 100%.

Table I

ELEMENTS	ABUNDANCE %*		
Carbon	^{12}C 100	^{13}C 1.08	
Hydrogen	^{1}H 100	^{2}H 0.016	
Nitrogen	^{14}N 100	^{15}N 0.38	
Oxygen	^{16}O 100	^{17}O 0.04	^{18}O 0.20
Fluorine	^{19}F 100		
Silicon	^{28}Si 100	^{29}Si 5.10	^{30}Si 3.35
Phosphorus	^{31}P 100		
Sulfur	^{32}S 100	^{33}S 0.78	^{34}S 4.40
Chlorine	^{35}Cl 100	^{37}Cl 32.5	
Bromine	^{79}Br 100	^{81}Br 98.0	
Iodine	^{127}I 100		

* Abundance calculated on the basis that the common isotope = 100%.

Suppose that a compound contains one carbon atom. Then about 1.08% of all the molecules will contain a ^{13}C atom, and these molecules will produce a $P+1$ peak about 1.08% the intensity of the parent peak; the ^{2}H atoms present will make an additional very small contribution to the $P+1$ peak. If a compound contains one sulfur atom, the $P+2$ peak will be about 4.4% of the parent peak. The $P+1$ and $P+2$ peaks are so designated in Figure 2.

Selection of likely molecular formulas appropriate to particular mass and isotope abundance measurements is greatly facilitated by the table constructed by Beynon.[3] This table, which has recently been extended[13] to mass 500, can be used for high resolution mass spectrometry.*

* Beynon's first table[3] is based on $O = 16.000000$. His expanded table[13] is based on the currently accepted standard, $C = 12.000000$.

Beyond about mass 250, use of the isotopes to determine a molecular formula loses its effectiveness. A reduced version of Beynon's table is presented as Appendix A. Its use will become more evident as we work through the spectra in this book. In practice, the measured isotope peaks are usually slightly higher than the calculated contributions because of incomplete resolution, bimolecular collisions (see below), contributions from a large $P-1$ peak, or because of impurities. The table is limited to compounds containing C, H, O, and N. The presence of S, Cl, or Br is usually readily apparent because of a large isotope contribution to $P+2$. We shall see that the number of chlorine and bromine atoms can be determined. Iodine, fluorine, and phosphorus are monoisotopic. Their presence can usually be deduced from a suspiciously small $P+1$ peak relative to the molecular weight, from the fragmentation pattern, from the other spectra with which we are concerned, or from the history of the compound.

It is difficult to overemphasize the importance of locating the parent peak. It will be stressed again that this gives an exact numerical molecular weight. Even in cases in which the parent peak is very small (and therefore an accurate determination of $P+1$ and $P+2$ is impossible), only a little extra information can often lead to identification. This information may be available from the source and history of the sample, from the fragmentation pattern, and from other spectra. Let us work through the selection of a molecular formula from the isotope abundance data obtained on an organic compound. We are given the following information:

m/e	%
150 (P)	100
151 ($P+1$)	10.2
152 ($P+2$)	0.88

The parent peak is mass 150; thus we have the molecular weight. The parent+2 ($P+2$) peak obviously does not allow for the presence of sulfur or halogen atoms. We look in Appendix A under mass 150. Our $P+1$ peak is 10.2% of the parent peak. We list the empirical formulas whose calculated isotope contribution to the $P+1$ peak falls—to be arbitrary—between 9.0 and 11.0; we also list the calculated $P+2$ values:

FORMULA	$P+1$	$P+2$
$C_7H_{10}N_4$	9.25	0.38
$C_8H_8NO_2$	9.23	0.78
$C_8H_{10}N_2O$	9.61	0.61
$C_8H_{12}N_3$	9.98	0.45
$C_9H_{10}O_2$	9.96	0.84
$C_9H_{12}NO$	10.34	0.68
$C_9H_{14}N_2$	10.71	0.52

On the basis of the "nitrogen rule" (p. 11), we immediately eliminate three of these formulas because they contain an odd number of nitrogen atoms. Our $P+2$ peak is 0.88% of the parent. This best fits $C_9H_{10}O_2$. However, $C_8H_{10}N_2O$ cannot be ruled out without additional evidence. Note that mass 150 is the sum of the masses of the common isotopes of these molecular formulas; the isotope masses used are whole numbers (12 for carbon, 14 for nitrogen, etc.).

When elements other than C, H, O, and N are present, their kind and number must be determined (see the discussion under the appropriate chemical class) and their mass subtracted from the molecular weight. The composition of the remainder of the molecule is then determined from Appendix A.

Quite often the organic chemist must identify a byproduct or an unexpected main product from a reaction. Under these circumstances, even rather complex molecules can be handled expeditiously. Since the compound has a history, an intelligent guess can be made as to what elements are present. The following example[18] may be instructive. In the course of polymerizing the fluorinated silicon-containing monomer, a crystalline

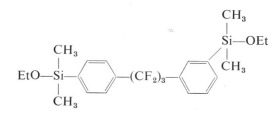

EtO—Si(CH_3)(CH_3)—C_6H_4—$(CF_2)_3$—C_6H_4—Si(CH_3)(CH_3)—OEt

sublimate was obtained as a by-product. The parent peak of the mass spectrum of the sublimate was m/e 434, and the base peak, m/e 419 (i.e., $P-15$). The $P+1$ peak was 31.2% of the parent peak, and the $P+2$ peak, 10.4%. On the assumption that the compound contained six fluorine and two silicon atoms, the molecular formula $C_{19}H_{20}F_6OSi_2$ was written. The intensities of the $P+1$ and $P+2$ peaks for this formula were calculated as follows:

CONTRIBUTOR	$P+1$	$P+2$	SOURCE
$C_{19}H_{20}$(mass 248)	20.85	2.06	Appendix A*
O	0.04	0.20	Table I
F_6	...	...	Table I
Si_2	10.20	6.70	Table I
	31.09	8.96	

* The C, H, and O content could have been obtained directly from Beynon's extended tables.[13]

The good agreement between the calculated and the determined values provided strong support for the molecular formula written. This information combined with the fragmentation pattern and the infrared and NMR spectra led to the following structure.

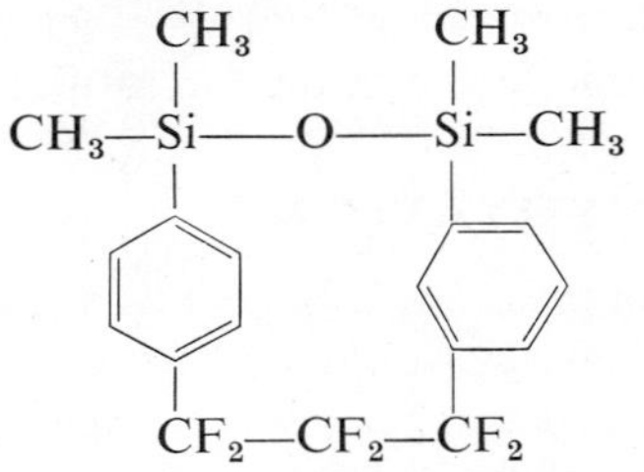

$$
\begin{array}{ccccc}
 & CH_3 & & CH_3 & \\
 & | & & | & \\
CH_3{-} & Si & {-}O{-} & Si & {-}CH_3 \\
 & | & & | & \\
 & C_6H_4 & & C_6H_4 & \\
 & | & & | & \\
 & CF_2 & {-}CF_2{-} & CF_2 &
\end{array}
$$

The foregoing is a good example of both the possibilities and limitations of spectrometric identification without any chemical manipulation on the compound. It is doubtful that even an experienced mass spectrometrist would have derived a molecular formula without some indication that silicon and fluorine were present. Confirmation is certainly easier than diagnosis.

V. RECOGNITION OF THE PARENT PEAK

There are two situations in which identification of the parent peak may be difficult.

1. The parent peak does not appear or is very weak. The obvious remedy in most cases is to run the spectrum at maximum sensitivity (and accept the resulting loss in resolution) and to use a larger sample. (Sometimes a large sample exaggerates the $P+1$ peak. See below.) Still the parent peak may not be evident, and other sources of information may be useful. The type of compound may be known, and the parent mass may be deduced from the breakdown pattern. For example, alcohols usually give a very weak parent peak, but often show a pronounced peak resulting from loss of water ($P-18$). A molecular weight determination, which can be done on the mass spectrometer (see below) or by any of the usual methods, or a combustion analysis together with consideration of the fragmentation pattern may help us to arrive at the parent mass. Preparation of a suitable derivative is another device that has been used in a limited way and will probably come to be used more extensively (p. 13).

2. The parent peak is present but is one of several peaks which may be as prominent or even more prominent. In this situation, the first question is that of purity. If the compound can be assumed to be pure, the usual problem is to distinguish the parent peak from a more prominent parent-1 peak. One good test is to reduce the energy of the bombarding electron beam to near the appearance potential. This will reduce the intensities of all peaks, but will increase the intensity of the parent peak relative to other peaks, including fragmentation peaks (but not parent peaks) of impurities. Another test frequently used is to increase the size of the sample, or increase the time the sample spends in the ionization chamber by decreasing the ion repeller voltage (Reference 1, pp. 55–57). In either case, the net effect is to increase the opportunity for bimolecular collisions to occur in the ion chamber. The most common result of a bimolecular collision of a parent radical ion containing a heteroatom (O, N, or S) is a contribution to the parent$+1$ peak (that is, the net effect is the transfer of a hydrogen atom from a neutral molecule to the parent ion).

$$RCH_2{-}\overset{+}{\underset{\cdot}{\ddot{O}}}{-}CH_2R + RCH_2{-}\underset{..}{\ddot{O}}{-}CH_2R \rightarrow$$

$$RCH_2{-}\overset{+}{\underset{H}{\ddot{O}}}{-}CH_2R + R\dot{C}H{-}\underset{..}{\ddot{O}}{-}CH_2R$$

Thus an increase in peak size relative to other peaks, as sample size is increased or the repeller voltage is decreased, designates that peak as the parent$+1$ peak and affords an indirect identification of the parent peak. Of course, the dependence of the $P+1$ peak on sample size must be kept in mind when this peak is used to establish a molecular formula of a compound containing a heteroatom.

Many peaks can be ruled out as possible parent peaks simply on grounds of reasonable structure requirements. The "nitrogen rule" is often helpful in this regard. It states that a molecule of even-numbered molecular weight must contain no nitrogen or an even number of nitrogen atoms; an odd-numbered molecular weight requires an odd number of nitrogen atoms. This rule holds for all compounds containing carbon, hydrogen, oxygen, nitrogen, sulfur, and the halogens, as well as many of the less usual atoms such as phosphorus, boron, silicon, arsenic, and the alkaline earths. A useful corollary states that cleavage of a single bond gives an odd-numbered ion fragment from an even-numbered molecular ion, and an even-numbered ion fragment from an odd-numbered molecular ion; for this corollary to hold, the ion fragment must contain all of the nitrogen (if any) of the molecular ion. Consideration of the breakdown pattern coupled with other information will also assist in identifying the parent peak. It should be kept in mind that Appendix A contains fragments and trivial formulas as well as molecular formulas.

The presence of appreciable amounts of impurities that give rise to prominent peaks near the parent peak can be troublesome. Here again, the expedient of reducing the energy of the electron beam will cause a relative increase in the intensity of the parent peak (and also of the parent peak of an impurity). The fragmentation pattern will often furnish clues. Another useful technique for detection of impurities is microeffusiometry. A fixed volume of sample is allowed to flow through the molecular leak, and the logarithms of the intensities of the peaks in question are plotted as a function of time. All peaks belonging to the same molecule will give lines of the same slope. Those due to other components of different molecular weight will give lines of different slopes.

The intensity of the parent peak depends on the stability of the parent ion. The most stable parent ions are those of purely aromatic systems. If substituents are present that have favorable modes of cleavage, the parent peak will be less intense, and the fragment peaks relatively more intense. In general, aromatics, conjugated olefins, saturated ring compounds, certain sulfur-containing compounds, and short straight-chain hydrocarbons will give a prominent parent peak. The parent peak will usually be recognizable in straight chain ketones, esters, acids, aldehydes, amides, ethers and halides. The parent peak is frequently not detectable in aliphatic alcohols, amines, nitrites, nitrates, nitro compounds, nitriles and in highly branched compounds.

VI. USE OF THE MOLECULAR FORMULA

If an organic chemist had to choose a single item of information above all others that are usually available to him from spectra or from chemical manipulations, he would certainly choose the molecular formula.

In addition to the kinds and numbers of atoms, the molecular formula gives the number of "unsaturated sites." This is intuitively obvious when C_6H_{14} is compared with C_6H_6, for example. There is a difference of eight H atoms, which means four "unsaturated sites." An "unsaturated site" is a double bond (C=C, C=O, etc.) or a ring. A triple bond counts as two double bonds. Thus, for C_6H_6, we could write such structures as

$$HC{\equiv}C{-}CH_2{-}CH_2{-}C{\equiv}CH$$
$$HC{\equiv}C{-}CH{=}CH{-}CH{=}CH_2$$

The number of "unsaturated sites" (Unsat.) can be calculated from the formula

$$\text{Unsat.} = \text{carbons} + 1 - \frac{\text{hydrogens}}{2} - \frac{\text{halogens}}{2} + \frac{\text{trivalent nitrogen}}{2}$$

Thus the compound C_7H_7NO would have $8 - 3.5 + 0.5 = 5$ "unsaturated sites." A possible structure is $C_6H_5C({=}O)NH_2$. Note that the divalent atoms (oxygen and sulfur) are not counted in the formula.

Terpenes often present a choice between a double bond and a ring structure. This question can readily be resolved on a microgram scale by catalytically hydrogenating the compound and rerunning the mass spectrum. If no other easily reducible groups are present, the increase in the mass of the molecular peak is a measure of the number of double bonds; the other "unsaturated sites" must be rings.

Such simple considerations give the chemist very ready information about structure. As another example, a compound containing a single oxygen atom may quickly be determined to be an ether or a carbonyl compound simply by counting "unsaturated sites."

VII. FRAGMENTATION

As a first impression, fragmenting a molecule with a huge excess of energy would seem a brute-force approach to molecular structure. It is very close to smashing a walnut with a sledge hammer. Seemingly, there is a lack of elegance to demolition. However, in recent years, the rationalizations used to correlate spectral patterns with structure can only be described as elegant. The insight of such pioneers as McLafferty, Beynon, Stenhagen, Ryhage, and Myerson have led to a number of rational mechanisms for fragmentation. These have been masterfully summarized and elaborated by Biemann.[1] Generally, the tendency has been to represent the molecular ion with a delocalized charge. Djerassi's approach[2] has been to localize the positive charge on either a π bond (except in conjugated systems), or on a heteroatom. This is, at least, a pedagogic *tour de force*. In chapter after chapter throughout three books,[2,20] the authors show consistently how the localized charge triggers rational fragmentation processes. Documentation of these processes, though persuasive, is still sparse. Readers are warned that the organic chemist can be carried away by his "plausible" mechanisms.*

In the first edition of this book, we discussed mechanisms in terms of single-electron shifts, which seems appropriate for unimolecular processes in the gas phase; these shifts were shown by the same curved arrow generally used by organic chemists to show two-electron shifts. The "fishhook" symbolism used by Djerassi et al.[2,20] is an apt device and will be used here. A single fishhook (⌒) designates the shift of a single electron. Cleavage of a bond requires the movement of two electrons. However, to prevent clutter, only one of a pair of fishhooks will be drawn. This practice can be illustrated for cleavage of a C—C bond next to a heteroatom (see p. 13).

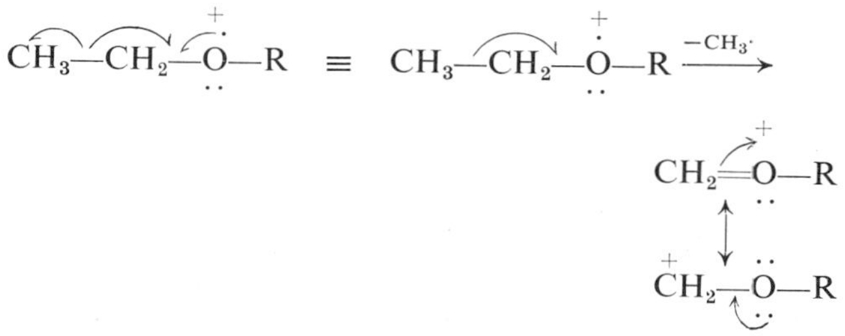

$$CH_3{-}CH_2{-}\overset{+}{\ddot{O}}{-}R \equiv CH_3{-}CH_2{-}\overset{+\cdot}{\ddot{O}}{-}R \xrightarrow{-CH_3\cdot} CH_2{=}\overset{+}{\ddot{O}}{-}R \leftrightarrow \overset{+}{C}H_2{-}\ddot{O}{-}R$$

The probability of cleavage of a particular bond is related to the bond strength, to the possibility of low-energy transitions, and to the stability of the fragments

* McLafferty suggests separate consideration of the effect of the positive ion and radical sites. F. W. McLafferty, *Chem. Comm.*, **1966,** 78.

both charged and uncharged formed in the fragmentation process. Our knowledge of pyrolytic cleavages can be used, to some extent, to predict likely modes of cleavage of the parent ion. Because of the extremely low vapor pressure in the mass spectrometer, there are very few fragment collisions; we are dealing largely with unimolecular decompositions. This assumption, backed by a file of reference spectra, is the basis for the vast amount of information available from the fragmentation pattern of a molecule. Whereas conventional organic chemistry deals with reactions initiated by chemical reagents or by thermal or actinic energy, mass spectrometry is concerned with the consequences suffered by an organic molecule struck by an ionizing electronic beam at a vapor pressure of about 10^{-5} mm Hg. A number of general rules for predicting prominent peaks in a spectrum can be written and rationalized, using standard concepts of physical organic chemistry.

1. The relative height of the parent peak is greatest for the straight-chain compound and decreases as the degree of branching increases.

2. The relative height of the parent peak usually decreases with increasing molecular weight in a homologous series. Fatty esters appear to be an exception.

3. Cleavage is favored at branched carbon atoms; the more branched, the more likely is cleavage. This is a consequence of the increased stability of a tertiary carbonium ion over a secondary, which in turn is more stable than a primary. Generally, the largest substituent at a branch is eliminated most readily as a radical, presumably because a long-chain radical can achieve some stability by delocalization of the lone electron.

4. Double bonds, cyclic structures, and especially aromatic (or heteroaromatic) rings stabilize the parent ion, and thus increase the probability of its appearance.

5. Double bonds favor allylic cleavage and give the resonance-stabilized allylic carbonium ion.

$$\overset{+}{CH_2}\dot{:}CH{-}CH_2{-}R \xrightarrow{-R\cdot} \overset{+}{C}H_2{-}CH{=}CH_2 \leftrightarrow CH_2{=}CH{-}\overset{+}{C}H_2$$

6. Saturated rings tend to lose side chains at the α-bond. This is merely a special case of branching (Rule 3). The positive charge tends to stay with the ring fragment.

7. In alkyl-substituted aromatic compounds, cleavage is very probable at the bond beta to the ring, giving the resonance-stabilized benzyl ion or, more likely, the tropylium ion directly.*

$$C_6H_5^{\cdot+}{-}CH_2{-}R \xrightarrow{-R\cdot} C_6H_5{=}CH_2^{+} \longleftrightarrow C_6H_5{-}\overset{+}{C}H_2$$

$$C_6H_5^{\cdot+}CH_2R \xrightarrow{-R\cdot} C_7H_7^{+} \longrightarrow C_7H_7^{+}\ \text{(tropylium)}$$

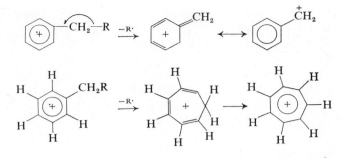

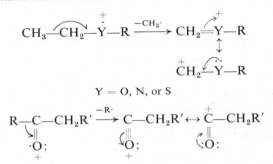

8. C—C bonds next to a heteroatom are frequently cleaved, leaving the charge on the fragment containing the heteroatom whose nonbonding electrons provide resonance stabilization.

$$CH_3{-}CH_2{-}\overset{+}{\dot{Y}}{-}R \xrightarrow{-CH_3\cdot} CH_2{=}\overset{+}{Y}{-}R \leftrightarrow \overset{+}{C}H_2{-}\ddot{Y}{-}R$$

Y = O, N, or S

$$R{-}\underset{\overset{\|}{\cdot O:^{+}}}{C}{-}CH_2R' \xrightarrow{-R\cdot} \underset{\overset{|||}{O:^{+}}}{C}{-}CH_2R' \leftrightarrow \underset{\overset{\|}{:O:}}{\overset{+}{C}}{-}CH_2R'$$

9. Cleavage is often associated with elimination of small stable neutral molecules such as carbon monoxide, olefins, water, ammonia, hydrogen sulfide, hydrogen cyanide, mercaptans, ketene, or alcohols. These cleavages often take place with rearrangements.

The frequent occurrence of rearrangement ions probably discouraged earlier use of mass spectrometry for structure determination. These ions are fragments whose origin cannot be described by simple cleavage of bonds in the parent ion, but are a result of intramolecular atomic rearrangement prior to fragmentation. Rearrangements involving migration of hydrogen atoms in molecules that contain a heteroatom are especially noticeable. Such rearrangements often account for prominent characteristic peaks, and are consequently very useful for our purpose. They can frequently be rationalized on the basis of low-energy transitions and increased stability of the products. Rearrangements resulting in elimination of a stable neutral molecule are common, and will be encountered in the discussion of mass spectra of chemical classes. Rearrangement peaks may be recognized by considering the corollary to the "nitrogen rule" (p. 11). Thus an even-numbered peak derived from an even-numbered molecular ion is a result of two cleavages, which may involve a rearrangement.

VIII. DERIVATIVES

If a compound has low volatility or if the parent mass cannot be determined, it may be possible to prepare a

* In accordance with the convention adopted in the first edition, the parent radical ion is depicted with a $\dot{+}$ symbol. When the charge can be localized on one particular atom, the odd electron is shown on that atom.

suitable derivative. The derivative selected should provide enhanced volatility, a predictable mode of cleavage, a simplified fragmentation pattern, or increased stability of the parent ion. Once the organic chemist learns to think of derivatives in these terms rather than as sharply melting crystals, the possibilities become obvious.

Compounds containing several polar groups may have very low volatility, e.g., sugars, amino acids, and dibasic carboxylic acids. Acetylation of hydroxyl and amino groups, and methylation of free acids are obvious and effective choices to increase volatility and give characteristic peaks. Perhaps less immediately obvious is the use of trimethylsilyl derivatives of hydroxyl, amino, sulfhydryl, and carboxylic acid groups.[21–25] Trimethylsilyl derivatives of sugars and of amino acids are volatile enough to pass through gas chromatographic columns. The parent peak of trimethylsilyl derivatives may not always be present, but the $P-15$ peak due to cleavage of one of the Si—CH_3 bonds is always prominent.

Reduction of ketones to hydrocarbons[26] has been used to elucidate the carbon skeleton of the ketone molecule. Polypeptides have been reduced with $LiAlH_4$ to give polyamino alcohols that were volatile and gave predictable fragmentation patterns.[27] Methylation and trifluoroacylation of tri- and tetrapeptides have been used to obtain mass spectra.[28]

IX. MASS SPECTRA OF SOME CHEMICAL CLASSES

Mass spectra of a number of chemical classes are briefly described in this section in terms of the most useful generalizations for identification. For more detail, the references cited (in particular, the thorough treatment by Budzikiewiez, Djerassi and Williams) should be consulted. The references are selective rather than comprehensive. A table of frequently encountered fragment ions is given in Appendix B. A table of fragments (uncharged) that are commonly eliminated is presented in Appendix C. A more exhaustive listing of common fragment ions has been compiled.[29]

Hydrocarbons

Saturated Hydrocarbons[11,30,31,32]

Most of the work in mass spectrometry has been done on hydrocarbons of interest to the petroleum industry. Rules 1 to 3 (p. 13) apply quite generally; rearrangement peaks, though common, are not usually intense (random rearrangements), and numerous reference spectra are available.

The parent peak (P) of a straight-chain, saturated hydrocarbon is always present, though of low intensity for long-chain compounds. The fragmentation pattern is characterized by clusters of peaks, and the corresponding peaks of each cluster are 14 (CH_2) mass units apart. The largest peak in each cluster represents a C_nH_{2n+1} fragment; this is accompanied by C_nH_{2n} and C_nH_{2n-1} fragments. The most intense fragments are at C_3 and C_4, and the fragment intensities decrease in a smooth curve down to $P-C_2H_5$; the $P-CH_3$ peak is characteristically very weak or missing. Compounds containing more than 8 carbon atoms show fairly similar spectra; identification then depends on the parent peak.

Spectra of branched saturated hydrocarbons are grossly similar to those of straight-chain compounds, but the smooth curve of decreasing intensities is broken by preferred fragmentation at each branch. Thus, compare Figures 3a and 3b.

In Figure 3b, the peaks at m/e 169 and 85 represent cleavage on either side of the branch with charge retention on the substituted carbon atom. Subtraction of the molecular weight from the sum of these fragments accounts for the fragment —CH—CH_3 (with a vertical bond on the CH). Note also the absence of the C_{11} fragment which cannot form by a single cleavage. Finally, the presence of a distinct $P-15$ peak also indicates a methyl branch. The fragment resulting from cleavage at a branch tends to lose a single hydrogen atom so that the resulting C_nH_{2n} peak is prominent and sometimes more intense than the corresponding C_nH_{2n+1} peak. Random rearrangements are common, and the use of reference compounds for final identification is good practice.

A saturated ring in a hydrocarbon increases the relative intensity of the parent peak, and favors cleavage at the bond connecting the ring to the rest of the molecule (Rule 6). Fragmentation of the ring is usually characterized by loss of two carbon atoms as C_2H_4 (28) and C_2H_5 (29). This tendency to lose even numbered fragments such as C_2H_4 gives a spectrum that contains a greater proportion of even-numbered mass ions than the spectrum of an acyclic hydrocarbon. As in branched hydrocarbons, C—C cleavage is accompanied by loss of a hydrogen atom. The characteristic peaks are therefore in the C_nH_{2n-1} and C_nH_{2n-2} series.

Olefins[11,33,34]

The parent peak of olefins, especially polyolefins, is usually distinct. Location of the double bond in acyclic olefins is difficult because of its facile migration in the fragments. In cyclic, especially polycyclic, olefins, location of the double bond is frequently evident as a result of a strong tendency for allylic cleavage without much double bond migration (Rule 5). Conjugation with a carbonyl group also fixes the position of the double bond. As with saturated hydrocarbons, acyclic

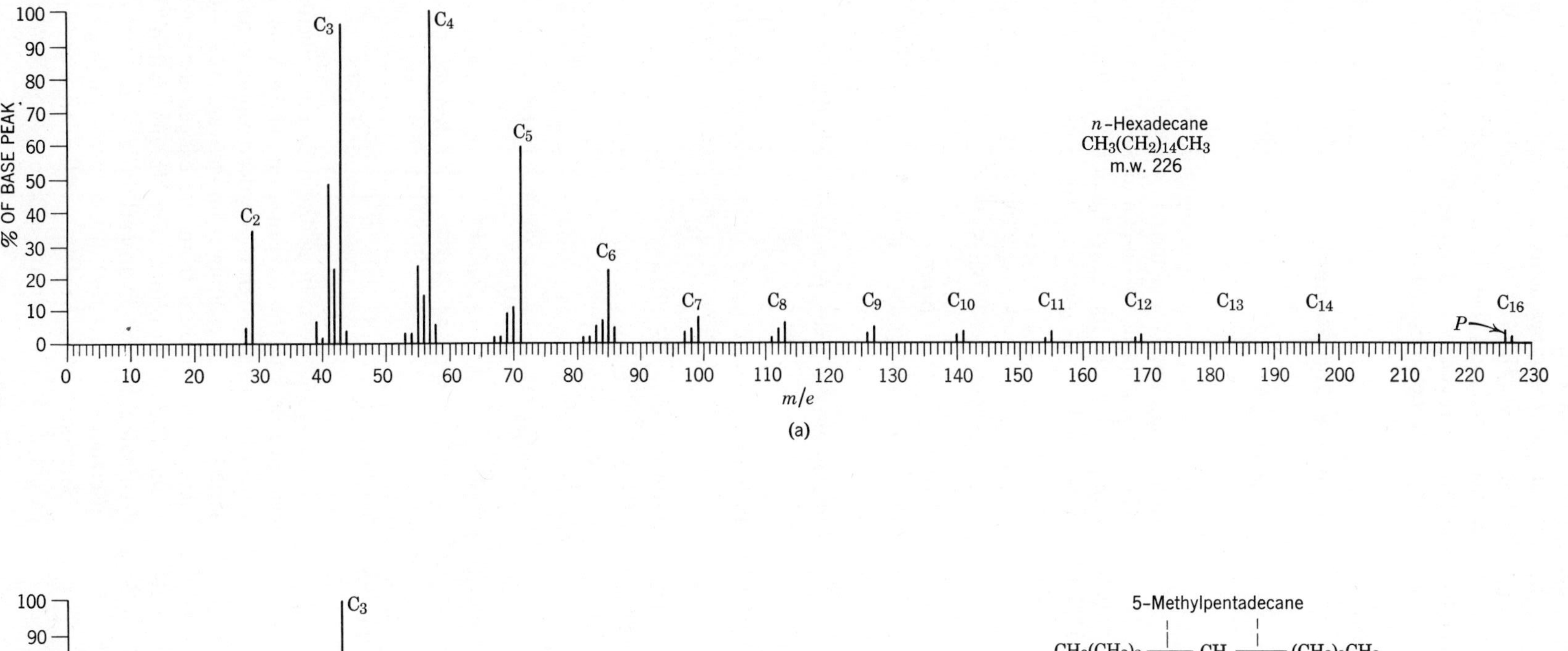

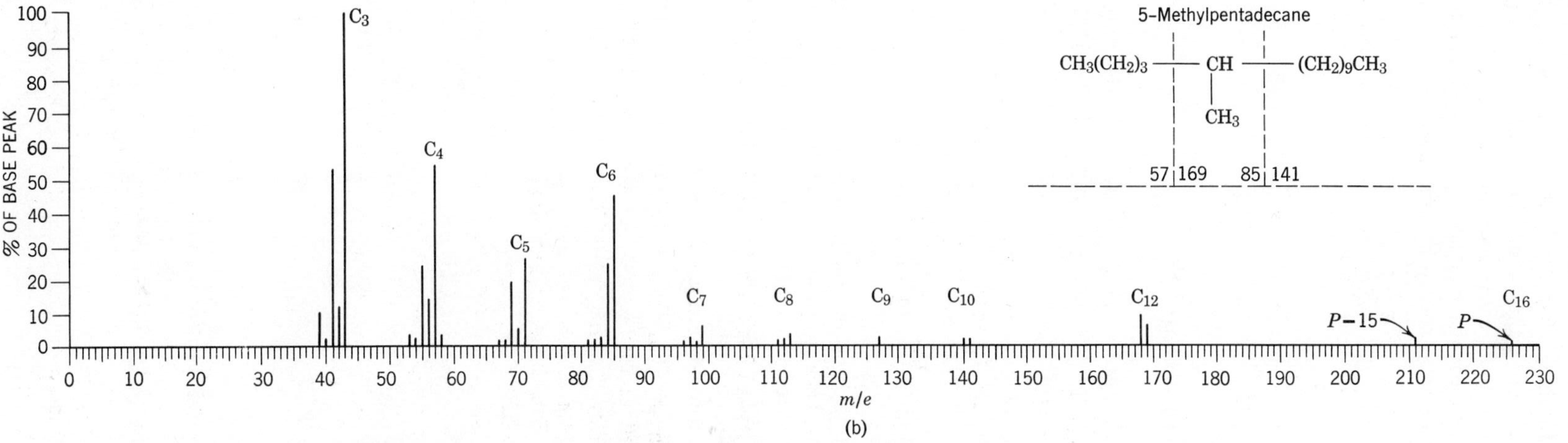

Fig. 3. Isomeric C_{16} hydrocarbons.

olefins are characterized by clusters of peaks at intervals of 14 units. In these clusters the C_nH_{2n-1} and C_nH_{2n} peaks are more intense than the C_nH_{2n+1} peaks.

Cyclic olefins usually show a distinct parent peak. A unique mode of cleavage is a type of homolytic retro-Diels-Alder reaction as shown by limonene.

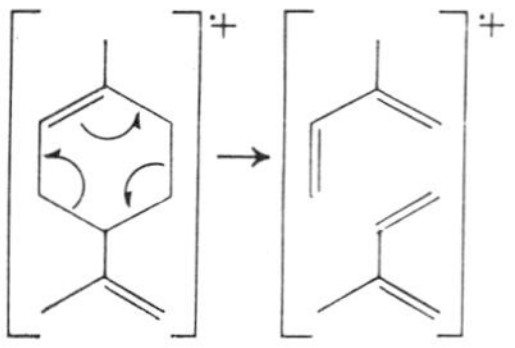

Aralkyl Hydrocarbons[35–38]

An aromatic ring in a molecule stabilizes the parent peak (Rule 4), which is usually sufficiently large that accurate measurements can be made on the $P+1$ and $P+2$ peaks.

A prominent peak (often the base peak) at *m/e* 91 ($C_6H_5CH_2^+$) is indicative of an alkyl substituted benzene ring. Branching at the α-carbon leads to masses higher than 91 by increments of 14, the largest substituent being eliminated most readily (Rule 3). The mere presence of a peak at mass 91, however, does not preclude branching at the α-carbon because this highly stabilized fragment may result from rearrangements. A distinct and sometimes prominent $P-1$ peak results from similar benzylic cleavage of a C—H bond.

It has been shown that in most cases the ion of mass 91 is a tropylium rather than a benzylic cation. This explains the ready loss of a methyl group from xylenes although toluene does not easily lose a methyl group.

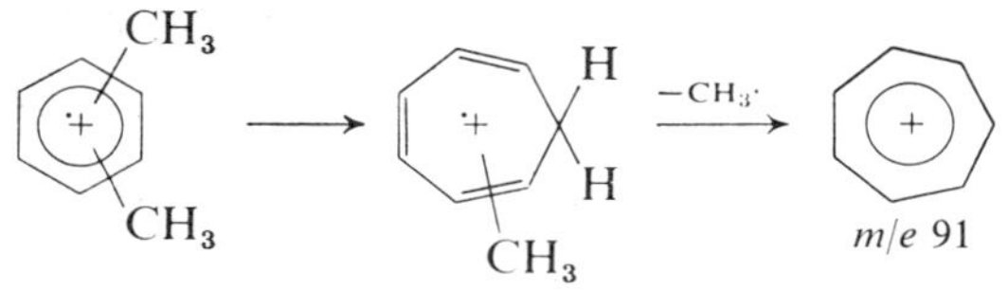

$-CH_3\cdot$

m/e 91

The frequently observed peak at *m/e* 65 results from elimination of a neutral acetylene molecule from the tropylium ion

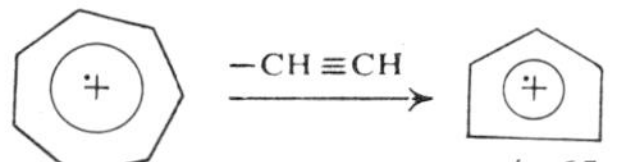

$-CH{\equiv}CH$

m/e 65

Hydrogen rearrangement with elimination of a neutral olefin molecule accounts for the peak at *m/e* 92 observed when the alkyl group is longer than C_2.

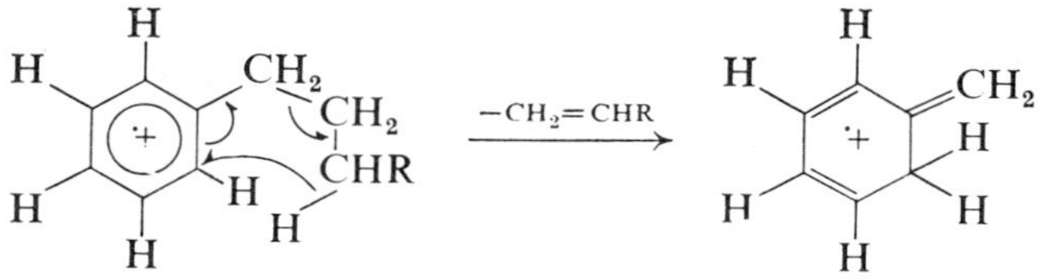

$-CH_2{=}CHR$

m/e 92

A characteristic cluster of ions due to α-cleavage and hydrogen rearrangements of monalkylbenzenes appears at *m/e* 77 ($C_6H_5^+$), 78 ($C_6H_6^+$), and 79 ($C_6H_7^+$).

Alkylated polyphenyls and alkylated polycyclic aromatic hydrocarbons exhibit the same β-cleavage as alkylbenzene compounds.

Hydroxy Compounds

Alcohols[39–45]

The parent peak of a primary or secondary alcohol is quite small and, for a tertiary alcohol, is undetectable. The parent peak of *n*-pentanol is extremely weak compared with its near homologs. The expedients mentioned (p. 11) may be used to obtain the molecular weight.

Cleavage of the C—C bond next to the oxygen atom is of general occurrence (Rule 8). Thus, primary alcohols show a prominent peak due to $CH_2{=}\overset{+}{O}H$ (*m/e* 31). Secondary and tertiary alcohols cleave analogously to give a prominent peak due to R(H)C=$\overset{+}{O}$H (*m/e* 45, 59, 73, etc.), and R(R′)C=$\overset{+}{O}$H (*m/e* 59, 73, 87 etc.), respectively. The largest substituent is expelled most readily (Rule 3).

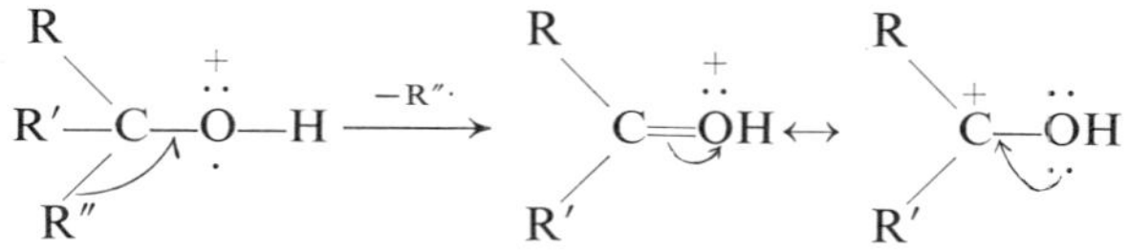

$$R'-\underset{R''}{\overset{R}{C}}-\overset{+}{O}-H \xrightarrow{-R''\cdot} \underset{R'}{\overset{R}{C}}{=}\overset{+}{O}H \leftrightarrow \underset{R'}{\overset{R}{\overset{+}{C}}}-OH$$

($R'' > R'$ or R) = alkyl

When R and/or R′ = H, a $P-1$ peak can usually be seen.

Primary alcohols, in addition to the principal C—C cleavage next to the oxygen atom, show a homologous series of peaks of progressively decreasing intensity at *m/e* 45, 59, 73, . . . , resulting from cleavage at C—C bonds successively removed from the oxygen atom. In long-chain (>C_6) alcohols, the fragmentation becomes dominated by the hydrocarbon pattern; in fact, the spectrum resembles that of the corresponding olefin.

The spectrum in the vicinity of the very weak or missing parent peak of a primary alcohol is sometimes complicated by weak $P-2$ (R—CH=O^+) and $P-3$ (R—C≡$\overset{+}{O}$) peaks.

A distinct and sometimes prominent peak can usually

be found at $P-18$ from loss of water. This peak is most noticeable in spectra of primary alcohols. This elimination by electron impact has been rationalized by a combined single electron and hydride ion shift.

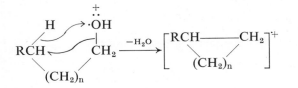

$$\mathrm{RCH(H)(CH_2)_n CH_2\overset{+}{\ddot{O}}H} \xrightarrow{-H_2O} \left[\mathrm{RCH{-}CH_2}\ (\mathrm{CH_2})_n\right]^{+\cdot}$$

The $P-18$ peak is frequently exaggerated by thermal decomposition of higher alcohols on hot inlet surfaces. Elimination of water, together with elimination of an olefin from primary alcohols, accounts for the presence of a peak at $P-(\text{olefin} + H_2O)$, i.e., a peak at $P-46$, $P-74$, $P-102$, ...

$$\mathrm{RCH(H)CH_2CH_2CH_2\dot{O}H^+} \xrightarrow[-H_2O]{-CH_2=CH_2} [\mathrm{CH_2{=}CHR}]^{+\cdot}$$

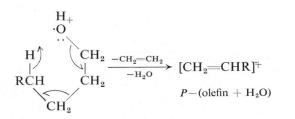

$P-(\text{olefin} + H_2O)$

The olefinic ion then decomposes by successive eliminations of ethylene.

Alcohols containing branched methyl groups (e.g., terpene alcohols) frequently show a fairly strong peak at $P-33$ resulting from loss of CH_3 and H_2O.

A peak at m/e 31 is quite diagnostic for a primary alcohol provided it is more intense than peaks at m/e 45, 59, 73 . . . . However, the first-formed ion of a secondary alcohol can decompose further to give a moderately intense m/e 31 ion.

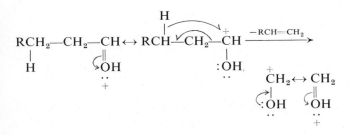

$$\mathrm{RCH_2{-}CH_2{-}CH(\overset{+}{\ddot{O}}H)} \leftrightarrow \mathrm{RCH(H){-}CH_2{-}\overset{+}{C}H(:\ddot{O}H)} \xrightarrow{-RCH=CH_2} \mathrm{\overset{+}{C}H_2{-}\ddot{O}H} \leftrightarrow \mathrm{CH_2{=}\overset{+}{\ddot{O}}H}$$

Figure 4 gives the characteristic spectra of isomeric primary, secondary, and tertiary C_5 alcohols.

Benzyl alcohols and their substituted homologs and analogs constitute a distinct class. Generally the parent peak is strong. A moderate benzylic peak ($P-OH$) is present as expected from cleavage beta to the ring. A complicated sequence leads to prominent $P-1$, $P-2$, and $P-3$ peaks. Loss of H_2O to give a distinct $P-18$ peak is a common feature, especially pronounced and mechanistically straightforward in some ortho-substituted benzyl alcohols.

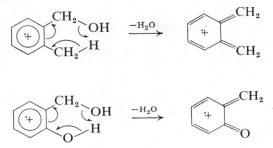

$$o\text{-}\mathrm{C_6H_4(CH_2OH)(CH_2H)}^{+\cdot} \xrightarrow{-H_2O} o\text{-}\mathrm{C_6H_4(=CH_2)_2}^{+\cdot}$$

$$o\text{-}\mathrm{C_6H_4(CH_2OH)(OH)}^{+\cdot} \xrightarrow{-H_2O} o\text{-}\mathrm{C_6H_4(=CH_2)(=O)}^{+\cdot}$$

The aromatic cluster at m/e 77, 78, and 79 resulting from complex degradation is usually prominent.

Phenols[46]

A conspicuous parent peak facilitates identification of phenols. In phenol itself, the parent peak is the base peak and the $P-1$ peak is small. In cresols, the $P-1$ peak is larger than the parent peak as a result of a facile benzylic C—H cleavage. A rearrangement peak at m/e 77 and peaks resulting from loss of CO ($P-28$) and CHO ($P-29$) are usually found in phenols.

Ethers

Aliphatic Ethers[47–51,51a]

The parent peak (two mass units larger than that of an analogous hydrocarbon) is small, but larger sample size will usually make the parent peak or the $P+1$ peak obvious (p. 11). The presence of an oxygen atom can be deduced from strong peaks at m/e 31, 45, 59, 73, ... These peaks represent the RO^+ and $ROCH_2^+$ fragments.

Fragmentation occurs in two principal ways:

(a) Cleavage of the C—C bond next to the oxygen atom ($\alpha\beta$ bond).

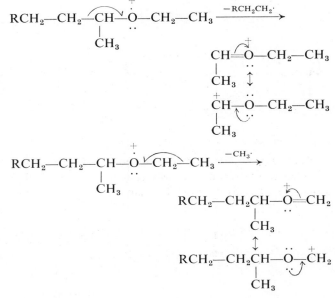

$$\mathrm{RCH_2{-}CH_2{-}CH(CH_3){-}\overset{+}{\ddot{O}}{-}CH_2{-}CH_3} \xrightarrow{-RCH_2CH_2\cdot} \mathrm{CH(CH_3){=}\overset{+}{O}{-}CH_2{-}CH_3} \leftrightarrow \mathrm{\overset{+}{C}H(CH_3){-}\ddot{O}{-}CH_2{-}CH_3}$$

$$\mathrm{RCH_2{-}CH_2{-}CH(CH_3){-}\overset{+}{\ddot{O}}{-}CH_2{-}CH_3} \xrightarrow{-CH_3\cdot} \mathrm{RCH_2{-}CH_2CH(CH_3){-}\overset{+}{O}{=}CH_2} \leftrightarrow \mathrm{RCH_2{-}CH_2CH(CH_3){-}\ddot{O}{-}\overset{+}{C}H_2}$$

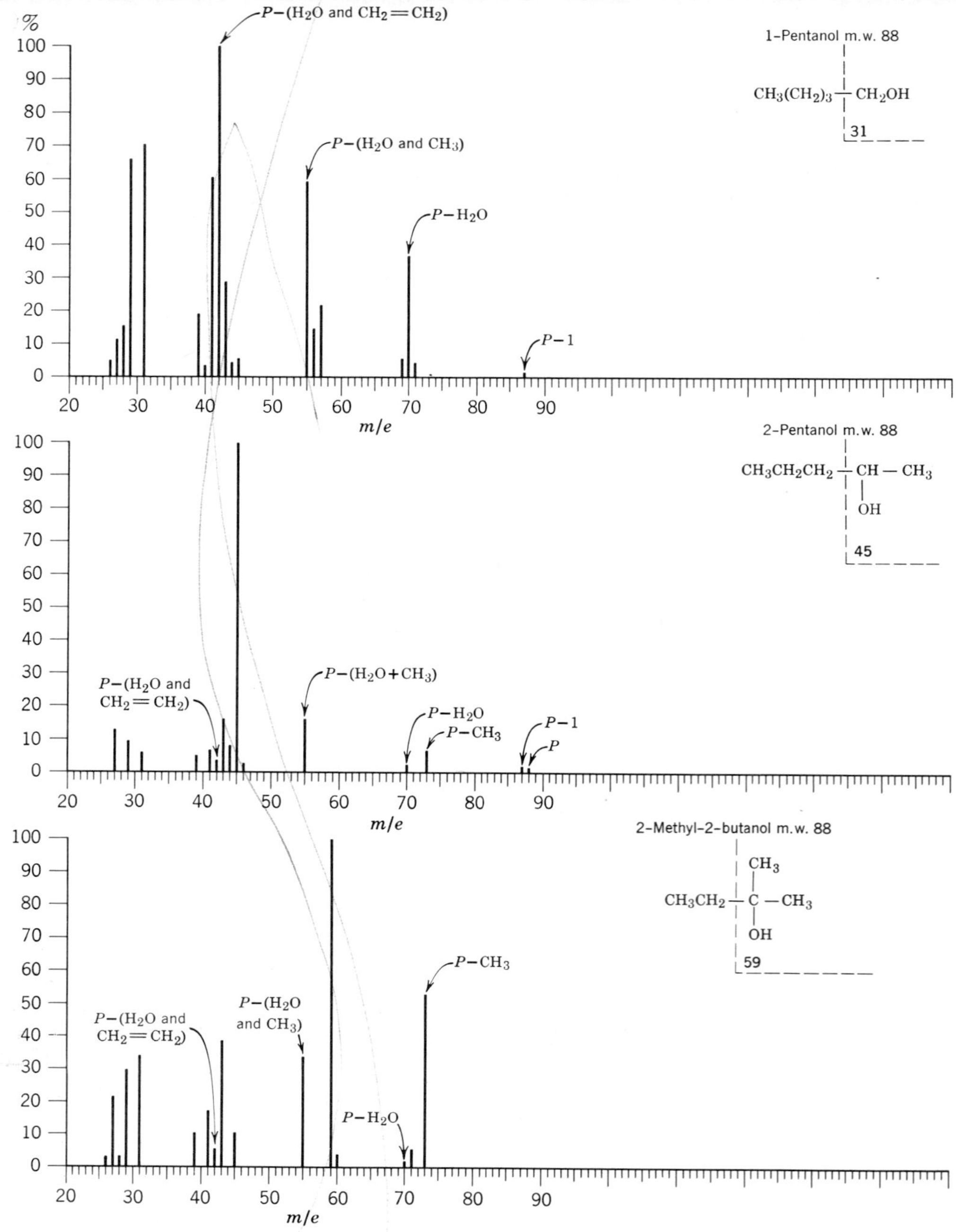

%
P−(H2O and CH2=CH2)
1-Pentanol m.w. 88
CH3(CH2)3 — CH2OH
31
P−(H2O and CH3)
P−H2O
P−1
m/e
2-Pentanol m.w. 88
CH3CH2CH2 — CH — CH3
OH
45
P−(H2O and CH2=CH2)
P−(H2O+CH3)
P−H2O
P−CH3
P−1
P
m/e
2-Methyl-2-butanol m.w. 88
CH3
CH3CH2 — C — CH3
OH
59
P−CH3
P−(H2O and CH3)
P−(H2O and CH2=CH2)
P−H2O
m/e

Fig. 4. Isomeric pentanols.

%
CH=ÖH+
CH3
Ethyl sec−butyl ether
m.w. 102
73
29
CH3 — CH2 — CH — O — CH2 — CH3
CH3
57
87
P
m/e

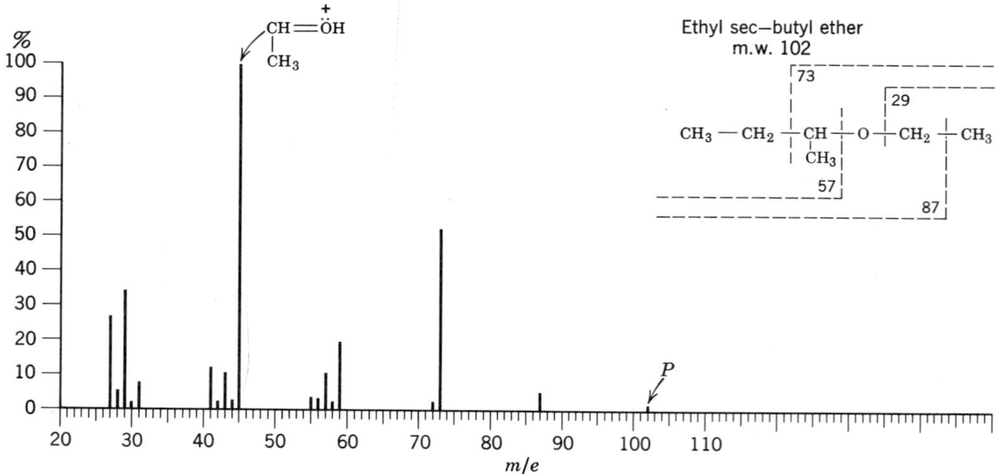

Fig. 5. Ethyl sec-butyl ether. Data from Reference 47.

One or the other of these oxygen-containing ions may account for the base peak. In the case shown, the first cleavage, i.e., at the branched carbon atom to lose the larger fragment, is preferred. However, the first-formed fragment decomposes further by the following process, often to give the base peak (Figure 5); the decomposition is important when the α—C is branched.

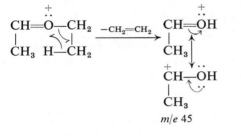

$$\underset{CH_3}{CH}{=}\overset{+}{\ddot{O}}{-}\underset{H-CH_2}{CH_2} \xrightarrow{-CH_2=CH_2} \underset{CH_3}{CH}{=}\overset{+}{O}H \longleftrightarrow \underset{CH_3}{\overset{+}{C}H}{-}\ddot{O}H$$

m/e 45

(b) C—O bond cleavage with the charge remaining on the alkyl fragment.

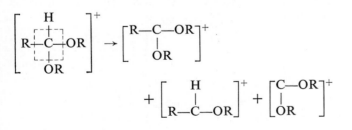

$$R{-}\overset{+}{\ddot{O}}{-}R' \xrightarrow{-\cdot\ddot{O}R'} \overset{+}{R}$$

$$R{-}\overset{+}{\ddot{O}}{-}R' \xrightarrow{-R\ddot{O}\cdot} \overset{+}{R'}$$

As expected, the spectrum of long chain ethers becomes dominated by the hydrocarbon pattern. Figure 5 is the spectrum of ethyl sec-butyl ether.

Acetals are a special class of ethers. Their mass spectra are characterized by an extremely weak parent peak, by the prominent peaks at *P* minus R, and *P* minus OR and a weak peak at *P* minus H. Each of these cleavages is mediated by an oxygen atom and thus facile. As usual, elimination of the largest group is preferred. As with aliphatic ethers, the first-formed oxygen-containing fragments can decompose further with hydrogen rearrangement and olefin elimination.

$$\left[R{-}\underset{OR}{\overset{H}{C}}{-}OR\right]^+ \rightarrow \left[R{-}\underset{OR}{C}{-}OR\right]^+ + \left[R{-}\overset{H}{C}{-}OR\right]^+ + \left[\underset{OR}{C}{-}OR\right]^+$$

Ketals behave similarly.

Aromatic Ethers[52–56]

The parent peak of aromatic ethers is prominent. Primary cleavage occurs at the bond beta to the ring, and the first-formed ion can decompose further. Thus anisole, m.w. 108, gives ions of *m/e* 93 and 65.

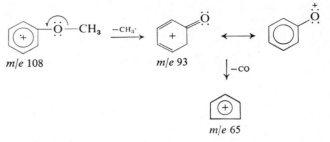

$$C_6H_5{-}\ddot{O}{-}CH_3^{+} \xrightarrow{-CH_3\cdot} C_6H_5O^{+} \xrightarrow{-CO} C_5H_5^{+}$$

m/e 108 → *m/e* 93 → *m/e* 65

The characteristic aromatic peaks at *m/e* 78 and 77 may arise from anisole as follows.

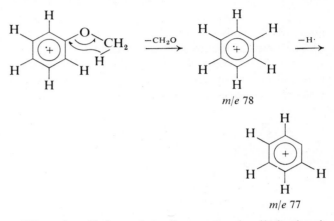

$$C_6H_5{-}O{-}CH_3^{+} \xrightarrow{-CH_2O} C_6H_6^{+} \xrightarrow{-H\cdot} C_6H_5^{+}$$

m/e 78 → *m/e* 77

When the alkyl portion of an aromatic alkyl ether is C_2 or larger, cleavage beta to the ring is accompanied by hydrogen rearrangement as noted above for alkylbenzenes. Clearly, cleavage is mediated by the ring rather than by the oxygen atom; C—C cleavage next to the oxygen atom is insignificant.

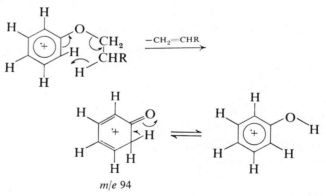

$$C_6H_5{-}O{-}CH_2{-}CH_2R^{+} \xrightarrow{-CH_2=CHR} C_6H_6O^{+} \rightleftharpoons C_6H_5OH^{+}$$

m/e 94

Diphenyl ethers show peaks at *P*−H, *P*−CO, and *P*−CHO by complex rearrangements.

Ketones

Aliphatic Ketones[57–59]

The parent peak of ketones is usually quite pronounced. Major fragmentation peaks of aliphatic ketones result from cleavage at the C—C bonds adjacent to the oxygen atom, the charge remaining with the oxygenated fragment. Thus, as with alcohols and ethers, cleavage is again at the C—C bond next to the oxygen atom.

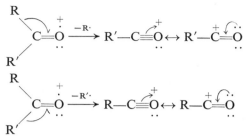

$$R(R')C{=}\overset{+}{\ddot{O}} \xrightarrow{-R\cdot} R'{-}C{\equiv}\overset{+}{O} \leftrightarrow R'{-}\overset{+}{C}{=}\ddot{O}$$

$$R(R')C{=}\overset{+}{\ddot{O}} \xrightarrow{-R'\cdot} R{-}C{\equiv}\overset{+}{O} \leftrightarrow R{-}\overset{+}{C}{=}\ddot{O}$$

This cleavage gives rise to a peak at *m/e* 43 or 57 or 71 . . . . The base peak very often results from loss of the larger alkyl group.

When one of the alkyl chains attached to the C=O group is C_3 or larger, cleavage of the C—C bond once-removed ($\alpha\beta$ bond) from the C=O group occurs with hydrogen rearrangement to give a major peak at *m/e* 58 or 72 or 86 . . . .

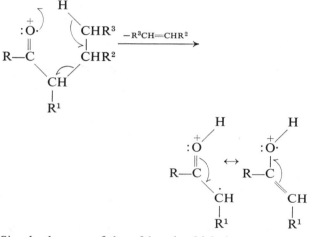

$$\text{R—C}(\text{=}\overset{+}{\text{O}}\cdot)\text{—CH(R}^1\text{)—CHR}^2\text{—CHR}^3\text{—H} \xrightarrow{-R^3CH=CHR^2}$$

$$\text{R—C}(\text{=}\overset{+}{\text{O}}\text{—H})\text{—}\dot{\text{C}}\text{H—R}^1 \leftrightarrow \text{R—}\dot{\text{C}}(\text{—}\overset{+}{\text{O}}\text{—H})\text{=CH—R}^1$$

Simple cleavage of the $\alpha\beta$ bond, which does not occur to any extent, would give an ion of low stability with two adjacent positive centers $R{-}\overset{+}{C}(O^-){-}\overset{+}{C}H_2$. When R is C_3 or longer, the first-formed ion can cleave again with hydrogen rearrangement.

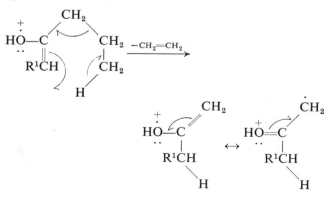

$$\overset{+}{\text{HO}}\text{—C(=CHR}^1\text{)—CH}_2\text{—CH}_2\text{—CH}_2\text{—H} \xrightarrow{-CH_2=CH_2}$$

$$\overset{+}{\text{HO}}\text{—C(=}\dot{\text{C}}\text{H}_2\text{)... : }\text{HO—C(CH}_2\text{)—R}^1\text{CH—H} \leftrightarrow \text{H}\overset{+}{\text{O}}\text{=C(}\dot{\text{C}}\text{H}_2\text{)—R}^1\text{CH—H}$$

Note that in long-chain ketones the hydrocarbon peaks are indistinguishable from the acyl peaks. The multiple cleavage modes in ketones sometimes make difficult the determination of the carbon chain configuration. Reduction of the carbonyl group to a methylene group yields the corresponding hydrocarbon whose fragmentation pattern leads to the carbon skeleton.

Cyclic Ketones[60–62]

The parent peak in cyclic ketones is prominent. As with aliphatic ketones, the primary cleavage of cyclic ketones is adjacent to the C=O group, but the ion thus formed must undergo further cleavage in order to produce a fragment. The base peak in the spectrum of cyclopentanone and of cyclohexanone is *m/e* 55. The mechanism is similar in both cases: hydrogen rearrangement from a primary radical to a conjugated secondary radical followed by formation of the resonance-stable ion, *m/e* 55.

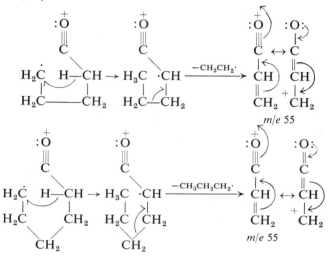

$$\dot{C}H_2\text{–}CH_2\text{–}CH_2\text{–}CH(\text{–}C{\equiv}\overset{+}{O}) \rightarrow H_3C\text{–}CH_2\text{–}CH_2\text{–}\dot{C}H\text{–}C{\equiv}\overset{+}{O} \xrightarrow{-CH_3CH_2\cdot} \overset{+}{O}{\equiv}C\text{–}CH{=}CH_2 \leftrightarrow O{=}C\text{–}CH{=}\overset{+}{C}H_2 \quad m/e\ 55$$

$$\text{(cyclohexanone)} \rightarrow \ldots \xrightarrow{-CH_3CH_2CH_2\cdot} \overset{+}{O}{\equiv}C\text{–}CH{=}CH_2 \leftrightarrow O{=}C\text{–}CH{=}\overset{+}{C}H_2 \quad m/e\ 55$$

The other prominent peaks at *m/e* 83 and 42 in the spectrum of cyclohexanone have been rationalized as follows.

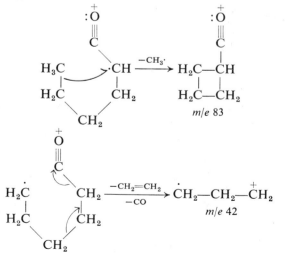

$$H_3C\text{–}H_2C\text{–}CH_2\text{–}CH_2\text{–}\dot{C}H\text{–}C{\equiv}\overset{+}{O} \xrightarrow{-CH_3\cdot} \text{(cyclopentanone ion, } H_2C\text{–}CH_2\text{–}H_2C\text{–}\dot{C}H\text{–}C{=}\overset{+}{O}) \quad m/e\ 83$$

$$\dot{H_2C}\text{–}H_2C\text{–}CH_2\text{–}CH_2\text{–}CH_2\text{–}C{\equiv}\overset{+}{O} \xrightarrow[-CO]{-CH_2=CH_2} \dot{C}H_2\text{–}CH_2\text{–}\overset{+}{C}H_2 \quad m/e\ 42$$

Aromatic Ketones[63,64]

The parent peak of aromatic ketones is prominent. Cleavage of aralkyl ketones occurs at the bond beta to the ring, leaving a characteristic $\mathrm{ArC{\equiv}\overset{+}{\ddot{O}}}$ fragment which usually accounts for the base peak. Loss of CO from this fragment gives the "phenyl" ion (*m/e* 77 in the case of acetophenone). Cleavage of the bond adjacent to the ring to form a $\mathrm{RC{\equiv}\overset{+}{O}}$ fragment is less important though somewhat enhanced by electron-withdrawing groups (and diminished by electron-donating groups) in the *para* position of the ring.

When the alkyl chain is C_3 or longer, cleavage of the C—C bond once-removed from the C═O group occurs with hydrogen rearrangement. This is the same cleavage noted for aliphatic ketones that proceeds through a cyclic transition state and results in elimination of an olefin and formation of a stable ion.

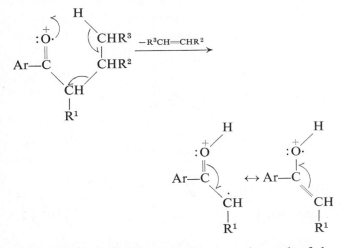

$$\mathrm{Ar{-}C(={\overset{+}{O}}\cdot\cdots H{-}CHR^3{-}CHR^2{-})CH{-}R^1} \xrightarrow{-\mathrm{R^3CH{=}CHR^2}}$$

$$\mathrm{Ar{-}C(={\overset{+}{O}}H){-}\dot{C}H{-}R^1} \leftrightarrow \mathrm{Ar{-}C(-{\overset{+}{O}}\cdot H){=}CH{-}R^1}$$

Unsymmetrical diarylketones cleave to give each of the $\mathrm{ArC{\equiv}\overset{+}{O}}$ ions expected.

Aldehydes

Aliphatic Aldehydes[65]

The parent peak of aliphatic aldehydes is usually discernible. Cleavage of the C—H and C—C bonds next to the oxygen atom results in a $P-1$ peak and in a $P-\mathrm{R}$ peak (*m/e* 29). The $P-1$ peak is a good diagnostic peak even for long-chain aldehydes, but the *m/e* 29 peak present in C_4 and higher aldehydes is due to the hydrocarbon $C_2H_5^+$ ion.

In the C_4 and higher aldehydes, cleavage of the C—C bond once removed from the C═O group occurs with hydrogen rearrangement to give a major peak at *m/e* 44, 58, or 72, . . . , depending on the α-substituents. This is the stablized ion formed through the cyclic transition state as shown for aliphatic ketones (R = H).

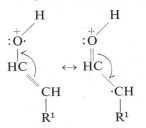

$$\mathrm{HC(-{\overset{+}{O}}\cdot H){=}CH{-}R^1} \leftrightarrow \mathrm{HC(={\overset{+}{O}}H){-}\dot{C}H{-}R^1}$$

In straight chain aldehydes, the other unique, diagnostic peaks are at $P-18$ (loss of water), $P-28$ (loss of ethylene), $P-43$ (loss of $\mathrm{CH_2{=}CH{-}O\cdot}$), and $P-44$ (loss of $\mathrm{CH_2{=}CH{-}OH}$). The rearrangements leading to these peaks have been rationalized (see Reference 2). As the chain lengthens, the hydrocarbon pattern (*m/e* 29, 43, 57, 71, . . .) becomes dominant. These features are evident in the spectrum of nonanal (Figure 6).

Aromatic Aldehydes[66,67]

Aromatic aldehydes are characterized by a large parent peak and by a parent-1 peak ($\mathrm{Ar{-}C{\equiv}\overset{+}{O}}$) that is always large and may be larger than the parent peak. The $P-1$ ion eliminates CO to give the phenyl ion (*m/e* 77), which in turn eliminates CH≡CH to give the $C_4H_3^+$ ion (*m/e* 51).

Carboxylic Acids

Aliphatic Acids[67–69]

The parent peak of a straight-chain monocarboxylic acid is weak but usually discernible. The most characteristic (sometimes the base) peak is *m/e* 60 due to cleavage of the bond once removed from the C═O group and hydrogen rearrangement. Branching at the α-carbon increases this fragment by the mass of the substituent. This is similar to the familiar ketone rearrangement (R = OH).

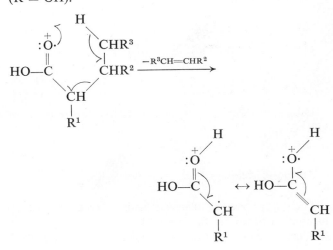

$$\mathrm{HO{-}C(={\overset{+}{O}}\cdot\cdots H{-}CHR^3{-}CHR^2{-})CH{-}R^1} \xrightarrow{-\mathrm{R^3CH{=}CHR^2}}$$

$$\mathrm{HO{-}C(={\overset{+}{O}}H){-}\dot{C}H{-}R^1} \leftrightarrow \mathrm{HO{-}C(-{\overset{+}{O}}\cdot H){=}CH{-}R^1}$$

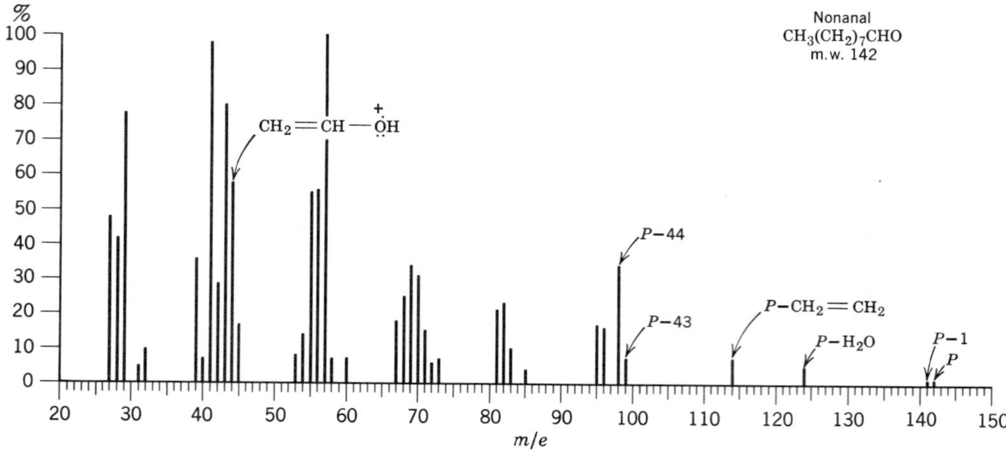

Fig. 6. Nonanal.

In short-chain acids, peaks at $P-OH$ and $P-COOH$ are prominent; these represent cleavage of bonds next to C═O. In long-chain acids, the spectrum consists of two series of peaks resulting from cleavage at each C—C bond with retention of charge either on the oxygen-containing fragment (*m/e* 45, 59, 73, 87, . . .) or on the alkyl fragment (*m/e* 29, 43, 57, 71, 85, . . .). As previously discussed, the hydrocarbon pattern also shows peaks at *m/e* 27, 28; 41, 42; 55, 56; 69, 70; . . . . In summary, besides the rearrangement peak, the spectrum of a long-chain acid resembles the series of "hydrocarbon" clusters at interval of 14 mass units. In each cluster, however, is a prominent peak at $C_nH_{2n-1}O_2$. Caproic acid (m.w. 116), for example, cleaves as follows:

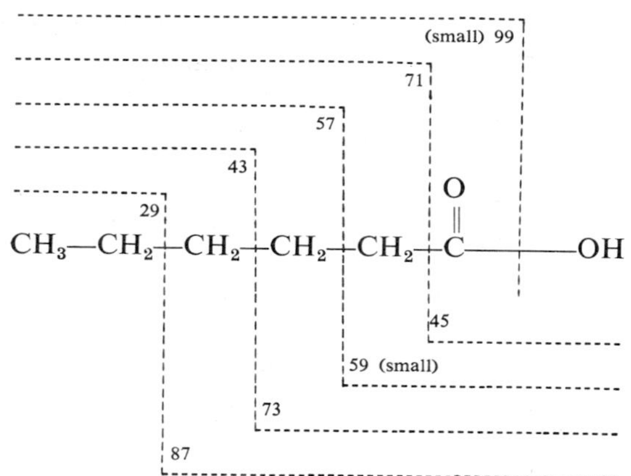

Dibasic acids are usually converted to esters to increase volatility.

Aromatic Acids[70–72]

The parent peak of aromatic acids is large. The other prominent peaks are formed by loss of OH ($P-17$) and of COOH ($P-45$). Loss of H_2O ($P-18$) is noted if a hydrogen-bearing ortho group is available. This is one example of the general "ortho effect" noted when the substituents can form a 6-membered transition state by hydrogen bonding to facilitate loss of a neutral molecule of H_2O, ROH or NH_3.

$-HZ$

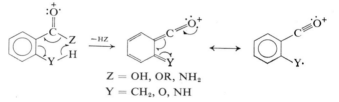

Z = OH, OR, NH_2
Y = CH_2, O, NH

Carboxylic Esters

Aliphatic Esters[73–80]

The parent peak of a methyl ester of a straight-chain aliphatic acid is usually distinct. Even waxes usually show a discernible parent peak. The parent peak is weak in the range *m/e* 130 to about 200, but becomes somewhat more intense beyond this range. The most characteristic peak is due to the familiar hydrogen rearrangement and cleavage one bond removed from the C═O group. Thus a methyl ester of an aliphatic acid unbranched at the α-carbon gives a strong peak at *m/e* 74, which, in fact, is the base peak in straight-chain methyl esters from C_6 to C_{26}. The alcohol moiety and/or the α-substituent can often be deduced by the location of the peak resulting from this cleavage.

$-R^3CH{=}CHR^2$

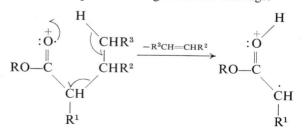

Four ions can result from bond cleavage next to C=O.

$$\left[\mathrm{R}\!\mid\!\overset{\displaystyle\mathrm{O}}{\overset{\|}{\mathrm{C}}}\mathrm{—OR'}\right]^{+} \rightarrow \mathrm{R}^{+} \text{ and } \left[\overset{\displaystyle\mathrm{O}}{\overset{\|}{\mathrm{C}}}\mathrm{—OR'}\right]^{+}$$

$$\left[\mathrm{R—}\overset{\displaystyle\mathrm{O}}{\overset{\|}{\mathrm{C}}}\!\mid\!\mathrm{OR'}\right]^{+} \rightarrow \mathrm{R—C{\equiv}\overset{+}{O}} \text{ and } [\mathrm{OR'}]^{+}$$

The ion R^+ is prominent in the short chain esters, but diminishes rapidly with increasing chain length and is barely perceptible in methyl caprate. The ion $\mathrm{R—C{\equiv}\overset{+}{O}}$ gives an excellent diagnostic peak for esters. In methyl esters it occurs at $P-31$. It is the base peak in methyl acetate, and is still 4% of the base peak in the C_{26} methylester. The ions $[\mathrm{OR'}]^+$ and $\left[\overset{\displaystyle\mathrm{O}}{\overset{\|}{\mathrm{C}}}\mathrm{OR'}\right]^{+}$ are usually of little importance.

The fragmentation pattern for methyl esters of straight-chain acids can be described in the same terms used for the pattern of the free acid. Cleavage at each C—C bond gives an alkyl ion (*m/e* 29, 43, 57, . . .) and an oxygen-containing ion, $C_nH_{2n-1}O_2^+$ (59, 73, 87, . . .). Thus there are hydrocarbon clusters at intervals of 14 mass units; in each cluster is a prominent peak at $C_nH_{2n-1}O_2$. The peak (*m/e* 87) representing the ion $[CH_2CH_2COOCH_3]^+$ is always more intense than its homologs, but the reason is not immediately obvious. However, it seems clear that the $C_nH_{2n-1}O_2$ ions do not all arise from simple cleavage.

Esters of long-chain alcohols show a diagnostic peak at *m/e* 61, 75, or 89, . . . from elimination of the alkyl moiety and transfer of two hydrogen atoms to the fragment containing the oxygen atoms.

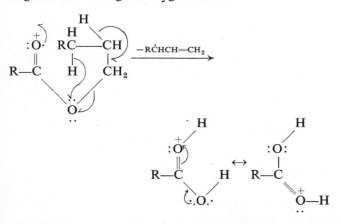

$$\xrightarrow{-\mathrm{R\dot{C}HCH{=}CH_2}}$$

$$\mathrm{R—C(=\overset{+}{O}—H)—\ddot{O}\cdot\;H} \leftrightarrow \mathrm{R—C(—\ddot{O}—H)=\overset{+}{O}—H}$$

The spectrum of methyl caprylate is presented as Figure 7. This spectrum illustrates one difficulty previously mentioned (p. 11) in using the $P+1$ peak to arrive at a molecular formula. The measured value for the $P+1$ peak is 12.9%. The calculated value (Appendix A) is 10.0%. The measured value is high due to an ion-molecule reaction because a relatively large sample was used in order to see the weak parent peak. The utility of the 5-galvanometer recorder is demonstrated by this spectrum; thus the $P+1$ peak can be measured accurately even though its intensity is only 0.11% of that of the base peak. The accuracy of the $P+2$ peak measurement is marginal.

Esters of fatty alcohols (except methyl esters) eliminate a molecule of acid in the same manner that alcohols eliminate water. A scheme similar to that for alcohols (p. 17) can be written. A possible alternative mechanism involves the carbonyl group.

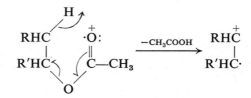

$$\mathrm{RHC(H)—R'HC—O—C(=\overset{+}{O}\cdot)—CH_3} \xrightarrow{-\mathrm{CH_3COOH}} \mathrm{R\overset{+}{H}C—R'HC\cdot}$$

Esters of dibasic acids $\mathrm{RO\overset{\|}{\underset{O}{C}}(CH_2)_n\overset{\|}{\underset{O}{C}}OR}$, in general, give recognizable parent peaks. Intense peaks are found at $(\mathrm{RO\underset{O}{\underset{\|}{C}}(CH_2)_n\underset{O}{\underset{\|}{C}}})^+$ and at $(\mathrm{RO\underset{O}{\underset{\|}{C}}(CH_2)_n})^+$.

Benzyl and Phenyl Esters

Benzyl acetate (also furfuryl acetate and other similar acetates) and phenyl acetate eliminate the neutral molecule ketene, frequently to form the base peak.

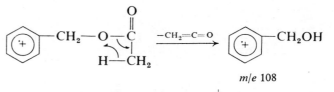

$$\mathrm{C_6H_5^{(+)}—CH_2—O—\overset{O}{\overset{\|}{C}}—CH_2—H} \xrightarrow{-\mathrm{CH_2{=}C{=}O}} \mathrm{C_6H_5^{(+)}—CH_2OH}$$

m/e 108

Of course, the *m/e* 43 peak ($\mathrm{CH_3C{\equiv}\overset{+}{O}}$) is prominent.

Esters of Aromatic Acids[66,70,81,82]

The parent peak of methyl esters of aromatic acids is prominent. As the size of the alcohol moiety increases, the intensity of the parent peak decreases rapidly to practically zero at C_5. The base peak results from elimination of ·OR, and elimination of ·COOR accounts for another prominent peak. In methyl esters, these peaks are at $P-31$, and $P-59$, respectively.

As the alkyl moiety increases in length, three modes of cleavage become important: rearrangement of one

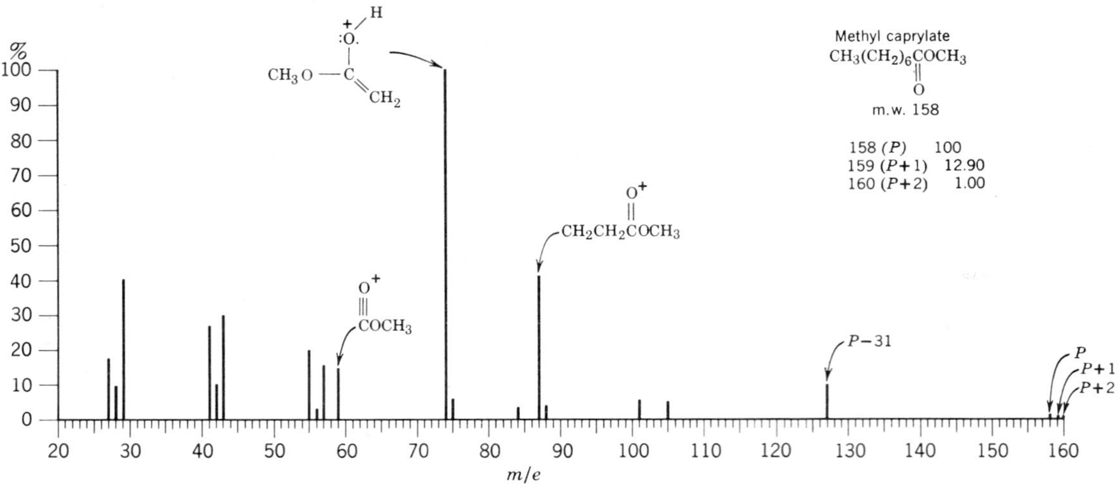

Fig. 7. Methyl caprylate.

hydrogen atom with elimination of a neutral olefin, rearrangement of two hydrogen atoms with elimination of an allylic radical, and retention of the positive charge by the alkyl group.

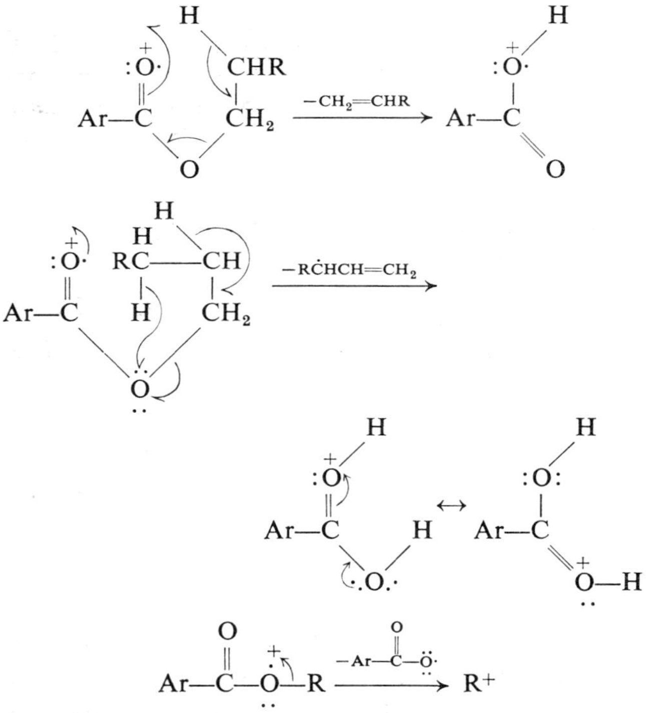

Appropriately, ortho-substituted benzoates eliminate ROH through the general "ortho" effect described above under aromatic acids. Thus the base peak in the spectrum of methyl salicylate is *m/e* 120; this ion eliminates carbon monoxide to give a strong peak at *m/e* 92.

A strong characteristic peak at mass 149 is found in the spectra of all esters of phthalic acid, starting with the diethyl ester. This peak is not significant in the dimethyl or methyl ethyl ester of phthalic acid, nor in esters of isophthalic or terephthalic acids, all of which give the expected peaks at $P-$R, $P-$2R, $P-$COOR, and $P-$2COOR. Since long-chain phthalate esters are widely used as plasticizers and in oil diffusion pumps (often, in the diffusion pump of the mass spectrometer inlet), a strong peak at *m/e* 149 may indicate contamination. The *m/e* 149 fragment is probably formed by two ester cleavages involving rearrangement of two hydrogen atoms and one hydrogen atom, followed by elimination of H_2O.

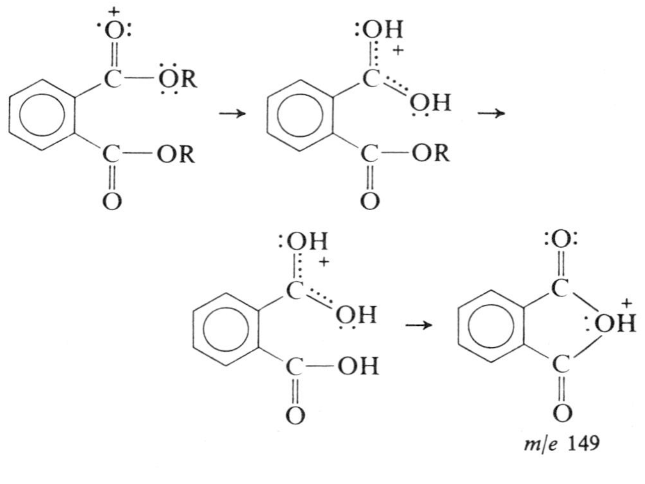

m/e 149

Lactones[83–85]

The parent peak of 5-membered ring lactones is distinct, but is weaker when an alkyl substituent is present at C_4. Facile cleavage of the side chain at C_4 (Rules 3 and 8) gives a strong peak at P minus alkyl.

The base peak (*m/e* 56) of γ-valerolactone and the

same strong peak of butyrolactone probably arise as follows.

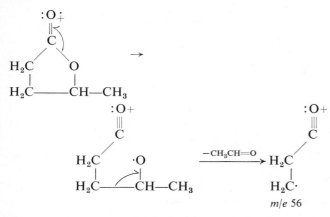

$$\text{[cyclic ion: } :O^{+}\!\!=\!C(\text{-}H_2C\text{-}H_2C\text{-}CH(CH_3)\text{-}O\text{-})] \rightarrow$$

$$:O^{+}\equiv C\text{-}H_2C\text{-}H_2C\text{-}CH(CH_3)\text{-}\cdot O \xrightarrow{-CH_3CH=O} :O^{+}\equiv C\text{-}H_2C\text{-}H_2C\cdot$$

m/e 56

Labeling experiments indicate that some of the *m/e* 56 peak in γ-valerolactone arises from the $C_4H_8^+$ ion. The other intense peaks in γ-valerolactone are at *m/e* 27 ($C_2H_3^+$), 28 ($C_2H_4^+$), 29 ($C_2H_5^+$), 41 ($C_3H_5^+$), and 43 ($C_3H_7^+$). In butyrolactone, there are strong peaks at *m/e* 27, 28, 29, 41, and 42 ($C_3H_6^+$).

Amines[86,87,87a]

Aliphatic Amines

The parent peak of an aliphatic monoamine is an odd number but is usually quite weak, and, in long-chain or highly branched amines, undetectable. The base peak frequently results from C—C cleavage next to the nitrogen atom (Rule 8); for primary amines unbranched at the α-atom, this is *m/e* 30. This cleavage accounts for the base peak in all primary amines and secondary and tertiary amines that are not branched at the α-carbon. Cleavage of the largest branch at the α-C atom is preferred.

$$R(R^1)(R^2)C\text{—}\overset{+}{\dot{N}}R^3R^4 \xrightarrow{-\cdot R^2} R(R^1)C\text{=}\overset{+}{N}R^3R^4 \longleftrightarrow R(R^1)\overset{+}{C}\text{—}\ddot{N}R^3R^4$$

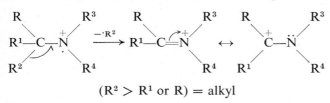

$$(R^2 > R^1 \text{ or } R) = \text{alkyl}$$

When R and/or R^1 = H, a $P-1$ peak is usually visible. This is the same type of cleavage noted (p. 16) for alcohols. The effect is more pronounced in amines because of the better resonance stabilization of the ion fragment by the less negative N atom compared with the O atom.

Primary straight-chain amines show a homologous series of peaks of progressively decreasing intensity (the cleavage at the ϵ bond is slightly more intense than at the neighboring bonds) at *m/e* 30, 44, 58, . . . , resulting from cleavage at C—C bonds successively removed from the nitrogen atom with retention of the charge on the N-containing fragment. These peaks are accompanied by the hydrocarbon pattern of C_nH_{2n+1}, C_nH_{2n}, and C_nH_{2n-1} ions. Thus we note characteristic clusters at intervals of 14 mass units, each cluster containing a peak due to a $C_nH_{2n+2}N$ ion. Because of the very facile cleavage to form the base peak, the fragmentation pattern in the high mass region becomes extremely weak.

A peak at *m/e* 30 is good though not conclusive evidence for a straight-chain primary amine. Further decomposition of the first-formed ion from a secondary or tertiary amine leads to a peak at *m/e* 30, 44, 58, or 72, ... This is a process similar to that described for aliphatic alcohols and ethers (pp. 16, 17), and similarly is enhanced by branching at one of the α-carbon atoms.

$$RCH_2\text{—}CH(CH_3)\text{—}\overset{+}{\dot{N}}H\text{—}CH_2CH_2R' \xrightarrow{-RCH_2\cdot} CH(CH_3)\text{=}\overset{+}{N}H\text{—}CH_2\text{—}CH_2R' \xrightarrow{-CH_2=CHR'} CH(CH_3)\text{=}\overset{+}{N}H_2$$

m/e 44

Cleavage of amino acid esters occurs at both C—C bonds next to the nitrogen atom, loss of the carbalkoxy group being preferred (a). The aliphatic amine fragment decomposes further to give a peak at *m/e* 30.

$$\overset{+}{N}H_2\text{=}CH\text{—}COOR' \xleftarrow{b} RCH_2CH_2\text{—}CH(\cdot\overset{+}{N}H_2)\text{—}COOR' \xrightarrow{a} RCH_2CH_2CH\text{=}\overset{+}{N}H_2 \xrightarrow{-RCH=CH_2} CH_2\text{=}\overset{+}{N}H_2$$

m/e 30

Cyclic Amines[88]

The parent peak of pyrrolidine is strong. Primary cleavage at the bonds next to the N atom leads either to loss of an α-H atom to give a strong $P-1$ peak, or to opening of the ring; the latter event is followed by elimination of ethylene to give $\cdot CH_2\overset{+}{N}H\text{=}CH_2$ (*m/e* 43, base peak), thence by loss of a hydrogen atom to give $CH_2\text{=}\overset{+}{N}\text{=}CH_2$ (*m/e* 42).

Piperidine likewise shows a strong parent and $P-1$ peak (base). Ring opening followed by several available sequences leads to characteristic peaks at m/e 70, 57, 56, 44, 43, 42, 30, 29, and 28. Substituents cleave at the ring junction (Rule 6).

Aromatic Amines[89–92]

The parent peak (odd number) of an aromatic monoamine is intense. Loss of one of the amino H atoms of aniline gives a moderately intense $P-1$ peak; loss of a neutral molecule of HCN followed by loss of a hydrogen atom gives prominent peaks at m/e 66 and 65, respectively.

It was noted (p. 19) that cleavage of alkylaryl ethers occurs with rearrangement at the O—C bond beta to the ring; i.e., cleavage was controlled by the ring rather than by the oxygen atom. In the case of alkylaryl amines, cleavage of the C—C bond next to the nitrogen atom is dominant.

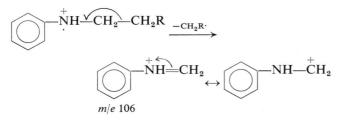

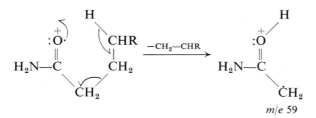

$$C_6H_5-\overset{+}{N}H-CH_2-CH_2R \xrightarrow{-CH_2R\cdot} C_6H_5-\overset{+}{N}H{=}CH_2 \leftrightarrow C_6H_5-NH-\overset{+}{C}H_2$$

m/e 106

Aliphatic Amides[93,94]

The parent peak of straight chain monoamides is usually discernible. The dominant modes of cleavage depend on the length of the acyl moiety, and on the lengths and number of the alkyl groups attached to the nitrogen atom.

The base peak in all straight-chain primary amides higher than propionamide results from the familiar cleavage of the $\alpha\beta$ C—C bond with rearrangement of a hydrogen atom.

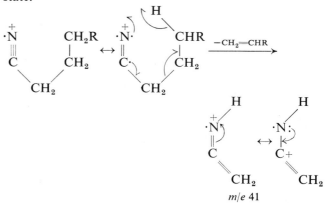

$$H_2N-C(=\overset{+}{O}\cdot)-CH_2-CH_2-CHR(H) \xrightarrow{-CH_2{=}CHR} H_2N-C(=\overset{+}{O}H)-\dot{C}H_2$$

m/e 59

Branching at the α-carbon gives a homologous peak at m/e 73 or 87, ...

Primary amides give a strong peak at m/e 44 from cleavage of the C—C bond at the C═O ($\overset{+}{O}{\equiv}C-\ddot{N}H_2 \leftrightarrow \ddot{O}{=}C{=}\overset{+}{N}H_2$); this is the base peak in C_1—C_3 primary amides and in isobutyramide. A moderate peak at m/e 86 results from $\gamma\delta$ C—C cleavage, possibly accompanied by cyclization.

$$R-CH_2-CH_2-CH_2-C(=O)-\overset{+}{\cdot N}H_2 \xrightarrow{-R\cdot} \text{cyclic } CH_2-CH_2-CH_2-C(=O)-\overset{+}{N}H_2$$

m/e 86

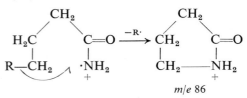

Secondary and tertiary amides with an available hydrogen on the α-carbon of the acyl moiety and methyl groups on the N atom show the dominant peak resulting from $\alpha\beta$ C—C cleavage with rearrangement of the γ-hydrogen atom. When the N-alkyl groups are C_2 or longer and the acyl moiety is shorter than C_3, another mode of cleavage predominates. This is cleavage of the N-alkyl group beta to the N atom, and cleavage of the C—N bond next to the O atom with rearrangement of an α-H atom of the acyl moiety.

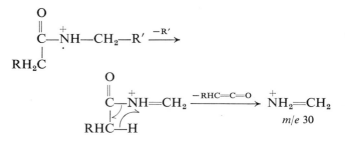

$$RH_2C-C(=O)-\overset{+}{\dot{N}}H-CH_2-R' \xrightarrow{-R'} RHC(H)-C(=O)-\overset{+}{N}H{=}CH_2 \xrightarrow{-RHC{=}C{=}O} \overset{+}{N}H_2{=}CH_2$$

m/e 30

Aliphatic Nitriles[69,95,96]

The parent peak of aliphatic nitriles (except for acetonitrile and propionitrile) are weak or absent, but the $P+1$ peak can usually be located by its behavior on increasing inlet pressure or decreasing repeller voltage (p. 11). A weak but diagnostically useful $P-1$ peak is formed by loss of an α-hydrogen to form the stable ion

$$R\dot{C}H-C{\equiv}\overset{\cdot +}{N} \leftrightarrow RCH{=}C{=}\overset{+}{\ddot{N}}.$$

The base peak of straight-chain nitriles between C_4 and C_9 is m/e 41. This peak is the ion resulting from hydrogen rearrangement in a 6-membered transition state.

$$\overset{+}{\cdot N}{\equiv}C-CH_2-CH_2-CH_2R \leftrightarrow \overset{+}{\cdot N}{=}\dot{C}-CH_2-CH_2-CHR(H) \xrightarrow{-CH_2{=}CHR} H-\overset{+}{N}{=}C{=}CH_2 \leftrightarrow H-\ddot{N}{=}\overset{+}{C}{=}CH_2$$

m/e 41

However, this peak lacks diagnostic value because of the presence of the C_3H_5 (*m/e* 41) in all molecules containing a hydrocarbon chain.

A peak at *m/e* 97 is characteristic and intense (sometimes the base peak) in straight-chain nitriles C_8 and higher. The following mechanism has been depicted

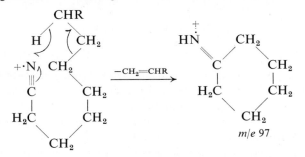

$$\text{cyclic } {}^{+\cdot}N\equiv C-CH_2\ldots \text{(CHR, H transfer)} \xrightarrow{-CH_2=CHR} \overset{+}{H\dot{N}}=C(CH_2)_5 \text{ ring}$$

m/e 97

Simple cleavage at each C—C bond (except the one next to the N atom) gives a characteristic series of homologous peaks of even mass number down the entire length of the chain (*m/e* 40, 54, 68, 82, . . .) due to the $(CH_2)_nC{\equiv}N^+$ ions. Accompanying these peaks are the usual peaks of the hydrocarbon pattern.

Nitro Compounds

Aliphatic Nitro Compounds[97,98,98a]

The parent peak (odd number) of an aliphatic mononitro compound is weak or absent (except in the lower homologs). The main peaks are attributable to the hydrocarbon fragments up to $P-NO_2$. Presence of a nitro group is indicated by an appreciable peak at *m/e* 30 (NO^+) and a smaller peak at mass 46 (NO_2^+).

Aromatic Nitro Compounds[98,99]

The parent peak of aromatic nitro compounds (odd number for one N atom) is strong. Prominent peaks result from elimination of an NO_2 radical ($P-46$, the base peak in nitrobenzene), and of a neutral NO molecule with rearrangement to form the phenoxy cation ($P-30$); both are good diagnostic peaks. Loss of CH≡CH from the $P-46$ ion accounts for a strong peak at $P-72$; loss of CO from the $P-30$ ion gives a peak at $P-58$. A diagnostic peak at *m/e* 30 results from the NO^+ ion.

The isomeric *o*-, *m*-, and *p*-nitroanilines give a strong parent peak (even number). They all give prominent peaks resulting from two sequences:

$$m/e\ 138\ (P) \xrightarrow{-NO_2} m/e\ 92 \xrightarrow{-HCN} m/e\ 65$$

$$m/e\ 138\ (P) \xrightarrow{-NO} m/e\ 108 \xrightarrow{-CO} m/e\ 80$$

Aside from differences in intensities, the three isomers give very similar spectra. The *m*- and *p*-compounds give a small peak at *m/e* 122 from loss of an O atom, whereas the *o*-compound eliminates $\cdot\ddot{O}H$ as follows to give a small peak at *m/e* 121.

$$o\text{-}C_6H_4(\overset{+}{N}(=O)\ddot{O}\cdot)(NH_2) \xrightarrow{-\cdot\ddot{O}H} C_6H_4(\overset{+}{N}{=}O)(=NH)$$

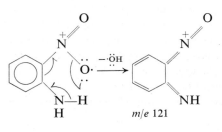

m/e 121

Aliphatic Nitrites[98,100]

The parent peak (odd number) of aliphatic nitrites (1 N present) is weak or absent. The peak at *m/e* 30 (NO^+) is always large and is often the base peak. There is a large peak at *m/e* 60 ($CH_2{=}\overset{+}{\ddot{O}}NO$) in all nitrites unbranched at the α-carbon; this represents cleavage of the C—C bond next to the ONO group. An α-branch can be identified by a peak at *m/e* 74, 88, or 102, ... Absence of a large peak at *m/e* 46 permits differentiation from nitro compounds. Hydrocarbon peaks are prominent, and their distribution and intensities describe the configuration of the carbon chain.

Aliphatic Nitrates[101]

The parent peak (odd number) of aliphatic nitrates (1 N present) is weak or absent. A prominent (frequently the base) peak is formed by cleavage of the C—C bond next to the ONO_2 group with loss of the heaviest alkyl group attached to the α-carbon.

$$R-\underset{R'}{CH}-\overset{+}{\ddot{O}}-NO_2 \xrightarrow{-R\cdot} \underset{R'}{CH}{=}\overset{+}{\ddot{O}}-NO_2$$

$$R > R'$$

The NO_2^+ peak at *m/e* 46 is also prominent. As in the case of aliphatic nitrites, the hydrocarbon fragment ions are distinct.

Sulfur Compounds

The contribution of the ^{34}S isotope to the $P+2$ peak, and often to a fragment + 2 peak, affords ready recognition of sulfur-containing compounds. A homologous series of sulfur-containing fragments is four mass units higher than the hydrocarbon fragment series. The number of sulfur atoms can be determined from the size of the contribution of the ^{34}S isotope to the $P+2$ peak. The mass of the sulfur atom(s) present is subtracted from the molecular weight. The formula of the rest of the molecule is now determined from the $P+1$ peak after subtracting the contribution of the ^{33}S isotope. The large correction applied to the $P+2$ peak makes this peak unreliable for use in Appendix A. In Compound 3 in Chapter 6, for example, the molecular weight is 206, and the molecule contains two sulfur atoms. The formula for the rest of the molecule is therefore found under mass 142, i.e., 206 minus (2 × 32). The corrected $P+1$ peak is 12.5 minus (2 × 0.78) which gives 10.9.

Aliphatic Mercaptans[102]

The parent peak of aliphatic mercaptans, except for higher tertiary mercaptans, is usually strong enough so that the $P+2$ peak can be accurately measured. In general, the cleavage modes resemble those of alcohols. Cleavage of the C—C bond ($\alpha\beta$ bond) next to the SH group gives the characteristic ion $CH_2{=}\overset{+}{\ddot{S}}H \leftrightarrow \overset{+}{C}H_2{-}\ddot{\overset{..}{S}}H$ (m/e 47). Cleavage at the $\beta\gamma$ bond gives a peak at m/e 61 of about one-half the intensity of the m/e 47 peak. Cleavage at the $\gamma\delta$ bond gives a small peak at m/e 75, and cleavage at the $\delta\epsilon$ bond gives a peak at m/e 89 that is more intense than the peak at m/e 75; presumably the m/e 89 ion is stabilized by cyclization.

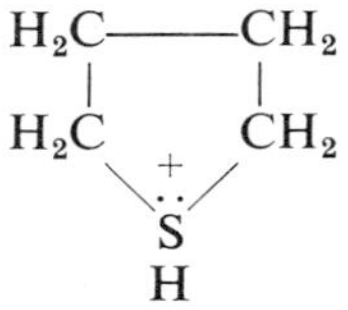

```
H2C———CH2
 |      |
H2C    CH2
   \ + /
    :S
     H
```

Again analogously to alcohols, primary mercaptans split out H_2S to give a strong $P-34$ peak, the resulting ion then eliminating ethylene; thus the homologous series $P-H_2S-(CH_2{=}CH_2)_n$ arises.

Secondary and tertiary mercaptans cleave at the α-C with loss of the largest group to give a prominent peak at m/e 61, 75, or 89, ... However, a peak at m/e 41 may also appear as a rearrangement peak in secondary and tertiary mercaptans. A peak at $P-33$ (loss of HS) is usually present in secondary mercaptans.

In long-chain mercaptans, the hydrocarbon pattern is superimposed on the mercaptan pattern. As in alcohols, the olefinic peaks (i.e., m/e 41, 55, 69, . . .) are as large or larger than the alkyl peaks (m/e 43, 57, 71, . . .).

Aliphatic Sulfides[102,102a]

The parent peak of aliphatic sulfides is usually intense enough so that the $P+2$ peak can be accurately measured. The cleavage modes generally resemble those of ethers. Cleavage of one or the other of the $\alpha\beta$ C—C bonds occurs, with loss of the largest group being favored. These first-formed ions decompose further with hydrogen transfer and elimination of an olefin. The steps shown for aliphatic ethers (p. 17) also occur for sulfides (with O replaced by S); the end result is the ion $RCH{=}\overset{+}{\ddot{S}}H$. For a sulfide unbranched at either α-C, this ion is $CH_2{=}\overset{+}{\ddot{S}}H$ (m/e 47), and its intensity may lead to confusion with the same ion derived from a mercaptan. However, the absence of $P-H_2S$ or $P-SH$ peaks in sulfide spectra makes the distinction.

A moderate to strong peak at m/e 61 is present in the spectrum of all except tertiary sulfides. When an α-methyl substituent is present, m/e 61 is the ion $CH_3CH{=}\overset{+}{\ddot{S}}H$ resulting from the double cleavage described above. Methyl primary sulfides cleave at the $\alpha\beta$ bond to give the m/e 61 ion, $CH_3{-}\overset{+}{\ddot{S}}{=}CH_2$.

However, a strong m/e 61 peak in the spectrum of a completely straight-chain sulfide calls for a different explanation. The following rationalization is offered.

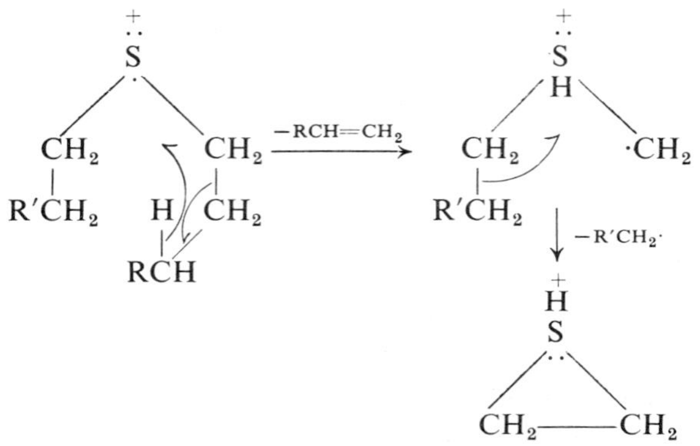

```
        +                                   +
        :S                                  :S
       /  \                                 / H
    CH2    CH2   --(-RCH=CH2)-->        CH2      ·CH2
    |       |                            |
  R'CH2   H  CH2                      R'CH2
           \ |                           | -R'CH2·
            RCH                          v
                                         +
                                         H
                                         S
                                       /  \
                                    CH2————CH2
                                     m/e 61
```

Sulfides give a characteristic ion by cleavage of the C—S bond with retention of charge on sulfur. The resulting $R\overset{+}{\ddot{S}}$ ion gives a peak at m/e 47, 61, or 75, ... The ion of m/e 103 seems especially favored possibly because of formation of a rearranged cyclic ion

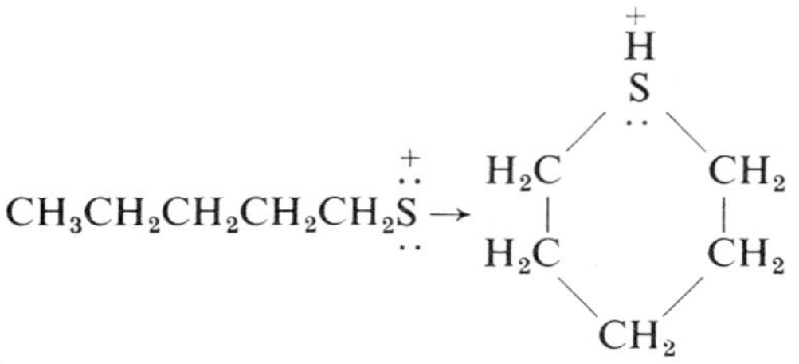

```
                                     +
                                     H
                                     S
                                   /  \
                     +       H2C       CH2
CH3CH2CH2CH2CH2S  →           |         |
                             H2C       CH2
                                \     /
                                  CH2
                                m/e 103
```

These features are illustrated by the spectrum of di-n-amyl sulfide (Figure 8).

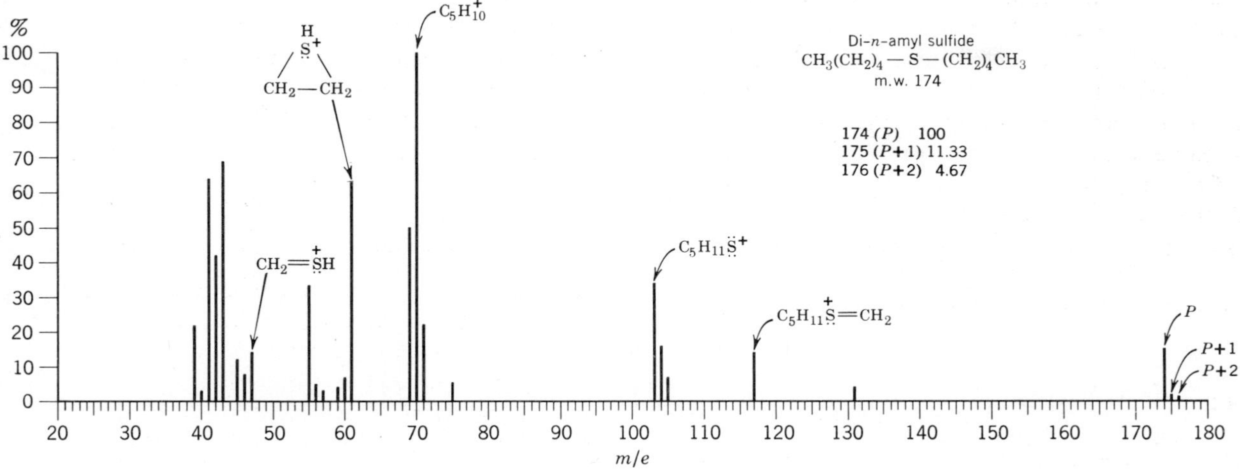

Fig. 8. Di-*n*-amyl sulfide. Data from Reference 102.

As with long-chain ethers, the hydrocarbon pattern may dominate the spectrum of long-chain sulfides; the C_nH_{2n} peaks seem especially prominent. In branched chain sulfides, cleavage at the branch may reduce the relative intensity of the characteristic sulfide peaks.

Aliphatic Disulphides[11]

Only a few disulfide spectra have been reported, and no mechanism studies have been done. The parent peak, at least up to C_{10} disulfides, is strong (Chapter 6, Compound No. 3).

A major peak results from cleavage of one of the C—S bonds with retention of the charge on the alkyl fragment. Another major peak results from the same cleavage with shift of a hydrogen atom to form the RSSH fragment which retains the charge. Other peaks apparently result from cleavage between the sulfur atoms without rearrangement, and with rearrangement of one or two hydrogen atoms to give, respectively, $R\overset{+}{S}$, $R\overset{+}{S}-1$, and $R\overset{+}{S}-2$.

Halogen Compounds

A compound that contains one chlorine atom will have a $P+2$ peak approximately one-third the intensity of the parent peak because of the presence of molecular ions containing the ^{37}Cl isotope. A compound that contains one bromine atom will have a $P+2$ peak almost equal in intensity to the parent peak because of the presence of molecular ions containing the ^{81}Br isotope. A compound that contains two chlorines, or two bromines, or one chlorine and one bromine, will show a distinct $P+4$ peak, in addition to the $P+2$ peak, because of the presence of molecular ions containing two atoms of the heavy isotope. In general, the number of chlorine and/or bromine atoms in a molecule can be ascertained by the number of alternate peaks beyond the parent peak. Thus, three Cl atoms in a molecule will give peaks at $P+2$, $P+4$, and $P+6$; in polychloro compounds, the peak of highest mass may be so weak as to escape notice.

The relative abundances of the peaks (parent, $P+2$, $P+4$, and so forth) have been calculated by Beynon[103] for compounds containing chlorine and bromine (atoms other than chlorine and bromine were ignored). A portion of these results is presented here, somewhat

Table II Intensities of Isotope Peaks (Relative to the Parent Peak) for Combinations of Bromine and Chlorine

HALOGEN PRESENT	% $P+2$	% $P+4$	% $P+6$	% $P+8$	% $P+10$	% $P+12$
Br	97.7					
Br_2	195.0	95.5				
Br_3	293.0	286.0	93.4			
Cl	32.6					
Cl_2	65.3	10.6				
Cl_3	99.8	31.9	3.47			
Cl_4	131.0	63.9	14.0	1.15		
Cl_5	163.0	106.0	34.7	5.66	0.37	
Cl_6	196.0	161.0	69.4	17.0	2.23	0.11
BrCl	130.0	31.9				
Br_2Cl	228.0	159.0	31.2			
Cl_2Br	163.0	74.4	10.4			

modified, as Table II. We can now tell what combination of chlorine and bromine atoms is present. It should be noted that Table II presents the isotope contributions in terms of percent of the parent peak.

The parent + 1 peak is still useful for arriving at an empirical formula by use of Appendix A, after we

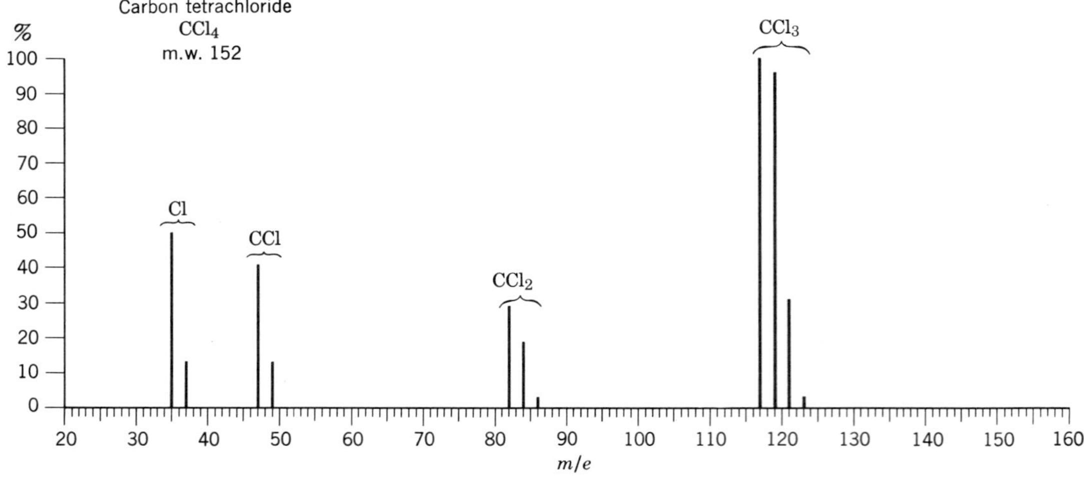

Fig. 9. Carbon tetrachloride.

subtract the masses of the appropriate number of chlorine and bromine atoms.

Unfortunately, the application of isotope contributions, though generally useful for aromatic halogen compounds is limited by the weak parent peak of many aliphatic halogen compounds of more than about six carbon atoms for a straight chain, or fewer for a branched chain. However, the halogen-containing fragments are recognizable by the ratio of the fragment + 2 peaks to fragment peaks in monochlorides or monobromides. In polychloro-or-bromo-compounds, these fragment + isotope peaks form a distinctive series of multiplets (Figure 9). Coincidence of another fragment ion with one of the isotope fragments, with disruption of the characteristic ratios, must always be kept in mind.

Neither fluorine nor iodine has a heavier isotope.

Aliphatic Chlorine Compounds[104,105]

The parent peak is detectable only in the lower monochlorides. Fragmentation of the parent ion is mediated by the chlorine atom, but to a much lesser degree than is the case in oxygen-, nitrogen-, or sulfur-containing compounds. Thus cleavage of a straight-chain monochloride at the C—C bond adjacent to the chlorine atom accounts for a small peak at *m/e* 49 (and, of course, the isotope peak at *m/e* 51).

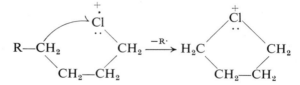

$$\mathrm{R{-}CH_2{-}\overset{+}{\dot{C}}l\!:} \xrightarrow{-\mathrm{R}\cdot} \mathrm{CH_2{=}\overset{+}{C}l\!:} \leftrightarrow \mathrm{\overset{+}{C}H_2{-}\ddot{C}l\!:}$$

Cleavage of the C—Cl bond leads to a small Cl^+ peak and to a R^+ peak which is prominent in the lower chlorides, but quite small when the chain is longer than about C_5.

Straight-chain chlorides longer than C_6 give $C_3H_6\overset{+}{Cl}$, $C_4H_8\overset{+}{Cl}$, and $C_5H_{10}\overset{+}{Cl}$ ions. Of these, the $C_4H_8\overset{+}{Cl}$ ion forms the most intense (sometimes the base) peak; a five-membered cyclic structure may explain its stability.

$$\mathrm{R{-}CH_2{-}CH_2{-}CH_2{-}CH_2{-}\overset{+}{\dot{C}}l} \xrightarrow{-\mathrm{R}\cdot} \mathrm{H_2C{<}(\overset{+}{C}l)(CH_2{-}CH_2){>}CH_2}$$

Loss of HCl occurs, possibly by 1,2-elimination, to give a peak (weak or moderate) at $P-36$.

In general, the spectrum of an aliphatic monochloride is dominated by the hydrocarbon pattern to a greater extent than that of a corresponding alcohol, amine, or mercaptan.

Aliphatic Bromides[104–106]

The remarks under aliphatic chlorides apply quite generally to the corresponding bromides.

Aliphatic Iodides[104,105]

Aliphatic iodides give the strongest parent peak of the aliphatic halides. Since iodine is monoisotopic, there is no distinctive isotope peak. The presence of an iodine atom can sometimes be deduced from isotope peaks that are suspiciously low in relation to the molecular weight, and from several distinctive peaks; in polyiodo compounds, the large interval between major peaks is characteristic.

Iodides cleave much as do chlorides and bromides, but the $C_4H_8\overset{+}{I}$ ion is not as evident as the corresponding chloride and bromide.

Aliphatic Fluorides[105,107–110]

Aliphatic fluorides give the weakest parent peak of the aliphatic halides. Fluorine is monoisotopic, and its detection in polyfluoro compounds depends on suspiciously small isotopic peaks relative to the molecular weight, on the intervals between peaks, and on characteristic peaks. Of these, the most characteristic is *m/e* 69 due to the ion CF_3^+, which is the base peak in all perfluorocarbons. Prominent peaks are noted at *m/e* 119, 169, 219 . . . ; these are increments of CF_2. The stable ions $C_3F_5^+$ and $C_4F_7^+$ give large peaks at *m/e* 131 and 181. The P—F peak is frequently visible in perfluorinated compounds. In monofluorides, cleavage of the $\alpha\beta$ C—C bond is less important than in the other monohalides, but cleavage of a C—H bond on the α—C is more so. This reversal is a consequence of the high electronegativity of the F atom, and is rationalized by placing the positive charge on the α-carbon. The secondary carbonium ion thus depicted by loss of a hydrogen atom is more stable than the primary carbonium ion resulting from loss of an alkyl radical.

$$[R—CH_2—F]^{+} \xrightarrow{-H\cdot} R—\overset{+}{C}H—F$$

$$\xrightarrow{-R\cdot} \overset{+}{C}H_2—F$$

Benzyl Halides[111]

The parent peak of benzyl halides is usually detectable. The benzyl (or tropylium) ion from loss of the halide is favored even over β-bond cleavage of an alkyl substituent. A substituted phenyl ion (α-bond cleavage) is prominent when the ring is polysubstituted.

Aromatic Halides[111–113]

The parent peak of an aryl halide is readily apparent. The $P-X$ peak is large for all compounds in which X is attached directly to the ring.

Heteroaromatic Compounds[92,114–118]

The parent peak of heteroaromatics and alkylated heteroaromatics is intense. Cleavage of the bond beta to the ring, as in alkyl benzenes, is the general rule; in pyridine, the position of substitution determines the ease of cleavage of the beta bond.

Localizing the charge of the parent ion on the heteroatom, rather than in the ring π structure, provides a satisfactory rationale for the observed mode of cleavage. The present treatment follows that used by Djerassi.[2]

The five-membered ring heteroaromatics (furan, thiophene, and pyrrole) show very similar ring cleavage patterns. The first step in each case is cleavage of the carbon-heteroatom bond

$-HC\equiv\dot{Y}$ → *m/e* 39

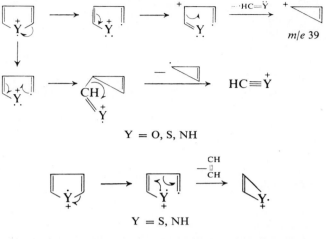

$HC\equiv\overset{+}{Y}$

Y = O, S, NH

$-CH\equiv CH$

Y = S, NH

Thus, in furan, there are two principal peaks: $C_3H_3^+$ (*m/e* 39), $HC\equiv\overset{+}{\ddot{O}}$ (*m/e* 29). In thiophene, there are three: $C_3H_3^+$ (*m/e* 39), $HC\equiv\overset{+}{\ddot{S}}$ (*m/e* 45), and $C_2H_2\overset{+}{\ddot{S}}$ (*m/e* 58). And in pyrrole, there are three: $C_3H_3^+$ (*m/e* 39), $HC\equiv\overset{+}{N}H$ (*m/e* 28) and $C_2H_2\overset{+}{N}H$ (*m/e* 41). Pyrrole also eliminates a neutral molecule of HCN to give an intense peak at *m/e* 40. The base peak in 2,5-dimethylfuran is *m/e* 43 ($CH_3C\equiv\overset{+}{O}$).

Cleavage of the β C—C bond in alkyl pryidines depends on the position of the ring substitution, being more pronounced when the alkyl group is in the 3-position. An alkyl group of more than three carbon atoms in the 2-position can undergo rearrangement of a hydrogen atom to the ring nitrogen.

$-RHC{=}CH_2$; CH_2, CH_2, RHC, H ; $\overset{+}{N}$H CH_2 ⟷ $\overset{+}{N}$H $\dot{C}H_2$

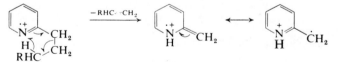

A similar cleavage is found in pyrazines since all ring substituents are necessarily ortho to one of the nitrogen atoms.

Other Classes

The following classes of organic compounds are discussed in Biemann's book (B),[1] or in Djerassi's books (D1, D2, D3).[2,20]

Alkaloids	D1, Chapter 5; D2; D3, Chapter 17; B, p. 305
Amino Acids & Peptides	D3, Chapter 26; B, Chapter 7
Antibiotics	D3, p. 172

Carbohydrates	D3, Chapter 27
Cyanides & Isothiocyanates	D1, Chapter 6
Estrogens	D3, Chapter 19
Glycerides	B, p. 255
Sapogenins	D3, Chapter 22
Silicones	B, p. 172
Steroids	B, Chapter 9; D3, Chapter 17, 20, 21, 22
Terpenes	B, p. 334; D3, Chapter 23, 24
Thioketals	D1, p. 58
Tropone & Tropolones	D1, Chapter 10

References

1. Biemann, K., *Mass Spectrometry, Applications to Organic Chemistry*, McGraw-Hill, New York, 1962. This is the first book on mass spectrometry addressed entirely to the organic chemist. The emphasis is on structure determinations of complex molecules.
2. Budzikiewicz, H., C. Djerassi, and D. H. Williams, *Interpretation of Mass Spectra of Organic Compounds*, Holden-Day, Inc., San Francisco, 1964.
3. Beynon, J. H., *Mass Spectrometry and Its Application to Organic Chemistry*, Elsevier, Amsterdam, 1960.
4. McLafferty, F. W., Ed., *Mass Spectrometry of Organic Ions*, Academic Press, New York, 1963.
5. McDowell, C. A. Ed., *Mass Spectrometry*, McGraw-Hill, New York, 1963.
6. Elliott, R. M. Ed., *Advances in Mass Spectrometry*, Vol. 2, Pergamon, London, 1963.
7. Reed, R. I., *Ion Production by Electron Impact*, Academic Press, London, 1962.
8. McLafferty, F. W., Mass Spectrometry, Chapt. 2, Vol. II, in *Determination of Organic Structure by Physical Methods*, F. C. Nachod and W. D. Phillips Ed., Academic Press, New York, 1962.
9. Waldron, J. D., Ed., *Advances in Mass Spectrometry*, Pergamon Press, London, 1959.
10. Kiser, R. W., *Introduction to Mass Spectroscopy and its Applications*, Prentice-Hall, Englewood Cliffs, N.J., 1965, Chapter 5.
10a. Bondarovich, H. A. and S. K. Freeman, Mass Spectrometry, Chapt. 4 in *Interpretive Spectroscopy*, S. K. Freeman Ed., Reinhold Publishing Corp., N.Y., 1965.
10b. Reed, R. I., *Application of Mass Spectrometry to Organic Chemistry*, Academic Press, N. Y., 1966.
11. "Catalog of Mass Spectra Data," American Petroleum Institute Res. Project No. 44, Carnegie Institute of Technology, Pittsburgh, Pa., and the Manufacturing Chemists Association Research Project, Agricultural and Mechanical College of Texas, College Station, Texas.
12. Index of Mass Spectral Data, A.S.T.M. Special Technical Publication No. 356, American Society for Testing and Materials, Philadelphia, 1963.
13. Beynon, J. H. and A. E. Williams, *Mass and Abundance Tables for Use in Mass Spectrometry*, Elsevier, Amsterdam, 1963.
13a. Cornu, A. and R. Massot, *Organic Analysis by High Resolution Mass Spectrometry, Atlas of Lines*, Les Presses Universitaires de France, Paris, 1965.
14. Lederberg, J., *Computation of Molecular Formulas for Mass Spectrometry*, Holden-Day, San Francisco, 1964.
15. Lederberg, J., *Tables and an Algorithm for Calculating Functional Groups of Organic Molecules in High Resolution Mass Spectrometry*, NASA Sci. Techn. Aerosp. Rep., N64-21426 (1964).
16. Kendrich, E., "A Mass Scale Based on $CH_2 = 14.0000$ for High-Resolution Mass Spectrometry of Organic Compounds," *Anal. Chem.*, **35,** 2146 (1963).
17. Biemann, K., P. Bommer, and D. M. Desiderio, Tetrahedron Letters, **1964,** 1725. Biemann, K., W. McMurray, Tetrahedron Letters, **1965,** 647. Biemann, K., *J. Pure Appl. Chem.*, **9,** 95 (1964).
18. Tunnicliff, D. D., P. A. Wadsworth, and D. O. Schissler, Mass and Abundance Tables. Shell Development Co., Emeryville, Calif.
19. Fuqua, S. A. and R. M. Silverstein, *J. Org. Chem.*, **29,** 395 (1964).
20. Budzikiewicz, H., C. Djerassi, and D. H. Williams, *Structure Elucidation of Natural Products by Mass Spectrometry*, Vols. I and II, Holden-Day, San Francisco, 1964.
21. Birkhofer, L. and A. Ritter, *Ber.*, **93,** 424 (1960).
22. Birkhofer, L. and A. Ritter, *Angew. Chem.*, int. ed., **4,** 417 (1965).
23. Sweeley, C. C. et al., *J. Am. Chem. Soc.*, **85,** 2497 (1963).
24. Makita, M., and W. W. Wells, *Anal. Biochem.*, **5,** 523 (1963).
25. Sharkey, A. G., R. A. Friedel, and S. H. Langer, *Anal. Chem.*, **29,** 770 (1957).
26. Siegel, H., and D. O. Schissler, *Anal. Chem.*, **28,** 1646 (1956).
27. Biemann, K., F. Gapp, and J. Seibl, *J. Am. Chem. Soc.*, **81,** 2274 (1959).
28. Weygand, F. et al. *Angew. Chem.*, int. ed., **2,** 485 (1963).
29. McLafferty, F. W., *Mass Spectral Correlations*, Advances in Chemistry Series No. 40. American Chemical Society, Washington, D.C., 1963.
30. Herlan, A., *Brennstoff.—Chem.*, **45,** 244 (1964).
31. Wibaut, J. P. and H. Brand, *Rec. trav. chim.*, **80,** 97 (1961).
32. O'Neal, M. J., and T. P. Wier, *Anal. Chem.*, **23,** 830 (1951).
33. McLafferty, F. W., *Anal. Chem.*, **31,** 2072 (1959).
34. Ref. 4, Chapt. 13.
35. Ref. 4, Chapt. 10.
36. Meyerson, S., *Appl. Spectroscopy*, **9,** 120 (1955).
37. King, A. B., *J. Chem. Phys.*, **42,** 3526 (1965).
38. Meyerson, S., H. Drews, and E. K. Fields, *J. Am. Chem. Soc.*, **86,** 4964 (1964).
39. Friedel, R. A., J. L. Shultz, and A. G. Sharkey, *Anal. Chem.*, **28,** 926 (1956).
40. Brown, R. A., W. S. Young, and N. Nicolaides, *Anal. Chem.*, **26,** 1653 (1954).
41. McFadden, W. H., M. Lounsbury, and A. L. Wahrhaftig, *Can. J. Chem.*, **36,** 990 (1958).
42. Ryhage, R. and E. Stenhagen, *J. Lipid Research*, **1,** 361 (1960).
43. Shannon, J. S., *Austral. J. Chem.*, **15,** 265 (1962).
44. Meyerson, S., P. N. Rylander, E. L. Eliel, and J. D. McCollum, *J. Am. Chem. Soc.*, **81,** 2606 (1959).
45. Eliel, E. L., J. D. McCollum, S. Meyerson, and P. N. Rylander, *J. Am. Chem. Soc.*, **83,** 2481 (1961).
46. Aczel, T., and H. E. Lumpkin, *Anal. Chem.*, **32,** 1819 (1960).
47. McLafferty, F. W., *Anal. Chem.*, **29,** 1782 (1957).
48. Ref. 3, pp. 362–367.
49. Friedel, R. A., and A. G. Sharkey, *Anal. Chem.*, **28,** 940 (1956).
50. von Mutzenbecker, G., Z. Pelah, D. H. Williams, H. Budzikiewicz, and C. Djerassi, *Steroids*, **2,** 475 (1963).
51. McFadden, W. H., J. Wasserman, J. Corse, R. E. Lundin, and R. Teranishi, *Anal. Chem.*, **36,** 1031 (1964).
51a. Djerassi, C., and C. Fenselau, *J. Am. Chem. Soc.*, **87,** 5747 (1965).
52. Wilson, J. M., *Experientia*, **16,** 403 (1960).

53. Barnes, C. S., and J. L. Occolowitz, *Austral. J. Chem.*, **16,** 219 (1963).
54. Pelah, Z., J. M. Wilson, M. Ohashi, H. Budzikiewicz, and C. Djerassi, *Tetrahedron*, **19,** 2233 (1963).
55. Ref. 3, pp. 272–273.
56. Reed, R. I., and J. M. Wilson, *Chem. and Ind.*, **1962,** 1428.
57. Sharkey, A. G., J. L. Shultz, and R. A. Friedel, *Anal. Chem.*, **28,** 934 (1956).
58. Ref. 3, pp. 294–302.
59. Ahlquist, L., R. Ryhage, E. Stenhagen, and E. von Sydow, *Arkiv Kemi*, **14,** 211 (1959).
60. Beynon, J. H., R. A. Saunders, and A. E. Williams, *Appl. Spectroscopy*, **14,** 95 (1960).
61. Natalis, P., *Bull. Soc. Chim. Belges*, **67,** 599 (1958).
62. Williams, D. H., H. Budzikiewicz, Z. Pelah, and C. Djerassi, *Monatsh.*, **95,** 166 (1964).
63. McLafferty, F. W., *Anal. Chem.*, **31,** 477 (1959).
64. Meyerson, S., and P. N. Rylander, *J. Am. Chem. Soc.*, **79,** 1058 (1957).
65. Gilpin, J. A., and F. W. McLafferty, *Anal. Chem.*, **29,** 990 (1957).
66. Aczel, T. and H. E. Lumpkin, *Anal. Chem.*, **33,** 386 (1961).
67. McCollum, J. D., and S. Meyerson, *J. Am. Chem. Soc.*, **85,** 1739 (1963).
67a. Happ, G. P., and D. W. Stewart, *J. Am. Chem. Soc.*, **74,** 4404 (1952).
68. Ref. 3, pp. 371–373.
69. Rol, N. C., *Rec. Trav. Chim.*, **84,** 413 (1965).
70. McLafferty, F. W., and R. S. Gohlke, *Anal. Chem.*, **31,** 2076 (1959).
71. Beynon, J. H., B. E. Job, and A. E. Williams, *Z. Naturforsch.*, **20,** 883 (1965).
72. Ref. 3, pp. 373–374.
73. Sharkey, A. G., J. L. Shultz, and R. A. Friedel, *Anal. Chem.*, **31,** 87 (1959).
74. Ryhage, R., and E. Stenhagen, *Arkiv Kemi*, **13,** 523 (1959). *Ibid.*, **14,** 483, 497 (1959).
75. Beynon, J. H., R. A. Saunders, and A. E. Williams, *Anal. Chem.*, **33,** 221 (1961).
76. Ref. 4, Chapt. 9.
77. Williams, D. H., H. Budzikiewicz, and C. Djerassi, *J. Am. Chem. Soc.*, **86,** 286 (1964).
78. Black, D. R., W. H. McFadden, and J. W. Corse, *J. Phys. Chem.*, **68,** 1237 (1964).
79. Ryhage, R., and E. Stenhagen, *Arkiv Kemi*, **23,** 167 (1964).
80. Kourey, R. E., B. L. Tuffley, and V. A. Yarborough, *Anal. Chem.*, **31,** 1760 (1959).
81. Emery, E. M., *Anal. Chem.*, **32,** 1495 (1960).
82. Aczel, T., and H. E. Lumpkin, *Anal. Chem.*, **34,** 33 (1962).
83. Friedman, L., and F. A. Long, *J. Am. Chem. Soc.*, **75,** 2832 (1953).
84. McFadden, W. H., E. A. Day, and M. J. Diamond, *Anal. Chem.*, **37,** 89 (1965).
85. Honhanen, E., T. Moisco, and P. Karvonen, *Acta Chem. Scand.*, **19,** 370 (1965).
86. Collin, J., *Bull. soc. roy. sci., Liège*, **21,** 446 (1952). *Ibid.*, **24,** 96 (1955). *Ibid.*, **25,** 441 (1956).
87. Gohlke, R. S., and F. W. McLafferty, *Anal. Chem.*, **34,** 1281 (1962).
87a. Djerassi, C., and C. Fenselau, *J. Am. Chem. Soc.*, **87,** 5752 (1965).
88. Gallegos, E. J., and R. W. Kiser, *J. Phys. Chem.*, **66,** 136, (1962).
89. Momigny, J., *Bull. soc. roy. sci., Liège*, **22,** 541 (1953).
90. Rylander, P. N., S. Meyerson, E. L. Eliel, and J. D. McCollum, *J. Am. Chem. Soc.*, **85,** 2723 (1963).
91. Ryhage, R., and E. Stenhagen, *Arkiv Kemi*, **15,** 545 (1960).
92. Spiteller, G., and M. Spiteller-Friedman, *Monatsh.*, **93,** 1395 (1962).
93. Gilpin, J. A., *Anal. Chem.*, **31,** 935 (1959).
94. Pelah, Z., M. A. Kielczewski, J. M. Wilson, M. Ohashi, H. Budzikiewicz, and C. Djerassi. *J. Am. Chem. Soc.*, **85,** 2470 (1963).
95. McLafferty, F. W., *Anal. Chem.* **34,** 26 (1962).
96. Beugelmans, R., D. H. Williams, H. Budzikiewicz, and C. Djerassi, *J. Am. Chem. Soc.*, **86,** 1386 (1964).
97. Collin, J., *Bull. soc. roy. sci., Liège*, **23,** 201 (1954).
98. Ref. 3, pp. 406–409.
98a. Aplin, J., M. Fischer, D. Becher, H. Budzekiewicz, and C. Djerassi, *J. Am. Chem. Soc.*, **87,** 4888 (1965).
99. Momigny, J., *Bull. Soc. roy. sci., Liège*, **25,** 93 (1956).
100. D'Or, L., and J. Collins, *Bull. soc. roy. sci., Liège*, **22,** 285 (1953).
101. Boschan, R., and S. R. Smith, U.S. Govt. Dept. of Comm. Office of Tech. Service, PB 151120, July 1957.
102. Levy, E. J., and W. H. Stahl, *Anal. Chem.*, **33,** 707 (1961).
102a. Sample, S., and C. Djerassi, *J. Am. Chem. Soc.*, **88,** 1937 (1966).
103. Ref. 3, p. 298.
104. Collin, J., *Bull. soc. roy. sci., Liège*, **25,** 426 (1956).
105. McLafferty, F. W., *Anal. Chem.*, **34,** 2 (1962).
106. McFadden, W. H., and M. Lounsbury, *Can. J. Chem.*, **40,** 1965 (1962).
107. Ref. 3, pp. 413–421.
108. Mohler, F. L., E. G. Bloom, J. H. Lengel, and C. E. Wise, *J. Am. Chem. Soc.*, **71,** 337 (1949).
109. Mohler, F. L., V. H. Dibeler, and R. M. Reese, *J. Research NBS*, **49,** 343 (1952).
110. Majer, J. R. in Stacey, Tatlow and Sharpe, Eds., *Advances in Fluorine Chemistry*, Vol. 2, Butterworths, London, 1961, p. 55.
111. McLafferty, F. W., *Anal. Chem.*, **34,** 16 (1962).
112. D'Or, L., J. Momigny, and A. M. Wirtz-Cordier, *Bull. Acad. Roy. Belg. Classe Scie.*, **47,** 811 (1961).
113. Dibeler, V. H., R. M. Reese, and F. L. Mohler, *J. Chem. Phys.*, **26,** 304 (1957).
114. Collin, J., *Bull. soc. roy. chim. Belges*, **69,** 449, 575 (1960).
115. Beynon, J. H., and A. E. Williams, *Applied Spectroscopy*, **13,** 101 (1959).
116. Kinney, I. W., and G. L. Cook, *Anal. Chem.*, **24,** 1609 (1959).
117. Budzikiewicz, H., C. Djerassi, H. H. Jackson, G. W. Kenner, D. J. Newman, and J. M. Wilson, *J. Chem. Soc.*, **1964,** 1949.
118. Ref. 1, p. 130, p. 132, pp. 134–135, and pp. 184–186.

APPENDIX A Masses and Isotopic Abundance Ratios for Various Combinations of Carbon, Hydrogen, Nitrogen and Oxygen *

	P + 1	P + 2
12		
C	1.08	
13		
CH	1.10	
14		
N	0.38	
CH_2	1.11	
15		
NH	0.40	
CH_3	1.13	
16		
O	0.04	0.20
NH_2	0.41	
CH_4	1.15	
17		
OH	0.06	0.20
NH_3	0.43	
CH_5	1.16	
18		
H_2O	0.07	0.20
NH_4	0.45	
19		
H_3O	0.09	0.20
24		
C_2	2.16	0.01
25		
C_2H	2.18	0.01
26		
CN	1.46	
C_2H_2	2.19	0.01
27		
CHN	1.48	
C_2H_3	2.21	0.01
28		
N_2	0.76	
CO	1.12	0.2
CH_2N	1.49	
C_2H_4	2.23	0.01
29		
N_2H	0.78	
CHO	1.14	0.20
CH_3N	1.51	
C_2H_5	2.24	0.01
30		
NO	0.42	0.20
N_2H_2	0.79	
CH_2O	1.15	0.20
CH_4N	1.53	0.01
C_2H_6	2.26	0.01
31		
NOH	0.44	0.20
N_2H_3	0.81	
CH_3O	1.17	0.20
CH_5N	1.54	
32		
O_2	0.08	0.40
NOH_2	0.45	0.20
N_2H_4	0.83	
CH_4O	1.18	0.20
33		
NOH_3	0.47	0.20
N_2H_5	0.84	
CH_5O	1.12	
34		
N_2H_6	0.86	
36		
C_3	3.24	0.04
37		
C_3H	3.26	0.04
38		
C_2N	2.54	0.02
C_3H_2	3.27	0.04
39		
C_2HN	2.56	0.02
C_3H_3	3.29	0.04
40		
CN_2	1.84	0.01
C_2O	2.20	0.21
C_2H_2N	2.58	0.02
C_3H_4	3.31	0.04
41		
CHN_2	1.86	
C_2HO	2.22	0.21
C_2H_3N	2.59	0.02
C_3H_5	3.32	0.04
42		
CNO	1.50	0.21
CH_2N_2	1.88	0.01
C_2H_2O	2.23	0.21
C_2H_4N	2.61	0.02
C_3H_6	3.34	0.04
43		
CHNO	1.52	0.21
CH_3N_2	1.89	0.01
C_2H_3O	2.25	0.21
C_2H_5N	2.62	0.02
C_3H_7	3.35	0.04
44		
N_2O	0.80	0.20
CO_2	1.16	0.40
CH_2NO	1.53	0.21
CH_4N_2	1.91	0.01
C_2H_4O	2.26	0.21
C_2H_6N	2.64	0.02
C_3H_8	3.37	0.04
45		
HN_2O	0.82	0.20
CHO_2	1.18	0.40
CH_3NO	1.55	0.21
CH_5N_2	1.92	0.01
C_2H_5O	2.28	0.21
C_2H_7N	2.66	0.02
46		
NO_2	0.46	0.40
N_2H_2O	0.83	0.20
CH_2O_2	1.19	0.40
CH_4NO	1.57	0.21
CH_6N_2	1.94	0.01
C_2H_6O	2.30	0.22
C_2H_8N	2.66	0.02
47		
CH_3O_2	1.21	0.40
CH_5NO	1.58	0.21
CH_7N_2	1.96	0.01
C_2H_7O	2.31	0.22
48		
CH_4O_2	1.22	0.40
C_4	4.32	0.07
49		
CH_5O_2	1.24	0.40
C_4H	4.34	0.07
50		
C_4H_2	4.34	0.07
51		
C_4H_3	4.37	0.07
52		
C_2N_2	2.92	0.03
C_3H_2N	3.66	0.05
C_4H_4	4.39	0.07
53		
C_2HN_2	2.94	0.03
C_3HO	3.30	0.24
C_3H_3N	3.67	0.05
C_4H_5	4.40	0.07
54		
C_2NO	2.58	0.22
$C_2H_2N_2$	2.96	0.03
C_3H_2O	3.31	0.24
C_3H_4N	3.69	0.05
C_4H_6	4.42	0.07
55		
C_2HNO	2.60	0.22
$C_2H_3N_2$	2.97	0.03
C_3H_3O	3.33	0.24
C_3H_5N	3.70	0.05
C_4H_7	4.43	0.08

* Adapted with permission from J. H. Beynon, *Mass Spectrometry and Its Application to Organic Chemistry*, Elsevier, Amsterdam, 1960.

	P + 1	P + 2
56		
CH_2N_3	2.26	0.02
C_2O_2	2.24	0.41
C_2H_2NO	2.61	0.22
$C_2H_4N_2$	2.99	0.03
C_3H_4O	3.35	0.24
C_3H_6N	3.72	0.05
C_4H_8	4.45	0.08
57		
CHN_2O	1.90	0.21
CH_3N_3	2.27	0.02
C_2HO_2	2.26	0.41
C_2H_3NO	2.63	0.22
$C_2H_5N_2$	3.00	0.03
C_3H_5O	3.36	0.24
C_3H_7N	3.74	0.05
C_4H_9	4.47	0.08
58		
CNO_2	1.54	0.41
CH_2N_2O	1.92	0.21
CH_4N_3	2.29	0.02
$C_2H_2O_2$	2.27	0.42
C_2H_4NO	2.65	0.22
$C_2H_6N_2$	3.02	0.03
C_3H_6O	3.38	0.24
C_3H_8N	3.75	0.05
C_4H_{10}	4.48	0.08
59		
$CHNO_2$	1.56	0.41
CH_3N_2O	1.93	0.21
CH_5N_3	2.31	0.02
$C_2H_3O_2$	2.29	0.42
C_2H_5NO	2.66	0.22
$C_2H_7N_2$	3.04	0.03
C_3H_7O	3.39	0.24
C_3H_9N	3.77	0.05
60		
CH_2NO_2	1.57	0.41
CH_4N_2O	1.95	0.21
CH_6N_3	2.32	0.02
$C_2H_4O_2$	2.30	0.04
C_2H_6NO	2.68	0.22
$C_2H_8N_2$	3.05	0.03
C_3H_8O	3.41	0.24
61		
CHO_3	1.21	0.60
CH_3NO_2	1.59	0.41
CH_5N_2O	1.96	0.21
CH_7N_3	2.34	0.02
$C_2H_5O_2$	2.32	0.42
C_2H_7NO	2.69	0.22
C_3H_9O	3.43	0.24
C_5H	5.42	0.12
62		
CH_2O_3	1.23	0.60
CH_4NO_2	1.60	0.41
CH_6N_2O	1.98	0.21
CH_8N_3	2.35	0.02

	P + 1	P + 2
$C_2H_6O_2$	2.34	0.42
C_5H_2	5.44	0.12
63		
CH_3O_3	1.25	0.60
CH_5NO_2	1.62	0.41
C_4HN	4.72	0.09
C_5H_3	5.45	0.12
64		
CH_4O_3	1.26	0.60
C_4H_2N	4.74	0.09
C_5H_4	5.47	0.12
65		
C_3HN_2	4.02	0.06
C_4HO	4.38	0.27
C_4H_3N	4.75	0.09
C_5H_5	5.48	0.12
66		
$C_3H_2N_2$	4.04	0.06
C_4H_2O	4.39	0.27
C_4H_4N	4.77	0.09
C_5H_6	5.50	0.12
67		
C_2HN_3	3.32	0.04
C_3HNO	3.68	0.25
$C_3H_3N_2$	4.05	0.06
C_4H_3O	4.41	0.27
C_4H_5N	4.78	0.09
C_5H_7	5.52	0.12
68		
$C_2H_2N_3$	3.34	0.04
C_3O_2	3.32	0.44
C_3H_2NO	3.69	0.25
$C_3H_4N_2$	4.07	0.06
C_4H_4O	4.43	0.28
C_4H_6N	4.80	0.09
C_5H_8	5.53	0.12
69		
CHN_4	2.62	0.03
C_2HN_2O	2.98	0.23
$C_2H_3N_3$	3.35	0.04
C_3HO_2	3.34	0.44
C_3H_3NO	3.71	0.25
$C_3H_5N_2$	4.09	0.06
C_4H_5O	4.44	0.28
C_4H_7N	4.82	0.09
C_5H_9	5.55	0.12
70		
CH_2N_4	2.64	0.03
C_2NO_2	2.62	0.42
$C_2H_2N_2O$	3.00	0.23
$C_2H_4N_3$	3.37	0.04
$C_3H_2O_2$	3.35	0.44
C_3H_4NO	3.73	0.25
$C_3H_6N_2$	4.10	0.07
C_4H_6O	4.46	0.28
C_4H_8N	4.83	0.09

	P + 1	P + 2
C_5H_{10}	5.56	0.13
71		
CHN_3O	2.28	0.22
CH_3N_4	2.65	0.03
C_2HNO_2	2.64	0.42
$C_2H_3N_2O$	3.01	0.23
$C_3H_5N_3$	3.39	0.04
$C_3H_3O_2$	3.37	0.44
C_3H_5NO	3.74	0.25
$C_3H_7N_2$	4.12	0.07
C_4H_7O	4.47	0.28
C_4H_9N	4.85	0.09
C_5H_{11}	5.58	0.13
72		
CH_2N_3O	2.30	0.22
CH_4N_4	2.67	0.03
$C_2H_2NO_2$	2.65	0.42
$C_2H_4N_2O$	3.03	0.23
$C_2H_6N_3$	3.40	0.44
$C_3H_4O_2$	3.38	0.44
C_3H_6NO	3.76	0.25
$C_3H_8N_2$	4.13	0.07
C_4H_8O	4.49	0.28
$C_4H_{10}N$	4.86	0.09
C_5H_{12}	5.60	0.13
73		
CHN_2O_2	1.94	0.41
CH_3N_3O	2.31	0.22
CH_5N_4	2.69	0.03
C_2HO_3	2.30	0.62
$C_2H_3NO_2$	2.67	0.42
$C_2H_5N_2O$	3.04	0.23
$C_2H_7N_3$	3.42	0.04
$C_3H_5O_2$	3.40	0.44
C_3H_7NO	3.77	0.25
$C_3H_9N_2$	4.15	0.07
C_4H_9O	4.51	0.28
$C_4H_{11}N$	4.88	0.10
C_6H	6.50	0.18
74		
$CH_2N_2O_2$	1.95	0.41
CH_4N_3O	2.33	0.22
CH_6N_4	2.70	0.03
$C_2H_2O_3$	2.31	0.62
$C_2H_4NO_2$	2.69	0.42
$C_2H_6N_2O$	3.06	0.23
$C_2H_8N_3$	3.43	0.05
$C_3H_6O_2$	3.42	0.44
C_3H_8NO	3.79	0.25
$C_3H_{10}N_2$	4.17	0.07
$C_4H_{10}O$	4.52	0.28
C_6H_2	6.52	0.18
75		
$CHNO_3$	1.60	0.61
$CH_3N_2O_2$	1.97	0.41
CH_5N_3O	2.34	0.22
CH_7N_4	2.72	0.03
$C_2H_3O_3$	2.33	0.62
$C_2H_5NO_2$	2.70	0.43

	P + 1	P + 2
$C_2H_7N_2O$	3.08	0.23
$C_2H_9N_3$	3.45	0.05
$C_3H_7O_2$	3.43	0.44
C_3H_9NO	3.81	0.25
C_5HN	5.80	0.14
C_6H_3	6.53	0.18
76		
CH_2NO_3	1.61	0.61
$CH_4N_2O_2$	1.99	0.41
CH_6N_3O	2.36	0.22
CH_8N_4	2.73	0.03
$C_2H_4O_3$	2.34	0.62
$C_2H_6NO_2$	2.72	0.43
$C_2H_8N_2O$	3.09	0.24
$C_3H_8O_2$	3.45	0.44
C_5H_2N	5.82	0.14
C_6H_4	6.55	0.18
77		
CHO_4	1.25	0.80
CH_3NO_3	1.63	0.61
$CH_5N_2O_2$	2.00	0.41
CH_7N_3O	2.38	0.22
$C_2H_5O_3$	2.39	0.62
$C_2H_7NO_2$	2.73	0.43
C_4HN_2	5.10	0.11
C_5HO	5.45	0.32
C_5H_3N	5.83	0.14
C_6H_5	6.56	0.18
78		
CH_2O_4	1.27	0.80
CH_4NO_3	1 64	0.61
$CH_6N_2O_2$	2.02	0.41
$C_2H_6O_3$	2.38	0.62
$C_4H_2N_2$	5.12	0.11
C_5H_2O	5.47	0.32
C_5H_4N	5.49	0.14
C_6H_6	6.58	0.18
79		
CH_3O_4	1.29	0.80
CH_5NO_3	1.66	0.61
C_3HN_3	4.40	0.08
C_4HNO	4.76	0.29
$C_4H_3N_2$	5.13	0.11
C_5H_3O	5.49	0.32
C_5H_5N	5.87	0.14
C_6H_7	6.60	0.18
80		
CH_4O_4	1.30	0.80
$C_3H_2N_3$	4.42	0.08
C_4H_2NO	4.78	0.29
$C_4H_4N_2$	5.15	0.11
C_5H_4O	5.51	0.32
C_5H_6N	5.88	0.14
C_6H_8	6.61	0 18
81		
C_2HN_4	3.70	0.05
C_3HN_2O	4.06	0 26

	P + 1	P + 2
$C_3H_3N_3$	4.43	0.08
C_4HO_2	4.42	0.48
C_4H_3NO	4.79	0.29
$C_4H_5N_2$	5.17	0.11
C_5H_5O	5.52	0.32
C_5H_7N	5.90	0.14
C_6H_9	6.63	0.18
82		
$C_2H_2N_4$	3.72	0.05
$C_3H_2N_2O$	4.08	0.36
$C_3H_4N_3$	4.45	0.08
$C_4H_2O_2$	4.43	0.48
C_4H_4NO	4.81	0.29
$C_4H_6N_2$	4.18	0.11
C_5H_6O	5.54	0.32
C_5H_8N	5.91	0.14
C_6H_{10}	6.64	0.19
83		
C_2HN_3O	3.36	0.24
$C_2H_3N_4$	3.74	0.06
C_3HNO_2	3.72	0.45
$C_3H_3N_2O$	4.09	0.27
$C_3H_5N_3$	4.47	0.08
$C_4H_3O_2$	4.45	0.48
C_4H_5NO	4.82	0.29
$C_4H_7N_2$	5.20	0.11
C_5H_7O	5.55	0.33
C_5H_9N	5.93	0.15
C_6H_{11}	6.66	0.19
84		
$C_2H_2N_3O$	3.38	0.24
$C_2H_4N_4$	3.75	0.06
$C_3H_2NO_2$	3.73	0.45
$C_3H_4N_2O$	4.11	0.27
$C_3H_6N_3$	4.48	0.81
$C_4H_4O_2$	4.47	0.48
C_4H_6NO	4.84	0.29
$C_4H_8N_2$	5.21	0.11
C_5H_8O	5.57	0.33
$C_5H_{10}N$	5.95	0.15
C_6H_{12}	6.68	0.19
85		
CHN_4O	2.66	0.23
$C_2HN_2O_2$	3.02	0.43
$C_2H_3N_3O$	3.39	0.24
$C_2H_5N_4$	3.77	0.06
C_3HO_3	3.38	0.64
$C_3H_3NO_2$	3.75	0.45
$C_3H_5N_2O$	4.12	0.27
$C_3H_7N_3$	4.50	0.08
$C_4H_5O_2$	4.48	0.48
C_4H_7NO	4.86	0.29
$C_4H_9N_2$	5.23	0.11
C_5H_9O	5.59	0.33
$C_5H_{11}N$	5.96	0.15
C_6H_{13}	6.69	0.19
C_7H	7.58	0.25
86		
CH_2N_4O	2.68	0.23
$C_2H_2N_2O_2$	3.03	0.43
$C_2H_4N_3O$	3.41	0.24
$C_2H_6N_4$	3.78	0.06
$C_3H_2O_3$	3.39	0.64
$C_3H_4NO_2$	3.77	0.45
$C_3H_6N_2O$	4.14	0.27
$C_3H_8N_3$	4.51	0.08
$C_4H_6O_2$	4.50	0.48
C_4H_8NO	4.87	0.30
$C_4H_{10}N_2$	5.25	0.11
$C_5H_{10}O$	5.60	0.33
$C_5H_{12}N$	5.98	0.15
C_6H_{14}	6.71	0.19
C_7H_2	7.60	0.25
87		
CHN_3O_2	2.32	0.42
CH_3N_4O	2.69	0.23
C_2HNO_3	2.68	0.62
$C_2H_3N_2O_2$	3.05	0.43
$C_2H_5N_3O$	3.43	0.25
$C_2H_7N_4$	3.80	0.06
$C_3H_3O_3$	3.41	0.64
$C_3H_5NO_2$	3.78	0.45
$C_3H_7N_2O$	4.16	0.27
$C_3H_9N_3$	4.53	0.08
$C_4H_7O_2$	4.51	0.48
C_4H_9NO	4.89	0.30
$C_4H_{11}N_2$	5.26	0.11
$C_5H_{11}O$	5.62	0.33
$C_5H_{13}N$	5.99	0.15
C_6HN	6.88	0.20
C_7H_3	7.61	0.25
88		
$CH_2N_3O_2$	2.34	0.42
CH_4N_4O	2.71	0.23
$C_2H_2NO_3$	2.69	0.63
$C_2H_4N_2O_2$	3.07	0.43
$C_2H_6N_3O$	3.44	0.25
$C_2H_8N_4$	3.82	0.06
$C_3H_4O_3$	3.42	0.64
$C_3H_6NO_2$	3.80	0.45
$C_3H_8N_2O$	4.17	0.27
$C_3H_{10}N_3$	4.55	0.08
$C_4H_8O_2$	4.53	0.48
$C_4H_{10}NO$	4.90	0.30
$C_4H_{12}N_2$	5.28	0.11
$C_5H_{12}O$	5.63	0.33
C_6H_2N	6.90	0.20
C_7H_4	7.63	0.25
89		
CHN_2O_3	1.98	0.61
$CH_3N_3O_2$	2.35	0.42
CH_5N_4O	2.73	0.23
C_2HO_4	2.33	0.82
$C_2H_3NO_3$	2.71	0.63
$C_2H_5N_2O_2$	3.08	0.44
$C_2H_7N_3O$	3.46	0.25
$C_2H_9N_4$	3.83	0.06
$C_3H_5O_3$	3.44	0.64
$C_3H_7NO_2$	3.81	0.46
$C_3H_9N_2O$	4.19	0.27
$C_3H_{11}N_3$	4.56	0.84
$C_4H_9O_2$	4.55	0.48
$C_4H_{11}NO$	4.92	0.30
C_5HN_2	6.18	0.16
C_6HO	6.54	0.38
C_6H_3N	6.91	0.20
C_7H_5	7.64	0.25
90		
$CH_2N_2O_3$	1.99	0.61
$CH_4N_3O_2$	2.37	0.42
CH_6N_4O	2.74	0.23
$C_2H_2O_4$	2.35	0.82
$C_2H_4NO_3$	2.72	0.63
$C_2H_6N_2O_2$	3.10	0.44
$C_2H_8N_3O$	3.47	0.25
$C_2H_{10}N_4$	3.85	0.06
$C_3H_6O_3$	3.46	0.64
$C_3H_8NO_2$	3.83	0.46
$C_3H_{10}N_2O$	4.20	0.27
$C_4H_{10}O_2$	4.56	0.48
$C_5H_2N_2$	6.20	0.16
C_6H_2O	6.56	0.38
C_6H_4N	6.93	0.20
C_7H_6	7.66	0.25
91		
$CHNO_4$	1.63	0.81
$CH_3N_2O_3$	2.01	0.61
$CH_5N_3O_2$	2.38	0.42
CH_7N_4O	2.76	0.23
$C_2H_3O_4$	2.37	0.82
$C_2H_5NO_3$	2.74	0.63
$C_2H_7N_2O_2$	3.11	0.44
$C_2H_9N_3O$	3.49	0.25
$C_3H_7O_3$	3.47	0.64
$C_3H_9NO_2$	3.85	0.46
C_4HN_3	5.48	0.12
C_5HNO	5.84	0.34
$C_5H_3N_2$	6.21	0.16
C_6H_3O	6.57	0.38
C_6H_5N	6.95	0.21
C_7H_7	7.68	0.25
92		
CH_2NO_4	1.65	0.81
$CH_4N_2O_3$	2.03	0.61
$CH_6N_3O_2$	2.40	0.42
CH_8N_4O	2.77	0.23
$C_2H_4O_4$	2.38	0.82
$C_2H_6NO_3$	2.76	0.63
$C_2H_8N_2O_2$	3.13	0.44
$C_3H_8O_3$	3.49	0.64
$C_4H_2N_3$	5.50	0.13
C_5H_2NO	5.86	0.34
$C_5H_4N_2$	6.23	0.16
C_6H_4O	6.59	0.38
C_6H_6N	6.96	0.21
C_7H_8	7.69	0.26
N_2O_4	9.19	0.80
93		
CH_3NO_4	1.67	0.81
$CH_5N_2O_3$	2.04	0.61
$CH_7N_3O_2$	2.42	0.42
$C_2H_5O_4$	2.40	0.82
$C_2H_7NO_3$	2.77	0.63
C_3HN_4	4.78	0.09
C_4HN_2O	5.14	0.31
$C_4H_3N_3$	5.52	0.13
C_5HO_2	5.50	0.52
C_5H_3NO	5.87	0.34
$C_5H_5N_2$	6.25	0.16
C_6H_5O	6.60	0.38
C_6H_7N	6.98	0.21
C_7H_9	7.71	0.26
94		
CH_4NO_4	1.68	0.81
$CH_6N_2O_3$	2.06	0.62
$C_2H_6O_4$	2.41	0.82
$C_3H_2N_4$	4.80	0.09
$C_4H_2N_2O$	5.16	0.31
$C_4H_4N_3$	5.53	0.13
$C_5H_2O_2$	5.51	0.52
C_5H_4NO	5.89	0.34
$C_5H_6N_2$	6.26	0.17
C_6H_6O	6.62	0.38
C_6H_8N	6.99	0.21
C_7H_{10}	7.72	0.26
95		
CH_5NO_4	1.70	0.81
C_3HN_3O	4.44	0.28
$C_3H_3N_4$	4.82	0.10
C_4HNO_2	4.80	0.49
$C_4H_3N_2O$	5.17	0.31
$C_4H_5N_3$	5.55	0.13
$C_5H_3O_2$	5.53	0.52
C_5H_5NO	5.90	0.34
$C_5H_7N_2$	6.28	0.17
C_6H_7O	6.64	0.39
C_6H_9N	7.01	0.21
C_7H_{11}	7.74	0.26
96		
$C_3H_2N_3O$	4.46	0.28
$C_3H_4N_4$	4.83	0.10
$C_4H_2NO_2$	4.81	0.49
$C_4H_4N_2O$	5.19	0.31
$C_4H_6N_3$	5.56	0.13
$C_5H_4O_2$	5.55	0.53
C_5H_6NO	5.92	0.35
$C_5H_8N_2$	6.29	0.17
C_6H_8O	6.65	0.39
$C_6H_{10}N$	7.03	0.21
C_7H_{12}	7.76	0.26
97		
C_2HN_4O	3.74	0.26
$C_3HN_2O_2$	4.10	0.47
$C_3H_3N_3O$	4.47	0.28
$C_3H_5N_4$	4.85	0.10
C_4HO_3	4.46	0.68
$C_4H_3NO_2$	4.83	0.49
$C_4H_5N_2O$	5.20	0.31
$C_4H_7N_3$	5.58	0.13
$C_5H_5O_2$	5.56	0.53

	P + 1	P + 2
C_5H_7NO	5.94	0.35
$C_5H_9N_2$	6.31	0.17
C_6H_9O	6.67	0.39
$C_6H_{11}N$	7.04	0.21
C_7H_{13}	7.77	0.26
C_8H	8.66	0.33
98		
$C_2H_2N_4O$	3.76	0.26
$C_3H_2N_2O_2$	4.12	0.47
$C_3H_4N_3O$	4.49	0.28
$C_3H_6N_4$	4.86	0.10
$C_4H_2O_3$	4.47	0.68
$C_4H_4NO_2$	4.85	0.49
$C_4H_6N_2O$	5.22	0.31
$C_4H_8N_3$	5.60	0.13
$C_5H_6O_2$	5.58	0.53
C_5H_8NO	5.95	0.35
$C_5H_{10}N_2$	6.33	0.17
$C_6H_{10}O$	6.68	0.39
$C_6H_{12}N$	7.06	0.21
C_7H_{14}	7.79	0.26
C_8H_2	8.68	0.33
99		
$C_2HN_3O_2$	3.40	0.44
$C_2H_3N_4O$	3.77	0.26
C_3HNO_3	3.76	0.65
$C_3H_3N_2O_2$	4.13	0.47
$C_3H_5N_3O$	4.51	0.28
$C_3H_7N_4$	4.88	0.10
$C_4H_3O_3$	4.49	0.68
$C_4H_5NO_2$	4.86	0.50
$C_4H_7N_2O$	5.24	0.31
$C_4H_9N_3$	5.61	0.13
$C_5H_7O_2$	5.59	0.53
C_5H_9NO	5.97	0.35
$C_5H_{11}N_2$	6.34	0.17
$C_6H_{11}O$	6.70	0.39
$C_6H_{13}N$	7.07	0.21
C_7HN	7.96	0.28
C_7H_{15}	7.80	0.26
C_8H_3	8.69	0.33
100		
$C_2H_2N_3O_2$	3.42	0.45
$C_2H_4N_4O$	3.79	0.26
$C_3H_2NO_3$	3.77	0.65
$C_3H_4N_2O_2$	4.15	0.47
$C_3H_6N_3O$	4.52	0.28
$C_3H_8N_4$	4.90	0.10
$C_4H_4O_3$	4.50	0.68
$C_4H_6NO_2$	4.88	0.50
$C_4H_8N_2O$	5.25	0.31
$C_4H_{10}N_3$	5.63	0.13
$C_5H_8O_2$	5.61	0.53
$C_5H_{10}NO$	5.98	0.35
$C_5H_{12}N_2$	6.36	0.17
$C_6H_{12}O$	6.72	0.39
$C_6H_{14}N$	7.09	0.22
C_7H_2N	7.98	0.28
C_7H_{16}	7.82	0.26
C_8H_4	8.71	0.33
101		
CHN_4O_2	2.70	0.43
$C_2HN_2O_3$	3.06	0.64
$C_2H_3N_3O_2$	3.43	0.45
$C_2H_5N_4O$	3.81	0.26
C_3HO_4	3.41	0.84
$C_3H_3NO_3$	3.79	0.65
$C_3H_5N_2O_2$	4.16	0.47
$C_3H_7N_3O$	4.54	0.28
$C_3H_9N_4$	4.91	0.10
$C_4H_5O_3$	4.52	0.68
$C_4H_7NO_2$	4.89	0.50
$C_4H_9N_2O$	5.27	0.31
$C_4H_{11}N_3$	5.64	0.13
$C_5H_9O_2$	5.63	0.53
$C_5H_{11}NO$	6.00	0.35
$C_5H_{13}N_2$	6.37	0.17
C_6HN_2	7.26	0.23
$C_6H_{13}O$	6.73	0.39
$C_6H_{15}N$	7.11	0.22
C_7HO	7.62	0.45
C_7H_3N	7.99	0.28
C_8H_5	8.73	0.33
102		
$CH_2N_4O_2$	2.72	0.43
$C_2H_2N_2O_3$	3.07	0.64
$C_2H_4N_3O_2$	3.45	0.45
$C_2H_6N_4O$	3.82	0.26
$C_3H_2O_4$	3.43	0.84
$C_3H_4NO_3$	3.81	0.66
$C_3H_6N_2O_2$	4.18	0.47
$C_3H_8N_3O$	4.55	0.28
$C_3H_{10}N_4$	4.93	0.10
$C_4H_6O_3$	4.54	0.68
$C_4H_8NO_2$	4.91	0.50
$C_4H_{10}N_2O$	5.28	0.32
$C_4H_{12}N_3$	5.66	0.13
$C_5H_{10}O_2$	5.64	0.53
$C_5H_{12}NO$	6.02	0.35
$C_5H_{14}N_2$	6.39	0.17
$C_6H_2N_2$	7.28	0.23
$C_6H_{14}O$	6.75	0.39
C_7H_2O	7.64	0.45
C_7H_4N	8.01	0.28
C_8H_6	8.74	0.34
103		
CHN_3O_3	2.36	0.62
$CH_3N_4O_2$	2.73	0.43
C_2HNO_4	2.72	0.83
$C_2H_3N_2O_3$	3.09	0.64
$C_2H_5N_3O_2$	3.46	0.45
$C_2H_7N_4O$	3.84	0.26
$C_3H_3O_4$	3.45	0.84
$C_3H_5NO_3$	3.82	0.66
$C_3H_7N_2O_2$	4.20	0.47
$C_3H_9N_3O$	4.57	0.29
$C_3H_{11}N_4$	4.94	0.10
$C_4H_7O_3$	4.55	0.68
$C_4H_9NO_2$	4.93	0.50
$C_4H_{11}N_2O$	5.30	0.32
$C_4H_{13}N_3$	5.68	0.14
C_5HN_3	6.56	0.18
$C_5H_{11}O_2$	5.66	0.53
$C_5H_{13}NO$	6.03	0.35
C_6HNO	6.92	0.40
$C_6H_3N_2$	7.30	0.23
C_7H_3O	7.65	0.45
C_7H_5N	8.03	0.28
C_8H_7	8.76	0.34
104		
$CH_2N_3O_3$	2.37	0.62
$CH_4N_4O_2$	2.75	0.43
$C_2H_2NO_4$	2.73	0.83
$C_2H_4N_2O_3$	3.11	0.64
$C_2H_6N_3O_2$	3.48	0.45
$C_2H_8N_4O$	3.85	0.26
$C_3H_4O_4$	3.46	0.84
$C_3H_6NO_3$	3.84	0.66
$C_3H_8N_2O_2$	4.21	0.47
$C_3H_{10}N_3O$	4.59	0.29
$C_3H_{12}N_4$	4.96	0.10
$C_4H_8O_3$	4.57	0.68
$C_4H_{10}NO_2$	4.94	0.50
$C_4H_{12}N_2O$	5.32	0.32
$C_5H_2N_3$	6.58	0.19
$C_5H_{12}O_2$	5.67	0.53
C_6H_2NO	6.94	0.41
$C_6H_4N_2$	7.31	0.23
C_7H_4O	7.67	0.45
C_7H_6N	8.04	0.28
C_8H_8	8.77	0.34
105		
CHN_2O_4	2.02	0.81
$CH_3N_3O_3$	2.39	0.62
$CH_5N_4O_2$	2.77	0.43
$C_2H_3NO_4$	2.75	0.83
$C_2H_5N_2O_3$	3.12	0.64
$C_2H_7N_3O_2$	3.50	0.45
$C_2H_9N_4O$	3.87	0.26
$C_3H_5O_4$	3.48	0.84
$C_3H_7NO_3$	3.85	0.66
$C_3H_9N_2O_2$	4.23	0.47
$C_3H_{11}N_3O$	4.60	0.29
C_4HN_4	5.86	0.15
$C_4H_9O_3$	4.58	0.68
$C_4H_{11}NO_2$	4.96	0.50
C_5HN_2O	6.22	0.36
$C_5H_3N_3$	6.60	0.19
C_6HO_2	6.58	0.58
C_6H_3NO	6.95	0.41
$C_6H_5N_2$	7.33	0.23
C_7H_5O	7.68	0.45
C_7H_7N	8.06	0.28
C_8H_9	8.79	0.34
106		
$CH_2N_2O_4$	2.03	0.82
$CH_4N_3O_3$	2.41	0.62
$CH_6N_4O_2$	2.78	0.43
$C_2H_4NO_4$	2.76	0.83
$C_2H_6N_2O_3$	3.14	0.64
$C_2H_8N_3O_2$	3.51	0.45
$C_2H_{10}N_4O$	3.89	0.26
$C_3H_6O_4$	3.49	0.85
$C_3H_8NO_3$	3.87	0.66
$C_3H_{10}N_2O_2$	4.24	0.47
$C_4H_2N_4$	5.88	0.15
$C_4H_{10}O_3$	4.60	0.68
$C_5H_2N_2O$	6.24	0.36
$C_5H_4N_3$	6.61	0.19
$C_6H_2O_2$	6.59	0.58
C_6H_4NO	6.97	0.41
$C_6H_6N_2$	7.34	0.23
C_7H_6O	7.70	0.46
C_7H_8N	8.07	0.28
C_8H_{10}	8.81	0.34
107		
$CH_3N_2O_4$	2.05	0.82
$CH_5N_3O_3$	2.42	0.62
$CH_7N_4O_2$	2.80	0.43
$C_2H_5NO_4$	2.78	0.83
$C_2H_7N_2O_3$	3.15	0.64
$C_2H_9N_3O_2$	3.53	0.45
$C_3H_7O_4$	3.51	0.85
$C_3H_9NO_3$	3.89	0.66
C_4HN_3O	5.52	0.33
$C_4H_3N_4$	5.90	0.15
C_5HNO_2	5.88	0.54
$C_5H_3N_2O$	6.25	0.37
$C_5H_5N_3$	6.63	0.19
$C_6H_3O_2$	6.61	0.58
C_6H_5NO	6.98	0.41
$C_6H_7N_2$	7.36	0.23
C_7H_7O	7.72	0.46
C_7H_9N	8.09	0.29
C_8H_{11}	8.82	0.34
108		
$CH_4N_2O_4$	2.06	0.82
$CH_6N_3O_3$	2.44	0.62
$CH_8N_4O_2$	2.81	0.43
$C_2H_6NO_4$	2.80	0.83
$C_2H_8N_2O_3$	3.17	0.64
$C_3H_8O_4$	3.53	0.85
$C_4H_2N_3O$	5.54	0.33
$C_4H_4N_4$	5.91	0.15
$C_5H_2NO_2$	5.90	0.54
$C_5H_4N_2O$	6.27	0.37
$C_5H_6N_3$	6.64	0.19
$C_6H_4O_2$	6.63	0.59
C_6H_6NO	7.00	0.41
$C_6H_8N_2$	7.38	0.24
C_7H_8O	7.73	0.46
$C_7H_{10}N$	8.11	0.29
C_8H_{12}	8.84	0.34
109		
$CH_5N_2O_4$	2.08	0.82
$CH_7N_3O_3$	2.45	0.62
$C_2H_7NO_4$	2.81	0.83
C_3HN_4O	4.82	0.30
$C_4HN_2O_2$	5.18	0.51
$C_4H_3N_3O$	5.55	0.33
$C_4H_5N_4$	5.93	0.15
C_5HO_3	5.54	0.73

	P + 1	P + 2
$C_5H_3NO_2$	5.91	0.55
$C_5H_5N_2O$	6.29	0.37
$C_5H_7N_3$	6.66	0.19
$C_6H_5O_2$	6.64	0.59
C_6H_7NO	7.02	0.41
$C_6H_9N_2$	7.39	0.24
C_7H_9O	7.75	0.46
$C_7H_{11}N$	8.12	0.29
C_8H_{13}	8.85	0.35
C_9H	9.74	0.42
110		
$CH_6N_2O_4$	2.10	0.82
$C_3H_2N_4O$	4.84	0.30
$C_4H_2N_2O_2$	5.20	0.51
$C_4H_4N_3O$	5.57	0.33
$C_4H_6N_4$	5.94	0.15
$C_5H_2O_3$	5.55	0.73
$C_5H_4NO_2$	5.93	0.55
$C_5H_6N_2O$	6.30	0.37
$C_5H_8N_3$	6.68	0.19
$C_6H_6O_2$	6.66	0.59
C_6H_8NO	7.03	0.41
$C_6H_{10}N_2$	7.41	0.24
$C_7H_{10}O$	7.76	0.46
$C_7H_{12}N$	8.14	0.29
C_8H_{14}	8.87	0.35
C_9H_2	9.76	0.42
111		
$C_3HN_3O_2$	4.48	0.48
$C_3H_3N_4O$	4.86	0.30
C_4HNO_3	4.84	0.69
$C_4H_3N_2O_2$	5.21	0.51
$C_4H_5N_3O$	5.59	0.33
$C_4H_7N_4$	5.96	0.15
$C_5H_3O_3$	5.57	0.73
$C_5H_5NO_2$	5.94	0.55
$C_5H_7N_2O$	6.32	0.37
$C_5H_9N_3$	6.69	0.19
$C_6H_7O_2$	6.67	0.59
C_6H_9NO	7.05	0.41
$C_6H_{11}N_2$	7.42	0.24
$C_7H_{11}O$	7.78	0.46
$C_7H_{13}N$	8.15	0.29
C_8HN	9.04	0.36
C_8H_{15}	8.89	0.35
C_9H_3	9.77	0.43
112		
$C_3H_2N_3O_2$	4.50	0.48
$C_3H_4N_4O$	4.87	0.30
$C_4H_2NO_3$	4.85	0.70
$C_4H_4N_2O_2$	5.23	0.51
$C_4H_6N_3O$	5.60	0.33
$C_4H_8N_4$	5.98	0.15
$C_5H_4O_3$	5.58	0.73
$C_5H_6NO_2$	5.96	0.55
$C_5H_8N_2O$	6.33	0.37
$C_5H_{10}N_3$	6.71	0.19
$C_6H_8O_2$	6.69	0.59
$C_6H_{10}NO$	7.06	0.41
$C_6H_{12}N_2$	7.44	0.24
$C_7H_{12}O$	7.80	0.46
$C_7H_{14}N$	8.17	0.29
C_8H_2N	9.06	0.36
C_8H_{16}	8.90	0.35
C_9H_4	9.79	0.43
113		
$C_2HN_4O_2$	3.78	0.46
$C_3HN_2O_3$	4.14	0.67
$C_3H_3N_3O_2$	4.51	0.48
$C_3H_5N_4O$	4.89	0.30
C_4HO_4	4.50	0.88
$C_4H_3NO_3$	4.87	0.70
$C_4H_5N_2O_2$	5.24	0.51
$C_4H_7N_3O$	5.62	0.33
$C_4H_9N_4$	5.99	0.15
$C_5H_5O_3$	5.60	0.73
$C_5H_7NO_2$	5.98	0.55
$C_5H_9N_2O$	6.35	0.37
$C_5H_{11}N_3$	6.72	0.19
$C_6H_9O_2$	6.71	0.59
$C_6H_{11}NO$	7.08	0.42
$C_6H_{13}N_2$	7.46	0.24
C_7HN_2	8.34	0.31
$C_7H_{13}O$	7.81	0.46
$C_7H_{15}N$	8.19	0.29
C_8HO	8.70	0.53
C_8H_3N	9.07	0.36
C_8H_{17}	8.92	0.35
C_9H_5	9.81	0.43
114		
$C_2H_2N_4O_2$	3.80	0.46
$C_3H_2N_2O_3$	4.15	0.67
$C_3H_4N_3O_2$	4.53	0.48
$C_3H_6N_4O$	4.90	0.30
$C_4H_2O_4$	4.51	0.88
$C_4H_4NO_3$	4.89	0.70
$C_4H_6N_2O_2$	5.26	0.51
$C_4H_8N_3O$	5.63	0.33
$C_4H_{10}N_4$	6.01	0.15
$C_5H_6O_3$	5.62	0.73
$C_5H_8NO_2$	5.99	0.55
$C_5H_{10}N_2O$	6.37	0.37
$C_5H_{12}N_3$	6.74	0.20
$C_6H_{10}O_2$	6.72	0.59
$C_6H_{12}NO$	7.10	0.42
$C_6H_{14}N_2$	7.47	0.24
$C_7H_2N_2$	8.36	0.31
$C_7H_{14}O$	7.83	0.47
$C_7H_{16}N$	8.20	0.29
C_8H_2O	8.72	0.53
C_8H_4N	9.09	0.37
C_8H_{18}	8.93	0.35
C_9H_6	9.82	0.43
115		
$C_2HN_3O_3$	3.44	0.65
$C_2H_3N_4O_2$	3.81	0.46
C_3HNO_4	3.80	0.86
$C_3H_3N_2O_3$	4.17	0.67
$C_3H_5N_3O_2$	4.54	0.48
$C_3H_7N_4O$	4.92	0.30
$C_4H_3O_4$	4.53	0.88
$C_4H_5NO_3$	4.90	0.70
$C_4H_7N_2O_2$	5.28	0.52
$C_4H_9N_3O$	5.65	0.33
$C_4H_{11}N_4$	6.02	0.16
$C_5H_7O_3$	5.63	0.73
$C_5H_9NO_2$	6.01	0.55
$C_5H_{11}N_2O$	6.38	0.37
$C_5H_{13}N_3$	6.76	0.20
C_6HN_3	7.64	0.25
$C_6H_{11}O_2$	6.74	0.59
$C_6H_{13}NO$	7.11	0.42
$C_6H_{15}N_2$	7.49	0.24
C_7HNO	8.00	0.48
$C_7H_3N_2$	8.38	0.31
$C_7H_{15}O$	7.84	0.47
$C_7H_{17}N$	8.22	0.30
C_8H_3O	8.73	0.54
C_8H_5N	9.11	0.37
C_9H_7	9.84	0.43
116		
$C_2H_2N_3O_3$	3.46	0.65
$C_2H_4N_4O_2$	3.83	0.46
$C_3H_2NO_4$	3.81	0.86
$C_3H_4N_2O_3$	4.19	0.67
$C_3H_6N_3O_2$	4.56	0.49
$C_3H_8N_4O$	4.94	0.30
$C_4H_4O_4$	4.54	0.88
$C_4H_6NO_3$	4.92	0.70
$C_4H_8N_2O_2$	5.29	0.52
$C_4H_{10}N_3O$	5.67	0.34
$C_4H_{12}N_4$	6.04	0.16
$C_5H_8O_3$	5.65	0.73
$C_5H_{10}NO_2$	6.02	0.55
$C_5H_{12}N_2O$	6.40	0.37
$C_5H_{14}N_3$	6.77	0.20
$C_6H_2N_3$	7.66	0.26
$C_6H_{12}O_2$	6.75	0.59
$C_6H_{14}NO$	7.13	0.42
$C_6H_{16}N_2$	7.50	0.24
C_7H_2NO	8.02	0.48
$C_7H_4N_2$	8.39	0.31
$C_7H_{16}O$	7.86	0.47
C_8H_4O	8.75	0.54
C_8H_6N	9.12	0.37
C_9H_8	9.85	0.43
117		
$C_2HN_2O_4$	3.10	0.84
$C_2H_3N_3O_3$	3.47	0.65
$C_2H_5N_4O_2$	3.85	0.46
$C_3H_3NO_4$	3.83	0.86
$C_3H_5N_2O_3$	4.20	0.67
$C_3H_7N_3O_2$	4.58	0.49
$C_3H_9N_4O$	4.95	0.30
$C_4H_5O_4$	4.56	0.88
$C_4H_7NO_3$	4.93	0.70
$C_4H_9N_2O_2$	5.31	0.52
$C_4H_{11}N_3O$	5.68	0.34
$C_4H_{13}N_4$	6.06	0.16
C_5HN_4	6.95	0.21
$C_5H_9O_3$	5.66	0.73
$C_5H_{11}NO_2$	6.04	0.55
$C_5H_{13}N_2O$	6.41	0.38
$C_5H_{15}N_3$	6.79	0.20
C_6HN_2O	7.30	0.43
$C_6H_3N_3$	7.68	0.26
$C_6H_{13}O_2$	6.77	0.60
$C_6H_{15}NO$	7.14	0.42
C_7HO_2	7.66	0.65
C_7H_3NO	8.03	0.48
$C_7H_5N_2$	8.41	0.31
C_8H_5O	8.76	0.54
C_8H_7N	9.14	0.37
C_9H_9	9.87	0.43
118		
$C_2H_2N_2O_4$	3.11	0.84
$C_2H_4N_3O_3$	3.49	0.65
$C_2H_6N_4O_2$	3.86	0.46
$C_3H_4NO_4$	3.84	0.86
$C_3H_6N_2O_3$	4.22	0.67
$C_3H_8N_3O_2$	4.59	0.49
$C_3H_{10}N_4O$	4.97	0.30
$C_4H_6O_4$	4.58	0.88
$C_4H_8NO_3$	4.95	0.70
$C_4H_{10}N_2O_2$	5.32	0 52
$C_4H_{12}N_3O$	5.70	0.34
$C_4H_{14}N_4$	6.07	0.16
$C_5H_2N_4$	6.96	0.21
$C_5H_{10}O_3$	5.68	0.73
$C_5H_{12}NO_2$	6.06	0.55
$C_5H_{14}N_2O$	6.43	0.38
$C_6H_2N_2O$	7.32	0.43
$C_6H_4N_3$	7.69	0.26
$C_6H_{14}O_2$	6.79	0.60
$C_7H_2O_2$	7.67	0.65
C_7H_4NO	8.05	0.48
$C_7H_6N_2$	8.42	0.31
C_8H_6O	8.78	0.54
C_8H_8N	9.15	0.37
C_9H_{10}	9.89	0.44
119		
$C_2H_3N_2O_4$	3.13	0.84
$C_2H_5N_3O_3$	3.50	0.65
$C_2H_7N_4O_2$	3.88	0.46
$C_3H_5NO_4$	3.86	0.86
$C_3H_7N_2O_3$	4.23	0.67
$C_3H_9N_3O_2$	4.61	0.49
$C_3H_{11}N_4O$	4.98	0.30
$C_4H_7O_4$	4.59	0.88
$C_4H_9NO_3$	4.97	0.70
$C_4H_{11}N_2O_2$	5.34	0.52
$C_4H_{13}N_3O$	5.71	0.34
C_5HN_3O	6.60	0.39
$C_5H_3N_4$	6.98	0.21
$C_5H_{11}O_3$	5.70	0.73
$C_5H_{13}NO_2$	6.07	0.56
C_6HNO_2	6.96	0.61
$C_6H_3N_2O$	7.33	0.43
$C_6H_5N_3$	7.71	0.26
$C_7H_3O_2$	7.69	0.66
C_7H_5NO	8.07	0.48
$C_7H_7N_2$	8.44	0.31
C_8H_7O	8.80	0.54
C_8H_9N	9.17	0.37
C_9H_{11}	9.90	0.44

	P + 1	P + 2
120		
$C_2H_4N_2O_4$	3.15	0.84
$C_2H_6N_3O_3$	3.52	0.65
$C_2H_8N_4O_2$	3.89	0.46
$C_3H_6NO_4$	3.88	0.86
$C_3H_8N_2O_3$	4.25	0.67
$C_3H_{10}N_3O_2$	4.62	0.49
$C_3H_{12}N_4O$	5.00	0.31
$C_4H_8O_4$	4.61	0.88
$C_4H_{10}NO_3$	4.98	0.70
$C_4H_{12}N_2O_2$	5.36	0.52
$C_5H_2N_3O$	6.62	0.39
$C_5H_4N_4$	6.99	0.21
$C_5H_{12}O_3$	5.71	0.74
$C_6H_2NO_2$	6.98	0.61
$C_6H_4N_2O$	7.35	0.43
$C_6H_6N_3$	7.72	0.26
$C_7H_4O_2$	7.71	0.66
C_7H_6NO	8.08	0.49
$C_7H_8N_2$	8.46	0.32
C_8H_8O	8.81	0.54
$C_8H_{10}N$	9.19	0.37
C_9H_{12}	9.92	0.44
121		
$C_2H_5N_2O_4$	3.16	0.84
$C_2H_7N_3O_3$	3.54	0.65
$C_2H_9N_4O_2$	3.91	0.46
$C_3H_7NO_4$	3.89	0.86
$C_3H_9N_2O_3$	4.27	0.67
$C_3H_{11}N_3O_2$	4.64	0.49
C_4HN_4O	5.90	0.35
$C_4H_9O_4$	4.62	0.89
$C_4H_{11}NO_3$	5.00	0.70
$C_5HN_2O_2$	6.26	0.57
$C_5H_3N_3O$	6.64	0.39
$C_5H_5N_4$	7.01	0.21
C_6HO_3	6.62	0.79
$C_6H_3NO_2$	6.99	0.61
$C_6H_5N_2O$	7.37	0.44
$C_6H_7N_3$	7.74	0.26
$C_7H_5O_2$	7.72	0.66
C_7H_7NO	8.10	0.49
$C_7H_9N_2$	8.47	0.32
C_8H_9O	8.83	0.54
$C_8H_{11}N$	9.20	0.38
C_9H_{13}	9.93	0.44
$C_{10}H$	10.82	0.53
122		
$C_2H_6N_2O_4$	3.18	0.84
$C_2H_8N_3O_3$	3.55	0.65
$C_2H_{10}N_4O_2$	3.93	0.46
$C_3H_8NO_4$	3.91	0.86
$C_3H_{10}N_2O_3$	4.28	0.67
$C_4H_2N_4O$	5.92	0.35
$C_4H_{10}O_4$	4.64	0.89
$C_5H_2N_2O_2$	6.28	0.57
$C_5H_4N_3O$	6.65	0.39
$C_5H_6N_4$	7.03	0.21
$C_6H_2O_3$	6.63	0.79
$C_6H_4NO_2$	7.01	0.61
$C_6H_6N_2O$	7.38	0.44
$C_6H_8N_3$	7.76	0.26
$C_7H_6O_2$	7.74	0.66
C_7H_8NO	8.11	0.49
$C_7H_{10}N_2$	8.49	0.32
$C_8H_{10}O$	8.84	0.54
$C_8H_{12}N$	9.22	0.38
C_9H_{14}	9.95	0.44
$C_{10}H_2$	10.84	0.53
123		
$C_2H_7N_2O_4$	3.19	0.84
$C_2H_9N_3O_3$	3.57	0.65
$C_3H_9NO_4$	3.92	0.86
$C_4HN_3O_2$	5.56	0.53
$C_4H_3N_4O$	5.94	0.35
C_5HNO_3	5.92	0.75
$C_5H_3N_2O_2$	6.29	0.57
$C_5H_5N_3O$	6.67	0.39
$C_5H_7N_4$	7.04	0.22
$C_6H_3O_3$	6.65	0.79
$C_6H_5NO_2$	7.02	0.61
$C_6H_7N_2O$	7.40	0.44
$C_6H_9N_3$	7.77	0.26
$C_7H_7O_2$	7.75	0.66
C_7H_9NO	8.13	0.49
$C_7H_{11}N_2$	8.50	0.32
$C_8H_{11}O$	8.86	0.55
$C_8H_{13}N$	9.23	0.38
C_9HN	10.12	0.46
C_9H_{15}	9.97	0.44
$C_{10}H_3$	10.85	0.53
124		
$C_2H_8N_2O_4$	3.21	0.84
$C_4H_2N_3O_2$	5.58	0.53
$C_4H_4N_4O$	5.95	0.35
$C_5H_2NO_3$	5.93	0.75
$C_5H_4N_2O_2$	6.31	0.57
$C_5H_6N_3O$	6.68	0.39
$C_5H_8N_4$	7.06	0.22
$C_6H_4O_3$	6.67	0.79
$C_6H_6NO_2$	7.04	0.61
$C_6H_8N_2O$	7.41	0.44
$C_6H_{10}N_3$	7.79	0.27
$C_7H_8O_2$	7.77	0.66
$C_7H_{10}NO$	8.15	0.49
$C_7H_{12}N_2$	8.52	0.32
$C_8H_{12}O$	8.88	0.55
$C_8H_{14}N$	9.25	0.38
C_9H_2N	10.14	0.46
C_9H_{16}	9.98	0.45
$C_{10}H_4$	10.87	0.53
125		
$C_3HN_4O_2$	4.86	0.50
$C_4HN_2O_3$	5.22	0.71
$C_4H_3N_3O_2$	5.59	0.53
$C_4H_5N_4O$	5.97	0.35
C_5HO_4	5.58	0.93
$C_5H_3NO_3$	5.95	0.75
$C_5H_5N_2O_2$	6.32	0.57
$C_5H_7N_3O$	6.70	0.39
$C_5H_9N_4$	7.07	0.22
$C_6H_5O_3$	6.68	0.79
$C_6H_7NO_2$	7.06	0.61
$C_6H_9N_2O$	7.43	0.44
$C_6H_{11}N_3$	7.80	0.27
$C_7H_9O_2$	7.79	0.66
$C_7H_{11}NO$	8.16	0.49
$C_7H_{13}N_2$	8.54	0.32
C_8HN_2	9.42	0.40
$C_8H_{13}O$	8.89	0.55
$C_8H_{15}N$	9.27	0.38
C_9HO	9.78	0.63
C_9H_3N	10.16	0.46
C_9H_{17}	10.00	0.45
$C_{10}H_5$	10.89	0.53
126		
$C_3H_2N_4O_2$	4.88	0.50
$C_4H_2N_2O_3$	5.24	0.71
$C_4H_4N_3O_2$	5.61	0.53
$C_4H_6N_4O$	5.98	0.35
$C_5H_2O_4$	5.59	0.93
$C_5H_4NO_3$	5.97	0.75
$C_5H_6N_2O_2$	6.34	0.57
$C_5H_8N_3O$	6.72	0.35
$C_5H_{10}N_4$	7.09	0.22
$C_6H_6O_3$	6.70	0.79
$C_6H_8NO_2$	7.07	0.62
$C_6H_{10}N_2O$	7.45	0.44
$C_6H_{12}N_3$	7.82	0.27
$C_7H_{10}O_2$	7.80	0.66
$C_7H_{12}NO$	8.18	0.49
$C_7H_{14}N_2$	8.55	0.32
$C_8H_2N_2$	9.44	0.40
$C_8H_{14}O$	8.91	0.55
$C_8H_{16}N$	9.28	0.38
C_9H_2O	9.80	0.63
C_9H_4N	10.17	0.46
C_9H_{18}	10.01	0.45
$C_{10}H_6$	10.90	0.54
127		
$C_3HN_3O_3$	4.52	0.68
$C_3H_3N_4O_2$	4.89	0.50
C_4HNO_4	4.88	0.90
$C_4H_3N_2O_3$	5.25	0.71
$C_4H_5N_3O_2$	5.63	0.53
$C_4H_7N_4O$	6.00	0.35
$C_5H_3O_4$	5.61	0.93
$C_5H_5NO_3$	5.98	0.75
$C_5H_7N_2O_2$	6.36	0.57
$C_5H_9N_3O$	6.73	0.40
$C_5H_{11}N_4$	7.11	0.22
$C_6H_7O_3$	6.71	0.79
$C_6H_9NO_2$	7.09	0.62
$C_6H_{11}N_2O$	7.46	0.44
$C_6H_{13}N_3$	7.84	0.27
C_7HN_3	8.73	0.34
$C_7H_{11}O_2$	7.82	0.67
$C_7H_{13}NO$	8.19	0.49
$C_7H_{15}N_2$	8.57	0.32
C_8HNO	9.08	0.57
$C_8H_3N_2$	9.46	0.40
$C_8H_{15}O$	8.92	0.55
$C_8H_{17}N$	9.30	0.38
C_9H_3O	9.81	0.63
C_9H_5N	10.19	0.47
C_9H_{19}	10.03	0.45
$C_{10}H_7$	10.92	0.54
128		
$C_3H_2N_3O_3$	4.54	0.68
$C_3H_4N_4O_2$	4.91	0.50
$C_4H_2NO_4$	4.89	0.90
$C_4H_4N_2O_3$	5.27	0.72
$C_4H_6N_3O_2$	5.64	0.53
$C_4H_8N_4O$	6.02	0.36
$C_5H_4O_4$	5.62	0.93
$C_5H_6NO_3$	6.00	0.75
$C_5H_8N_2O_2$	6.37	0.57
$C_5H_{10}N_3O$	6.75	0.40
$C_5H_{12}N_4$	7.12	0.22
$C_6H_8O_3$	6.73	0.79
$C_6H_{10}NO_2$	7.10	0.62
$C_6H_{12}N_2O$	7.48	0.44
$C_6H_{14}N_3$	7.85	0.27
$C_7H_2N_3$	8.74	0.34
$C_7H_{12}O_2$	7.83	0.67
$C_7H_{14}NO$	8.21	0.50
$C_7H_{16}N_2$	8.58	0.33
C_8H_2NO	9.10	0.57
$C_8H_4N_2$	9.47	0.40
$C_8H_{16}O$	8.94	0.55
$C_8H_{18}N$	9.31	0.39
C_9H_4O	9.83	0.63
C_9H_6N	10.20	0.47
C_9H_{20}	10.05	0.45
$C_{10}H_8$	10.94	0.54
129		
$C_3HN_2O_4$	4.18	0.87
$C_3H_3N_3O_3$	4.55	0.69
$C_3H_5N_4O_2$	4.93	0.50
$C_4H_3NO_4$	4.91	0.90
$C_4H_5N_2O_3$	5.28	0.72
$C_4H_7N_3O_2$	5.66	0.54
$C_4H_9N_4O$	6.03	0.36
$C_5H_5O_4$	5.64	0.93
$C_5H_7NO_3$	6.01	0.75
$C_5H_9N_2O_2$	6.39	0.57
$C_5H_{11}N_3O$	6.76	0.40
$C_5H_{13}N_4$	7.14	0.22
C_6HN_4	8.03	0.28
$C_6H_9O_3$	6.75	0.79
$C_6H_{11}NO_2$	7.12	0.62
$C_6H_{13}N_2O$	7.49	0.44
$C_6H_{15}N_3$	7.87	0.27
C_7HN_2O	8.38	0.51
$C_7H_3N_3$	8.76	0.34
$C_7H_{13}O_2$	7.85	0.67
$C_7H_{15}NO$	8.23	0.50
$C_7H_{17}N_2$	8.60	0.33
C_8HO_2	8.74	0.74
C_8H_3NO	9.11	0.57
$C_8H_5N_2$	9.49	0.40
$C_8H_{17}O$	8.96	0.55
$C_8H_{19}N$	9.33	0.39
C_9H_5O	9.85	0.63
C_9H_7N	10.22	0.47
$C_{10}H_9$	10.95	0.54

	P + 1	P + 2
130		
$C_3H_2N_2O_4$	4.19	0.87
$C_3H_4N_3O_3$	4.57	0.69
$C_3H_6N_4O_2$	4.94	0.50
$C_4H_4NO_4$	4.92	0.90
$C_4H_6N_2O_3$	5.30	0.72
$C_4H_8N_3O_2$	5.67	0.54
$C_4H_{10}N_4O$	6.05	0.36
$C_5H_6O_4$	5.66	0.93
$C_5H_8NO_3$	6.03	0.75
$C_5H_{10}N_2O_2$	6.40	0.58
$C_5H_{12}N_3O$	6.78	0.40
$C_5H_{14}N_4$	7.15	0.22
$C_6H_2N_4$	8.04	0.29
$C_6H_{10}O_3$	6.76	0.79
$C_6H_{12}NO_2$	7.14	0.62
$C_6H_{14}N_2O$	7.51	0.45
$C_6H_{16}N_3$	7.88	0.27
$C_7H_2N_2O$	8.40	0.51
$C_7H_4N_3$	8.77	0.34
$C_7H_{14}O_2$	7.87	0.67
$C_7H_{16}NO$	8.24	0.50
$C_7H_{18}N_2$	8.62	0.33
$C_8H_2O_2$	8.76	0.74
C_8H_4NO	9.13	0.57
$C_8H_6N_2$	9.50	0.40
$C_8H_{18}O$	8.97	0.56
C_9H_6O	9.86	0.63
C_9H_8N	10.24	0.47
$C_{10}H_{10}$	10.97	0.54
131		
$C_3H_3N_2O_4$	4.21	0.87
$C_3H_5N_3O_3$	4.58	0.69
$C_3H_7N_4O_2$	4.96	0.50
$C_4H_5NO_4$	4.94	0.90
$C_4H_7N_2O_3$	5.32	0.72
$C_4H_9N_3O_2$	5.69	0.54
$C_4H_{11}N_4O$	6.06	0.36
$C_5H_7O_4$	5.67	0.93
$C_5H_9NO_3$	6.05	0.75
$C_5H_{11}N_2O_2$	6.42	0.58
$C_5H_{13}N_3O$	6.80	0.40
$C_5H_{15}N_4$	7.17	0.22
C_6HN_3O	7.68	0.46
$C_6H_3N_4$	8.06	0.29
$C_6H_{11}O_3$	6.78	0.80
$C_6H_{13}NO_2$	7.15	0.62
$C_6H_{15}N_2O$	7.53	0.45
$C_6H_{17}N_3$	7.90	0.27
C_7HNO_2	8.04	0.68
$C_7H_3N_2O$	8.41	0.51
$C_7H_5N_3$	8.79	0.34
$C_7H_{15}O_2$	7.88	0.67
$C_7H_{17}NO$	8.26	0.50
$C_8H_3O_2$	8.77	0.74
C_8H_5NO	9.15	0.57
$C_8H_7N_2$	9.52	0.41
C_9H_7O	9.88	0.64
C_9H_9N	10.25	0.47
$C_{10}H_{11}$	10.98	0.54
132		
$C_3H_4N_2O_4$	4.23	0.87
$C_3H_6N_3O_3$	4.60	0.69
$C_3H_8N_4O_2$	4.97	0.50
$C_4H_6NO_4$	4.96	0.90
$C_4H_8N_2O_3$	5.33	0.72
$C_4H_{10}N_3O_2$	5.71	0.54
$C_4H_{12}N_4O$	6.08	0.36
$C_5H_8O_4$	5.69	0.93
$C_5H_{10}NO_3$	6.06	0.76
$C_5H_{12}N_2O_2$	6.44	0.58
$C_5H_{14}N_3O$	6.81	0.40
$C_5H_{16}N_4$	7.19	0.23
$C_6H_2N_3O$	7.70	0.46
$C_6H_4N_4$	8.07	0.29
$C_6H_{12}O_3$	6.97	0.80
$C_6H_{14}NO_2$	7.17	0.62
$C_6H_{16}N_2O$	7.54	0.45
$C_7H_2NO_2$	8.06	0.68
$C_7H_4N_2O$	8.43	0.51
$C_7H_6N_3$	8.81	0.34
$C_7H_{16}O_2$	7.90	0.67
$C_8H_4O_2$	8.79	0.74
C_8H_6NO	9.16	0.57
$C_8H_8N_2$	9.54	0.41
C_9H_8O	9.89	0.64
$C_9H_{10}N$	10.27	0.47
$C_{10}H_{12}$	11.00	0.55
133		
$C_3H_5N_2O_4$	4.24	0.87
$C_3H_7N_3O_3$	4.62	0.69
$C_3H_9N_4O_2$	4.99	0.51
$C_4H_7NO_4$	4.97	0.90
$C_4H_9N_2O_3$	5.35	0.72
$C_4H_{11}N_3O_2$	5.72	0.54
$C_4H_{13}N_4O$	6.10	0.36
C_5HN_4O	6.98	0.41
$C_5H_9O_4$	5.70	0.94
$C_5H_{11}NO_3$	6.08	0.76
$C_5H_{13}N_2O_2$	6.45	0.58
$C_5H_{15}N_3O$	6.83	0.40
$C_6HN_2O_2$	7.34	0.63
$C_6H_3N_3O$	7.72	0.46
$C_6H_5N_4$	8.09	0.29
$C_6H_{13}O_3$	6.81	0.80
$C_6H_{15}NO_2$	7.18	0.62
C_7HO_3	7.70	0.86
$C_7H_3NO_2$	8.07	0.69
$C_7H_5N_2O$	8.45	0.51
$C_7H_7N_3$	8.82	0.35
$C_8H_5O_2$	8.80	0.74
C_8H_7NO	9.18	0.57
$C_8H_9N_2$	9.55	0.41
C_9H_9O	9.91	0.64
$C_9H_{11}N$	10.28	0.48
$C_{10}H_{13}$	11.01	0.55
$C_{11}H$	11.90	0.64
134		
$C_3H_6N_2O_4$	4.26	0.87
$C_3H_8N_3O_3$	4.63	0.69
$C_3H_{10}N_4O_2$	5.01	0.51
$C_4H_8NO_4$	4.99	0.90
$C_4H_{10}N_2O_3$	5.36	0.72
$C_4H_{12}N_3O_2$	5.74	0.54
$C_4H_{14}N_4O$	6.11	0.36
$C_5H_2N_4O$	7.00	0.41
$C_5H_{10}O_4$	5.72	0.94
$C_5H_{12}NO_3$	6.09	0.76
$C_5H_{14}N_2O_2$	6.47	0.58
$C_6H_2N_2O_2$	7.36	0.64
$C_6H_4N_3O$	7.73	0.46
$C_6H_6N_4$	8.11	0.29
$C_6H_{14}O_3$	6.83	0.80
$C_7H_2O_3$	7.71	0.86
$C_7H_4NO_2$	8.09	0.69
$C_7H_6N_2O$	8.46	0.52
$C_7H_8N_3$	8.84	0.35
$C_8H_6O_2$	8.82	0.74
C_8H_8NO	9.19	0.58
$C_8H_{10}N_2$	9.57	0.41
$C_9H_{10}O$	9.93	0.64
$C_9H_{12}N$	10.30	0.48
$C_{10}H_{14}$	11.03	0.55
$C_{11}H_2$	11.92	0.65
135		
$C_3H_7N_2O_4$	4.27	0.87
$C_3H_9N_3O_3$	4.65	0.69
$C_3H_{11}N_4O_2$	5.02	0.51
$C_4H_9NO_4$	5.00	0.90
$C_4H_{11}N_2O_3$	5.38	0.72
$C_4H_{13}N_3O_2$	5.75	0.54
$C_5HN_3O_2$	6.64	0.59
$C_5H_3N_4O$	7.02	0.41
$C_5H_{11}O_4$	5.74	0.94
$C_5H_{13}NO_3$	6.11	0.76
C_6HNO_3	7.00	0.81
$C_6H_3N_2O_2$	7.37	0.64
$C_6H_5N_3O$	7.75	0.46
$C_6H_7N_4$	8.12	0.29
$C_7H_3O_3$	7.73	0.86
$C_7H_5NO_2$	8.10	0.69
$C_7H_7N_2O$	8.48	0.52
$C_7H_9N_3$	8.85	0.35
$C_8H_7O_2$	8.84	0.74
C_8H_9NO	9.21	0.58
$C_8H_{11}N_2$	9.58	0.41
$C_9H_{11}O$	9.94	0.64
$C_9H_{13}N$	10.32	0.48
$C_{10}HN$	11.20	0.57
$C_{10}H_{15}$	11.05	0.55
$C_{11}H_3$	11.94	0.65
136		
$C_3H_8N_2O_4$	4.29	0.87
$C_3H_{10}N_3O_3$	4.66	0.69
$C_3H_{12}N_4O_2$	5.04	0.51
$C_4H_{10}NO_4$	5.02	0.90
$C_4H_{12}N_2O_3$	5.40	0.72
$C_5H_2N_3O_2$	6.66	0.59
$C_5H_4N_4O$	7.03	0.42
$C_5H_{12}O_4$	5.75	0.94
$C_6H_2NO_3$	7.01	0.81
$C_6H_4N_2O_2$	7.39	0.64
$C_6H_6N_3O$	7.76	0.46
$C_6H_8N_4$	8.14	0.29
$C_7H_4O_3$	7.75	0.86
$C_7H_6NO_2$	8.12	0.69
$C_7H_8N_2O$	8.49	0.52
$C_7H_{10}N_3$	8.87	0.35
$C_8H_8O_2$	8.85	0.75
$C_8H_{10}NO$	9.23	0.58
$C_8H_{12}N_2$	9.60	0.41
$C_9H_{12}O$	9.96	0.64
$C_9H_{14}N$	10.33	0.48
$C_{10}H_2N$	11.22	0.57
$C_{10}H_{16}$	11.06	0.55
$C_{11}H_4$	11.95	0.65
137		
$C_3H_9N_2O_4$	4.31	0.88
$C_3H_{11}N_3O_3$	4.68	0.69
$C_4HN_4O_2$	5.94	0.55
$C_4H_{11}NO_4$	5.04	0.90
$C_5HN_2O_3$	6.30	0.77
$C_5H_3N_3O_2$	6.67	0.59
$C_5H_5N_4O$	7.05	0.42
C_6HO_4	6.66	0.99
$C_6H_3NO_3$	7.03	0.81
$C_6H_5N_2O_2$	7.41	0.64
$C_6H_7N_3O$	7.78	0.47
$C_6H_9N_4$	8.15	0.29
$C_7H_5O_3$	7.76	0.86
$C_7H_7NO_2$	8.14	0.69
$C_7H_9N_2O$	8.51	0.52
$C_7H_{11}N_3$	8.89	0.35
$C_8H_9O_2$	8.87	0.75
$C_8H_{11}NO$	9.24	0.58
$C_8H_{13}N_2$	9.62	0.41
C_9HN_2	10.50	0.50
$C_9H_{13}O$	9.97	0.65
$C_9H_{15}N$	10.35	0.48
$C_{10}HO$	10.86	0.73
$C_{10}H_3N$	11.24	0.57
$C_{10}H_{17}$	11.08	0.56
$C_{11}H_5$	11.97	0.65
138		
$C_3H_{10}N_2O_4$	4.32	0.88
$C_4H_2N_4O_2$	5.96	0.55
$C_5H_2N_2O_3$	6.32	0.77
$C_5H_4N_3O_2$	6.69	0.59
$C_5H_6N_4O$	7.06	0.42
$C_6H_2O_4$	6.67	0.99
$C_6H_4NO_3$	7.05	0.81
$C_6H_6N_2O_2$	7.42	0.64
$C_6H_8N_3O$	7.80	0.47
$C_6H_{10}N_4$	8.17	0.30
$C_7H_6O_3$	7.78	0.86
$C_7H_8NO_2$	8.15	0.69
$C_7H_{10}N_2O$	8.53	0.52
$C_7H_{12}N_3$	8.90	0.35
$C_8H_{10}O_2$	8.88	0.75
$C_8H_{12}NO$	9.26	0.58
$C_8H_{14}N_2$	9.63	0.42
$C_9H_2N_2$	10.52	0.50
$C_9H_{14}O$	9.99	0.65
$C_9H_{16}N$	10.36	0.48
$C_{10}H_2O$	10.88	0.73

	P + 1	P + 2
$C_{10}H_4N$	11.25	0.57
$C_{10}H_{18}$	11.09	0.56
$C_{11}H_6$	11.98	0.65
139		
$C_4H_3N_3O_3$	5.60	0.73
$C_4H_3N_4O_2$	5.97	0.55
C_5HNO_4	5.96	0.95
$C_5H_3N_2O_3$	6.33	0.77
$C_5H_5N_3O_2$	6.71	0.59
$C_5H_7N_4O$	7.03	0.42
$C_6H_3O_4$	6.69	0.99
$C_6H_5NO_3$	7.06	0.82
$C_6H_7N_2O_2$	7.44	0.64
$C_6H_9N_3O$	7.81	0.47
$C_6H_{11}N_4$	8.19	0.30
$C_7H_7O_3$	7.79	0.86
$C_7H_9NO_2$	8.17	0.69
$C_7H_{11}N_2O$	8.54	0.52
$C_7H_{13}N_3$	8.92	0.35
C_8HN_3	9.81	0.43
$C_8H_{11}O_2$	8.90	0.75
$C_8H_{13}NO$	9.27	0.58
$C_8H_{15}N_2$	9.65	0.42
C_9HNO	10.16	0.66
$C_9H_3N_2$	10.54	0.50
$C_9H_{15}O$	10.01	0.65
$C_9H_{17}N$	10.38	0.49
$C_{10}H_3O$	10.89	0.74
$C_{10}H_5N$	11.27	0.58
$C_{10}H_{19}$	11.11	0.56
$C_{11}H_7$	12.00	0.66
140		
$C_4H_2N_3O_3$	5.62	0.73
$C_4H_4N_4O_2$	5.99	0.55
$C_5H_2NO_4$	5.97	0.95
$C_5H_4N_2O_3$	6.35	0.77
$C_5H_6N_3O_2$	6.72	0.60
$C_5H_8N_4O$	7.10	0.42
$C_6H_4O_4$	6.70	0.99
$C_6H_6NO_3$	7.08	0.82
$C_6H_8N_2O_2$	7.45	0.64
$C_6H_{10}N_3O$	7.83	0.47
$C_6H_{12}N_4$	8.20	0.30
$C_7H_8O_3$	7.81	0.87
$C_7H_{10}NO_2$	8.18	0.69
$C_7H_{12}N_2O$	8.56	0.52
$C_7H_{14}N_3$	8.93	0.36
$C_8H_2N_3$	9.82	0.43
$C_8H_{12}O_2$	8.92	0.75
$C_8H_{14}NO$	9.29	0.58
$C_8H_{16}N_2$	9.66	0.42
C_9H_2NO	10.18	0.67
$C_9H_4N_2$	10.55	0.50
$C_9H_{16}O$	10.02	0.65
$C_9H_{18}N$	10.40	0.49
$C_{10}H_4O$	10.91	0.74
$C_{10}H_6N$	11.28	0.58
$C_{10}H_{20}$	11.13	0.56
$C_{11}H_8$	12.02	0.66
141		
$C_4HN_2O_4$	5.26	0.92
$C_4H_3N_3O_3$	5.63	0.73
$C_4H_5N_4O_2$	6.01	0.56
$C_5H_3NO_4$	5.99	0.95
$C_5H_5N_2O_3$	6.36	0.77
$C_5H_7N_3O_2$	6.74	0.60
$C_5H_9N_4O$	7.11	0.42
$C_6H_5O_4$	6.72	0.99
$C_6H_7NO_3$	7.09	0.82
$C_6H_9N_2O_2$	7.47	0.64
$C_6H_{11}N_3O$	7.84	0.47
$C_6H_{13}N_4$	8.22	0.30
C_7HN_4	9.11	0.37
$C_7H_9O_3$	7.83	0.87
$C_7H_{11}NO_2$	8.20	0.70
$C_7H_{13}N_2O$	8.57	0.53
$C_7H_{15}N_3$	8.95	0.36
C_8HN_2O	9.46	0.60
$C_8H_3N_3$	9.84	0.44
$C_8H_{13}O_2$	8.93	0.75
$C_8H_{15}NO$	9.31	0.59
$C_8H_{17}N_2$	9.68	0.42
C_9HO_2	9.82	0.83
C_9H_3NO	10.19	0.67
$C_9H_5N_2$	10.57	0.50
$C_9H_{17}O$	10.04	0.65
$C_9H_{19}N$	10.41	0.49
$C_{10}H_5O$	10.93	0.74
$C_{10}H_7N$	11.30	0.58
$C_{10}H_{21}$	11.14	0.56
$C_{11}H_9$	12.03	0.66
142		
$C_4H_2N_2O_4$	5.27	0.92
$C_4H_4N_3O_3$	5.65	0.74
$C_4H_6N_4O_2$	6.02	0.56
$C_5H_4NO_4$	6.01	0.95
$C_5H_6N_2O_3$	6.38	0.77
$C_5H_8N_3O_2$	6.75	0.60
$C_5H_{10}N_4O$	7.13	0.42
$C_6H_6O_4$	6.74	0.99
$C_6H_8NO_3$	7.11	0.82
$C_6H_{10}N_2O_2$	7.49	0.64
$C_6H_{12}N_3O$	7.86	0.47
$C_6H_{14}N_4$	8.23	0.30
$C_7H_2N_4$	9.12	0.37
$C_7H_{10}O_3$	7.84	0.87
$C_7H_{12}NO_2$	8.22	0.70
$C_7H_{14}N_2O$	8.59	0.53
$C_7H_{16}N_3$	8.97	0.36
$C_8H_2N_2O$	9.48	0.60
$C_8H_4N_3$	9.85	0.44
$C_8H_{14}O_2$	8.95	0.75
$C_8H_{16}NO$	9.32	0.59
$C_8H_{18}N_2$	9.70	0.42
$C_9H_2O_2$	9.84	0.83
C_9H_4NO	10.21	0.67
$C_9H_6N_2$	10.58	0.51
$C_9H_{18}O$	10.05	0.65
$C_9H_{20}N$	10.43	0.49
$C_{10}H_6O$	10.94	0.74
$C_{10}H_8N$	11.32	0.58
$C_{10}H_{22}$	11.16	0.56
$C_{11}H_{10}$	12.05	0.66
143		
$C_4H_3N_2O_4$	5.29	0.92
$C_4H_5N_3O_3$	5.66	0.74
$C_4H_7N_4O_2$	6.04	0.56
$C_5H_5NO_4$	6.02	0.95
$C_5H_7N_2O_3$	6.40	0.78
$C_5H_9N_3O_2$	6.77	0.60
$C_5H_{11}N_4O$	7.14	0.42
$C_6H_7O_4$	6.75	0.99
$C_6H_9NO_3$	7.13	0.82
$C_6H_{11}N_2O_2$	7.50	0.65
$C_6H_{13}N_3O$	7.88	0.47
$C_6H_{15}N_4$	8.25	0.30
C_7HN_3O	8.76	0.54
$C_7H_3N_4$	9.14	0.37
$C_7H_{11}O_3$	7.86	0.87
$C_7H_{13}NO_2$	8.23	0.70
$C_7H_{15}N_2O$	8.61	0.53
$C_7H_{17}N_3$	8.98	0.36
C_8HNO_2	9.12	0.77
$C_8H_3N_2O$	9.50	0.60
$C_8H_5N_3$	9.87	0.44
$C_8H_{15}O_2$	8.96	0.76
$C_8H_{17}NO$	9.34	0.59
$C_8H_{19}N_2$	9.71	0.42
$C_9H_3O_2$	9.85	0.83
C_9H_5NO	10.23	0.67
$C_9H_7N_2$	10.60	0.51
$C_9H_{19}O$	10.07	0.65
$C_9H_{21}N$	10.44	0.49
$C_{10}H_7O$	10.96	0.74
$C_{10}H_9N$	11.33	0.58
$C_{11}H_{11}$	12.06	0.66
144		
$C_4H_4N_2O_4$	5.31	0.92
$C_4H_6N_3O_3$	5.68	0.74
$C_4H_8N_4O_2$	6.05	0.56
$C_5H_6NO_4$	6.04	0.95
$C_5H_8N_2O_3$	6.41	0.78
$C_5H_{10}N_3O_2$	6.79	0.60
$C_5H_{12}N_4O$	7.16	0.42
$C_6H_8O_4$	6.77	1.00
$C_6H_{10}NO_3$	7.14	0.82
$C_6H_{12}N_2O_2$	7.52	0.65
$C_6H_{14}N_3O$	7.89	0.47
$C_6H_{16}N_4$	8.27	0.30
$C_7H_2N_3O$	8.78	0.54
$C_7H_4N_4$	9.15	0.38
$C_7H_{12}O_3$	7.87	0.87
$C_7H_{14}NO_2$	8.25	0.70
$C_7H_{16}N_2O$	8.62	0.53
$C_7H_{18}N_3$	9.00	0.36
$C_8H_2NO_2$	9.14	0.77
$C_8H_4N_2O$	9.51	0.60
$C_8H_6N_3$	9.89	0.44
$C_8H_{16}O_2$	8.98	0.76
$C_8H_{18}NO$	9.35	0.59
$C_8H_{20}N_2$	9.73	0.43
$C_9H_4O_2$	9.87	0.84
C_9H_6NO	10.24	0.67
$C_9H_8N_2$	10.62	0.51
$C_9H_{20}O$	10.09	0.66
$C_{10}H_8O$	10.97	0.74
$C_{10}H_{10}N$	11.35	0.58
$C_{11}H_{12}$	12.08	0.67
145		
$C_4H_5N_2O_4$	5.32	0.92
$C_4H_7N_3O_3$	5.70	0.74
$C_4H_9N_4O_2$	6.07	0.56
$C_5H_7NO_4$	6.05	0.96
$C_5H_9N_2O_3$	6.43	0.78
$C_5H_{11}N_3O_2$	6.80	0.60
$C_5H_{13}N_4O$	7.18	0.43
C_6HN_4O	8.07	0.49
$C_6H_9O_4$	6.78	1.00
$C_6H_{11}NO_3$	7.16	0.82
$C_6H_{13}N_2O_2$	7.53	0.65
$C_6H_{15}N_3O$	7.91	0.48
$C_6H_{17}N_4$	8.28	0.31
$C_7HN_2O_2$	8.42	0.71
$C_7H_3N_3O$	8.80	0.54
$C_7H_5N_4$	9.17	0.38
$C_7H_{13}O_3$	7.89	0.87
$C_7H_{15}NO_2$	8.26	0.70
$C_7H_{17}N_2O$	8.64	0.53
$C_7H_{19}N_3$	9.01	0.36
C_8HO_3	8.78	0.94
$C_8H_3NO_2$	9.15	0.77
$C_8H_5N_2O$	9.53	0.61
$C_8H_7N_3$	9.90	0.44
$C_8H_{17}O_2$	9.00	0.76
$C_8H_{19}NO$	9.37	0.59
$C_9H_5O_2$	9.88	0.84
C_9H_7NO	10.26	0.67
$C_9H_9N_2$	10.63	0.51
$C_{10}H_9O$	10.99	0.75
$C_{10}H_{11}N$	11.36	0.59
$C_{11}H_{13}$	12.10	0.67
$C_{12}H$	12.98	0.77
146		
$C_4H_6N_2O_4$	5.34	0.92
$C_4H_8N_3O_3$	5.71	0.74
$C_4H_{10}N_4O_2$	6.09	0.56
$C_5H_8NO_4$	6.07	0.96
$C_5H_{10}N_2O_3$	6.44	0.78
$C_5H_{12}N_3O_2$	6.82	0.60
$C_5H_{14}N_4O$	7.19	0.43
$C_6H_2N_4O$	8.08	0.49
$C_6H_{10}O_4$	6.80	1.00
$C_6H_{12}NO_3$	7.17	0.82
$C_6H_{14}N_2O_2$	7.55	0.65
$C_6H_{16}N_3O$	7.92	0.48
$C_6H_{18}N_4$	8.30	0.31
$C_7H_2N_2O_2$	8.44	0.71
$C_7H_4N_3O$	8.81	0.55
$C_7H_6N_4$	9.19	0.38
$C_7H_{14}O_3$	7.91	0.87
$C_7H_{16}NO_2$	8.28	0.70
$C_7H_{18}N_2O$	8.65	0.53
$C_8H_2O_3$	8.79	0.94
$C_8H_4NO_2$	9.17	0.77
$C_8H_6N_2O$	9.54	0.61
$C_8H_8N_3$	9.92	0.44
$C_8H_{18}O_2$	9.01	0.76
$C_9H_6O_2$	9.90	0.84

	P + 1	P + 2
C_9H_8NO	10.27	0.68
$C_9H_{10}N_2$	10.65	0.51
$C_{10}H_{10}O$	11.01	0.75
$C_{10}H_{12}N$	11.38	0.59
$C_{11}H_{14}$	12.11	0.67
$C_{12}H_2$	13.00	0.77
147		
$C_4H_7N_2O_4$	5.35	0.92
$C_4H_9N_3O_3$	5.73	0.74
$C_4H_{11}N_4O_2$	6.10	0.56
$C_5H_9NO_4$	6.09	0.96
$C_5H_{11}N_2O_3$	6.46	0.78
$C_5H_{13}N_3O_2$	6.83	0.60
$C_5H_{15}N_4O$	7.21	0.43
$C_6HN_3O_2$	7.72	0.66
$C_6H_3N_4O$	8.10	0.49
$C_6H_{11}O_4$	6.82	1.00
$C_6H_{13}NO_3$	7.19	0.82
$C_6H_{15}N_2O_2$	7.57	0.65
$C_6H_{17}N_3O$	7.94	0.48
C_7HNO_3	8.08	0.89
$C_7H_3N_2O_2$	8.45	0.72
$C_7H_5N_3O$	8.83	0.55
$C_7H_7N_4$	9.20	0.38
$C_7H_{15}O_3$	7.92	0.87
$C_7H_{17}NO_2$	8.30	0.70
$C_8H_3O_3$	8.81	0.94
$C_8H_5NO_2$	9.19	0.78
$C_8H_7N_2O$	9.56	0.61
$C_8H_9N_3$	9.93	0.44
$C_9H_7O_2$	9.92	0.84
C_9H_9NO	10.29	0.68
$C_9H_{11}N_2$	10.66	0.51
$C_{10}H_{11}O$	11.02	0.75
$C_{10}H_{13}N$	11.40	0.59
$C_{11}HN$	12.28	0.69
$C_{11}H_{15}$	12.13	0.67
$C_{12}H_3$	13.02	0.78
148		
$C_4H_8N_2O_4$	5.37	0.92
$C_4H_{10}N_3O_3$	5.74	0.74
$C_4H_{12}N_4O_2$	6.12	0.56
$C_5H_{10}NO_4$	6.10	0.96
$C_5H_{12}N_2O_3$	6.48	0.78
$C_5H_{14}N_3O_2$	6.85	0.60
$C_5H_{16}N_4O$	7.22	0.43
$C_6H_2N_3O_2$	7.74	0.66
$C_6H_4N_4O$	8.11	0.49
$C_6H_{12}O_4$	6.83	1.00
$C_6H_{14}NO_3$	7.21	0.83
$C_6H_{16}N_2O_2$	7.58	0.65
$C_7H_2NO_3$	8.10	0.89
$C_7H_4N_2O_2$	8.47	0.72
$C_7H_6N_3O$	8.84	0.55
$C_7H_8N_4$	9.22	0.38
$C_7H_{16}O_3$	7.94	0.88
$C_8H_4O_3$	8.83	0.94
$C_8H_6NO_2$	9.20	0.78
$C_8H_8N_2O$	9.58	0.61
$C_8H_{10}N_3$	9.95	0.45
$C_9H_8O_2$	9.93	0.84
$C_9H_{10}NO$	10.31	0.68
$C_9H_{12}N_2$	10.68	0.52
$C_{10}H_{12}O$	11.04	0.75
$C_{10}H_{14}N$	11.41	0.59
$C_{11}H_2N$	12.30	0.69
$C_{11}H_{16}$	12.14	0.67
$C_{12}H_4$	13.03	0.78
149		
$C_4H_9N_2O_4$	5.39	0.92
$C_4H_{11}N_3O_3$	5.76	0.74
$C_4H_{13}N_4O_2$	6.13	0.56
$C_5HN_4O_2$	7.02	0.62
$C_5H_{11}NO_4$	6.12	0.96
$C_5H_{13}N_2O_3$	6.49	0.78
$C_5H_{15}N_3O_2$	6.87	0.61
$C_6HN_2O_3$	7.38	0.84
$C_6H_3N_3O_2$	7.75	0.66
$C_6H_5N_4O$	8.13	0.49
$C_6H_{13}O_4$	6.85	1.00
$C_6H_{15}NO_3$	7.22	0.83
C_7HO_4	7.74	1.06
$C_7H_3NO_3$	8.11	0.89
$C_7H_5N_2O_2$	8.49	0.72
$C_7H_7N_3O$	8.86	0.55
$C_7H_9N_4$	9.23	0.38
$C_8H_5O_3$	8.84	0.95
$C_8H_7NO_2$	9.22	0.78
$C_8H_9N_2O$	9.59	0.61
$C_8H_{11}N_3$	9.97	0.45
$C_9H_9O_2$	9.95	0.84
$C_9H_{11}NO$	10.32	0.68
$C_9H_{13}N_2$	10.70	0.52
$C_{10}HN_2$	11.59	0.61
$C_{10}H_{13}O$	11.05	0.75
$C_{10}H_{15}N$	11.43	0.59
$C_{11}HO$	11.94	0.85
$C_{11}H_3N$	12.32	0.69
$C_{11}H_{17}$	12.16	0.67
$C_{12}H_5$	13.05	0.78
150		
$C_4H_{10}N_2O_4$	5.40	0.92
$C_4H_{12}N_3O_3$	5.78	0.74
$C_4H_{14}N_4O_2$	6.15	0.56
$C_5H_2N_4O_2$	7.04	0.62
$C_5H_{12}NO_4$	6.13	0.96
$C_5H_{14}N_2O_3$	6.51	0.78
$C_6H_2N_2O_3$	7.40	0.84
$C_6H_4N_3O_2$	7.77	0.67
$C_6H_6N_4O$	8.15	0.49
$C_6H_{14}O_4$	6.86	1.00
$C_7H_2O_4$	7.75	1.06
$C_7H_4NO_3$	8.13	0.89
$C_7H_6N_2O_2$	8.50	0.72
$C_7H_8N_3O$	8.88	0.55
$C_7H_{10}N_4$	9.25	0.38
$C_8H_6O_3$	8.86	0.95
$C_8H_8NO_2$	9.23	0.78
$C_8H_{10}N_2O$	9.61	0.61
$C_8H_{12}N_3$	9.98	0.45
$C_9H_{10}O_2$	9.96	0.84
$C_9H_{12}NO$	10.34	0.68
$C_9H_{14}N_2$	10.71	0.52
$C_{10}H_2N_2$	11.60	0.61
$C_{10}H_{14}O$	11.07	0.75
$C_{10}H_{16}N$	11.44	0.60
$C_{11}H_2O$	11.96	0.85
$C_{11}H_4N$	12.33	0.70
$C_{11}H_{18}$	12.18	0.68
$C_{12}H_6$	13.06	0.78
151		
$C_4H_{11}N_2O_4$	5.42	0.92
$C_4H_{13}N_3O_3$	5.79	0.74
$C_5HN_3O_3$	6.68	0.79
$C_5H_3N_4O_2$	7.06	0.62
$C_5H_{13}NO_4$	6.15	0.96
C_6HNO_4	7.04	1.01
$C_6H_3N_2O_3$	7.41	0.84
$C_6H_5N_3O_2$	7.79	0.67
$C_6H_7N_4O$	8.16	0.50
$C_7H_3O_4$	7.77	1.06
$C_7H_5NO_3$	8.14	0.89
$C_7H_7N_2O_2$	8.52	0.72
$C_7H_9N_3O$	8.89	0.55
$C_7H_{11}N_4$	9.27	0.39
$C_8H_7O_3$	8.87	0.95
$C_8H_9NO_2$	9.25	0.78
$C_8H_{11}N_2O$	9.62	0.62
$C_8H_{13}N_3$	10.00	0.45
C_9HN_3	10.89	0.54
$C_9H_{11}O_2$	9.98	0.85
$C_9H_{13}NO$	10.36	0.68
$C_9H_{15}N_2$	10.73	0.52
$C_{10}HNO$	11.24	0.77
$C_{10}H_3N_2$	11.62	0.61
$C_{10}H_{15}O$	11.09	0.76
$C_{10}H_{17}N$	11.46	0.60
$C_{11}H_3O$	11.97	0.85
$C_{11}H_5N$	12.35	0.70
$C_{11}H_{19}$	12.19	0.68
$C_{12}H_7$	13.08	0.79
152		
$C_4H_{12}N_2O_4$	5.43	0.92
$C_5H_2N_3O_3$	6.70	0.79
$C_5H_4N_4O_2$	7.07	0.62
$C_6H_2NO_4$	7.05	1.01
$C_6H_4N_2O_3$	7.43	0.84
$C_6H_6N_3O_2$	7.80	0.67
$C_6H_8N_4O$	8.18	0.50
$C_7H_4O_4$	7.79	1.06
$C_7H_6NO_3$	8.16	0.89
$C_7H_8N_2O_2$	8.53	0.72
$C_7H_{10}N_3O$	8.91	0.55
$C_7H_{12}N_4$	9.28	0.39
$C_8H_8O_3$	8.89	0.95
$C_8H_{10}NO_2$	9.27	0.78
$C_8H_{12}N_2O$	9.64	0.62
$C_8H_{14}N_3$	10.01	0.45
$C_9H_2N_3$	10.90	0.54
$C_9H_{12}O_2$	10.00	0.85
$C_9H_{14}NO$	10.37	0.68
$C_9H_{16}N_2$	10.74	0.52
$C_{10}H_2NO$	11.26	0.78
$C_{10}H_4N_2$	11.63	0.62
$C_{10}H_{16}O$	11.10	0.76
$C_{10}H_{18}N$	11.48	0.60
$C_{11}H_4O$	11.99	0.86
$C_{11}H_6N$	12.36	0.70
$C_{11}H_{20}$	12.21	0.68
$C_{12}H_8$	13.10	0.79
153		
$C_5HN_2O_4$	6.34	0.97
$C_5H_3N_3O_3$	6.71	0.80
$C_5H_5N_4O_2$	7.09	0.62
$C_6H_3NO_4$	7.07	1.02
$C_6H_5N_2O_3$	7.44	0.84
$C_6H_7N_3O_2$	7.82	0.67
$C_6H_9N_4O$	8.19	0.50
$C_7H_5O_4$	7.80	1.07
$C_7H_7NO_3$	8.18	0.89
$C_7H_9N_2O_2$	8.55	0.72
$C_7H_{11}N_3O$	8.92	0.56
$C_7H_{13}N_4$	9.30	0.39
C_8HN_4	10.19	0.47
$C_8H_9O_3$	8.91	0.95
$C_8H_{11}NO_2$	9.28	0.78
$C_8H_{13}N_2O$	9.66	0.62
$C_8H_{15}N_3$	10.03	0.45
C_9HN_2O	10.54	0.70
$C_9H_3N_3$	10.92	0.54
$C_9H_{13}O_2$	10.01	0.85
$C_9H_{15}NO$	10.39	0.69
$C_9H_{17}N_2$	10.76	0.52
$C_{10}HO_2$	10.90	0.94
$C_{10}H_3NO$	11.28	0.78
$C_{10}H_5N_2$	11.65	0.62
$C_{10}H_{17}O$	11.12	0.76
$C_{10}H_{19}N$	11.49	0.60
$C_{11}H_5O$	12.01	0.86
$C_{11}H_7N$	12.38	0.70
$C_{11}H_{21}$	12.22	0.68
$C_{12}H_9$	13.11	0.79
154		
$C_5H_2N_2O_4$	6.35	0.97
$C_5H_4N_3O_3$	6.73	0.80
$C_5H_6N_4O_2$	7.10	0.62
$C_6H_4NO_4$	7.09	1.02
$C_6H_6N_2O_3$	7.46	0.84
$C_6H_8N_3O_2$	7.83	0.67
$C_6H_{10}N_4O$	8.21	0.50
$C_7H_6O_4$	7.82	1.07
$C_7H_8NO_3$	8.19	0.90
$C_7H_{10}N_2O_2$	8.57	0.73
$C_7H_{12}N_3O$	8.94	0.56
$C_7H_{14}N_4$	9.31	0.39
$C_8H_2N_4$	10.20	0.47
$C_8H_{10}O_3$	8.92	0.95
$C_8H_{12}NO_2$	9.30	0.79
$C_8H_{14}N_2O$	9.67	0.62
$C_8H_{16}N_3$	10.05	0.46
$C_9H_2N_2O$	10.56	0.70
$C_9H_4N_3$	10.93	0.54
$C_9H_{14}O_2$	10.03	0.85
$C_9H_{16}NO$	10.40	0.69
$C_9H_{18}N_2$	10.78	0.53
$C_{10}H_2O_2$	10.92	0.94
$C_{10}H_4NO$	11.29	0.78

	P + 1	P + 2
$C_{10}H_6N_2$	11.67	0.62
$C_{10}H_{18}O$	11.13	0.76
$C_{10}H_{20}N$	11.51	0.60
$C_{11}H_6O$	12.02	0.86
$C_{11}H_8N$	12.40	0.70
$C_{11}H_{22}$	12.24	0.68
$C_{12}H_{10}$	13.13	0.79
155		
$C_5H_3N_2O_4$	6.37	0.97
$C_5H_5N_3O_3$	6.75	0.80
$C_5H_7N_4O_2$	7.12	0.62
$C_6H_5NO_4$	7.10	1.02
$C_6H_7N_2O_3$	7.48	0.84
$C_6H_9N_3O_2$	7.85	0.67
$C_6H_{11}N_4O$	8.23	0.50
$C_7H_7O_4$	7.83	1.07
$C_7H_9NO_3$	8.21	0.90
$C_7H_{11}N_2O_2$	8.58	0.73
$C_7H_{13}N_3O$	8.96	0.56
$C_7H_{15}N_4$	9.33	0.39
C_8HN_3O	9.84	0.64
$C_8H_3N_4$	10.22	0.47
$C_8H_{11}O_3$	8.94	0.95
$C_8H_{13}NO_2$	9.31	0.79
$C_8H_{15}N_2O$	9.69	0.62
$C_8H_{17}N_3$	10.06	0.46
C_9HNO_2	10.20	0.87
$C_9H_3N_2O$	10.58	0.71
$C_9H_5N_3$	10.95	0.54
$C_9H_{15}O_2$	10.04	0.85
$C_9H_{17}NO$	10.42	0.69
$C_9H_{19}N_2$	10.79	0.53
$C_{10}H_3O_2$	10.93	0.94
$C_{10}H_5NO$	11.31	0.78
$C_{10}H_7N_2$	11.68	0.62
$C_{10}H_{19}O$	11.15	0.76
$C_{10}H_{21}N$	11.52	0.60
$C_{11}H_7O$	12.04	0.86
$C_{11}H_9N$	12.41	0.71
$C_{11}H_{23}$	12.26	0.69
$C_{12}H_{11}$	13.14	0.79
156		
$C_5H_4N_2O_4$	6.39	0.98
$C_5H_6N_3O_3$	6.76	0.80
$C_5H_8N_4O_2$	7.14	0.62
$C_6H_6NO_4$	7.12	1.02
$C_6H_8N_2O_3$	7.49	0.85
$C_6H_{10}N_3O_2$	7.87	0.67
$C_6H_{12}N_4O$	8.24	0.50
$C_7H_8O_4$	7.85	1.07
$C_7H_{10}NO_3$	8.22	0.90
$C_7H_{12}N_2O_2$	8.60	0.73
$C_7H_{14}N_3O$	8.97	0.56
$C_7H_{16}N_4$	9.35	0.39
$C_8H_2N_3O$	9.86	0.64
$C_8H_4N_4$	10.24	0.47
$C_8H_{12}O_3$	8.95	0.96
$C_8H_{14}NO_2$	9.33	0.79
$C_8H_{16}N_2O$	9.70	0.62
$C_8H_{18}N_3$	10.08	0.46
$C_9H_2NO_2$	10.22	0.87
$C_9H_4N_2O$	10.59	0.71

	P + 1	P + 2
$C_9H_6N_3$	10.97	0.55
$C_9H_{16}O_2$	10.06	0.85
$C_9H_{18}NO$	10.43	0.69
$C_9H_{20}N_2$	10.81	0.53
$C_{10}H_4O_2$	10.95	0.94
$C_{10}H_6NO$	11.32	0.78
$C_{10}H_8N_2$	11.70	0.62
$C_{10}H_{20}O$	11.17	0.77
$C_{10}H_{22}N$	11.54	0.61
$C_{11}H_8O$	12.05	0.86
$C_{11}H_{10}N$	12.43	0.71
$C_{11}H_{24}$	12.27	0.69
$C_{12}H_{12}$	13.16	0.80
157		
$C_5H_5N_2O_4$	6.40	0.98
$C_5H_7N_3O_3$	6.78	0.80
$C_5H_9N_4O_2$	7.15	0.62
$C_6H_7NO_4$	7.13	1.02
$C_6H_9N_2O_3$	7.51	0.85
$C_6H_{11}N_3O_2$	7.88	0.67
$C_6H_{13}N_4O$	8.26	0.50
C_7HN_4O	9.15	0.57
$C_7H_9O_4$	7.87	1.07
$C_7H_{11}NO_3$	8.24	0.90
$C_7H_{13}N_2O_2$	8.61	0.73
$C_7H_{15}N_3O$	8.99	0.56
$C_7H_{17}N_4$	9.36	0.39
$C_8HN_2O_2$	9.50	0.80
$C_8H_3N_3O$	9.88	0.64
$C_8H_5N_4$	10.25	0.48
$C_8H_{13}O_3$	8.97	0.96
$C_8H_{15}NO_2$	9.35	0.79
$C_8H_{17}N_2O$	9.72	0.62
$C_8H_{19}N_3$	10.09	0.46
C_9HO_3	9.86	1.03
$C_9H_3NO_2$	10.23	0.87
$C_9H_5N_2O$	10.61	0.71
$C_9H_7N_3$	10.98	0.55
$C_9H_{17}O_2$	10.08	0.86
$C_9H_{19}NO$	10.45	0.69
$C_9H_{21}N_2$	10.82	0.53
$C_{10}H_5O_2$	10.96	0.94
$C_{10}H_7NO$	11.34	0.78
$C_{10}H_9N_2$	11.71	0.63
$C_{10}H_{21}O$	11.18	0.77
$C_{10}H_{23}N$	11.56	0.61
$C_{11}H_9O$	12.07	0.86
$C_{11}H_{11}N$	12.44	0.71
$C_{12}H_{13}$	13.18	0.80
$C_{13}H$	14.06	0.91
158		
$C_5H_6N_2O_4$	6.42	0.98
$C_5H_8N_3O_3$	6.79	0.80
$C_5H_{10}N_4O_2$	7.17	0.63
$C_6H_8NO_4$	7.15	1.02
$C_6H_{10}N_2O_3$	7.52	0.85
$C_6H_{12}N_3O_2$	7.90	0.68
$C_6H_{14}N_4O$	8.27	0.50
$C_7H_2N_4O$	9.16	0.58
$C_7H_{10}O_4$	7.88	1.07
$C_7H_{12}NO_3$	8.26	0.90

	P + 1	P + 2
$C_7H_{14}N_2O_2$	8.63	0.73
$C_7H_{16}N_3O$	9.00	0.56
$C_7H_{18}N_4$	9.38	0.40
$C_8H_2N_2O_2$	9.52	0.81
$C_8H_4N_3O$	9.89	0.64
$C_8H_6N_4$	10.27	0.48
$C_8H_{14}O_3$	8.99	0.96
$C_8H_{16}NO_2$	9.36	0.79
$C_8H_{18}N_2O$	9.74	0.63
$C_8H_{20}N_3$	10.11	0.46
$C_9H_2O_3$	9.88	1.04
$C_9H_4NO_2$	10.25	0.87
$C_9H_6N_2O$	10.62	0.71
$C_9H_8N_3$	11.00	0.55
$C_9H_{18}O_2$	10.09	0.86
$C_9H_{20}NO$	10.47	0.69
$C_9H_{22}N_2$	10.84	0.53
$C_{10}H_6O_2$	10.98	0.95
$C_{10}H_8NO$	11.36	0.79
$C_{10}H_{10}N_2$	11.73	0.63
$C_{10}H_{22}O$	11.20	0.77
$C_{11}H_{10}O$	12.09	0.87
$C_{11}H_{12}N$	12.46	0.71
$C_{12}H_{14}$	13.19	0.80
$C_{13}H_2$	14.08	0.92
159		
$C_5H_7N_2O_4$	6.43	0.98
$C_5H_9N_3O_3$	6.81	0.80
$C_5H_{11}N_4O_2$	7.18	0.63
$C_6H_9NO_4$	7.17	1.02
$C_6H_{11}N_2O_3$	7.54	0.85
$C_6H_{13}N_3O_2$	7.91	0.68
$C_6H_{15}N_4O$	8.29	0.51
$C_7HN_3O_2$	8.80	0.75
$C_7H_3N_4O$	9.18	0.58
$C_7H_{11}O_4$	7.90	1.07
$C_7H_{13}NO_3$	8.27	0.90
$C_7H_{15}N_2O_2$	8.65	0.73
$C_7H_{17}N_3O$	9.02	0.56
$C_7H_{19}N_4$	9.39	0.40
C_8HNO_3	9.16	0.97
$C_8H_3N_2O_2$	9.53	0.81
$C_8H_5N_3O$	9.91	0.64
$C_8H_7N_4$	10.28	0.48
$C_8H_{15}O_3$	9.00	0.96
$C_8H_{17}NO_2$	9.38	0.79
$C_8H_{19}N_2O$	9.75	0.63
$C_8H_{21}N_3$	10.13	0.46
$C_9H_3O_3$	9.89	1.04
$C_9H_5NO_2$	10.27	0.87
$C_9H_7N_2O$	10.64	0.71
$C_9H_9N_3$	11.01	0.55
$C_9H_{19}O_2$	10.11	0.86
$C_9H_{21}NO$	10.48	0.70
$C_{10}H_7O_2$	11.00	0.95
$C_{10}H_9NO$	11.37	0.79
$C_{10}H_{11}N_2$	11.75	0.63
$C_{11}H_{11}O$	12.10	0.87
$C_{11}H_{13}N$	12.48	0.71
$C_{12}HN$	13.37	0.82
$C_{12}H_{15}$	13.21	0.80
$C_{13}H_3$	14.10	0.92

	P + 1	P + 2
160		
$C_5H_8N_2O_4$	6.45	0.98
$C_5H_{10}N_3O_3$	6.83	0.80
$C_5H_{12}N_4O_2$	7.20	0.63
$C_6H_{10}NO_4$	7.18	1.02
$C_6H_{12}N_2O_3$	7.56	0.85
$C_6H_{14}N_3O_2$	7.93	0.68
$C_6H_{16}N_4O$	8.31	0.51
$C_7H_2N_3O_2$	8.82	0.75
$C_7H_4N_4O$	9.19	0.58
$C_7H_{12}O_4$	7.91	1.07
$C_7H_{14}NO_3$	8.29	0.90
$C_7H_{16}N_2O_2$	8.66	0.73
$C_7H_{18}N_3O$	9.04	0.57
$C_7H_{20}N_4$	9.41	0.40
$C_8H_2NO_3$	9.18	0.97
$C_8H_4N_2O_2$	9.55	0.81
$C_8H_6N_3O$	9.92	0.64
$C_8H_8N_4$	10.30	0.48
$C_8H_{16}O_3$	9.02	0.96
$C_8H_{18}NO_2$	9.39	0.79
$C_8H_{20}N_2O$	9.77	0.63
$C_9H_4O_3$	9.91	1.04
$C_9H_6NO_2$	10.28	0.88
$C_9H_8N_2O$	10.66	0.71
$C_9H_{10}N_3$	11.03	0.55
$C_9H_{20}O_2$	10.12	0.86
$C_{10}H_8O_2$	11.01	0.95
$C_{10}H_{10}NO$	11.39	0.79
$C_{10}H_{12}N_2$	11.76	0.63
$C_{11}H_{12}O$	12.12	0.87
$C_{11}H_{14}N$	12.49	0.72
$C_{12}H_2N$	13.38	0.82
$C_{12}H_{16}$	13.22	0.80
$C_{13}H_4$	14.11	0.92
161		
$C_5H_9N_2O_4$	6.47	0.98
$C_5H_{11}N_3O_3$	6.84	0.80
$C_5H_{13}N_4O_2$	7.22	0.63
$C_6HN_4O_2$	8.10	0.69
$C_6H_{11}NO_4$	7.20	1.03
$C_6H_{13}N_2O_3$	7.57	0.85
$C_6H_{15}N_3O_2$	7.95	0.68
$C_6H_{17}N_4O$	8.32	0.51
$C_7HN_2O_3$	8.46	0.92
$C_7H_3N_3O_2$	8.84	0.75
$C_7H_5N_4O$	9.21	0.58
$C_7H_{13}O_4$	7.93	1.08
$C_7H_{15}NO_3$	8.30	0.90
$C_7H_{17}N_2O_2$	8.68	0.74
$C_7H_{19}N_3O$	9.05	0.57
C_8HO_4	8.82	1.14
$C_8H_3NO_3$	9.19	0.98
$C_8H_5N_2O_2$	9.57	0.81
$C_8H_7N_3O$	9.94	0.65
$C_8H_9N_4$	10.32	0.48
$C_8H_{17}O_3$	9.03	0.96
$C_8H_{19}NO_2$	9.41	0.80
$C_9H_5O_3$	9.92	1.04
$C_9H_7NO_2$	10.30	0.88
$C_9H_9N_2O$	10.67	0.72
$C_9H_{11}N_3$	11.05	0.56

	P + 1	P + 2
$C_{10}H_9O_2$	11.03	0.95
$C_{10}H_{11}NO$	11.40	0.79
$C_{10}H_{13}N_2$	11.78	0.63
$C_{11}HN_2$	12.67	0.74
$C_{11}H_{13}O$	12.13	0.87
$C_{11}H_{15}N$	12.51	0.72
$C_{12}HO$	13.02	0.98
$C_{12}H_3N$	13.40	0.83
$C_{12}H_{17}$	13.24	0.81
$C_{13}H_5$	14.13	0.92

162

	P + 1	P + 2
$C_5H_{10}N_2O_4$	6.48	0.98
$C_5H_{12}N_3O_3$	6.86	0.81
$C_5H_{14}N_4O_2$	7.23	0.63
$C_6H_2N_4O_2$	8.12	0.69
$C_6H_{12}NO_4$	7.21	1.03
$C_6H_{14}N_2O_3$	7.59	0.85
$C_6H_{16}N_3O_2$	7.96	0.68
$C_6H_{18}N_4O$	8.34	0.51
$C_7H_2N_2O_3$	8.48	0.92
$C_7H_4N_3O_2$	8.85	0.75
$C_7H_6N_4O$	9.23	0.58
$C_7H_{14}O_4$	7.95	1.08
$C_7H_{16}NO_3$	8.32	0.91
$C_7H_{18}N_2O_2$	8.69	0.74
$C_8H_2O_4$	8.83	1.15
$C_8H_4NO_3$	9.21	0.98
$C_8H_6N_2O_2$	9.58	0.81
$C_8H_8N_3O$	9.96	0.65
$C_8H_{10}N_4$	10.33	0.48
$C_8H_{18}O_3$	9.05	0.96
$C_9H_6O_3$	9.94	1.04
$C_9H_8NO_2$	10.31	0.88
$C_9H_{10}N_2O$	10.69	0.72
$C_9H_{12}N_3$	11.06	0.56
$C_{10}H_{10}O_2$	11.04	0.95
$C_{10}H_{12}NO$	11.42	0.79
$C_{10}H_{14}N_2$	11.79	0.64
$C_{11}H_2N_2$	12.68	0.74
$C_{11}H_{14}O$	12.15	0.87
$C_{11}H_{16}N$	12.52	0.72
$C_{12}H_2O$	13.04	0.98
$C_{12}H_4N$	13.41	0.83
$C_{12}H_{18}$	13.26	0.81
$C_{13}H_6$	14.14	0.92

163

	P + 1	P + 2
$C_5H_{11}N_2O_4$	6.50	0.98
$C_5H_{13}N_3O_3$	6.87	0.81
$C_5H_{15}N_4O_2$	7.25	0.63
$C_6HN_3O_3$	7.76	0.87
$C_6H_3N_4O_2$	8.14	0.69
$C_6H_{13}NO_4$	7.23	1.03
$C_6H_{15}N_2O_3$	7.60	0.85
$C_6H_{17}N_3O_2$	7.98	0.68
C_7HNO_4	8.12	1.09
$C_7H_3N_2O_3$	8.49	0.92
$C_7H_5N_3O_2$	8.87	0.75
$C_7H_7N_4O$	9.24	0.58
$C_7H_{15}O_4$	7.96	1.08
$C_7H_{17}NO_3$	8.34	0.91
$C_8H_3O_4$	8.85	1.15
$C_8H_5NO_3$	9.22	0.98
$C_8H_7N_2O_2$	9.60	0.81
$C_8H_9N_3O$	9.97	0.65
$C_8H_{11}N_4$	10.35	0.49
$C_9H_7O_3$	9.96	1.04
$C_9H_9NO_2$	10.33	0.88
$C_9H_{11}N_2O$	10.70	0.72
$C_9H_{13}N_3$	11.08	0.56
$C_{10}HN_3$	11.97	0.66
$C_{10}H_{11}O_2$	11.06	0.95
$C_{10}H_{13}NO$	11.44	0.80
$C_{10}H_{15}N_2$	11.81	0.64
$C_{11}HNO$	12.32	0.89
$C_{11}H_3N_2$	12.70	0.74
$C_{11}H_{15}O$	12.17	0.88
$C_{11}H_{17}N$	12.54	0.72
$C_{12}H_3O$	13.05	0.98
$C_{12}H_5N$	13.43	0.83
$C_{12}H_{19}$	13.27	0.81
$C_{13}H_7$	14.16	0.93

164

	P + 1	P + 2
$C_5H_{12}N_2O_4$	6.51	0.98
$C_5H_{14}N_3O_3$	6.89	0.81
$C_5H_{16}N_4O_2$	7.26	0.63
$C_6H_2N_3O_3$	7.78	0.87
$C_6H_4N_4O_2$	8.15	0.70
$C_6H_{14}NO_4$	7.25	1.03
$C_6H_{16}N_2O_3$	7.62	0.86
$C_7H_2NO_4$	8.13	1.09
$C_7H_4N_2O_3$	8.51	0.92
$C_7H_6N_3O_2$	8.88	0.75
$C_7H_8N_4O$	9.26	0.59
$C_7H_{16}O_4$	7.98	1.08
$C_8H_4O_4$	8.87	1.15
$C_8H_6NO_3$	9.24	0.98
$C_8H_8N_2O_2$	9.61	0.81
$C_8H_{10}N_3O$	9.99	0.65
$C_8H_{12}N_4$	10.36	0.49
$C_9H_8O_3$	9.97	1.05
$C_9H_{10}NO_2$	10.35	0.88
$C_9H_{12}N_2O$	10.72	0.72
$C_9H_{14}N_3$	11.09	0.56
$C_{10}H_2N_3$	11.98	0.66
$C_{10}H_{12}O_2$	11.08	0.96
$C_{10}H_{14}NO$	11.45	0.80
$C_{10}H_{16}N_2$	11.83	0.64
$C_{11}H_2NO$	12.34	0.90
$C_{11}H_4N_2$	12.71	0.74
$C_{11}H_{16}O$	12.18	0.88
$C_{11}H_{18}N$	12.56	0.72
$C_{12}H_4O$	13.07	0.98
$C_{12}H_6N$	13.45	0.83
$C_{12}H_{20}$	13.29	0.81
$C_{13}H_8$	14.18	0.93

165

	P + 1	P + 2
$C_5H_{13}N_2O_4$	6.53	0.98
$C_5H_{15}N_3O_3$	6.91	0.81
$C_6HN_2O_4$	7.42	1.04
$C_6H_3N_3O_3$	7.79	0.87
$C_6H_5N_4O_2$	8.17	0.70
$C_6H_{15}NO_4$	7.26	1.03
$C_7H_3NO_4$	8.15	1.09
$C_7H_5N_2O_3$	8.52	0.92
$C_7H_7N_3O_2$	8.90	0.75
$C_7H_9N_4O$	9.27	0.59
$C_8H_5O_4$	8.88	1.15
$C_8H_7NO_3$	9.26	0.98
$C_8H_9N_2O_2$	9.63	0.82
$C_8H_{11}N_3O$	10.00	0.65
$C_8H_{13}N_4$	10.38	0.49
C_9HN_4	11.27	0.58
$C_9H_9O_3$	9.99	1.05
$C_9H_{11}NO_2$	10.36	0.88
$C_9H_{13}N_2O$	10.74	0.72
$C_9H_{15}N_3$	11.11	0.56
$C_{10}HN_2O$	11.62	0.82
$C_{10}H_3N_3$	12.00	0.66
$C_{10}H_{13}O_2$	11.09	0.96
$C_{10}H_{15}NO$	11.47	0.80
$C_{10}H_{17}N_2$	11.84	0.64
$C_{11}HO_2$	11.98	1.05
$C_{11}H_3NO$	12.36	0.90
$C_{11}H_5N_2$	12.73	0.74
$C_{11}H_{17}O$	12.20	0.88
$C_{11}H_{19}N$	12.57	0.73
$C_{12}H_5O$	13.09	0.99
$C_{12}H_7N$	13.46	0.84
$C_{12}H_{21}$	13.30	0.81
$C_{13}H_9$	14.19	0.93

166

	P + 1	P + 2
$C_5H_{14}N_2O_4$	6.55	0.99
$C_6H_2N_2O_4$	7.44	1.04
$C_6H_4N_3O_3$	7.81	0.87
$C_6H_6N_4O_2$	8.18	0.70
$C_7H_4NO_4$	8.17	1.09
$C_7H_6N_2O_3$	8.54	0.92
$C_7H_8N_3O_2$	8.92	0.76
$C_7H_{10}N_4O$	9.29	0.59
$C_8H_6O_4$	8.90	1.15
$C_8H_8NO_3$	9.27	0.98
$C_8H_{10}N_2O_2$	9.65	0.82
$C_8H_{12}N_3O$	10.02	0.65
$C_8H_{14}N_4$	10.40	0.49
$C_9H_2N_4$	11.28	0.58
$C_9H_{10}O_3$	10.00	1.05
$C_9H_{12}NO_2$	10.38	0.89
$C_9H_{14}N_2O$	10.75	0.72
$C_9H_{16}N_3$	11.13	0.56
$C_{10}H_2N_2O$	11.64	0.82
$C_{10}H_4N_3$	12.01	0.66
$C_{10}H_{14}O_2$	11.11	0.96
$C_{10}H_{16}NO$	11.48	0.80
$C_{10}H_{18}N_2$	11.86	0.64
$C_{11}H_2O_2$	12.00	1.06
$C_{11}H_4NO$	12.37	0.90
$C_{11}H_6N_2$	12.75	0.75
$C_{11}H_{18}O$	12.21	0.88
$C_{11}H_{20}N$	12.59	0.73
$C_{12}H_6O$	13.10	0.99
$C_{12}H_8N$	13.48	0.84
$C_{12}H_{22}$	13.32	0.82
$C_{13}H_{10}$	14.21	0.93

167

	P + 1	P + 2
$C_6H_3N_2O_4$	7.45	1.04
$C_6H_5N_3O_3$	7.83	0.87
$C_6H_7N_4O_2$	8.20	0.70
$C_7H_5NO_4$	8.18	1.10
$C_7H_7N_2O_3$	8.56	0.93
$C_7H_9N_3O_2$	8.93	0.76
$C_7H_{11}N_4O$	9.31	0.59
$C_8H_7O_4$	8.91	1.15
$C_8H_9NO_3$	9.29	0.99
$C_8H_{11}N_2O_2$	9.66	0.82
$C_8H_{13}N_3O$	10.04	0.66
$C_8H_{15}N_4$	10.41	0.49
C_9HN_3O	10.93	0.74
$C_9H_3N_4$	11.30	0.58
$C_9H_{11}O_3$	10.02	1.05
$C_9H_{13}NO_2$	10.39	0.89
$C_9H_{15}N_2O$	10.77	0.73
$C_9H_{17}N_3$	11.14	0.57
$C_{10}HNO_2$	11.28	0.98
$C_{10}H_3N_2O$	11.66	0.82
$C_{10}H_5N_3$	12.03	0.66
$C_{10}H_{15}O_2$	11.12	0.96
$C_{10}H_{17}NO$	11.50	0.80
$C_{10}H_{19}N_2$	11.87	0.65
$C_{11}H_3O_2$	12.01	1.06
$C_{11}H_5NO$	12.39	0.90
$C_{11}H_7N_2$	12.76	0.75
$C_{11}H_{19}O$	12.23	0.88
$C_{11}H_{21}N$	12.60	0.73
$C_{12}H_7O$	13.12	0.99
$C_{12}H_9N$	13.49	0.84
$C_{12}H_{23}$	13.34	0.82
$C_{13}H_{11}$	14.22	0.94

168

	P + 1	P + 2
$C_6H_4N_2O_4$	7.47	1.04
$C_6H_6N_3O_3$	7.84	0.87
$C_6H_8N_4O_2$	8.22	0.70
$C_7H_6NO_4$	8.20	1.10
$C_7H_8N_2O_3$	8.57	0.93
$C_7H_{10}N_3O_2$	8.95	0.76
$C_7H_{12}N_4O$	9.32	0.59
$C_8H_8O_4$	8.93	1.15
$C_8H_{10}NO_3$	9.30	0.99
$C_8H_{12}N_2O_2$	9.68	0.82
$C_8H_{14}N_3O$	10.05	0.66
$C_8H_{16}N_4$	10.43	0.49
$C_9H_2N_3O$	10.94	0.74
$C_9H_4N_4$	11.32	0.58
$C_9H_{12}O_3$	10.04	1.05
$C_9H_{14}NO_2$	10.41	0.89
$C_9H_{16}N_2O$	10.78	0.73
$C_9H_{18}N_3$	11.16	0.57
$C_{10}H_2NO_2$	11.30	0.98
$C_{10}H_4N_2O$	11.67	0.82
$C_{10}H_6N_3$	12.05	0.67
$C_{10}H_{16}O_2$	11.14	0.96
$C_{10}H_{18}NO$	11.52	0.80
$C_{10}H_{20}N_2$	11.89	0.65
$C_{11}H_4O_2$	12.03	1.06
$C_{11}H_6NO$	12.40	0.90
$C_{11}H_8N_2$	12.78	0.75
$C_{11}H_{20}O$	12.25	0.89
$C_{11}H_{22}N$	12.62	0.73

	P + 1	P + 2
$C_{12}H_{8}O$	13.13	0.99
$C_{12}H_{10}N$	13.51	0.84
$C_{12}H_{24}$	13.35	0.82
$C_{13}H_{12}$	14.24	0.94

169

	P + 1	P + 2
$C_{6}H_{5}N_{2}O_{4}$	7.48	1.05
$C_{6}H_{7}N_{3}O_{3}$	7.86	0.87
$C_{6}H_{9}N_{4}O_{2}$	8.23	0.70
$C_{7}H_{7}NO_{4}$	8.21	1.10
$C_{7}H_{9}N_{2}O_{3}$	8.59	0.93
$C_{7}H_{11}N_{3}O_{2}$	8.96	0.76
$C_{7}H_{13}N_{4}O$	9.34	0.59
$C_{8}HN_{4}O$	10.23	0.67
$C_{8}H_{9}O_{4}$	8.95	1.16
$C_{8}H_{11}NO_{3}$	9.32	0.99
$C_{8}H_{13}N_{2}O_{2}$	9.69	0.82
$C_{8}H_{15}N_{3}O$	10.07	0.66
$C_{8}H_{17}N_{4}$	10.44	0.50
$C_{9}HN_{2}O_{2}$	10.58	0.91
$C_{9}H_{3}N_{3}O$	10.96	0.75
$C_{9}H_{5}N_{4}$	11.33	0.59
$C_{9}H_{13}O_{3}$	10.05	1.05
$C_{9}H_{15}NO_{2}$	10.43	0.89
$C_{9}H_{17}N_{2}O$	10.80	0.73
$C_{9}H_{19}N_{3}$	11.17	0.57
$C_{10}HO_{3}$	10.94	1.14
$C_{10}H_{3}NO_{2}$	11.31	0.98
$C_{10}H_{5}N_{2}O$	11.69	0.82
$C_{10}H_{7}N_{3}$	12.06	0.67
$C_{10}H_{17}O_{2}$	11.16	0.96
$C_{10}H_{19}NO$	11.53	0.81
$C_{10}H_{21}N_{2}$	11.91	0.65
$C_{11}H_{5}O_{2}$	12.05	1.06
$C_{11}H_{7}NO$	12.42	0.91
$C_{11}H_{9}N_{2}$	12.79	0.75
$C_{11}H_{21}O$	12.26	0.89
$C_{11}H_{23}N$	12.64	0.73
$C_{12}H_{9}O$	13.15	1.00
$C_{12}H_{11}N$	13.53	0.84
$C_{12}H_{25}$	13.37	0.82
$C_{13}H_{13}$	14.26	0.94
$C_{14}H$	15.14	1.07

170

	P + 1	P + 2
$C_{6}H_{6}N_{2}O_{4}$	7.50	1.05
$C_{6}H_{8}N_{3}O_{3}$	7.87	0.87
$C_{6}H_{10}N_{4}O_{2}$	8.25	0.70
$C_{7}H_{8}NO_{4}$	8.23	1.10
$C_{7}H_{10}N_{2}O_{3}$	8.60	0.93
$C_{7}H_{12}N_{3}O_{2}$	8.98	0.76
$C_{7}H_{14}N_{4}O$	9.35	0.59
$C_{8}H_{2}N_{4}O$	10.24	0.68
$C_{8}H_{10}O_{4}$	8.96	1.16
$C_{8}H_{12}NO_{3}$	9.34	0.99
$C_{8}H_{14}N_{2}O_{2}$	9.71	0.82
$C_{8}H_{16}N_{3}O$	10.08	0.66
$C_{8}H_{18}N_{4}$	10.46	0.50
$C_{9}H_{2}N_{2}O_{2}$	10.60	0.91
$C_{9}H_{4}N_{3}O$	10.97	0.75
$C_{9}H_{6}N_{4}$	11.35	0.59
$C_{9}H_{14}O_{3}$	10.07	1.06
$C_{9}H_{16}NO_{2}$	10.44	0.89
$C_{9}H_{18}N_{2}O$	10.82	0.73
$C_{9}H_{20}N_{3}$	11.19	0.57
$C_{10}H_{2}O_{3}$	10.96	1.14
$C_{10}H_{4}NO_{2}$	11.33	0.98
$C_{10}H_{6}N_{2}O$	11.70	0.83
$C_{10}H_{8}N_{3}$	12.08	0.67
$C_{10}H_{18}O_{2}$	11.17	0.97
$C_{10}H_{20}NO$	11.55	0.81
$C_{10}H_{22}N_{2}$	11.92	0.65
$C_{11}H_{6}O_{2}$	12.06	1.06
$C_{11}H_{8}NO$	12.44	0.91
$C_{11}H_{10}N_{2}$	12.81	0.75
$C_{11}H_{22}O$	12.28	0.89
$C_{11}H_{24}N$	12.65	0.74
$C_{12}H_{10}O$	13.17	1.00
$C_{12}H_{12}N$	13.54	0.85
$C_{12}H_{26}$	13.38	0.83
$C_{13}H_{14}$	14.27	0.94
$C_{14}H_{2}$	15.16	1.07

171

	P + 1	P + 2
$C_{6}H_{7}N_{2}O_{4}$	7.52	1.05
$C_{6}H_{9}N_{3}O_{3}$	7.89	0.88
$C_{6}H_{11}N_{4}O_{2}$	8.26	0.70
$C_{7}H_{9}NO_{4}$	8.25	1.10
$C_{7}H_{11}N_{2}O_{3}$	8.62	0.93
$C_{7}H_{13}N_{3}O_{2}$	9.00	0.76
$C_{7}H_{15}N_{4}O$	9.37	0.60
$C_{8}HN_{3}O_{2}$	9.88	0.84
$C_{8}H_{3}N_{4}O$	10.26	0.68
$C_{8}H_{11}O_{4}$	8.98	1.16
$C_{8}H_{13}NO_{3}$	9.35	0.99
$C_{8}H_{15}N_{2}O_{2}$	9.73	0.83
$C_{8}H_{17}N_{3}O$	10.10	0.66
$C_{8}H_{19}N_{4}$	10.48	0.50
$C_{9}HNO_{3}$	10.24	1.07
$C_{9}H_{3}N_{2}O_{2}$	10.61	0.91
$C_{9}H_{5}N_{3}O$	10.99	0.75
$C_{9}H_{7}N_{4}$	11.36	0.59
$C_{9}H_{15}O_{3}$	10.08	1.06
$C_{9}H_{17}NO_{2}$	10.46	0.89
$C_{9}H_{19}N_{2}O$	10.83	0.73
$C_{9}H_{21}N_{3}$	11.21	0.57
$C_{10}H_{3}O_{3}$	10.97	1.14
$C_{10}H_{5}NO_{2}$	11.35	0.99
$C_{10}H_{7}N_{2}O$	11.72	0.83
$C_{10}H_{9}N_{3}$	12.09	0.67
$C_{10}H_{19}O_{2}$	11.19	0.97
$C_{10}H_{21}NO$	11.56	0.81
$C_{10}H_{23}N_{2}$	11.94	0.65
$C_{11}H_{7}O_{2}$	12.08	1.07
$C_{11}H_{9}NO$	12.45	0.91
$C_{11}H_{11}N_{2}$	12.83	0.76
$C_{11}H_{23}O$	12.29	0.89
$C_{11}H_{25}N$	12.67	0.74
$C_{12}H_{11}O$	13.18	1.00
$C_{12}H_{13}N$	13.56	0.85
$C_{13}HN$	14.45	0.97
$C_{13}H_{15}$	14.29	0.94
$C_{14}H_{3}$	15.18	1.07

172

	P + 1	P + 2
$C_{6}H_{8}N_{2}O_{4}$	7.53	1.05
$C_{6}H_{10}N_{3}O_{3}$	7.91	0.88
$C_{6}H_{12}N_{4}O_{2}$	8.28	0.71
$C_{7}H_{10}NO_{4}$	8.26	1.10
$C_{7}H_{12}N_{2}O_{3}$	8.64	0.93
$C_{7}H_{14}N_{3}O_{2}$	9.01	0.76
$C_{7}H_{16}N_{4}O$	9.39	0.60
$C_{8}H_{2}N_{3}O_{2}$	9.90	0.84
$C_{8}H_{4}N_{4}O$	10.27	0.68
$C_{8}H_{12}O_{4}$	8.99	1.16
$C_{8}H_{14}NO_{3}$	9.37	0.99
$C_{8}H_{16}N_{2}O_{2}$	9.74	0.83
$C_{8}H_{18}N_{3}O$	10.12	0.66
$C_{8}H_{20}N_{4}$	10.49	0.50
$C_{9}H_{2}NO_{3}$	10.26	1.07
$C_{9}H_{4}N_{2}O_{2}$	10.63	0.91
$C_{9}H_{6}N_{3}O$	11.01	0.75
$C_{9}H_{8}N_{4}$	11.38	0.59
$C_{9}H_{16}O_{3}$	10.10	1.06
$C_{9}H_{18}NO_{2}$	10.47	0.90
$C_{9}H_{20}N_{2}O$	10.85	0.73
$C_{9}H_{22}N_{3}$	11.22	0.57
$C_{10}H_{4}O_{3}$	10.99	1.15
$C_{10}H_{6}NO_{2}$	11.36	0.99
$C_{10}H_{8}N_{2}O$	11.74	0.83
$C_{10}H_{10}N_{3}$	12.11	0.67
$C_{10}H_{20}O_{2}$	11.20	0.97
$C_{10}H_{22}NO$	11.58	0.81
$C_{10}H_{24}N_{2}$	11.95	0.65
$C_{11}H_{8}O_{2}$	12.09	1.07
$C_{11}H_{10}NO$	12.47	0.91
$C_{11}H_{12}N_{2}$	12.84	0.76
$C_{11}H_{24}O$	12.31	0.89
$C_{12}H_{12}O$	13.20	1.00
$C_{12}H_{14}N$	13.57	0.85
$C_{13}H_{2}N$	14.46	0.97
$C_{13}H_{16}$	14.30	0.95
$C_{14}H_{4}$	15.19	1.07

173

	P + 1	P + 2
$C_{6}H_{9}N_{2}O_{4}$	7.55	1.05
$C_{6}H_{11}N_{3}O_{3}$	7.92	0.88
$C_{6}H_{13}N_{4}O_{2}$	8.30	0.71
$C_{7}HN_{4}O_{2}$	9.18	0.78
$C_{7}H_{11}NO_{4}$	8.28	1.10
$C_{7}H_{13}N_{2}O_{3}$	8.65	0.93
$C_{7}H_{15}N_{3}O_{2}$	9.03	0.77
$C_{7}H_{17}N_{4}O$	9.40	0.60
$C_{8}HN_{2}O_{3}$	9.54	1.01
$C_{8}H_{3}N_{3}O_{2}$	9.92	0.84
$C_{8}H_{5}N_{4}O$	10.29	0.68
$C_{8}H_{13}O_{4}$	9.01	1.16
$C_{8}H_{15}NO_{3}$	9.38	0.99
$C_{8}H_{17}N_{2}O_{2}$	9.76	0.83
$C_{8}H_{19}N_{3}O$	10.13	0.66
$C_{8}H_{21}N_{4}$	10.51	0.50
$C_{9}HO_{4}$	9.90	1.24
$C_{9}H_{3}NO_{3}$	10.27	1.08
$C_{9}H_{5}N_{2}O_{2}$	10.65	0.91
$C_{9}H_{7}N_{3}O$	11.02	0.75
$C_{9}H_{9}N_{4}$	11.40	0.59
$C_{9}H_{17}O_{3}$	10.12	1.06
$C_{9}H_{19}NO_{2}$	10.49	0.90
$C_{9}H_{21}N_{2}O$	10.86	0.74
$C_{9}H_{23}N_{3}$	11.24	0.58
$C_{10}H_{5}O_{3}$	11.00	1.15
$C_{10}H_{7}NO_{2}$	11.38	0.99
$C_{10}H_{9}N_{2}O$	11.75	0.83
$C_{10}H_{11}N_{3}$	12.13	0.67
$C_{10}H_{21}O_{2}$	11.22	0.97
$C_{10}H_{23}NO$	11.60	0.81
$C_{11}H_{9}O_{2}$	12.11	1.07
$C_{11}H_{11}NO$	12.48	0.91
$C_{11}H_{13}N_{2}$	12.86	0.76
$C_{12}HN_{2}$	13.75	0.87
$C_{12}H_{13}O$	13.21	1.00
$C_{12}H_{15}N$	13.59	0.85
$C_{13}HO$	14.10	1.12
$C_{13}H_{3}N$	14.48	0.97
$C_{13}H_{17}$	14.32	0.95
$C_{14}H_{5}$	15.21	1.07

174

	P + 1	P + 2
$C_{6}H_{10}N_{2}O_{4}$	7.56	1.05
$C_{6}H_{12}N_{3}O_{3}$	7.94	0.88
$C_{6}H_{14}N_{4}O_{2}$	8.31	0.71
$C_{7}H_{2}N_{4}O_{2}$	9.20	0.78
$C_{7}H_{12}NO_{4}$	8.29	1.10
$C_{7}H_{14}N_{2}O_{3}$	8.67	0.93
$C_{7}H_{16}N_{3}O_{2}$	9.04	0.77
$C_{7}H_{18}N_{4}O$	9.42	0.60
$C_{8}H_{2}N_{2}O_{3}$	9.56	1.01
$C_{8}H_{4}N_{3}O_{2}$	9.93	0.85
$C_{8}H_{6}N_{4}O$	10.31	0.68
$C_{8}H_{14}O_{4}$	9.03	1.16
$C_{8}H_{16}NO_{3}$	9.40	1.00
$C_{8}H_{18}N_{2}O_{2}$	9.77	0.83
$C_{8}H_{20}N_{3}O$	10.15	0.67
$C_{8}H_{22}N_{4}$	10.52	0.50
$C_{9}H_{2}O_{4}$	9.91	1.24
$C_{9}H_{4}NO_{3}$	10.29	1.08
$C_{9}H_{6}N_{2}O_{2}$	10.66	0.92
$C_{9}H_{8}N_{3}O$	11.04	0.75
$C_{9}H_{10}N_{4}$	11.41	0.60
$C_{9}H_{18}O_{3}$	10.13	1.06
$C_{9}H_{20}NO_{2}$	10.51	0.90
$C_{9}H_{22}N_{2}O$	10.88	0.74
$C_{10}H_{6}O_{3}$	11.02	1.15
$C_{10}H_{8}NO_{2}$	11.39	0.99
$C_{10}H_{10}N_{2}O$	11.77	0.83
$C_{10}H_{12}N_{3}$	12.14	0.68
$C_{10}H_{22}O_{2}$	11.24	0.97
$C_{11}H_{10}O_{2}$	12.13	1.07
$C_{11}H_{12}NO$	12.50	0.92
$C_{11}H_{14}N_{2}$	12.87	0.76
$C_{12}H_{2}N_{2}$	13.76	0.88
$C_{12}H_{14}O$	13.23	1.01
$C_{12}H_{16}N$	13.61	0.85
$C_{13}H_{2}O$	14.12	1.12
$C_{13}H_{4}N$	14.49	0.97
$C_{13}H_{18}$	14.34	0.95
$C_{14}H_{6}$	15.22	1.08

175

	P + 1	P + 2
$C_{6}H_{11}N_{2}O_{4}$	7.58	1.05
$C_{6}H_{13}N_{3}O_{3}$	7.95	0.88
$C_{6}H_{15}N_{4}O_{2}$	8.33	0.71
$C_{7}HN_{3}O_{3}$	8.84	0.95

	P + 1	P + 2
$C_7H_3N_4O_2$	9.22	0.78
$C_7H_{13}NO_4$	8.31	1.11
$C_7H_{15}N_2O_3$	8.68	0.94
$C_7H_{17}N_3O_2$	9.06	0.77
$C_7H_{19}N_4O$	9.43	0.60
C_8HNO_4	9.20	1.18
$C_8H_3N_2O_3$	9.57	1.01
$C_8H_5N_3O_2$	9.95	0.85
$C_8H_7N_4O$	10.32	0.68
$C_8H_{17}NO_3$	9.42	1.00
$C_8H_{19}N_2O_2$	9.79	0.83
$C_8H_{21}N_3O$	10.16	0.67
$C_8H_{15}O_4$	9.04	1.16
$C_9H_3O_4$	9.93	1.24
$C_9H_5NO_3$	10.30	1.08
$C_9H_7N_2O_2$	10.68	0.92
$C_9H_9N_3O$	11.05	0.76
$C_9H_{11}N_4$	11.43	0.60
$C_9H_{19}O_3$	10.15	1.06
$C_9H_{21}NO_2$	10.52	0.90
$C_{10}H_7O_3$	11.04	1.15
$C_{10}H_9NO_2$	11.41	0.99
$C_{10}H_{11}N_2O$	11.78	0.83
$C_{10}H_{13}N_3$	12.16	0.68
$C_{11}HN_3$	13.05	0.78
$C_{11}H_{11}O_2$	12.14	1.07
$C_{11}H_{13}NO$	12.52	0.92
$C_{11}H_{15}N_2$	12.89	0.77
$C_{12}HNO$	13.40	1.03
$C_{12}H_3N_2$	13.78	0.88
$C_{12}H_{15}O$	13.25	1.01
$C_{12}H_{17}N$	13.62	0.86
$C_{13}H_3O$	14.14	1.12
$C_{13}H_5N$	14.51	0.98
$C_{13}H_{19}$	14.35	0.95
$C_{14}H_7$	15.24	1.08
176		
$C_6H_{12}N_2O_4$	7.60	1.05
$C_6H_{14}N_3O_3$	7.97	0.88
$C_6H_{16}N_4O_2$	8.34	0.71
$C_7H_2N_3O_3$	8.86	0.95
$C_7H_4N_4O_2$	9.23	0.78
$C_7H_{14}NO_4$	8.33	1.11
$C_7H_{16}N_2O_3$	8.70	0.94
$C_7H_{18}N_3O_2$	9.08	0.77
$C_7H_{20}N_4O$	9.45	0.60
$C_8H_2NO_4$	9.22	1.18
$C_8H_4N_2O_3$	9.59	1.01
$C_8H_6N_3O_2$	9.96	0.85
$C_8H_8N_4O$	10.34	0.69
$C_8H_{16}O_4$	9.06	1.17
$C_8H_{18}NO_3$	9.43	1.00
$C_8H_{20}N_2O_2$	9.81	0.83
$C_9H_4O_4$	9.95	1.24
$C_9H_6NO_3$	10.32	1.08
$C_9H_8N_2O_2$	10.70	0.92
$C_9H_{10}N_3O$	11.07	0.76
$C_9H_{12}N_4$	11.44	0.60
$C_9H_{20}O_3$	10.16	1.07
$C_{10}H_8O_3$	11.05	1.15
$C_{10}H_{10}NO_2$	11.43	0.99
$C_{10}H_{12}N_2O$	11.80	0.84
$C_{10}H_{14}N_3$	12.17	0.68
$C_{11}H_2N_3$	13.06	0.79
$C_{11}H_{12}O_2$	12.16	1.08
$C_{11}H_{14}NO$	12.53	0.92
$C_{11}H_{16}N_2$	12.91	0.77
$C_{12}H_2NO$	13.42	1.03
$C_{12}H_4N_2$	13.79	0.88
$C_{12}H_{16}O$	13.26	1.01
$C_{12}H_{18}N$	13.64	0.86
$C_{13}H_4O$	14.15	1.13
$C_{13}H_6N$	14.53	0.98
$C_{13}H_{20}$	14.37	0.96
$C_{14}H_8$	15.26	1.08
177		
$C_6H_{13}N_2O_4$	7.61	1.06
$C_6H_{15}N_3O_3$	7.99	0.88
$C_6H_{17}N_4O_2$	8.36	0.71
$C_7HN_2O_4$	8.50	1.12
$C_7H_3N_3O_3$	8.87	0.95
$C_7H_5N_4O_2$	9.25	0.78
$C_7H_{15}NO_4$	8.34	1.11
$C_7H_{17}N_2O_3$	8.72	0.94
$C_7H_{19}N_3O_2$	9.09	0.77
$C_8H_3NO_4$	9.23	1.18
$C_8H_5N_2O_3$	9.61	1.01
$C_8H_7N_3O_2$	9.98	0.85
$C_8H_9N_4O$	10.35	0.69
$C_8H_{17}O_4$	9.07	1.17
$C_8H_{19}NO_3$	9.45	1.00
$C_9H_5O_4$	9.96	1.25
$C_9H_7NO_3$	10.34	1.08
$C_9H_9N_2O_2$	10.71	0.92
$C_9H_{11}N_3O$	11.09	0.76
$C_9H_{13}N_4$	11.46	0.60
$C_{10}HN_4$	12.35	0.70
$C_{10}H_9O_3$	11.07	1.16
$C_{10}H_{11}NO_2$	11.44	1.00
$C_{10}H_{13}N_2O$	11.82	0.84
$C_{10}H_{15}N_3$	12.19	0.68
$C_{11}HN_2O$	12.71	0.94
$C_{11}H_3N_3$	13.08	0.79
$C_{11}H_{13}O_2$	12.17	1.08
$C_{11}H_{15}NO$	12.55	0.92
$C_{11}H_{17}N_2$	12.92	0.77
$C_{12}HO_2$	13.06	1.18
$C_{12}H_3NO$	13.44	1.03
$C_{12}H_5N_2$	13.81	0.88
$C_{12}H_{17}O$	13.28	1.01
$C_{12}H_{19}N$	13.65	0.86
$C_{13}H_5O$	14.17	1.13
$C_{13}H_7N$	14.54	0.98
$C_{13}H_{21}$	14.38	0.96
$C_{14}H_9$	15.27	1.08
178		
$C_6H_{14}N_2O_4$	7.63	1.06
$C_6H_{16}N_3O_3$	8.00	0.88
$C_6H_{18}N_4O_2$	8.38	0.71
$C_7H_2N_2O_4$	8.52	1.12
$C_7H_4N_3O_3$	8.89	0.95
$C_7H_6N_4O_2$	9.26	0.79
$C_7H_{16}NO_4$	8.36	1.11
$C_7H_{18}N_2O_3$	8.73	0.94
$C_8H_4NO_4$	9.25	1.18
$C_8H_6N_2O_3$	9.62	1.02
$C_8H_8N_3O_2$	10.00	0.85
$C_8H_{10}N_4O$	10.37	0.69
$C_8H_{18}O_4$	9.09	1.17
$C_9H_6O_4$	9.98	1.25
$C_9H_8NO_3$	10.35	1.08
$C_9H_{10}N_2O_2$	10.73	0.92
$C_9H_{12}N_3O$	11.10	0.76
$C_9H_{14}N_4$	11.48	0.60
$C_{10}H_2N_4$	12.36	0.70
$C_{10}H_{10}O_3$	11.08	1.16
$C_{10}H_{12}NO_2$	11.46	1.00
$C_{10}H_{14}N_2O$	11.83	0.84
$C_{10}H_{16}N_3$	12.21	0.68
$C_{11}H_2N_2O$	12.72	0.94
$C_{11}H_4N_3$	13.10	0.79
$C_{11}H_{14}O_2$	12.19	1.08
$C_{11}H_{16}NO$	12.56	0.92
$C_{11}H_{18}N_2$	12.94	0.77
$C_{12}H_2O_2$	13.08	1.19
$C_{12}H_4NO$	13.45	1.03
$C_{12}H_6N_2$	13.83	0.88
$C_{12}H_{18}O$	13.29	1.01
$C_{12}H_{20}N$	13.67	0.86
$C_{13}H_6O$	14.18	1.13
$C_{13}H_8N$	14.56	0.98
$C_{13}H_{22}$	14.40	0.96
$C_{14}H_{10}$	15.29	1.09
179		
$C_6H_{15}N_2O_4$	7.64	1.06
$C_6H_{17}N_3O_3$	8.02	0.89
$C_7H_3N_2O_4$	8.53	1.12
$C_7H_5N_3O_3$	8.91	0.95
$C_7H_7N_4O_2$	9.28	0.79
$C_7H_{17}NO_4$	8.37	1.11
$C_8H_5NO_4$	9.26	1.18
$C_8H_7N_2O_3$	9.64	1.02
$C_8H_9N_3O_2$	10.01	0.85
$C_8H_{11}N_4O$	10.39	0.69
$C_9H_7O_4$	9.99	1.25
$C_9H_9NO_3$	10.37	1.09
$C_9H_{11}N_2O_2$	10.74	0.92
$C_9H_{13}N_3O$	11.12	0.76
$C_9H_{15}N_4$	11.49	0.60
$C_{10}HN_3O$	12.01	0.86
$C_{10}H_3N_4$	12.38	0.71
$C_{10}H_{11}O_3$	11.10	1.16
$C_{10}H_{13}NO_2$	11.47	1.00
$C_{10}H_{15}N_2O$	11.85	0.84
$C_{10}H_{17}N_3$	12.22	0.69
$C_{11}HNO_2$	12.36	1.10
$C_{11}H_3N_2O$	12.74	0.95
$C_{11}H_5N_3$	13.11	0.79
$C_{11}H_{15}O_2$	12.21	1.08
$C_{11}H_{17}NO$	12.58	0.93
$C_{11}H_{19}N_2$	12.95	0.77
$C_{12}H_3O_2$	13.09	1.19
$C_{12}H_5NO$	13.47	1.04
$C_{12}H_7N_2$	13.84	0.89
$C_{12}H_{19}O$	13.31	1.02
$C_{12}H_{21}N$	13.69	0.87
$C_{13}H_7O$	14.20	1.13
$C_{13}H_9N$	14.57	0.99
$C_{13}H_{23}$	14.42	0.96
$C_{14}H_{11}$	15.30	1.09
180		
$C_6H_{16}N_2O_4$	7.66	1.06
$C_7H_4N_2O_4$	8.55	1.12
$C_7H_6N_3O_3$	8.92	0.96
$C_7H_8N_4O_2$	9.30	0.79
$C_8H_6NO_4$	9.28	1.18
$C_8H_8N_2O_3$	9.65	1.02
$C_8H_{10}N_3O_2$	10.03	0.85
$C_8H_{12}N_4O$	10.40	0.69
$C_9H_8O_4$	10.01	1.25
$C_9H_{10}NO_3$	10.38	1.09
$C_9H_{12}N_2O_2$	10.76	0.93
$C_9H_{14}N_3O$	11.13	0.77
$C_9H_{16}N_4$	11.51	0.61
$C_{10}H_2N_3O$	12.02	0.86
$C_{10}H_4N_4$	12.40	0.71
$C_{10}H_{12}O_3$	11.12	1.16
$C_{10}H_{14}NO_2$	11.49	1.00
$C_{10}H_{16}N_2O$	11.86	0.84
$C_{10}H_{18}N_3$	12.24	0.69
$C_{11}H_2NO_2$	12.38	1.10
$C_{11}H_4N_2O$	12.75	0.95
$C_{11}H_6N_3$	13.13	0.80
$C_{11}H_{16}O_2$	12.22	1.08
$C_{11}H_{18}NO$	12.60	0.93
$C_{11}H_{20}N_2$	12.97	0.78
$C_{12}H_4O_2$	13.11	1.19
$C_{12}H_6NO$	13.48	1.04
$C_{12}H_8N_2$	13.86	0.89
$C_{12}H_{20}O$	13.33	1.02
$C_{12}H_{22}N$	13.70	0.87
$C_{13}H_8O$	14.22	1.13
$C_{13}H_{10}N$	14.59	0.99
$C_{13}H_{24}$	14.43	0.97
$C_{14}H_{12}$	15.32	1.09
181		
$C_7H_5N_2O_4$	8.56	1.13
$C_7H_7N_3O_3$	8.94	0.96
$C_7H_9N_4O_2$	9.31	0.79
$C_8H_7NO_4$	9.30	1.19
$C_8H_9N_2O_3$	9.67	1.02
$C_8H_{11}N_3O_2$	10.04	0.86
$C_8H_{13}N_4O$	10.42	0.69
C_9HN_4O	11.31	0.78
$C_9H_9O_4$	10.03	1.25
$C_9H_{11}NO_3$	10.40	1.09
$C_9H_{13}N_2O_2$	10.78	0.93
$C_9H_{15}N_3O$	11.15	0.77
$C_9H_{17}N_4$	11.52	0.61
$C_{10}HN_2O_2$	11.66	1.02
$C_{10}H_3N_3O$	12.04	0.86
$C_{10}H_5N_4$	12.41	0.71
$C_{10}H_{13}O_3$	11.13	1.16
$C_{10}H_{15}NO_2$	11.51	1.00
$C_{10}H_{17}N_2O$	11.88	0.85
$C_{10}H_{19}N_3$	12.25	0.69

	P + 1	P + 2
$C_{11}HO_3$	12.02	1.26
$C_{11}H_3NO_2$	12.39	1.10
$C_{11}H_5N_2O$	12.77	0.95
$C_{11}H_7N_3$	13.14	0.80
$C_{11}H_{17}O_2$	12.24	1.09
$C_{11}H_{19}NO$	12.61	0.93
$C_{11}H_{21}N_2$	12.99	0.78
$C_{12}H_5O_2$	13.13	1.19
$C_{12}H_7NO$	13.50	1.04
$C_{12}H_9N_2$	13.87	0.89
$C_{12}H_{21}O$	13.34	1.02
$C_{12}H_{23}N$	13.72	0.87
$C_{13}H_9O$	14.23	1.14
$C_{13}H_{11}N$	14.61	0.99
$C_{13}H_{25}$	14.45	0.97
$C_{14}H_{13}$	15.34	1.09
$C_{15}H$	16.23	1.23

182

	P + 1	P + 2
$C_7H_6N_2O_4$	8.58	1.13
$C_7H_8N_3O_3$	8.95	0.96
$C_7H_{10}N_4O_2$	9.33	0.79
$C_8H_8NO_4$	9.31	1.19
$C_8H_{10}N_2O_3$	9.69	1.02
$C_8H_{12}N_3O_2$	10.06	0.86
$C_8H_{14}N_4O$	10.43	0.70
$C_9H_2N_4O$	11.32	0.79
$C_9H_{10}O_4$	10.04	1.25
$C_9H_{12}NO_3$	10.42	1.09
$C_9H_{14}N_2O_2$	10.79	0.93
$C_9H_{16}N_3O$	11.17	0.77
$C_9H_{18}N_4$	11.54	0.61
$C_{10}H_2N_2O_2$	11.68	1.02
$C_{10}H_4N_3O$	12.05	0.87
$C_{10}H_6N_4$	12.43	0.71
$C_{10}H_{14}O_3$	11.15	1.16
$C_{10}H_{16}NO_2$	11.52	1.01
$C_{10}H_{18}N_2O$	11.90	0.85
$C_{10}H_{20}N_3$	12.27	0.69
$C_{11}H_2O_3$	12.04	1.26
$C_{11}H_4NO_2$	12.41	1.11
$C_{11}H_6N_2O$	12.79	0.95
$C_{11}H_8N_3$	13.16	0.80
$C_{11}H_{18}O_2$	12.25	1.09
$C_{11}H_{20}NO$	12.63	0.93
$C_{11}H_{22}N_2$	13.00	0.78
$C_{12}H_6O_2$	13.14	1.19
$C_{12}H_8NO$	13.52	1.04
$C_{12}H_{10}N_2$	13.89	0.89
$C_{12}H_{22}O$	13.36	1.02
$C_{12}H_{24}N$	13.73	0.87
$C_{13}H_{10}O$	14.25	1.14
$C_{13}H_{12}N$	14.62	0.99
$C_{13}H_{26}$	14.46	0.97
$C_{14}H_{14}$	15.35	1.10
$C_{15}H_2$	16.24	1.21

183

	P + 1	P + 2
$C_7H_7N_2O_4$	8.60	1.13
$C_7H_9N_3O_3$	8.97	0.96
$C_7H_{11}N_4O_2$	9.34	0.79
$C_8H_9NO_4$	9.33	1.19
$C_8H_{11}N_2O_3$	9.70	1.02
$C_8H_{13}N_3O_2$	10.08	0.86
$C_8H_{15}N_4O$	10.45	0.70
$C_9HN_3O_2$	10.96	0.95
$C_9H_3N_4O$	11.34	0.79
$C_9H_{11}O_4$	10.06	1.26
$C_9H_{13}NO_3$	10.43	1.09
$C_9H_{15}N_2O_2$	10.81	0.93
$C_9H_{17}N_3O$	11.18	0.77
$C_9H_{19}N_4$	11.56	0.61
$C_{10}HNO_3$	11.32	1.18
$C_{10}H_3N_2O_2$	11.70	1.03
$C_{10}H_5N_3O$	12.07	0.87
$C_{10}H_7N_4$	12.44	0.71
$C_{10}H_{15}O_3$	11.16	1.17
$C_{10}H_{17}NO_2$	11.54	1.01
$C_{10}H_{19}N_2O$	11.91	0.85
$C_{10}H_{21}N_3$	12.29	0.69
$C_{11}H_3O_3$	12.05	1.26
$C_{11}H_5NO_2$	12.43	1.11
$C_{11}H_7N_2O$	12.80	0.95
$C_{11}H_9N_3$	13.18	0.80
$C_{11}H_{19}O_2$	12.27	1.09
$C_{11}H_{21}NO$	12.64	0.93
$C_{11}H_{23}N_2$	13.02	0.78
$C_{12}H_7O_2$	13.16	1.20
$C_{12}H_9NO$	13.53	1.05
$C_{12}H_{11}N_2$	13.91	0.90
$C_{12}H_{23}O$	13.37	1.02
$C_{12}H_{25}N$	13.75	0.87
$C_{13}H_{11}O$	14.26	1.14
$C_{13}H_{13}N$	14.64	0.99
$C_{13}H_{27}$	14.48	0.97
$C_{14}HN$	15.53	1.12
$C_{14}H_{15}$	15.37	1.10
$C_{15}H_3$	16.26	1.23

184

	P + 1	P + 2
$C_7H_8N_2O_4$	8.61	1.13
$C_7H_{10}N_3O_3$	8.99	0.96
$C_7H_{12}N_4O_2$	9.36	0.80
$C_8H_{10}NO_4$	9.34	1.19
$C_8H_{12}N_2O_3$	9.72	1.03
$C_8H_{14}N_3O_2$	10.09	0.86
$C_8H_{16}N_4O$	10.47	0.70
$C_9H_2N_3O_2$	10.98	0.95
$C_9H_4N_4O$	11.35	0.79
$C_9H_{12}O_4$	10.07	1.26
$C_9H_{14}NO_3$	10.45	1.09
$C_9H_{16}N_2O_2$	10.82	0.93
$C_9H_{18}N_3O$	11.20	0.77
$C_9H_{20}N_4$	11.57	0.61
$C_{10}H_2NO_3$	11.34	1.18
$C_{10}H_4N_2O_2$	11.71	1.03
$C_{10}H_6N_3O$	12.09	0.87
$C_{10}H_8N_4$	12.46	0.71
$C_{10}H_{16}O_3$	11.18	1.17
$C_{10}H_{18}NO_2$	11.55	1.01
$C_{10}H_{20}N_2O$	11.93	0.85
$C_{10}H_{22}N_3$	12.30	0.70
$C_{11}H_4O_3$	12.07	1.27
$C_{11}H_6NO_2$	12.44	1.11
$C_{11}H_8N_2O$	12.82	0.96
$C_{11}H_{10}N_3$	13.19	0.80
$C_{11}H_{20}O_2$	12.29	1.09
$C_{11}H_{22}NO$	12.66	0.94
$C_{11}H_{24}N_2$	13.03	0.78
$C_{12}H_8O_2$	13.17	1.20
$C_{12}H_{10}NO$	13.55	1.05
$C_{12}H_{12}N_2$	13.92	0.90
$C_{12}H_{24}O$	13.39	1.03
$C_{12}H_{26}N$	13.77	0.88
$C_{13}H_{12}O$	14.28	1.14
$C_{13}H_{14}N$	14.65	1.00
$C_{13}H_{28}$	14.50	0.97
$C_{14}H_2N$	15.54	1.13
$C_{14}H_{16}$	15.38	1.10
$C_{15}H_4$	16.27	1.24

185

	P + 1	P + 2
$C_7H_9N_2O_4$	8.63	1.13
$C_7H_{11}N_3O_3$	9.00	0.96
$C_7H_{13}N_4O_2$	9.38	0.80
$C_8HN_4O_2$	10.27	0.88
$C_8H_{11}NO_4$	9.36	1.19
$C_8H_{13}N_2O_3$	9.73	1.03
$C_8H_{15}N_3O_2$	10.11	0.86
$C_8H_{17}N_4O$	10.48	0.70
$C_9HN_2O_3$	10.62	1.11
$C_9H_3N_3O_2$	11.00	0.95
$C_9H_5N_4O$	11.37	0.79
$C_9H_{13}O_4$	10.09	1.26
$C_9H_{15}NO_3$	10.46	1.10
$C_9H_{17}N_2O_2$	10.84	0.93
$C_9H_{19}N_3O$	11.21	0.77
$C_9H_{21}N_4$	11.59	0.62
$C_{10}HO_4$	10.98	1.35
$C_{10}H_3NO_3$	11.35	1.19
$C_{10}H_5N_2O_2$	11.73	1.03
$C_{10}H_7N_3O$	12.10	0.87
$C_{10}H_9N_4$	12.48	0.72
$C_{10}H_{17}O_3$	11.20	1.17
$C_{10}H_{19}NO_2$	11.57	1.01
$C_{10}H_{21}N_2O$	11.94	0.85
$C_{10}H_{23}N_3$	12.32	0.70
$C_{11}H_5O_3$	12.08	1.27
$C_{11}H_7NO_2$	12.46	1.11
$C_{11}H_9N_2O$	12.83	0.96
$C_{11}H_{11}N_3$	13.21	0.81
$C_{11}H_{21}O_2$	12.30	1.09
$C_{11}H_{23}NO$	12.68	0.94
$C_{11}H_{25}N_2$	13.05	0.79
$C_{12}H_9O_2$	13.19	1.20
$C_{12}H_{11}NO$	13.56	1.05
$C_{12}H_{13}N_2$	13.94	0.90
$C_{12}H_{25}O$	13.41	1.03
$C_{12}H_{27}N$	13.78	0.88
$C_{13}HN_2$	14.83	1.02
$C_{13}H_{13}O$	14.30	1.15
$C_{13}H_{15}N$	14.67	1.00
$C_{14}HO$	15.18	1.27
$C_{14}H_3N$	15.56	1.13
$C_{14}H_{17}$	15.40	1.10
$C_{15}H_5$	16.29	1.24

186

	P + 1	P + 2
$C_7H_{10}N_2O_4$	8.64	1.13
$C_7H_{12}N_3O_3$	9.02	0.97
$C_7H_{14}N_4O_2$	9.39	0.80
$C_8H_2N_4O_2$	10.28	0.88
$C_8H_{12}NO_4$	9.38	1.19
$C_8H_{14}N_2O_3$	9.75	1.03
$C_8H_{16}N_3O_2$	10.12	0.86
$C_8H_{18}N_4O$	10.50	0.70
$C_9H_2N_2O_3$	10.64	1.11
$C_9H_4N_3O_2$	11.01	0.95
$C_9H_6N_4O$	11.39	0.79
$C_9H_{14}O_4$	10.11	1.26
$C_9H_{16}NO_3$	10.48	1.10
$C_9H_{18}N_2O_2$	10.86	0.94
$C_9H_{20}N_3O$	11.23	0.78
$C_9H_{22}N_4$	11.60	0.62
$C_{10}H_2O_4$	10.99	1.35
$C_{10}H_4NO_3$	11.37	1.19
$C_{10}H_6N_2O_2$	11.74	1.03
$C_{10}H_8N_3O$	12.12	0.87
$C_{10}H_{10}N_4$	12.49	0.72
$C_{10}H_{18}O_3$	11.21	1.17
$C_{10}H_{20}NO_2$	11.59	1.01
$C_{10}H_{22}N_2O$	11.96	0.86
$C_{10}H_{24}N_3$	12.33	0.70
$C_{11}H_6O_3$	12.10	1.27
$C_{11}H_8NO_2$	12.47	1.11
$C_{11}H_{10}N_2O$	12.85	0.96
$C_{11}H_{12}N_3$	13.22	0.81
$C_{11}H_{22}O_2$	12.32	1.10
$C_{11}H_{24}NO$	12.69	0.94
$C_{11}H_{26}N_2$	13.07	0.79
$C_{12}H_{10}O_2$	13.21	1.20
$C_{12}H_{12}NO$	13.58	1.05
$C_{12}H_{14}N_2$	13.95	0.90
$C_{12}H_{26}O$	13.42	1.03
$C_{13}H_2N_2$	14.84	1.02
$C_{13}H_{14}O$	14.31	1.15
$C_{13}H_{16}N$	14.69	1.00
$C_{14}H_2O$	15.20	1.27
$C_{14}H_4N$	15.57	1.13
$C_{14}H_{18}$	15.42	1.11
$C_{15}H_6$	16.31	1.24

187

	P + 1	P + 2
$C_7H_{11}N_2O_4$	8.66	1.13
$C_7H_{13}N_3O_3$	9.03	0.97
$C_7H_{15}N_4O_2$	9.41	0.80
$C_8HN_3O_3$	9.92	1.04
$C_8H_3N_4O_2$	10.30	0.88
$C_8H_{13}NO_4$	9.39	1.20
$C_8H_{15}N_2O_3$	9.77	1.03
$C_8H_{17}N_3O_2$	10.14	0.87
$C_8H_{19}N_4O$	10.51	0.70
C_9HNO_4	10.28	1.28
$C_9H_3N_2O_3$	10.65	1.11
$C_9H_5N_3O_2$	11.03	0.95
$C_9H_7N_4O$	11.40	0.80
$C_9H_{15}O_4$	10.12	1.26
$C_9H_{17}NO_3$	10.50	1.10
$C_9H_{19}N_2O_2$	10.87	0.94
$C_9H_{21}N_3O$	11.25	0.78
$C_9H_{23}N_4$	11.62	0.62
$C_{10}H_3O_4$	11.01	1.35
$C_{10}H_5NO_3$	11.39	1.19

	P + 1	P + 2
$C_{10}H_7N_2O_2$	11.76	1.03
$C_{10}H_9N_3O$	12.13	0.88
$C_{10}H_{11}N_4$	12.51	0.72
$C_{10}H_{19}O_3$	11.23	1.17
$C_{10}H_{21}NO_2$	11.60	1.01
$C_{10}H_{23}N_2O$	11.98	0.86
$C_{10}H_{25}N_3$	12.35	0.70
$C_{11}H_7O_3$	12.12	1.27
$C_{11}H_9NO_2$	12.49	1.12
$C_{11}H_{11}N_2O$	12.87	0.96
$C_{11}H_{13}N_3$	13.24	0.81
$C_{11}H_{23}O_2$	12.33	1.10
$C_{11}H_{25}NO$	12.71	0.94
$C_{12}HN_3$	14.13	0.93
$C_{12}H_{11}O_2$	13.22	1.20
$C_{12}H_{13}NO$	13.60	1.05
$C_{12}H_{15}N_2$	13.97	0.90
$C_{13}HNO$	14.48	1.17
$C_{13}H_3N_2$	14.86	1.03
$C_{13}H_{15}O$	14.33	1.15
$C_{13}H_{17}N$	14.70	1.00
$C_{14}H_3O$	15.22	1.28
$C_{14}H_5N$	15.59	1.13
$C_{14}H_{19}$	15.43	1.11
$C_{15}H_7$	16.32	1.24
188		
$C_7H_{12}N_2O_4$	8.68	1.14
$C_7H_{14}N_3O_3$	9.05	0.97
$C_7H_{16}N_4O_2$	9.42	0.80
$C_8H_2N_3O_3$	9.94	1.05
$C_8H_4N_4O_2$	10.31	0.88
$C_8H_{14}NO_4$	9.41	1.20
$C_8H_{16}N_2O_3$	9.78	1.03
$C_8H_{18}N_3O_2$	10.16	0.87
$C_8H_{20}N_4O$	10.53	0.71
$C_9H_2NO_4$	10.30	1.28
$C_9H_4N_2O_3$	10.67	1.12
$C_9H_6N_3O_2$	11.04	0.96
$C_9H_8N_4O$	11.42	0.80
$C_9H_{16}O_4$	10.14	1.26
$C_9H_{18}NO_3$	10.51	1.10
$C_9H_{20}N_2O_2$	10.89	0.94
$C_9H_{22}N_3O$	11.26	0.78
$C_9H_{24}N_4$	11.64	0.62
$C_{10}H_4O_4$	11.03	1.35
$C_{10}H_6NO_3$	11.40	1.19
$C_{10}H_8N_2O_2$	11.78	1.03
$C_{10}H_{10}N_3O$	12.15	0.88
$C_{10}H_{12}N_4$	12.52	0.72
$C_{10}H_{20}O_3$	11.24	1.18
$C_{10}H_{22}NO_2$	11.62	1.02
$C_{10}H_{24}N_2O$	11.99	0.86
$C_{11}H_8O_3$	12.13	1.27
$C_{11}H_{10}NO_2$	12.51	1.12
$C_{11}H_{12}N_2O$	12.88	0.96
$C_{11}H_{14}N_3$	13.26	0.81
$C_{11}H_{24}O_2$	12.35	1.10
$C_{12}H_2N_3$	14.14	0.93
$C_{12}H_{12}O_2$	13.24	1.21
$C_{12}H_{14}NO$	13.61	1.06
$C_{12}H_{16}N_2$	13.99	0.91
$C_{13}H_2NO$	14.50	1.18

	P + 1	P + 2
$C_{13}H_4N_2$	14.88	1.03
$C_{13}H_{16}O$	14.34	1.15
$C_{13}H_{18}N$	14.72	1.01
$C_{14}H_4O$	15.23	1.28
$C_{14}H_6N$	15.61	1.14
$C_{14}H_{20}$	15.45	1.11
$C_{15}H_8$	16.34	1.25
189		
$C_7H_{13}N_2O_4$	8.69	1.14
$C_7H_{15}N_3O_3$	9.07	0.97
$C_7H_{17}N_4O_2$	9.44	0.80
$C_8HN_2O_4$	9.58	1.21
$C_8H_3N_3O_3$	9.95	1.05
$C_8H_5N_4O_2$	10.33	0.88
$C_8H_{15}NO_4$	9.42	1.20
$C_8H_{17}N_2O_3$	9.80	1.03
$C_8H_{19}N_3O_2$	10.17	0.87
$C_8H_{21}N_4O$	10.55	0.71
$C_9H_3NO_4$	10.31	1.28
$C_9H_5N_2O_3$	10.69	1.12
$C_9H_7N_3O_2$	11.06	0.96
$C_9H_9N_4O$	11.43	0.80
$C_9H_{17}O_4$	10.15	1.26
$C_9H_{19}NO_3$	10.53	1.10
$C_9H_{21}N_2O_2$	10.90	0.94
$C_9H_{23}N_3O$	11.28	0.78
$C_{10}H_5O_4$	11.04	1.35
$C_{10}H_7NO_3$	11.42	1.19
$C_{10}H_9N_2O_2$	11.79	1.04
$C_{10}H_{11}N_3O$	12.17	0.88
$C_{10}H_{13}N_4$	12.54	0.72
$C_{10}H_{21}O_3$	11.26	1.18
$C_{10}H_{23}NO_2$	11.63	1.02
$C_{11}HN_4$	13.43	0.83
$C_{11}H_9O_3$	12.15	1.28
$C_{11}H_{11}NO_2$	12.52	1.12
$C_{11}H_{13}N_2O$	12.90	0.97
$C_{11}H_{15}N_3$	13.27	0.81
$C_{12}HN_2O$	13.79	1.08
$C_{12}H_3N_3$	14.16	0.93
$C_{12}H_{13}O_2$	13.25	1.21
$C_{12}H_{15}NO$	13.63	1.06
$C_{12}H_{17}N_2$	14.00	0.91
$C_{13}HO_2$	14.14	1.33
$C_{13}H_3NO$	14.52	1.18
$C_{13}H_5N_2$	14.89	1.03
$C_{13}H_{17}O$	14.36	1.16
$C_{13}H_{19}N$	14.73	1.01
$C_{14}H_5O$	15.25	1.28
$C_{14}H_7N$	15.62	1.14
$C_{14}H_{21}$	15.46	1.11
$C_{15}H_9$	16.35	1.25
190		
$C_7H_{14}N_2O_4$	8.71	1.14
$C_7H_{16}N_3O_3$	9.08	0.97
$C_7H_{18}N_4O_2$	9.46	0.80
$C_8H_2N_2O_4$	9.60	1.21
$C_8H_4N_3O_3$	9.97	1.05
$C_8H_6N_4O_2$	10.35	0.89
$C_8H_{16}NO_4$	9.44	1.20
$C_8H_{18}N_2O_3$	9.81	1.03

	P + 1	P + 2
$C_8H_{20}N_3O_2$	10.19	0.87
$C_8H_{22}N_4O$	10.56	0.71
$C_9H_4NO_4$	10.33	1.28
$C_9H_6N_2O_3$	10.70	1.12
$C_9H_8N_3O_2$	11.08	0.96
$C_9H_{10}N_4O$	11.45	0.80
$C_9H_{18}O_4$	10.17	1.27
$C_9H_{20}NO_3$	10.54	1.10
$C_9H_{22}N_2O_2$	10.92	0.94
$C_{10}H_6O_4$	11.06	1.35
$C_{10}H_8NO_3$	11.43	1.20
$C_{10}H_{10}N_2O_2$	11.81	1.03
$C_{10}H_{12}N_3O$	12.18	0.88
$C_{10}H_{14}N_4$	12.56	0.73
$C_{10}H_{22}O_3$	11.28	1.18
$C_{11}H_2N_4$	13.44	0.84
$C_{11}H_{10}O_3$	12.16	1.28
$C_{11}H_{12}NO_2$	12.54	1.12
$C_{11}H_{14}N_2O$	12.91	0.97
$C_{11}H_{16}N_3$	13.29	0.82
$C_{12}H_2N_2O$	13.80	1.08
$C_{12}H_4N_3$	14.18	0.93
$C_{12}H_{14}O_2$	13.27	1.21
$C_{12}H_{16}NO$	13.64	1.06
$C_{12}H_{18}N_2$	14.02	0.91
$C_{13}H_2O_2$	14.16	1.33
$C_{13}H_4NO$	14.53	1.18
$C_{13}H_6N_2$	14.91	1.03
$C_{13}H_{18}O$	14.38	1.16
$C_{13}H_{20}N$	14.75	1.01
$C_{14}H_6O$	15.26	1.28
$C_{14}H_8N$	15.64	1.14
$C_{14}H_{22}$	15.48	1.12
$C_{15}H_{10}$	16.37	1.25
191		
$C_7H_{15}N_2O_4$	8.72	1.14
$C_7H_{17}N_3O_3$	9.10	0.97
$C_7H_{19}N_4O_2$	9.47	0.81
$C_8H_3N_2O_4$	9.61	1.22
$C_8H_5N_3O_3$	9.99	1.05
$C_8H_7N_4O_2$	10.36	0.89
$C_8H_{17}NO_4$	9.46	1.20
$C_8H_{19}N_2O_3$	9.83	1.04
$C_8H_{21}N_3O_2$	10.20	0.87
$C_9H_5NO_4$	10.34	1.28
$C_9H_7N_2O_3$	10.72	1.12
$C_9H_9N_3O_2$	11.09	0.96
$C_9H_{11}N_4O$	11.47	0.80
$C_9H_{19}O_4$	10.19	1.27
$C_9H_{21}NO_3$	10.56	1.11
$C_{10}H_7O_4$	11.07	1.36
$C_{10}H_9NO_3$	11.45	1.20
$C_{10}H_{11}N_2O_2$	11.82	1.04
$C_{10}H_{13}N_3O$	12.20	0.88
$C_{10}H_{15}N_4$	12.57	0.73
$C_{11}HN_3O$	13.09	0.99
$C_{11}H_3N_4$	13.46	0.84
$C_{11}H_{11}O_3$	12.18	1.28
$C_{11}H_{13}NO_2$	12.55	1.12
$C_{11}H_{15}N_2O$	12.93	0.97
$C_{11}H_{17}N_3$	13.30	0.82
$C_{12}HNO_2$	13.44	1.23

	P + 1	P + 2
$C_{12}H_3N_2O$	13.82	1.08
$C_{12}H_5N_3$	14.19	0.93
$C_{12}H_{15}O_2$	13.29	1.21
$C_{12}H_{17}NO$	13.66	1.06
$C_{12}H_{19}N_2$	14.03	0.91
$C_{13}H_3O_2$	14.17	1.33
$C_{13}H_5NO$	14.55	1.18
$C_{13}H_7N_2$	14.92	1.04
$C_{13}H_{19}O$	14.39	1.16
$C_{13}H_{21}N$	14.77	1.01
$C_{14}H_7O$	15.28	1.29
$C_{14}H_9N$	15.65	1.14
$C_{14}H_{23}$	15.50	1.12
$C_{15}H_{11}$	16.39	1.25
192		
$C_7H_{16}N_2O_4$	8.74	1.14
$C_7H_{18}N_3O_3$	9.11	0.97
$C_7H_{20}N_4O_2$	9.49	0.81
$C_8H_4N_2O_4$	9.63	1.22
$C_8H_6N_3O_3$	10.00	1.05
$C_8H_8N_4O_2$	10.38	0.89
$C_8H_{18}NO_4$	9.47	1.20
$C_8H_{20}N_2O_3$	9.85	1.04
$C_9H_6NO_4$	10.36	1.29
$C_9H_8N_2O_3$	10.73	1.12
$C_9H_{10}N_3O_2$	11.11	0.96
$C_9H_{12}N_4O$	11.48	0.80
$C_9H_{20}O_4$	10.20	1.27
$C_{10}H_8O_4$	11.09	1.36
$C_{10}H_{10}NO_3$	11.47	1.20
$C_{10}H_{12}N_2O_2$	11.84	1.04
$C_{10}H_{14}N_3O$	12.21	0.89
$C_{10}H_{16}N_4$	12.59	0.73
$C_{11}H_2N_3O$	13.10	0.99
$C_{11}H_4N_4$	13.48	0.84
$C_{11}H_{12}O_3$	12.20	1.28
$C_{11}H_{14}NO_2$	12.57	1.13
$C_{11}H_{16}N_2O$	12.95	0.97
$C_{11}H_{18}N_3$	13.32	0.82
$C_{12}H_2NO_2$	13.46	1.24
$C_{12}H_4N_2O$	13.83	1.09
$C_{12}H_6N_3$	14.21	0.94
$C_{12}H_{16}O_2$	13.30	1.22
$C_{12}H_{18}NO$	13.68	1.06
$C_{12}H_{20}N_2$	14.05	0.92
$C_{13}H_4O_2$	14.19	1.33
$C_{13}H_6NO$	14.56	1.18
$C_{13}H_8N_2$	14.94	1.04
$C_{13}H_{20}O$	14.41	1.16
$C_{13}H_{22}N$	14.78	1.02
$C_{14}H_8O$	15.30	1.29
$C_{14}H_{10}N$	15.67	1.15
$C_{14}H_{24}$	15.51	1.12
$C_{15}H_{12}$	16.40	1.26
193		
$C_7H_{17}N_2O_4$	8.76	1.14
$C_7H_{19}N_3O_3$	9.13	0.98
$C_8H_5N_2O_4$	9.64	1.22
$C_8H_7N_3O_3$	10.02	1.05
$C_8H_9N_4O_2$	10.39	0.89
$C_8H_{19}NO_4$	9.49	1.20

	P + 1	P + 2
$C_9H_7NO_4$	10.38	1.29
$C_9H_9N_2O_3$	10.75	1.13
$C_9H_{11}N_3O_2$	11.12	0.96
$C_9H_{13}N_4O$	11.50	0.81
$C_{10}HN_4O$	12.39	0.91
$C_{10}H_9O_4$	11.11	1.36
$C_{10}H_{11}NO_3$	11.48	1.20
$C_{10}H_{13}N_2O_2$	11.86	1.04
$C_{10}H_{15}N_3O$	12.23	0.89
$C_{10}H_{17}N_4$	12.60	0.73
$C_{11}HN_2O_2$	12.74	1.15
$C_{11}H_3N_3O$	13.12	0.99
$C_{11}H_5N_4$	13.49	0.84
$C_{11}H_{13}O_3$	12.21	1.28
$C_{11}H_{15}NO_2$	12.59	1.13
$C_{11}H_{17}N_2O$	12.96	0.97
$C_{11}H_{19}N_3$	13.34	0.82
$C_{12}HO_3$	13.10	1.39
$C_{12}H_3NO_2$	13.48	1.24
$C_{12}H_5N_2O$	13.85	1.09
$C_{12}H_7N_3$	14.22	0.94
$C_{12}H_{17}O_2$	13.32	1.22
$C_{12}H_{19}NO$	13.69	1.07
$C_{12}H_{21}N_2$	14.07	0.92
$C_{13}H_5O_2$	14.21	1.33
$C_{13}H_7NO$	14.58	1.19
$C_{13}H_9N_2$	14.96	1.04
$C_{13}H_{21}O$	14.42	1.16
$C_{13}H_{23}N$	14.80	1.02
$C_{14}H_9O$	15.31	1.29
$C_{14}H_{11}N$	15.69	1.15
$C_{14}H_{25}$	15.53	1.12
$C_{15}H_{13}$	16.42	1.26
$C_{16}H$	17.31	1.40

194

	P + 1	P + 2
$C_7H_{18}N_2O_4$	8.77	1.14
$C_8H_6N_2O_4$	9.66	1.22
$C_8H_8N_3O_3$	10.03	1.06
$C_8H_{10}N_4O_2$	10.41	0.89
$C_9H_8NO_4$	10.39	1.29
$C_9H_{10}N_2O_3$	10.77	1.13
$C_9H_{12}N_3O_2$	11.14	0.97
$C_9H_{14}N_4O$	11.51	0.81
$C_{10}H_2N_4O$	12.40	0.91
$C_{10}H_{10}O_4$	11.12	1.36
$C_{10}H_{12}NO_3$	11.50	1.20
$C_{10}H_{14}N_2O_2$	11.87	1.05
$C_{10}H_{16}N_3O$	12.25	0.89
$C_{10}H_{18}N_4$	12.62	0.74
$C_{11}H_2N_2O_2$	12.76	1.15
$C_{11}H_4N_3O$	13.13	1.00
$C_{11}H_6N_4$	13.51	0.85
$C_{11}H_{14}O_3$	12.23	1.28
$C_{11}H_{16}NO_2$	12.60	1.13
$C_{11}H_{18}N_2O$	12.98	0.98
$C_{11}H_{20}N_3$	13.35	0.82
$C_{12}H_2O_3$	13.12	1.39
$C_{12}H_4NO_2$	13.49	1.24
$C_{12}H_6N_2O$	13.87	1.09
$C_{12}H_8N_3$	14.24	0.94
$C_{12}H_{18}O_2$	13.33	1.22
$C_{12}H_{20}NO$	13.71	1.07
$C_{12}H_{22}N_2$	14.08	0.92
$C_{13}H_6O_2$	14.22	1.34
$C_{13}H_8NO$	14.60	1.19
$C_{13}H_{10}N_2$	14.97	1.04
$C_{13}H_{22}O$	14.44	1.17
$C_{13}H_{24}N$	14.81	1.02
$C_{14}H_{10}O$	15.33	1.29
$C_{14}H_{12}N$	15.70	1.15
$C_{14}H_{26}$	15.54	1.13
$C_{15}H_{14}$	16.43	1.26
$C_{16}H_2$	17.32	1.41

195

	P + 1	P + 2
$C_8H_7N_2O_4$	9.68	1.22
$C_8H_9N_3O_3$	10.05	1.06
$C_8H_{11}N_4O_2$	10.43	0.89
$C_9H_9NO_4$	10.41	1.29
$C_9H_{11}N_2O_3$	10.78	1.13
$C_9H_{13}N_3O_2$	11.16	0.97
$C_9H_{15}N_4O$	11.53	0.81
$C_{10}HN_3O_2$	12.05	1.07
$C_{10}H_3N_4O$	12.42	0.91
$C_{10}H_{11}O_4$	11.14	1.36
$C_{10}H_{13}NO_3$	11.51	1.21
$C_{10}H_{15}N_2O_2$	11.89	1.05
$C_{10}H_{17}N_3O$	12.26	0.89
$C_{10}H_{19}N_4$	12.64	0.74
$C_{11}HNO_3$	12.40	1.31
$C_{11}H_3N_2O_2$	12.78	1.15
$C_{11}H_5N_3O$	13.15	1.00
$C_{11}H_7N_4$	13.52	0.85
$C_{11}H_{15}O_3$	12.24	1.29
$C_{11}H_{17}NO_2$	12.62	1.13
$C_{11}H_{19}N_2O$	12.99	0.98
$C_{11}H_{21}N_3$	13.37	0.83
$C_{12}H_3O_3$	13.13	1.39
$C_{12}H_5NO_2$	13.51	1.24
$C_{12}H_7N_2O$	13.88	1.09
$C_{12}H_9N_3$	14.26	0.94
$C_{12}H_{19}O_2$	13.35	1.22
$C_{12}H_{21}NO$	13.72	1.07
$C_{12}H_{23}N_2$	14.10	0.92
$C_{13}H_7O_2$	14.24	1.34
$C_{13}H_9NO$	14.61	1.19
$C_{13}H_{11}N_2$	14.99	1.05
$C_{13}H_{23}O$	14.46	1.17
$C_{13}H_{25}N$	14.83	1.02
$C_{14}H_{11}O$	15.34	1.30
$C_{14}H_{13}N$	15.72	1.15
$C_{14}H_{27}$	15.56	1.13
$C_{15}HN$	16.61	1.29
$C_{15}H_{15}$	16.45	1.27
$C_{16}H_3$	17.34	1.41

196

	P + 1	P + 2
$C_8H_8N_2O_4$	9.69	1.22
$C_8H_{10}N_3O_3$	10.07	1.06
$C_8H_{12}N_4O_2$	10.44	0.90
$C_9H_{10}NO_4$	10.42	1.29
$C_9H_{12}N_2O_3$	10.80	1.13
$C_9H_{14}N_3O_2$	11.17	0.97
$C_9H_{16}N_4O$	11.55	0.81
$C_{10}H_2N_3O_2$	12.06	1.07
$C_{10}H_4N_4O$	12.44	0.91
$C_{10}H_{12}O_4$	11.15	1.37
$C_{10}H_{14}NO_3$	11.53	1.21
$C_{10}H_{16}N_2O_2$	11.90	1.05
$C_{10}H_{18}N_3O$	12.28	0.89
$C_{10}H_{20}N_4$	12.65	0.74
$C_{11}H_2NO_3$	12.42	1.31
$C_{11}H_4N_2O_2$	12.79	1.15
$C_{11}H_6N_3O$	13.17	1.00
$C_{11}H_8N_4$	13.54	0.85
$C_{11}H_{16}O_3$	12.26	1.29
$C_{11}H_{18}NO_2$	12.63	1.13
$C_{11}H_{20}N_2O$	13.01	0.98
$C_{11}H_{22}N_3$	13.38	0.83
$C_{12}H_4O_3$	13.15	1.40
$C_{12}H_6NO_2$	13.52	1.24
$C_{12}H_8N_2O$	13.90	1.09
$C_{12}H_{10}N_3$	14.27	0.95
$C_{12}H_{20}O_2$	13.37	1.22
$C_{12}H_{22}NO$	13.74	1.07
$C_{12}H_{24}N_2$	14.11	0.92
$C_{13}H_8O_2$	14.25	1.34
$C_{13}H_{10}NO$	14.63	1.19
$C_{13}H_{12}N_2$	15.00	1.05
$C_{13}H_{24}O$	14.47	1.17
$C_{13}H_{26}N$	14.85	1.03
$C_{14}H_{12}O$	15.36	1.30
$C_{14}H_{14}N$	15.73	1.16
$C_{14}H_{28}$	15.58	1.13
$C_{15}H_2N$	16.62	1.29
$C_{15}H_{16}$	16.47	1.27
$C_{16}H_4$	17.35	1.41

197

	P + 1	P + 2
$C_8H_9N_2O_4$	9.71	1.23
$C_8H_{11}N_3O_3$	10.08	1.06
$C_8H_{13}N_4O_2$	10.46	0.90
$C_9HN_4O_2$	11.35	0.99
$C_9H_{11}NO_4$	10.44	1.29
$C_9H_{13}N_2O_3$	10.81	1.13
$C_9H_{15}N_3O_2$	11.19	0.97
$C_9H_{17}N_4O$	11.56	0.81
$C_{10}HN_2O_3$	11.70	1.23
$C_{10}H_3N_3O_2$	12.08	1.07
$C_{10}H_5N_4O$	12.45	0.91
$C_{10}H_{13}O_4$	11.17	1.37
$C_{10}H_{15}NO_3$	11.55	1.21
$C_{10}H_{17}N_2O_2$	11.92	1.05
$C_{10}H_{19}N_3O$	12.29	0.90
$C_{10}H_{21}N_4$	12.67	0.74
$C_{11}HO_4$	12.06	1.46
$C_{11}H_3NO_3$	12.43	1.31
$C_{11}H_5N_2O_2$	12.81	1.16
$C_{11}H_7N_3O$	13.18	1.00
$C_{11}H_9N_4$	13.56	0.85
$C_{11}H_{17}O_3$	12.28	1.29
$C_{11}H_{19}NO_2$	12.65	1.14
$C_{11}H_{21}N_2O$	13.03	0.98
$C_{11}H_{23}N_3$	13.40	0.83
$C_{12}H_5O_3$	13.16	1.40
$C_{12}H_7NO_2$	13.54	1.25
$C_{12}H_9N_2O$	13.91	1.10
$C_{12}H_{11}N_3$	14.29	0.95
$C_{12}H_{21}O_2$	13.38	1.23
$C_{12}H_{23}NO$	13.76	1.08
$C_{12}H_{25}N_2$	14.13	0.93
$C_{13}H_9O_2$	14.27	1.34
$C_{13}H_{11}NO$	14.64	1.20
$C_{13}H_{13}N_2$	15.02	1.05
$C_{13}H_{25}O$	14.49	1.17
$C_{13}H_{27}N$	14.86	1.03
$C_{14}HN_2$	15.91	1.18
$C_{14}H_{13}O$	15.38	1.30
$C_{14}H_{15}N$	15.75	1.16
$C_{14}H_{29}$	15.59	1.13
$C_{15}HO$	16.26	1.44
$C_{15}H_3N$	16.64	1.30
$C_{15}H_{17}$	16.48	1.27
$C_{16}H_5$	17.37	1.42

198

	P + 1	P + 2
$C_8H_{10}N_2O_4$	9.72	1.23
$C_8H_{12}N_3O_3$	10.10	1.06
$C_8H_{14}N_4O$	10.47	0.90
$C_9H_2N_4O_2$	11.36	0.99
$C_9H_{12}NO_4$	10.46	1.30
$C_9H_{14}N_2O_3$	10.83	1.13
$C_9H_{16}N_3O_2$	11.20	0.97
$C_9H_{18}N_4O$	11.58	0.82
$C_{10}H_2N_2O_3$	11.72	1.23
$C_{10}H_4N_3O_2$	12.09	1.07
$C_{10}H_6N_4O$	12.47	0.92
$C_{10}H_{14}O_4$	11.19	1.37
$C_{10}H_{16}NO_3$	11.56	1.21
$C_{10}H_{18}N_2O_2$	11.94	1.05
$C_{10}H_{20}N_3O$	12.31	0.90
$C_{10}H_{22}N_4$	12.68	0.74
$C_{11}H_2O_4$	12.08	1.47
$C_{11}H_4NO_3$	12.45	1.31
$C_{11}H_6N_2O_2$	12.82	1.16
$C_{11}H_8N_3O$	13.20	1.01
$C_{11}H_{10}N_4$	13.57	0.85
$C_{11}H_{18}O_3$	12.29	1.29
$C_{11}H_{20}NO_2$	12.67	1.14
$C_{11}H_{22}N_2O$	13.04	0.99
$C_{11}H_{24}N_3$	13.42	0.83
$C_{12}H_6O_3$	13.18	1.40
$C_{12}H_8NO_2$	13.56	1.25
$C_{12}H_{10}N_2O$	13.93	1.10
$C_{12}H_{12}N_3$	14.30	0.95
$C_{12}H_{22}O_2$	13.40	1.23
$C_{12}H_{24}NO$	13.77	1.08
$C_{12}H_{26}N_2$	14.15	0.93
$C_{13}H_{10}O_2$	14.29	1.35
$C_{13}H_{12}NO$	14.66	1.20
$C_{13}H_{14}N_2$	15.04	1.05
$C_{13}H_{26}O$	14.50	1.18
$C_{13}H_{28}N$	14.88	1.03
$C_{14}H_2N_2$	15.92	1.18
$C_{14}H_{14}O$	15.39	1.30
$C_{14}H_{16}N$	15.77	1.16
$C_{14}H_{30}$	15.61	1.14
$C_{15}H_2O$	16.28	1.44
$C_{15}H_4N$	16.65	1.30
$C_{15}H_{18}$	16.50	1.27
$C_{16}H_6$	17.39	1.42

	P + 1	P + 2
199		
$C_8H_{11}N_2O_4$	9.74	1.23
$C_8H_{13}N_3O_3$	10.11	1.06
$C_8H_{15}N_4O_2$	10.49	0.90
$C_9HN_3O_3$	11.00	1.15
$C_9H_3N_4O_2$	11.38	0.99
$C_9H_{13}NO_4$	10.47	1.30
$C_9H_{15}N_2O_3$	10.85	1.14
$C_9H_{17}N_3O_2$	11.22	0.98
$C_9H_{19}N_4O$	11.59	0.82
$C_{10}HNO_4$	11.36	1.39
$C_{10}H_3N_2O_3$	11.73	1.23
$C_{10}H_5N_3O_2$	12.11	1.07
$C_{10}H_7N_4O$	12.48	0.92
$C_{10}H_{15}O_4$	11.20	1.37
$C_{10}H_{17}NO_3$	11.58	1.21
$C_{10}H_{19}N_2O_2$	11.95	1.01
$C_{10}H_{21}N_3O$	12.33	0.90
$C_{10}H_{23}N_4$	12.70	0.75
$C_{11}H_3O_4$	12.09	1.47
$C_{11}H_5NO_3$	12.47	1.31
$C_{11}H_7N_2O_2$	12.84	1.16
$C_{11}H_9N_3O$	13.21	1.01
$C_{11}H_{11}N_4$	13.59	0.86
$C_{11}H_{19}O_3$	12.31	1.29
$C_{11}H_{21}NO_2$	12.68	1.14
$C_{11}H_{23}N_2O$	13.06	0.99
$C_{11}H_{25}N_3$	13.43	0.84
$C_{12}H_7O_3$	13.20	1.40
$C_{12}H_9NO_2$	13.57	1.25
$C_{12}H_{11}N_2O$	13.95	1.10
$C_{12}H_{13}N_3$	14.32	0.95
$C_{12}H_{23}O_2$	13.41	1.23
$C_{12}H_{25}NO$	13.79	1.08
$C_{12}H_{27}N_2$	14.16	0.93
$C_{13}HN_3$	15.21	1.08
$C_{13}H_{11}O_2$	14.30	1.35
$C_{13}H_{13}NO$	14.68	1.20
$C_{13}H_{15}N_2$	15.05	1.06
$C_{13}H_{27}O$	14.52	1.18
$C_{13}H_{29}N$	14.89	1.03
$C_{14}HNO$	15.57	1.33
$C_{14}H_3N_2$	15.94	1.19
$C_{14}H_{15}O$	15.41	1.31
$C_{14}H_{17}N$	15.78	1.16
$C_{15}H_3O$	16.30	1.44
$C_{15}H_5N$	16.67	1.30
$C_{15}H_{19}$	16.51	1.28
$C_{16}H_7$	17.40	1.42
200		
$C_8H_{12}N_2O_4$	9.76	1.23
$C_8H_{14}N_3O_3$	10.13	1.07
$C_8H_{16}N_4O_2$	10.51	0.90
$C_9H_2N_3O_3$	11.02	1.15
$C_9H_4N_4O_2$	11.39	0.99
$C_9H_{14}NO_4$	10.49	1.30
$C_9H_{16}N_2O_3$	10.86	1.14
$C_9H_{18}N_3O_2$	11.24	0.98
$C_9H_{20}N_4O$	11.61	0.82
$C_{10}H_2NO_4$	11.38	1.39
$C_{10}H_4N_2O_3$	11.75	1.23
$C_{10}H_6N_3O_2$	12.13	1.08
$C_{10}H_8N_4O$	12.50	0.92
$C_{10}H_{16}O_4$	11.22	1.37
$C_{10}H_{18}NO_3$	11.59	1.21
$C_{10}H_{20}N_2O_2$	11.97	1.06
$C_{10}H_{22}N_3O$	12.34	0.90
$C_{10}H_{24}N_4$	12.72	0.75
$C_{11}H_4O_4$	12.11	1.47
$C_{11}H_6NO_3$	12.48	1.32
$C_{11}H_8N_2O_2$	12.86	1.16
$C_{11}H_{10}N_3O$	13.23	1.01
$C_{11}H_{12}N_4$	13.60	0.86
$C_{11}H_{20}O_3$	12.32	1.30
$C_{11}H_{22}NO_2$	12.70	1.14
$C_{11}H_{24}N_2O$	13.07	0.99
$C_{11}H_{26}N_3$	13.45	0.84
$C_{12}H_8O_3$	13.21	1.40
$C_{12}H_{10}NO_2$	13.59	1.25
$C_{12}H_{12}N_2O$	13.96	1.10
$C_{12}H_{14}N_3$	13.34	0.96
$C_{12}H_{24}O_2$	13.43	1.23
$C_{12}H_{26}NO$	13.80	1.08
$C_{12}H_{28}N_2$	14.18	0.93
$C_{13}H_2N_3$	15.22	1.08
$C_{13}H_{12}O_2$	14.32	1.35
$C_{13}H_{14}NO$	14.69	1.20
$C_{13}H_{16}N_2$	15.07	1.06
$C_{13}H_{28}O$	14.54	1.18
$C_{14}H_2NO$	15.58	1.33
$C_{14}H_4N_2$	15.96	1.19
$C_{14}H_{16}O$	15.42	1.31
$C_{14}H_{18}N$	15.80	1.17
$C_{15}H_4O$	16.31	1.44
$C_{15}H_6N$	16.69	1.30
$C_{15}H_{20}$	16.53	1.28
$C_{16}H_8$	17.42	1.42
201		
$C_8H_{13}N_2O_4$	9.77	1.23
$C_8H_{15}N_3O_3$	10.15	1.07
$C_8H_{17}N_4O_2$	10.52	0.90
$C_9HN_2O_4$	10.66	1.32
$C_9H_3N_3O_3$	11.04	1.16
$C_9H_5N_4O_2$	11.41	1.00
$C_9H_{15}NO_4$	10.50	1.30
$C_9H_{17}N_2O_3$	10.88	1.14
$C_9H_{19}N_3O_2$	11.25	0.98
$C_9H_{21}N_4O$	11.63	0.82
$C_{10}H_3NO_4$	11.39	1.39
$C_{10}H_5N_2O_3$	11.77	1.23
$C_{10}H_7N_3O_2$	12.14	1.08
$C_{10}H_9N_4O$	12.52	0.92
$C_{10}H_{17}O_4$	11.23	1.37
$C_{10}H_{19}NO_3$	11.61	1.22
$C_{10}H_{21}N_2O_2$	11.98	1.06
$C_{10}H_{23}N_3O$	12.36	0.90
$C_{10}H_{25}N_4$	12.73	0.75
$C_{11}H_5O_4$	12.12	1.47
$C_{11}H_7NO_3$	12.50	1.32
$C_{11}H_9N_2O_2$	12.87	1.16
$C_{11}H_{11}N_3O$	13.25	1.01
$C_{11}H_{13}N_4$	13.62	0.86
$C_{11}H_{21}O_3$	12.34	1.30
$C_{11}H_{23}NO_2$	12.71	1.14
$C_{11}H_{25}N_2O$	13.09	0.99
$C_{11}H_{27}N_3$	13.46	0.84
$C_{12}HN_4$	14.51	0.98
$C_{12}H_9O_3$	13.23	1.41
$C_{12}H_{11}NO_2$	13.60	1.26
$C_{12}H_{13}N_2O$	13.98	1.11
$C_{12}H_{15}N_3$	14.35	0.96
$C_{12}H_{25}O_2$	13.45	1.23
$C_{12}H_{27}NO$	13.82	1.08
$C_{13}HN_2O$	14.87	1.23
$C_{13}H_3N_3$	15.24	1.08
$C_{13}H_{13}O_2$	14.33	1.35
$C_{13}H_{15}NO$	14.71	1.21
$C_{13}H_{17}N_2$	15.08	1.06
$C_{14}HO_2$	15.22	1.48
$C_{14}H_3NO$	15.60	1.33
$C_{14}H_5N_2$	15.97	1.19
$C_{14}H_{17}O$	15.44	1.31
$C_{14}H_{19}N$	15.81	1.17
$C_{15}H_5O$	16.33	1.45
$C_{15}H_7N$	16.70	1.31
$C_{15}H_{21}$	16.55	1.28
$C_{16}H_9$	17.43	1.43
202		
$C_8H_{14}N_2O_4$	9.79	1.23
$C_8H_{16}N_3O_3$	10.16	1.07
$C_8H_{18}N_4O_2$	10.54	0.91
$C_9H_2N_2O_4$	10.68	1.32
$C_9H_4N_3O_3$	11.05	1.16
$C_9H_6N_4O_2$	11.43	1.00
$C_9H_{16}NO_4$	10.52	1.30
$C_9H_{18}N_2O_3$	10.89	1.14
$C_9H_{20}N_3O_2$	11.27	0.98
$C_9H_{22}N_4O$	11.64	0.82
$C_{10}H_4NO_4$	11.41	1.39
$C_{10}H_6N_2O_3$	11.78	1.24
$C_{10}H_8N_3O_2$	12.16	1.08
$C_{10}H_{10}N_4O$	12.53	0.92
$C_{10}H_{18}O_4$	11.25	1.38
$C_{10}H_{20}NO_3$	11.63	1.22
$C_{10}H_{22}N_2O_2$	12.00	1.06
$C_{10}H_{24}N_3O$	12.37	0.91
$C_{10}H_{26}N_4$	12.75	0.75
$C_{11}H_6O_4$	12.14	1.47
$C_{11}H_8NO_3$	12.51	1.32
$C_{11}H_{10}N_2O_2$	12.89	1.17
$C_{11}H_{12}N_3O$	13.26	1.01
$C_{11}H_{14}N_4$	13.64	0.86
$C_{11}H_{22}O_3$	12.36	1.30
$C_{11}H_{24}NO_2$	12.73	1.15
$C_{11}H_{26}N_2O$	13.11	0.99
$C_{12}H_2N_4$	14.53	0.98
$C_{12}H_{10}O_3$	13.25	1.41
$C_{12}H_{12}NO_2$	13.62	1.26
$C_{12}H_{14}N_2O$	13.99	1.11
$C_{12}H_{16}N_3$	14.37	0.96
$C_{12}H_{26}O_2$	13.46	1.24
$C_{13}H_2N_2O$	14.88	1.23
$C_{13}H_4N_3$	15.26	1.09
$C_{13}H_{14}O_2$	14.35	1.35
$C_{13}H_{16}NO$	14.72	1.21
$C_{13}H_{18}N_2$	15.10	1.06
$C_{14}H_2O_2$	15.24	1.48
$C_{14}H_4NO$	15.61	1.34
$C_{14}H_6N_2$	15.99	1.19
$C_{14}H_{18}O$	15.46	1.31
$C_{14}H_{20}N$	15.83	1.17
$C_{15}H_6O$	16.34	1.45
$C_{15}H_8N$	16.72	1.31
$C_{15}H_{22}$	16.56	1.28
$C_{16}H_{10}$	17.45	1.43
203		
$C_8H_{15}N_2O_4$	9.80	1.23
$C_8H_{17}N_3O_3$	10.18	1.07
$C_8H_{19}N_4O_2$	10.55	0.91
$C_9H_3N_2O_4$	10.69	1.32
$C_9H_5N_3O_3$	11.07	1.16
$C_9H_7N_4O_2$	11.44	1.00
$C_9H_{17}NO_4$	10.54	1.30
$C_9H_{19}N_2O_3$	10.91	1.14
$C_9H_{21}N_3O_2$	11.28	0.98
$C_9H_{23}N_4O$	11.66	0.82
$C_{10}H_5NO_4$	11.42	1.40
$C_{10}H_7N_2O_3$	11.80	1.24
$C_{10}H_9N_3O_2$	12.17	1.08
$C_{10}H_{11}N_4O$	12.55	0.93
$C_{10}H_{19}O_4$	11.27	1.38
$C_{10}H_{21}NO_3$	11.64	1.22
$C_{10}H_{23}N_2O_2$	12.02	1.06
$C_{10}H_{25}N_3O$	12.39	0.91
$C_{11}H_7O_4$	12.16	1.48
$C_{11}H_9NO_3$	12.53	1.32
$C_{11}H_{11}N_2O_2$	12.90	1.17
$C_{11}H_{13}N_3O$	13.28	1.02
$C_{11}H_{15}N_4$	13.65	0.86
$C_{11}H_{23}O_3$	12.37	1.30
$C_{11}H_{25}NO_2$	12.75	1.15
$C_{12}HN_3O$	14.17	1.13
$C_{12}H_3N_4$	14.54	0.98
$C_{12}H_{11}O_3$	13.26	1.41
$C_{12}H_{13}NO_2$	13.64	1.26
$C_{12}H_{15}N_2O$	14.01	1.11
$C_{12}H_{17}N_3$	14.38	0.96
$C_{13}HNO_2$	14.52	1.38
$C_{13}H_3N_2O$	14.90	1.23
$C_{13}H_5N_3$	15.27	1.09
$C_{13}H_{15}O_2$	14.37	1.36
$C_{13}H_{17}NO$	14.74	1.21
$C_{13}H_{19}N_2$	15.12	1.06
$C_{14}H_3O_2$	15.26	1.48
$C_{14}H_5NO$	15.63	1.34
$C_{14}H_7N_2$	16.00	1.20
$C_{14}H_{19}O$	15.47	1.32
$C_{14}H_{21}N$	15.85	1.17
$C_{15}H_7O$	16.36	1.45
$C_{15}H_9N$	16.73	1.31
$C_{15}H_{23}$	16.58	1.29
$C_{16}H_{11}$	17.47	1.43
204		
$C_8H_{16}N_2O_4$	9.82	1.24
$C_8H_{18}N_3O_3$	10.19	1.07
$C_8H_{20}N_4O_2$	10.57	0.91
$C_9H_4N_2O_4$	10.71	1.32

	P + 1	P + 2
$C_9H_6N_3O_3$	11.08	1.16
$C_9H_8N_4O_2$	11.46	1.00
$C_9H_{18}NO_4$	10.55	1.31
$C_9H_{20}N_2O_3$	10.93	1.14
$C_9H_{22}N_3O_2$	11.30	0.98
$C_9H_{24}N_4O$	11.67	0.83
$C_{10}H_6NO_4$	11.44	1.40
$C_{10}H_8N_2O_3$	11.81	1.24
$C_{10}H_{10}N_3O_2$	12.19	1.08
$C_{10}H_{12}N_4O$	12.56	0.93
$C_{10}H_{20}O_4$	11.28	1.38
$C_{10}H_{22}NO_3$	11.66	1.22
$C_{10}H_{24}N_2O_2$	12.03	1.06
$C_{11}H_8O_4$	12.17	1.48
$C_{11}H_{10}NO_3$	12.55	1.32
$C_{11}H_{12}N_2O_2$	12.92	1.17
$C_{11}H_{14}N_3O$	13.29	1.02
$C_{11}H_{16}N_4$	13.67	0.87
$C_{11}H_{24}O_3$	12.39	1.30
$C_{12}H_2N_3O$	14.18	1.13
$C_{12}H_4N_4$	14.56	0.99
$C_{12}H_{12}O_3$	13.28	1.41
$C_{12}H_{14}NO_2$	13.65	1.26
$C_{12}H_{16}N_2O$	14.03	1.11
$C_{12}H_{18}N_3$	14.40	0.96
$C_{13}H_2NO_2$	14.54	1.38
$C_{13}H_4N_2O$	14.91	1.24
$C_{13}H_6N_3$	15.29	1.09
$C_{13}H_{16}O_2$	14.38	1.36
$C_{13}H_{18}NO$	14.76	1.21
$C_{13}H_{20}N_2$	15.13	1.07
$C_{14}H_4O_2$	15.27	1.49
$C_{14}H_6NO$	15.65	1.34
$C_{14}H_8N_2$	16.02	1.20
$C_{14}H_{20}O$	15.49	1.32
$C_{14}H_{22}N$	15.86	1.18
$C_{15}H_8O$	16.38	1.45
$C_{15}H_{10}N$	16.75	1.31
$C_{15}H_{24}$	16.59	1.29
$C_{16}H_{12}$	17.48	1.43

205

	P + 1	P + 2
$C_8H_{17}N_2O_4$	9.84	1.24
$C_8H_{19}N_3O_3$	10.21	1.07
$C_8H_{21}N_4O_2$	10.59	0.91
$C_9H_5N_2O_4$	10.73	1.32
$C_9H_7N_3O_3$	11.10	1.16
$C_9H_9N_4O_2$	11.47	1.00
$C_9H_{19}NO_4$	10.57	1.31
$C_9H_{21}N_2O_3$	10.94	1.15
$C_9H_{23}N_3O_2$	11.32	0.99
$C_{10}H_7NO_4$	11.46	1.40
$C_{10}H_9N_2O_3$	11.83	1.24
$C_{10}H_{11}N_3O_2$	12.21	1.09
$C_{10}H_{13}N_4O$	12.58	0.93
$C_{10}H_{21}O_4$	11.30	1.38
$C_{10}H_{23}NO_3$	11.67	1.22
$C_{11}HN_4O$	13.47	1.04
$C_{11}H_9O_4$	12.19	1.48
$C_{11}H_{11}NO_3$	12.56	1.33
$C_{11}H_{13}N_2O_2$	12.94	1.17
$C_{11}H_{15}N_3O$	13.31	1.02
$C_{11}H_{17}N_4$	13.68	0.87
$C_{12}HN_2O_2$	13.82	1.29
$C_{12}H_3N_3O$	14.20	1.14
$C_{12}H_5N_4$	14.57	0.99
$C_{12}H_{13}O_3$	13.29	1.41
$C_{12}H_{15}NO_2$	13.67	1.26
$C_{12}H_{17}N_2O$	14.04	1.11
$C_{12}H_{19}N_3$	14.42	0.97
$C_{13}HO_3$	14.18	1.53
$C_{13}H_3NO_2$	14.56	1.38
$C_{13}H_5N_2O$	14.93	1.24
$C_{13}H_7N_3$	15.30	1.09
$C_{13}H_{17}O_2$	14.40	1.36
$C_{13}H_{19}NO$	14.77	1.21
$C_{13}H_{21}N_2$	15.15	1.07
$C_{14}H_5O_2$	15.29	1.49
$C_{14}H_7NO$	15.66	1.34
$C_{14}H_9N_2$	16.04	1.20
$C_{14}H_{21}O$	15.50	1.32
$C_{14}H_{23}N$	15.88	1.18
$C_{15}H_9O$	16.39	1.46
$C_{15}H_{11}N$	16.77	1.32
$C_{15}H_{25}$	16.61	1.29
$C_{16}H_{13}$	17.50	1.44
$C_{17}H$	18.39	1.59

206

	P + 1	P + 2
$C_8H_{18}N_2O_4$	9.85	1.24
$C_8H_{20}N_3O_3$	10.23	1.08
$C_8H_{22}N_4O_2$	10.60	0.91
$C_9H_6N_2O_4$	10.74	1.32
$C_9H_8N_3O_3$	11.12	1.16
$C_9H_{10}N_4O_2$	11.49	1.01
$C_9H_{20}NO_4$	10.58	1.31
$C_9H_{22}N_2O_3$	10.96	1.15
$C_{10}H_8NO_4$	11.47	1.40
$C_{10}H_{10}N_2O_3$	11.85	1.24
$C_{10}H_{12}N_3O_2$	12.22	1.09
$C_{10}H_{14}N_4O$	12.60	0.93
$C_{10}H_{22}O_4$	11.31	1.38
$C_{11}H_2N_4O$	13.48	1.04
$C_{11}H_{10}O_4$	12.20	1.48
$C_{11}H_{12}NO_3$	12.58	1.33
$C_{11}H_{14}N_2O_2$	12.95	1.17
$C_{11}H_{16}N_3O$	13.33	1.02
$C_{11}H_{18}N_4$	13.70	0.87
$C_{12}H_2N_2O_2$	13.84	1.29
$C_{12}H_4N_3O$	14.22	1.14
$C_{12}H_6N_4$	14.59	0.99
$C_{12}H_{14}O_3$	13.31	1.42
$C_{12}H_{16}NO_2$	13.68	1.27
$C_{12}H_{18}N_2O$	14.06	1.12
$C_{12}H_{20}N_3$	14.43	0.97
$C_{13}H_2O_3$	14.20	1.53
$C_{13}H_4NO_2$	14.57	1.39
$C_{13}H_6N_2O$	14.95	1.24
$C_{13}H_8N_3$	15.32	1.10
$C_{13}H_{18}O_2$	14.41	1.36
$C_{13}H_{20}NO$	14.79	1.22
$C_{13}H_{22}N_2$	15.16	1.07
$C_{14}H_6O_2$	15.30	1.49
$C_{14}H_8NO$	15.68	1.35
$C_{14}H_{10}N_2$	16.05	1.21
$C_{14}H_{22}O$	15.52	1.32
$C_{14}H_{24}N$	15.89	1.18
$C_{15}H_{10}O$	16.41	1.46
$C_{15}H_{12}N$	16.78	1.32
$C_{15}H_{26}$	16.63	1.29
$C_{16}H_{14}$	17.51	1.44
$C_{17}H_2$	18.40	1.59

207

	P + 1	P + 2
$C_8H_{19}N_2O_4$	9.87	1.24
$C_8H_{21}N_3O_3$	10.24	1.08
$C_9H_7N_2O_4$	10.76	1.33
$C_9H_9N_3O_3$	11.13	1.17
$C_9H_{11}N_4O_2$	11.51	1.01
$C_9H_{21}NO_4$	10.60	1.31
$C_{10}H_9NO_4$	11.49	1.40
$C_{10}H_{11}N_2O_3$	11.86	1.25
$C_{10}H_{13}N_3O_2$	12.24	1.09
$C_{11}H_{15}N_4O$	12.61	0.93
$C_{11}HN_3O_2$	13.13	1.20
$C_{11}H_3N_4O$	13.50	1.04
$C_{11}H_{11}O_4$	12.22	1.48
$C_{11}H_{13}NO_3$	12.59	1.33
$C_{11}H_{15}N_2O_2$	12.97	1.18
$C_{11}H_{17}N_3O$	13.34	1.02
$C_{11}H_{19}N_4$	13.72	0.87
$C_{12}HNO_3$	13.48	1.44
$C_{12}H_3N_2O_2$	13.86	1.29
$C_{12}H_5N_3O$	14.23	1.14
$C_{12}H_7N_4$	14.61	0.99
$C_{12}H_{15}O_3$	13.33	1.42
$C_{12}H_{17}NO_2$	13.70	1.27
$C_{12}H_{19}N_2O$	14.07	1.12
$C_{12}H_{21}N_3$	14.45	0.97
$C_{13}H_3O_3$	14.21	1.54
$C_{13}H_5NO_2$	14.59	1.39
$C_{13}H_7N_2O$	14.96	1.24
$C_{13}H_9N_3$	15.34	1.10
$C_{13}H_{19}O_2$	14.43	1.37
$C_{13}H_{21}NO$	14.80	1.22
$C_{13}H_{23}N_2$	15.18	1.07
$C_{14}H_7O_2$	15.32	1.49
$C_{14}H_9NO$	15.69	1.35
$C_{14}H_{11}N_2$	16.07	1.21
$C_{14}H_{23}O$	15.54	1.33
$C_{14}H_{25}N$	15.91	1.18
$C_{15}H_{11}O$	16.42	1.46
$C_{15}H_{13}N$	16.80	1.32
$C_{15}H_{27}$	16.64	1.30
$C_{16}HN$	17.69	1.47
$C_{16}H_{15}$	17.53	1.44
$C_{17}H_3$	18.42	1.60

208

	P + 1	P + 2
$C_8H_{20}N_2O_4$	9.88	1.24
$C_9H_8N_2O_4$	10.77	1.33
$C_9H_{10}N_3O_3$	11.15	1.17
$C_9H_{12}N_4O_2$	11.52	1.01
$C_{10}H_{10}NO_4$	11.50	1.40
$C_{10}H_{12}N_2O_3$	11.88	1.25
$C_{10}H_{14}N_3O_2$	12.25	1.09
$C_{10}H_{16}N_4O$	12.63	0.94
$C_{11}H_2N_3O_2$	13.14	1.20
$C_{11}H_4N_4O$	13.52	1.05
$C_{11}H_{12}O_4$	12.24	1.49
$C_{11}H_{14}NO_3$	12.61	1.33
$C_{11}H_{16}N_2O_2$	12.98	1.18
$C_{11}H_{18}N_3O$	13.36	1.03
$C_{11}H_{20}N_4$	13.73	0.88
$C_{12}H_2NO_3$	13.50	1.44
$C_{12}H_4N_2O_2$	13.87	1.29
$C_{12}H_6N_3O$	14.25	1.14
$C_{12}H_8N_4$	14.62	1.00
$C_{12}H_{16}O_3$	13.34	1.42
$C_{12}H_{18}NO_2$	13.72	1.27
$C_{12}H_{20}N_2O$	14.09	1.12
$C_{12}H_{22}N_3$	14.46	0.97
$C_{13}H_4O_3$	14.23	1.54
$C_{13}H_6NO_2$	14.60	1.39
$C_{13}H_8N_2O$	14.98	1.24
$C_{13}H_{10}N_3$	15.35	1.10
$C_{13}H_{20}O_2$	14.45	1.37
$C_{13}H_{22}NO$	14.82	1.22
$C_{13}H_{24}N_2$	15.20	1.08
$C_{14}H_8O_2$	15.34	1.50
$C_{14}H_{10}NO$	15.71	1.35
$C_{14}H_{12}N_2$	16.08	1.21
$C_{14}H_{24}O$	15.55	1.33
$C_{14}H_{26}N$	15.93	1.19
$C_{15}H_{12}O$	16.44	1.46
$C_{15}H_{14}N$	16.81	1.33
$C_{15}H_{28}$	16.66	1.30
$C_{16}H_2N$	17.70	1.47
$C_{16}H_{16}$	17.55	1.45
$C_{17}H_4$	18.43	1.60

209

	P + 1	P + 2
$C_9H_9N_2O_4$	10.79	1.33
$C_9H_{11}N_3O_3$	11.16	1.17
$C_9H_{13}N_4O_2$	11.54	1.01
$C_{10}HN_4O_2$	12.43	1.11
$C_{10}H_{11}NO_4$	11.52	1.41
$C_{10}H_{13}N_2O_3$	11.89	1.25
$C_{10}H_{15}N_3O_2$	12.27	1.09
$C_{10}H_{17}N_4O$	12.64	0.94
$C_{11}HN_2O_3$	12.78	1.35
$C_{11}H_3N_3O_2$	13.16	1.20
$C_{11}H_5N_4O$	13.53	1.05
$C_{11}H_{13}O_4$	12.25	1.49
$C_{11}H_{15}NO_3$	12.63	1.33
$C_{11}H_{17}N_2O_2$	13.00	1.18
$C_{11}H_{19}N_3O$	13.37	1.03
$C_{11}H_{21}N_4$	13.75	0.88
$C_{12}HO_4$	13.14	1.60
$C_{12}H_3NO_3$	13.51	1.44
$C_{12}H_5N_2O_2$	13.89	1.29
$C_{12}H_7N_3O$	14.26	1.15
$C_{12}H_9N_4$	14.64	1.00
$C_{12}H_{17}O_3$	13.36	1.42
$C_{12}H_{19}NO_2$	13.73	1.27
$C_{12}H_{21}N_2O$	14.11	1.12
$C_{12}H_{23}N_3$	14.48	0.98
$C_{13}H_5O_3$	14.25	1.54
$C_{13}H_7NO_2$	14.62	1.39
$C_{13}H_9N_2O$	14.99	1.25
$C_{13}H_{11}N_3$	15.37	1.10

	P + 1	P + 2
$C_{13}H_{21}O_2$	14.46	1.37
$C_{13}H_{23}NO$	14.84	1.22
$C_{13}H_{25}N_2$	15.21	1.08
$C_{14}H_9O_2$	15.35	1.50
$C_{14}H_{11}NO$	15.73	1.35
$C_{14}H_{13}N_2$	16.10	1.21
$C_{14}H_{25}O$	15.57	1.33
$C_{14}H_{27}N$	15.94	1.19
$C_{15}HN_2$	16.99	1.35
$C_{15}H_{13}O$	16.46	1.47
$C_{15}H_{15}N$	16.83	1.33
$C_{15}H_{29}$	16.67	1.30
$C_{16}HO$	17.35	1.61
$C_{16}H_3N$	17.72	1.48
$C_{16}H_{17}$	17.56	1.45
$C_{17}H_5$	18.45	1.60

210

	P + 1	P + 2
$C_9H_{10}N_2O_4$	10.81	1.33
$C_9H_{12}N_3O_3$	11.18	1.17
$C_9H_{14}N_4O_2$	11.55	1.01
$C_{10}H_2N_4O_2$	12.44	1.11
$C_{10}H_{12}NO_4$	11.54	1.41
$C_{10}H_{14}N_2O_3$	11.91	1.25
$C_{10}H_{16}N_3O_2$	12.29	1.09
$C_{10}H_{18}N_4O$	12.66	0.94
$C_{11}H_2N_2O_3$	12.80	1.35
$C_{11}H_4N_3O_2$	13.17	1.20
$C_{11}H_6N_4O$	13.55	1.05
$C_{11}H_{14}O_4$	12.27	1.49
$C_{11}H_{16}NO_3$	12.64	1.34
$C_{11}H_{18}N_2O_2$	13.02	1.18
$C_{11}H_{20}N_3O$	13.39	1.03
$C_{11}H_{22}N_4$	13.76	0.88
$C_{12}H_2O_4$	13.16	1.60
$C_{12}H_4NO_3$	13.53	1.45
$C_{12}H_6N_2O_2$	13.90	1.30
$C_{12}H_8N_3O$	14.28	1.15
$C_{12}H_{10}N_4$	14.65	1.00
$C_{12}H_{18}O_3$	13.37	1.43
$C_{12}H_{20}NO_2$	13.75	1.28
$C_{12}H_{22}N_2O$	14.12	1.13
$C_{12}H_{24}N_3$	14.50	0.98
$C_{13}H_6O_3$	14.26	1.54
$C_{13}H_8NO_2$	14.64	1.40
$C_{13}H_{10}N_2O$	15.01	1.25
$C_{13}H_{12}N_3$	15.38	1.11
$C_{13}H_{22}O_2$	14.48	1.37
$C_{13}H_{24}NO$	14.85	1.23
$C_{13}H_{26}N_2$	15.23	1.08
$C_{14}H_{10}O_2$	15.37	1.50
$C_{14}H_{12}NO$	15.74	1.36
$C_{14}H_{14}N_2$	16.12	1.22
$C_{14}H_{26}O$	15.58	1.33
$C_{14}H_{28}N$	15.96	1.19
$C_{15}H_2N_2$	17.00	1.36
$C_{15}H_{14}O$	16.47	1.47
$C_{15}H_{16}N$	16.85	1.33
$C_{15}H_{30}$	16.69	1.31
$C_{16}H_2O$	17.36	1.61
$C_{16}H_4N$	17.74	1.48
$C_{16}H_{18}$	17.58	1.45
$C_{17}H_6$	18.47	1.61

211

	P + 1	P + 2
$C_9H_{11}N_2O_4$	10.82	1.33
$C_9H_{13}N_3O_3$	11.20	1.17
$C_9H_{15}N_4O_2$	11.57	1.01
$C_{10}HN_3O_3$	12.08	1.27
$C_{10}H_3N_4O_2$	12.46	1.12
$C_{10}H_{13}NO_4$	11.55	1.41
$C_{10}H_{15}N_2O_3$	11.93	1.25
$C_{10}H_{17}N_3O_2$	12.30	1.10
$C_{10}H_{19}N_4O$	12.68	0.94
$C_{11}HNO_4$	12.44	1.51
$C_{11}H_3N_2O_3$	12.82	1.36
$C_{11}H_5N_3O_2$	13.19	1.20
$C_{11}H_7N_4O$	13.56	1.05
$C_{11}H_{15}O_4$	12.28	1.49
$C_{11}H_{17}NO_3$	12.66	1.34
$C_{11}H_{19}N_2O_2$	13.03	1.18
$C_{11}H_{21}N_3O$	13.41	1.03
$C_{11}H_{23}N_4$	13.78	0.88
$C_{12}H_3O_4$	13.17	1.60
$C_{12}H_5NO_3$	13.55	1.45
$C_{12}H_7N_2O_2$	13.92	1.30
$C_{12}H_9N_3O$	14.30	1.15
$C_{12}H_{11}N_4$	14.67	1.60
$C_{12}H_{19}O_3$	13.39	1.43
$C_{12}H_{21}NO_2$	13.76	1.28
$C_{12}H_{23}N_2O$	14.14	1.13
$C_{12}H_{25}N_3$	14.51	0.98
$C_{13}H_7O_3$	14.28	1.54
$C_{13}H_9NO_2$	14.65	1.40
$C_{13}H_{11}N_2O$	15.03	1.25
$C_{13}H_{13}N_3$	15.40	1.11
$C_{13}H_{23}O_2$	14.49	1.38
$C_{13}H_{25}NO$	14.87	1.23
$C_{13}H_{27}N_2$	15.24	1.08
$C_{14}HN_3$	16.29	1.24
$C_{14}H_{11}O_2$	15.38	1.50
$C_{14}H_{13}NO$	15.76	1.36
$C_{14}H_{15}N_2$	16.13	1.22
$C_{14}H_{27}O$	15.60	1.34
$C_{14}H_{29}N$	15.97	1.19
$C_{15}HNO$	16.65	1.50
$C_{15}H_3N_2$	17.02	1.36
$C_{15}H_{15}O$	16.49	1.47
$C_{15}H_{17}N$	16.86	1.33
$C_{15}H_{31}$	16.71	1.31
$C_{16}H_3O$	17.38	1.62
$C_{16}H_5N$	17.75	1.48
$C_{16}H_{19}$	17.59	1.45
$C_{17}H_7$	18.48	1.61

212

	P + 1	P + 2
$C_9H_{12}N_2O_4$	10.84	1.34
$C_9H_{14}N_3O_3$	11.21	1.18
$C_9H_{16}N_4O_2$	11.59	1.02
$C_{10}H_2N_3O_3$	12.10	1.27
$C_{10}H_4N_4O_2$	12.47	1.12
$C_{10}H_{14}NO_4$	11.57	1.41
$C_{10}H_{16}N_2O_3$	11.94	1.25
$C_{10}H_{18}N_3O_2$	12.32	1.10
$C_{10}H_{20}N_4O$	12.69	0.94
$C_{11}H_2NO_4$	12.46	1.51
$C_{11}H_4N_2O_3$	12.83	1.36
$C_{11}H_6N_3O_2$	13.21	1.21
$C_{11}H_8N_4O$	13.58	1.06
$C_{11}H_{16}O_4$	12.30	1.49
$C_{11}H_{18}NO_3$	12.67	1.34
$C_{11}H_{20}N_2O_2$	13.05	1.19
$C_{11}H_{22}N_3O$	13.42	1.03
$C_{11}H_{24}N_4$	13.80	0.88
$C_{12}H_4O_4$	13.19	1.60
$C_{12}H_6NO_3$	13.56	1.45
$C_{12}H_8N_2O_2$	13.94	1.30
$C_{12}H_{10}N_3O$	14.31	1.15
$C_{12}H_{12}N_4$	14.69	1.01
$C_{12}H_{20}O_3$	13.41	1.43
$C_{12}H_{22}NO_2$	13.78	1.28
$C_{12}H_{24}N_2O$	14.15	1.13
$C_{12}H_{26}N_3$	14.53	0.98
$C_{13}H_8O_3$	14.29	1.55
$C_{13}H_{10}NO_2$	14.67	1.40
$C_{13}H_{12}N_2O$	15.04	1.25
$C_{13}H_{14}N_3$	15.42	1.11
$C_{13}H_{24}O_2$	14.51	1.38
$C_{13}H_{26}NO$	14.88	1.23
$C_{13}H_{28}N_2$	15.26	1.09
$C_{14}H_2N_3$	16.31	1.25
$C_{14}H_{12}O_2$	15.40	1.50
$C_{14}H_{14}NO$	15.77	1.36
$C_{14}H_{16}N_2$	16.15	1.22
$C_{14}H_{28}O$	15.62	1.34
$C_{14}H_{30}N$	15.99	1.20
$C_{15}H_2NO$	16.66	1.50
$C_{15}H_4N_2$	17.04	1.36
$C_{15}H_{16}O$	16.50	1.47
$C_{15}H_{18}N$	16.88	1.34
$C_{15}H_{32}$	16.72	1.31
$C_{16}H_4O$	17.39	1.62
$C_{16}H_6N$	17.77	1.48
$C_{16}H_{20}$	17.61	1.46
$C_{17}H_8$	18.50	1.61

213

	P + 1	P + 2
$C_9H_3N_2O_4$	10.86	1.34
$C_9H_{15}N_3O_3$	11.23	1.18
$C_9H_{17}N_4O_2$	11.60	1.02
$C_{10}HN_2O_4$	11.74	1.43
$C_{10}H_3N_3O_2$	12.12	1.27
$C_{10}H_5N_4O_2$	12.49	1.12
$C_{10}H_{15}NO_4$	11.58	1.41
$C_{10}H_{17}N_2O_3$	11.96	1.26
$C_{10}H_{19}N_3O_2$	12.33	1.10
$C_{10}H_{21}N_4O$	12.71	0.95
$C_{11}H_3NO_4$	12.47	1.51
$C_{11}H_5N_2O_3$	12.85	1.36
$C_{11}H_7N_3O_2$	13.22	1.21
$C_{11}H_9N_4O$	13.60	1.06
$C_{11}H_{17}O_4$	12.32	1.50
$C_{11}H_{19}NO_3$	12.69	1.34
$C_{11}H_{21}N_2O_2$	13.06	1.19
$C_{11}H_{23}N_3O$	13.44	1.04
$C_{11}H_{25}N_4$	13.81	0.89
$C_{12}H_5O_4$	13.20	1.60
$C_{12}H_7NO_3$	13.58	1.45
$C_{12}H_9N_2O_2$	13.95	1.30
$C_{12}H_{11}N_3O$	14.33	1.15
$C_{12}H_{13}N_4$	14.70	1.01
$C_{12}H_{21}O_3$	13.42	1.43
$C_{12}H_{23}NO_2$	13.80	1.28
$C_{12}H_{25}N_2O$	14.17	1.13
$C_{12}H_{27}N_3$	14.54	0.99
$C_{13}HN_4$	15.59	1.14
$C_{13}H_9O_3$	14.31	1.55
$C_{13}H_{11}NO_2$	14.68	1.40
$C_{13}H_{13}N_2O$	15.06	1.26
$C_{13}H_{15}N_3$	15.43	1.11
$C_{13}H_{25}O_2$	14.53	1.38
$C_{13}H_{27}NO$	14.90	1.23
$C_{13}H_{29}N_2$	15.28	1.09
$C_{14}HN_2O$	15.95	1.39
$C_{14}H_3N_3$	16.32	1.25
$C_{14}H_{13}O_2$	15.42	1.51
$C_{14}H_{15}NO$	15.79	1.36
$C_{14}H_{17}N_2$	16.16	1.22
$C_{14}H_{29}O$	15.63	1.34
$C_{14}H_{31}N$	16.01	1.20
$C_{15}HO_2$	16.30	1.64
$C_{15}H_3NO$	16.68	1.50
$C_{15}H_5N_2$	17.05	1.36
$C_{15}H_{17}O$	16.52	1.48
$C_{15}H_{19}N$	16.90	1.34
$C_{16}H_5O$	17.41	1.62
$C_{16}H_7N$	17.78	1.49
$C_{16}H_{21}$	17.63	1.46
$C_{17}H_9$	18.51	1.61

214

	P + 1	P + 2
$C_9H_{14}N_2O_4$	10.87	1.34
$C_9H_{16}N_3O_3$	11.24	1.18
$C_9H_{18}N_4O_2$	11.62	1.02
$C_{10}H_2N_2O_4$	11.76	1.43
$C_{10}H_4N_3O_3$	12.13	1.28
$C_{10}H_6N_4O_2$	12.51	1.12
$C_{10}H_{16}NO_4$	11.60	1.42
$C_{10}H_{18}N_2O_3$	11.97	1.26
$C_{10}H_{20}N_3O_2$	12.35	1.10
$C_{10}H_{22}N_4O$	12.72	0.95
$C_{11}H_4NO_4$	12.49	1.52
$C_{11}H_6N_2O_3$	12.86	1.36
$C_{11}H_8N_3O_2$	13.24	1.21
$C_{11}H_{10}N_4O$	13.61	1.06
$C_{11}H_{18}O_4$	12.33	1.50
$C_{11}H_{20}NO_3$	12.71	1.34
$C_{11}H_{22}N_2O_2$	13.08	1.19
$C_{11}H_{24}N_3O$	13.45	1.04
$C_{11}H_{26}N_4$	13.83	0.89
$C_{12}H_6O_4$	13.22	1.61
$C_{12}H_8NO_3$	13.59	1.45
$C_{12}H_{10}N_2O_2$	13.97	1.31
$C_{12}H_{12}N_3O$	14.34	1.16
$C_{12}H_{14}N_4$	14.72	1.01
$C_{12}H_{22}O_3$	13.44	1.43
$C_{12}H_{24}NO_2$	13.81	1.28
$C_{12}H_{26}N_2O$	14.19	1.14
$C_{12}H_{28}N_3$	14.56	0.99
$C_{13}H_2N_4$	15.61	1.14
$C_{13}H_{10}O_3$	14.33	1.55
$C_{13}H_{12}NO_2$	14.70	1.40
$C_{13}H_{14}N_2O$	15.07	1.26

	P + 1	P + 2
$C_{13}H_{16}N_3$	15.45	1.12
$C_{13}H_{26}O_2$	14.54	1.38
$C_{13}H_{28}NO$	14.92	1.24
$C_{13}H_{30}N_2$	15.29	1.09
$C_{14}H_2N_2O$	15.96	1.39
$C_{14}H_4N_3$	16.34	1.25
$C_{14}H_{14}O_2$	15.43	1.51
$C_{14}H_{16}NO$	15.81	1.37
$C_{14}H_{18}N_2$	16.18	1.23
$C_{14}H_{30}O$	15.65	1.34
$C_{15}H_2O_2$	16.32	1.64
$C_{15}H_4NO$	16.69	1.51
$C_{15}H_6N_2$	17.07	1.37
$C_{15}H_{18}O$	16.54	1.48
$C_{15}H_{20}N$	16.91	1.34
$C_{16}H_6O$	17.43	1.63
$C_{16}H_8N$	17.80	1.49
$C_{16}H_{22}$	17.64	1.46
$C_{17}H_{10}$	18.53	1.62

215

	P + 1	P + 2
$C_9H_{15}N_2O_4$	10.89	1.34
$C_9H_{17}N_3O_3$	11.26	1.18
$C_9H_{19}N_4O_2$	11.63	1.02
$C_{10}H_3N_2O_4$	11.77	1.44
$C_{10}H_5N_3O_3$	12.15	1.28
$C_{10}H_7N_4O_2$	12.52	1.12
$C_{10}H_{17}NO_4$	11.62	1.42
$C_{10}H_{19}N_2O_3$	11.99	1.26
$C_{10}H_{21}N_3O_2$	12.37	1.10
$C_{10}H_{23}N_4O$	12.74	0.95
$C_{11}H_5NO_4$	12.50	1.52
$C_{11}H_7N_2O_3$	12.88	1.37
$C_{11}H_9N_3O_2$	13.25	1.21
$C_{11}H_{11}N_4O$	13.63	1.06
$C_{11}H_{19}O_4$	12.35	1.50
$C_{11}H_{21}NO_3$	12.72	1.35
$C_{11}H_{23}N_2O_2$	13.10	1.19
$C_{11}H_{25}N_3O$	13.47	1.04
$C_{11}H_{27}N_4$	13.84	0.89
$C_{12}H_7O_4$	13.24	1.61
$C_{12}H_9NO_3$	13.61	1.46
$C_{12}H_{11}N_2O_2$	13.98	1.31
$C_{12}H_{13}N_3O$	14.36	1.16
$C_{12}H_{15}N_4$	14.73	1.01
$C_{12}H_{23}O_3$	13.45	1.44
$C_{12}H_{25}NO_2$	13.83	1.29
$C_{12}H_{27}N_2O$	14.20	1.14
$C_{12}H_{29}N_3$	14.58	0.99
$C_{13}HN_3O$	15.25	1.28
$C_{13}H_3N_4$	15.62	1.14
$C_{13}H_{11}O_3$	14.34	1.55
$C_{13}H_{13}NO_2$	14.72	1.41
$C_{13}H_{15}N_2O$	15.09	1.26
$C_{13}H_{17}N_3$	15.46	1.12
$C_{13}H_{27}O_2$	14.56	1.38
$C_{13}H_{29}NO$	14.93	1.24
$C_{14}HNO_2$	15.60	1.54
$C_{14}H_3N_2O$	15.98	1.39
$C_{14}H_5N_3$	16.35	1.25
$C_{14}H_{15}O_2$	15.45	1.51
$C_{14}H_{17}NO$	15.82	1.37
$C_{14}H_{19}N_2$	16.20	1.23
$C_{15}H_3O_2$	16.34	1.65
$C_{15}H_5NO$	16.71	1.51
$C_{15}H_7N_2$	17.08	1.37
$C_{15}H_{19}O$	16.55	1.48
$C_{15}H_{21}N$	16.93	1.34
$C_{16}H_7O$	17.44	1.63
$C_{16}H_9N$	17.82	1.49
$C_{16}H_{23}$	17.66	1.47
$C_{17}H_{11}$	18.55	1.62

216

	P + 1	P + 2
$C_9H_{16}N_2O_4$	10.90	1.34
$C_9H_{18}N_3O_3$	11.28	1.18
$C_9H_{20}N_4O_2$	11.65	1.02
$C_{10}H_4N_2O_4$	11.79	1.44
$C_{10}H_6N_3O_3$	12.16	1.28
$C_{10}H_8N_4O_2$	12.54	1.13
$C_{10}H_{18}NO_4$	11.63	1.42
$C_{10}H_{20}N_2O_3$	12.01	1.26
$C_{10}H_{22}N_3O_2$	12.38	1.11
$C_{10}H_{24}N_4O$	12.76	0.95
$C_{11}H_6NO_4$	12.52	1.52
$C_{11}H_8N_2O_3$	12.90	1.37
$C_{11}H_{10}N_3O_2$	13.27	1.21
$C_{11}H_{12}N_4O$	13.64	1.06
$C_{11}H_{20}O_4$	12.36	1.50
$C_{11}H_{22}NO_3$	12.74	1.35
$C_{11}H_{24}N_2O_2$	13.11	1.19
$C_{11}H_{26}N_3O$	13.49	1.04
$C_{11}H_{28}N_4$	13.86	0.89
$C_{12}H_8O_4$	13.25	1.61
$C_{12}H_{10}NO_3$	13.63	1.46
$C_{12}H_{12}N_2O_2$	14.00	1.31
$C_{12}H_{14}N_3O$	14.38	1.16
$C_{12}H_{16}N_4$	14.75	1.01
$C_{12}H_{24}O_3$	13.47	1.44
$C_{12}H_{26}NO_2$	13.84	1.29
$C_{12}H_{28}N_2O$	14.22	1.14
$C_{13}H_2N_3O$	15.26	1.29
$C_{13}H_4N_4$	15.64	1.14
$C_{13}H_{12}O_3$	14.36	1.56
$C_{13}H_{14}NO_2$	14.73	1.41
$C_{13}H_{16}N_2O$	15.11	1.26
$C_{13}H_{18}N_3$	15.48	1.12
$C_{13}H_{28}O_2$	14.57	1.39
$C_{14}H_2NO_2$	15.62	1.54
$C_{14}H_4N_2O$	15.99	1.40
$C_{14}H_6N_3$	16.37	1.26
$C_{14}H_{16}O_2$	15.46	1.51
$C_{14}H_{18}NO$	15.84	1.37
$C_{14}H_{20}N_2$	16.21	1.23
$C_{15}H_4O_2$	16.35	1.65
$C_{15}H_6NO$	16.73	1.51
$C_{15}H_8N_2$	17.10	1.37
$C_{15}H_{20}O$	16.57	1.49
$C_{15}H_{22}N$	16.94	1.35
$C_{16}H_8O$	17.46	1.63
$C_{16}H_{10}N$	17.83	1.50
$C_{16}H_{24}$	17.67	1.47
$C_{17}H_{12}$	18.56	1.62

217

	P + 1	P + 2
$C_9H_{17}N_2O_4$	10.92	1.34
$C_9H_{19}N_3O_3$	11.29	1.18
$C_9H_{21}N_4O_2$	11.67	1.03
$C_{10}H_5N_2O_4$	11.81	1.44
$C_{10}H_7N_3O_3$	12.18	1.28
$C_{10}H_9N_4O_2$	12.55	1.13
$C_{10}H_{19}NO_4$	11.65	1.42
$C_{10}H_{21}N_2O_3$	12.02	1.26
$C_{10}H_{23}N_3O_2$	12.40	1.11
$C_{10}H_{25}N_4O$	12.77	0.95
$C_{11}H_7NO_4$	12.54	1.52
$C_{11}H_9N_2O_3$	12.91	1.37
$C_{11}H_{11}N_3O_2$	13.29	1.22
$C_{11}H_{13}N_4O$	13.66	1.07
$C_{11}H_{21}O_4$	12.38	1.50
$C_{11}H_{23}NO_3$	12.75	1.35
$C_{11}H_{25}N_2O_2$	13.13	1.20
$C_{11}H_{27}N_3O$	13.50	1.05
$C_{12}HN_4O$	14.55	1.19
$C_{12}H_9O_4$	13.27	1.61
$C_{12}H_{11}NO_3$	13.64	1.46
$C_{12}H_{13}N_2O_2$	14.02	1.31
$C_{12}H_{15}N_3O$	14.39	1.16
$C_{12}H_{17}N_4$	14.77	1.02
$C_{12}H_{25}O_3$	13.49	1.44
$C_{12}H_{27}NO_2$	13.86	1.29
$C_{13}HN_2O_2$	14.91	1.43
$C_{13}H_3N_3O$	15.28	1.29
$C_{13}H_5N_4$	15.65	1.15
$C_{13}H_{13}O_3$	14.37	1.56
$C_{13}H_{15}NO_2$	14.75	1.41
$C_{13}H_{17}N_2O$	15.12	1.27
$C_{13}H_{19}N_3$	15.50	1.12
$C_{14}HO_3$	15.26	1.68
$C_{14}H_3NO_2$	15.64	1.54
$C_{14}H_5N_2O$	16.01	1.40
$C_{14}H_7N_3$	16.39	1.26
$C_{14}H_{17}O_2$	15.48	1.52
$C_{14}H_{19}NO$	15.58	1.37
$C_{14}H_{21}N_2$	16.23	1.23
$C_{15}H_5O_2$	16.37	1.65
$C_{15}H_7NO$	16.74	1.51
$C_{15}H_9N_2$	17.12	1.38
$C_{15}H_{21}O$	16.58	1.49
$C_{15}H_{23}N$	16.96	1.35
$C_{16}H_9O$	17.47	1.63
$C_{16}H_{11}N$	17.85	1.50
$C_{16}H_{25}$	17.69	1.47
$C_{17}H_{13}$	18.58	1.63
$C_{18}H$	19.47	1.79

218

	P + 1	P + 2
$C_9H_{18}N_2O_4$	10.93	1.35
$C_9H_{20}N_3O_3$	11.31	1.19
$C_9H_{22}N_4O_2$	11.68	1.03
$C_{10}H_6N_2O_4$	11.82	1.44
$C_{10}H_8N_3O_3$	12.20	1.28
$C_{10}H_{10}N_4O_2$	12.57	1.13
$C_{10}H_{20}NO_4$	11.66	1.42
$C_{10}H_{22}N_2O_3$	12.04	1.27
$C_{10}H_{24}N_3O_2$	12.41	1.11
$C_{10}H_{26}N_4O$	12.79	0.96
$C_{11}H_8NO_4$	12.55	1.52
$C_{11}H_{10}N_2O_3$	12.93	1.37
$C_{11}H_{12}N_3O_2$	13.30	1.22
$C_{11}H_{14}N_4O$	13.68	1.07
$C_{11}H_{22}O_4$	12.40	1.51
$C_{11}H_{24}NO_3$	12.77	1.35
$C_{11}H_{26}N_2O_2$	13.14	1.20
$C_{12}H_2N_4O$	14.56	1.19
$C_{12}H_{10}O_4$	13.28	1.61
$C_{12}H_{12}NO_3$	13.66	1.46
$C_{12}H_{14}N_2O_2$	14.03	1.31
$C_{12}H_{16}N_3O$	14.41	1.17
$C_{12}H_{18}N_4$	14.78	1.02
$C_{12}H_{26}O_3$	13.50	1.44
$C_{13}H_2N_2O_2$	14.92	1.44
$C_{13}H_4N_3O$	15.30	1.29
$C_{13}H_6N_4$	15.67	1.15
$C_{13}H_{14}O_3$	14.39	1.56
$C_{13}H_{16}NO_2$	14.76	1.41
$C_{13}H_{18}N_2O$	15.14	1.27
$C_{13}H_{20}N_3$	15.51	1.13
$C_{14}H_2O_3$	15.28	1.69
$C_{14}H_4NO_2$	15.65	1.54
$C_{14}H_6N_2O$	16.03	1.40
$C_{14}H_8N_3$	16.40	1.26
$C_{14}H_{18}O_2$	15.50	1.52
$C_{14}H_{20}NO$	15.87	1.38
$C_{14}H_{22}N_2$	16.24	1.24
$C_{15}H_6O_2$	16.38	1.66
$C_{15}H_8NO$	16.76	1.52
$C_{15}H_{10}N_2$	17.13	1.38
$C_{15}H_{22}O$	16.60	1.49
$C_{15}H_{24}N$	16.98	1.35
$C_{16}H_{10}O$	17.49	1.64
$C_{16}H_{12}N$	17.86	1.50
$C_{16}H_{26}$	17.71	1.47
$C_{17}H_{14}$	18.59	1.63
$C_{18}H_2$	19.48	1.79

219

	P + 1	P + 2
$C_9H_{19}N_2O_4$	10.95	1.35
$C_9H_{21}N_3O_3$	11.32	1.19
$C_9H_{23}N_4O_2$	11.70	1.03
$C_{10}H_7N_2O_4$	11.84	1.44
$C_{10}H_9N_3O_3$	12.21	1.29
$C_{10}H_{11}N_4O_2$	12.59	1.13
$C_{10}H_{21}NO_4$	11.68	1.42
$C_{10}H_{23}N_2O_3$	12.05	1.27
$C_{10}H_{25}N_3O_2$	12.43	1.11
$C_{11}H_9NO_4$	12.57	1.53
$C_{11}H_{11}N_2O_3$	12.94	1.37
$C_{11}H_{13}N_3O_2$	13.32	1.22
$C_{11}H_{15}N_4O$	13.69	1.07
$C_{11}H_{23}O_4$	12.41	1.51
$C_{11}H_{25}NO_3$	12.79	1.35
$C_{12}HN_3O_2$	14.21	1.34
$C_{12}H_3N_4O$	14.58	1.19
$C_{12}H_{11}O_4$	13.30	1.62
$C_{12}H_{13}NO_3$	13.67	1.47
$C_{12}H_{15}N_2O_2$	14.05	1.32
$C_{12}H_{17}N_3O$	14.42	1.17
$C_{12}H_{19}N_4$	14.80	1.02
$C_{13}HNO_3$	14.56	1.59
$C_{13}H_3N_2O_2$	14.94	1.44
$C_{13}H_5N_3O$	15.31	1.29

	P + 1	P + 2
$C_{13}H_{7}N_{4}$	15.69	1.15
$C_{13}H_{15}O_{3}$	14.41	1.56
$C_{13}H_{17}NO_{2}$	14.78	1.42
$C_{13}H_{19}N_{2}O$	15.15	1.27
$C_{13}H_{21}N_{3}$	15.53	1.13
$C_{14}H_{3}O_{3}$	15.29	1.69
$C_{14}H_{5}NO_{2}$	15.67	1.55
$C_{14}H_{7}N_{2}O$	16.04	1.40
$C_{14}H_{9}N_{3}$	16.42	1.26
$C_{14}H_{19}O_{2}$	15.51	1.52
$C_{14}H_{21}NO$	15.89	1.38
$C_{14}H_{23}N_{2}$	16.26	1.24
$C_{15}H_{7}O_{2}$	16.40	1.66
$C_{15}H_{9}NO$	16.77	1.52
$C_{15}H_{11}N_{2}$	17.15	1.38
$C_{15}H_{23}O$	16.62	1.49
$C_{15}H_{25}N$	16.99	1.36
$C_{16}H_{11}O$	17.51	1.64
$C_{16}H_{13}N$	17.88	1.50
$C_{16}H_{27}$	17.72	1.48
$C_{17}HN$	18.77	1.66
$C_{17}H_{15}$	18.61	1.63
$C_{18}H_{3}$	19.50	1.80

220

	P + 1	P + 2
$C_{9}H_{20}N_{2}O_{4}$	10.97	1.35
$C_{9}H_{22}N_{3}O_{3}$	11.34	1.19
$C_{9}H_{24}N_{4}O_{2}$	11.71	1.03
$C_{10}H_{8}N_{2}O_{4}$	11.85	1.44
$C_{10}H_{10}N_{3}O_{3}$	12.23	1.29
$C_{10}H_{12}N_{4}O_{2}$	12.60	1.13
$C_{10}H_{22}NO_{4}$	11.70	1.43
$C_{10}H_{24}N_{2}O_{3}$	12.07	1.27
$C_{11}H_{10}NO_{4}$	12.58	1.53
$C_{11}H_{12}N_{2}O_{3}$	12.96	1.38
$C_{11}H_{14}N_{3}O_{2}$	13.33	1.22
$C_{11}H_{16}N_{4}O$	13.71	1.07
$C_{11}H_{24}O_{4}$	12.43	1.51
$C_{12}H_{2}N_{3}O_{2}$	14.22	1.34
$C_{12}H_{4}N_{4}O$	14.60	1.19
$C_{12}H_{12}O_{4}$	13.32	1.62
$C_{12}H_{14}NO_{3}$	13.69	1.47
$C_{12}H_{16}N_{2}O_{2}$	14.06	1.32
$C_{12}H_{18}N_{3}O$	14.44	1.17
$C_{12}H_{20}N_{4}$	14.81	1.02
$C_{13}H_{2}NO_{3}$	14.58	1.59
$C_{13}H_{4}N_{2}O_{2}$	14.95	1.44
$C_{13}H_{6}N_{3}O$	15.33	1.30
$C_{13}H_{8}N_{4}$	15.70	1.15
$C_{13}H_{16}O_{3}$	14.42	1.57
$C_{13}H_{18}NO_{2}$	14.80	1.42
$C_{13}H_{20}N_{2}O$	15.17	1.27
$C_{13}H_{22}N_{3}$	15.54	1.13
$C_{14}H_{4}O_{3}$	15.31	1.69
$C_{14}H_{6}NO_{2}$	15.68	1.55
$C_{14}H_{8}N_{2}O$	16.06	1.41
$C_{14}H_{10}N_{3}$	16.43	1.27
$C_{14}H_{20}O_{2}$	15.53	1.52
$C_{14}H_{22}NO$	15.90	1.38
$C_{14}H_{24}N_{2}$	16.28	1.24
$C_{15}H_{8}O_{2}$	16.42	1.66
$C_{15}H_{10}NO$	16.79	1.52
$C_{15}H_{12}N_{2}$	17.16	1.38
$C_{15}H_{24}O$	16.63	1.50
$C_{15}H_{26}N$	17.01	1.36
$C_{16}H_{12}O$	17.52	1.64
$C_{16}H_{14}N$	17.90	1.51
$C_{16}H_{28}$	17.74	1.48
$C_{17}H_{2}N$	18.78	1.66
$C_{17}H_{16}$	18.63	1.64
$C_{18}H_{4}$	19.52	1.80

221

	P + 1	P + 2
$C_{9}H_{21}N_{2}O_{4}$	10.98	1.35
$C_{9}H_{23}N_{3}O_{3}$	11.36	1.19
$C_{10}H_{9}N_{2}O_{4}$	11.87	1.45
$C_{10}H_{11}N_{3}O_{3}$	12.24	1.29
$C_{10}H_{13}N_{4}O_{2}$	12.62	1.14
$C_{10}H_{23}NO_{4}$	11.71	1.43
$C_{11}HN_{4}O_{2}$	13.51	1.25
$C_{11}H_{11}NO_{4}$	12.60	1.53
$C_{11}H_{13}N_{2}O_{3}$	12.98	1.38
$C_{11}H_{15}N_{3}O_{2}$	13.35	1.23
$C_{11}H_{17}N_{4}O$	13.72	1.08
$C_{12}HN_{2}O_{3}$	13.86	1.49
$C_{12}H_{3}N_{3}O_{2}$	14.24	1.34
$C_{12}H_{5}N_{4}O$	14.61	1.20
$C_{12}H_{13}O_{4}$	13.33	1.62
$C_{12}H_{15}NO_{3}$	13.71	1.47
$C_{12}H_{17}N_{2}O_{2}$	14.08	1.32
$C_{12}H_{19}N_{3}O$	14.46	1.17
$C_{12}H_{21}N_{4}$	14.83	1.03
$C_{13}HO_{4}$	14.22	1.74
$C_{13}H_{3}NO_{3}$	14.60	1.59
$C_{13}H_{5}N_{2}O_{2}$	14.97	1.44
$C_{13}H_{7}N_{3}O$	15.34	1.30
$C_{13}H_{9}N_{4}$	15.72	1.16
$C_{13}H_{17}O_{3}$	14.44	1.57
$C_{13}H_{19}NO_{2}$	14.81	1.42
$C_{13}H_{21}N_{2}O$	15.19	1.28
$C_{13}H_{23}N_{3}$	15.56	1.13
$C_{14}H_{5}O_{3}$	15.33	1.69
$C_{14}H_{7}NO_{2}$	15.70	1.55
$C_{14}H_{9}N_{2}O$	16.07	1.41
$C_{14}H_{11}N_{3}$	16.45	1.27
$C_{14}H_{21}O_{2}$	15.54	1.53
$C_{14}H_{23}NO$	15.92	1.38
$C_{14}H_{25}N_{2}$	16.29	1.24
$C_{15}H_{9}O_{2}$	16.43	1.66
$C_{15}H_{11}NO$	16.81	1.52
$C_{15}H_{13}N_{2}$	17.18	1.39
$C_{15}H_{25}O$	16.65	1.50
$C_{15}H_{27}N$	17.02	1.36
$C_{16}HN_{2}$	18.07	1.54
$C_{16}H_{13}O$	17.54	1.64
$C_{16}H_{15}N$	17.91	1.51
$C_{16}H_{29}$	17.75	1.48
$C_{17}HO$	18.43	1.80
$C_{17}H_{3}N$	18.80	1.67
$C_{17}H_{17}$	18.64	1.64
$C_{18}H_{5}$	19.53	1.80

222

	P + 1	P + 2
$C_{9}H_{22}N_{2}O_{4}$	11.00	1.35
$C_{10}H_{10}N_{2}O_{4}$	11.89	1.45
$C_{10}H_{12}N_{3}O_{3}$	12.26	1.29
$C_{10}H_{14}N_{4}O_{2}$	12.63	1.14
$C_{11}H_{2}N_{4}O_{2}$	13.52	1.25
$C_{11}H_{12}NO_{4}$	12.62	1.53
$C_{11}H_{14}N_{2}O_{3}$	12.99	1.38
$C_{11}H_{16}N_{3}O_{2}$	13.37	1.23
$C_{11}H_{18}N_{4}O$	13.74	1.08
$C_{12}H_{2}N_{2}O_{3}$	13.88	1.49
$C_{12}H_{4}N_{3}O_{2}$	14.25	1.34
$C_{12}H_{6}N_{4}O$	14.63	1.20
$C_{12}H_{14}O_{4}$	13.35	1.62
$C_{12}H_{16}NO_{3}$	13.72	1.47
$C_{12}H_{18}N_{2}O_{2}$	14.10	1.32
$C_{12}H_{20}N_{3}O$	14.47	1.18
$C_{12}H_{22}N_{4}$	14.85	1.03
$C_{13}H_{2}O_{4}$	14.24	1.74
$C_{13}H_{4}NO_{3}$	14.61	1.59
$C_{13}H_{6}N_{2}O_{2}$	14.99	1.45
$C_{13}H_{8}N_{3}O$	15.36	1.30
$C_{13}H_{10}N_{4}$	15.73	1.16
$C_{13}H_{18}O_{3}$	14.45	1.57
$C_{13}H_{20}NO_{2}$	14.83	1.42
$C_{13}H_{22}N_{2}O$	15.20	1.28
$C_{13}H_{24}N_{3}$	15.58	1.14
$C_{14}H_{6}O_{3}$	15.34	1.70
$C_{14}H_{8}NO_{2}$	15.72	1.55
$C_{14}H_{10}N_{2}O$	16.09	1.41
$C_{14}H_{12}N_{3}$	16.47	1.27
$C_{14}H_{22}O_{2}$	15.56	1.53
$C_{14}H_{24}NO$	15.93	1.39
$C_{14}H_{26}N_{2}$	16.31	1.25
$C_{15}H_{10}O_{2}$	16.45	1.67
$C_{15}H_{12}NO$	16.82	1.53
$C_{15}H_{14}N_{2}$	17.20	1.39
$C_{15}H_{26}O$	16.66	1.50
$C_{15}H_{28}N$	17.04	1.36
$C_{16}H_{2}N_{2}$	18.09	1.54
$C_{16}H_{14}O$	17.55	1.65
$C_{16}H_{16}N$	17.93	1.51
$C_{16}H_{30}$	17.77	1.49
$C_{17}H_{2}O$	18.44	1.80
$C_{17}H_{4}N$	18.82	1.67
$C_{17}H_{18}$	18.66	1.64
$C_{18}H_{6}$	19.55	1.81

223

	P + 1	P + 2
$C_{10}H_{11}N_{2}O_{4}$	11.90	1.45
$C_{10}H_{13}N_{3}O_{3}$	12.28	1.29
$C_{10}H_{15}N_{4}O_{2}$	12.65	1.14
$C_{11}HN_{3}O_{3}$	13.16	1.40
$C_{11}H_{3}N_{4}O_{2}$	13.54	1.25
$C_{11}H_{13}NO_{4}$	12.63	1.53
$C_{11}H_{15}N_{2}O_{3}$	13.01	1.38
$C_{11}H_{17}N_{3}O_{2}$	13.38	1.23
$C_{11}H_{19}N_{4}O$	13.76	1.08
$C_{12}HNO_{4}$	13.52	1.65
$C_{12}H_{3}N_{2}O_{3}$	13.90	1.50
$C_{12}H_{5}N_{3}O_{2}$	14.27	1.35
$C_{12}H_{7}N_{4}O$	14.64	1.20
$C_{12}H_{15}O_{4}$	13.36	1.62
$C_{12}H_{17}NO_{3}$	13.74	1.47
$C_{12}H_{19}N_{2}O_{2}$	14.11	1.33
$C_{12}H_{21}N_{3}O$	14.49	1.18
$C_{12}H_{23}N_{4}$	14.86	1.03
$C_{13}H_{3}O_{4}$	14.25	1.74
$C_{13}H_{5}NO_{3}$	14.63	1.59
$C_{13}H_{7}N_{2}O_{2}$	15.00	1.45
$C_{13}H_{9}N_{3}O$	15.38	1.30
$C_{13}H_{11}N_{4}$	15.75	1.16
$C_{13}H_{19}O_{3}$	14.47	1.57
$C_{13}H_{21}NO_{2}$	14.84	1.43
$C_{13}H_{23}N_{2}O$	15.22	1.28
$C_{13}H_{25}N_{3}$	15.59	1.14
$C_{14}H_{7}O_{3}$	15.36	1.70
$C_{14}H_{9}NO_{2}$	15.73	1.56
$C_{14}H_{11}N_{2}O$	16.11	1.41
$C_{14}H_{13}N_{3}$	16.48	1.27
$C_{14}H_{23}O_{2}$	15.58	1.53
$C_{14}H_{25}NO$	15.95	1.39
$C_{14}H_{27}N_{2}$	16.32	1.25
$C_{15}HN_{3}$	17.37	1.42
$C_{15}H_{11}O_{2}$	16.46	1.67
$C_{15}H_{13}NO$	16.84	1.53
$C_{15}H_{15}N_{2}$	17.21	1.39
$C_{15}H_{27}O$	16.68	1.50
$C_{15}H_{29}N$	17.06	1.37
$C_{16}HNO$	17.73	1.68
$C_{16}H_{3}N_{2}$	18.10	1.54
$C_{16}H_{15}O$	17.57	1.65
$C_{16}H_{17}N$	17.94	1.52
$C_{16}H_{31}$	17.79	1.49
$C_{17}H_{3}O$	18.46	1.80
$C_{17}H_{5}N$	18.83	1.67
$C_{17}H_{19}$	18.67	1.64
$C_{18}H_{7}$	19.56	1.81

224

	P + 1	P + 2
$C_{10}H_{12}N_{2}O_{4}$	11.92	1.45
$C_{10}H_{14}N_{3}O_{3}$	12.29	1.30
$C_{10}H_{16}N_{4}O_{2}$	12.67	1.14
$C_{11}H_{2}N_{3}O_{3}$	13.18	1.40
$C_{11}H_{4}N_{4}O_{2}$	13.56	1.25
$C_{11}H_{14}NO_{4}$	12.65	1.54
$C_{11}H_{16}N_{2}O_{3}$	13.02	1.38
$C_{11}H_{18}N_{3}O_{2}$	13.40	1.23
$C_{11}H_{20}N_{4}O$	13.77	1.08
$C_{12}H_{2}NO_{4}$	13.54	1.65
$C_{12}H_{4}N_{2}O_{3}$	13.91	1.50
$C_{12}H_{6}N_{3}O_{2}$	14.29	1.35
$C_{12}H_{8}N_{4}O$	14.66	1.20
$C_{12}H_{16}O_{4}$	13.38	1.63
$C_{12}H_{18}NO_{3}$	13.75	1.48
$C_{12}H_{20}N_{2}O_{2}$	14.13	1.33
$C_{12}H_{22}N_{3}O$	14.50	1.18
$C_{12}H_{24}N_{4}$	14.88	1.03
$C_{13}H_{4}O_{4}$	14.27	1.74
$C_{13}H_{6}NO_{3}$	14.64	1.60
$C_{13}H_{8}N_{2}O_{2}$	15.02	1.45
$C_{13}H_{10}N_{3}O$	15.39	1.31
$C_{13}H_{12}N_{4}$	15.77	1.16
$C_{13}H_{20}O_{3}$	14.49	1.57
$C_{13}H_{22}NO_{2}$	14.86	1.43
$C_{13}H_{24}N_{2}O$	15.23	1.28
$C_{13}H_{26}N_{3}$	15.61	1.14
$C_{14}H_{8}O_{3}$	15.37	1.70
$C_{14}H_{10}NO_{2}$	15.75	1.56
$C_{14}H_{12}N_{2}O$	16.12	1.42
$C_{14}H_{14}N_{3}$	16.50	1.28
$C_{14}H_{24}O_{2}$	15.59	1.53

	P + 1	P + 2
$C_{14}H_{26}NO$	15.97	1.39
$C_{14}H_{28}N_2$	16.34	1.25
$C_{15}H_2N_3$	17.39	1.42
$C_{15}H_{12}O_2$	16.48	1.67
$C_{15}H_{14}NO$	16.85	1.53
$C_{15}H_{16}N_2$	17.23	1.40
$C_{15}H_{28}O$	16.70	1.51
$C_{15}H_{30}N$	17.07	1.37
$C_{16}H_2NO$	17.74	1.68
$C_{16}H_4N_2$	18.12	1.55
$C_{16}H_{16}O$	17.59	1.65
$C_{16}H_{18}N$	17.96	1.52
$C_{16}H_{32}$	17.80	1.49
$C_{17}H_4O$	18.47	1.81
$C_{17}H_6N$	18.85	1.68
$C_{17}H_{20}$	18.69	1.65
$C_{18}H_8$	19.58	1.81

225

	P + 1	P + 2
$C_{10}H_{13}N_2O_4$	11.93	1.45
$C_{10}H_{15}N_3O_3$	12.31	1.30
$C_{10}H_{17}N_4O_2$	12.68	1.14
$C_{11}HN_2O_4$	12.82	1.56
$C_{11}H_3N_3O_3$	13.20	1.41
$C_{11}H_5N_4O_2$	13.57	1.25
$C_{11}H_{15}NO_4$	12.66	1.54
$C_{11}H_{17}N_2O_3$	13.04	1.39
$C_{11}H_{19}N_3O_2$	13.41	1.23
$C_{11}H_{21}N_4O$	13.79	1.08
$C_{12}H_3NO_4$	13.55	1.65
$C_{12}H_5N_2O_3$	13.93	1.50
$C_{12}H_7N_3O_2$	14.30	1.35
$C_{12}H_9N_4O$	14.68	1.20
$C_{12}H_{17}O_4$	13.40	1.63
$C_{12}H_{19}NO_3$	13.77	1.48
$C_{12}H_{21}N_2O_2$	14.14	1.33
$C_{12}H_{23}N_3O$	14.52	1.18
$C_{12}H_{25}N_4$	14.89	1.04
$C_{13}H_5O_4$	14.28	1.75
$C_{13}H_7NO_3$	14.66	1.60
$C_{13}H_9N_2O_2$	15.03	1.45
$C_{13}H_{11}N_3O$	15.41	1.31
$C_{13}H_{13}N_4$	15.78	1.17
$C_{13}H_{21}O_3$	14.50	1.58
$C_{13}H_{23}NO_2$	14.88	1.43
$C_{13}H_{25}N_2O$	15.25	1.29
$C_{13}H_{27}N_3$	15.62	1.14
$C_{14}HN_4$	16.67	1.30
$C_{14}H_9O_3$	15.39	1.70
$C_{14}H_{11}NO_2$	15.76	1.56
$C_{14}H_{13}N_2O$	16.14	1.42
$C_{14}H_{15}N_3$	16.51	1.28
$C_{14}H_{25}O_2$	15.61	1.54
$C_{14}H_{27}NO$	15.98	1.39
$C_{14}H_{29}N_2$	16.36	1.25
$C_{15}HN_2O$	17.03	1.56
$C_{15}H_3N_3$	17.40	1.42
$C_{15}H_{13}O_2$	16.50	1.67
$C_{15}H_{15}NO$	16.87	1.54
$C_{15}H_{17}N_2$	17.24	1.40
$C_{15}H_{29}O$	16.71	1.51
$C_{15}H_{31}N$	17.09	1.37
$C_{16}HO_2$	17.38	1.82
$C_{16}H_3NO$	17.76	1.68
$C_{16}H_5N_2$	18.13	1.55
$C_{16}H_{17}O$	17.60	1.66
$C_{16}H_{19}N$	17.98	1.52
$C_{16}H_{33}$	17.82	1.49
$C_{17}H_5O$	18.49	1.81
$C_{17}H_7N$	18.86	1.68
$C_{17}H_{21}$	18.71	1.65
$C_{18}H_9$	19.60	1.81

226

	P + 1	P + 2
$C_{10}H_{14}N_2O_4$	11.95	1.46
$C_{10}H_{16}N_3O_3$	12.32	1.30
$C_{10}H_{18}N_4O_2$	12.70	1.15
$C_{11}H_2N_2O_4$	12.84	1.56
$C_{11}H_4N_3O_3$	13.21	1.41
$C_{11}H_6N_4O_2$	13.59	1.26
$C_{11}H_{16}NO_4$	12.68	1.54
$C_{11}H_{18}N_2O_3$	13.06	1.39
$C_{11}H_{20}N_3O_2$	13.43	1.24
$C_{11}H_{22}N_4O$	13.80	1.09
$C_{12}H_4NO_4$	13.57	1.65
$C_{12}H_6N_2O_3$	13.94	1.50
$C_{12}H_8N_3O_2$	14.32	1.35
$C_{12}H_{10}N_4O$	14.69	1.21
$C_{12}H_{18}O_4$	13.41	1.63
$C_{12}H_{20}NO_3$	13.79	1.48
$C_{12}H_{22}N_2O_2$	14.16	1.33
$C_{12}H_{24}N_3O$	14.54	1.18
$C_{12}H_{26}N_4$	14.91	1.04
$C_{13}H_6O_4$	14.30	1.75
$C_{13}H_8NO_3$	14.68	1.60
$C_{13}H_{10}N_2O_2$	15.05	1.46
$C_{13}H_{12}N_3O$	15.42	1.31
$C_{13}H_{14}N_4$	15.80	1.17
$C_{13}H_{22}O_3$	14.52	1.58
$C_{13}H_{24}NO_2$	14.89	1.43
$C_{13}H_{26}N_2O$	15.27	1.29
$C_{13}H_{28}N_3$	15.64	1.15
$C_{14}H_2N_4$	16.69	1.31
$C_{14}H_{10}O_3$	15.41	1.71
$C_{14}H_{12}NO_2$	15.78	1.56
$C_{14}H_{14}N_2O$	16.15	1.42
$C_{14}H_{16}N_3$	16.53	1.28
$C_{14}H_{26}O_2$	15.62	1.54
$C_{14}H_{28}NO$	16.00	1.40
$C_{14}H_{30}N_2$	16.37	1.26
$C_{15}H_2N_2O$	17.04	1.56
$C_{15}H_4N_3$	17.42	1.43
$C_{15}H_{14}O_2$	16.51	1.68
$C_{15}H_{16}NO$	16.89	1.54
$C_{15}H_{18}N_2$	17.26	1.40
$C_{15}H_{30}O$	16.73	1.51
$C_{15}H_{32}N$	17.10	1.37
$C_{16}H_2O_2$	17.40	1.82
$C_{16}H_4NO$	17.77	1.69
$C_{16}H_6N_2$	18.15	1.55
$C_{16}H_{18}O$	17.62	1.66
$C_{16}H_{20}N$	17.99	1.52
$C_{16}H_{34}$	17.83	1.50
$C_{17}H_6O$	18.51	1.81
$C_{17}H_8N$	18.88	1.68
$C_{17}H_{22}$	18.72	1.65
$C_{18}H_{10}$	19.61	1.82

227

	P + 1	P + 2
$C_{10}H_{15}N_2O_4$	11.97	1.46
$C_{10}H_{17}N_3O_3$	12.34	1.30
$C_{10}H_{19}N_4O_2$	12.71	1.15
$C_{11}H_3N_2O_4$	12.85	1.56
$C_{11}H_5N_3O_3$	13.23	1.41
$C_{11}H_7N_4O_2$	13.60	1.26
$C_{11}H_{17}NO_4$	12.70	1.54
$C_{11}H_{19}N_2O_3$	13.07	1.39
$C_{11}H_{21}N_3O_2$	13.45	1.24
$C_{11}H_{23}N_4O$	13.82	1.09
$C_{12}H_5NO_4$	13.59	1.65
$C_{12}H_7N_2O_3$	13.96	1.50
$C_{12}H_9N_3O_2$	14.33	1.36
$C_{12}H_{11}N_4O$	14.71	1.21
$C_{12}H_{19}O_4$	13.43	1.63
$C_{12}H_{21}NO_3$	13.80	1.48
$C_{12}H_{23}N_2O_2$	14.18	1.33
$C_{12}H_{25}N_3O$	14.55	1.19
$C_{12}H_{27}N_4$	14.93	1.04
$C_{13}H_7O_4$	14.32	1.75
$C_{13}H_9NO_3$	14.69	1.60
$C_{13}H_{11}N_2O_2$	15.07	1.46
$C_{13}H_{13}N_3O$	15.44	1.31
$C_{13}H_{15}N_4$	15.81	1.17
$C_{13}H_{23}O_3$	14.53	1.58
$C_{13}H_{25}NO_2$	14.91	1.44
$C_{13}H_{27}N_2O$	15.28	1.29
$C_{13}H_{29}N_3$	15.66	1.15
$C_{14}HN_3O$	16.33	1.45
$C_{14}H_3N_4$	16.70	1.31
$C_{14}H_{11}O_3$	15.42	1.71
$C_{14}H_{13}NO_2$	15.80	1.57
$C_{14}H_{15}N_2O$	16.17	1.42
$C_{14}H_{17}N_3$	16.55	1.28
$C_{14}H_{27}O_2$	15.64	1.54
$C_{14}H_{29}NO$	16.01	1.40
$C_{14}H_{31}N_2$	16.39	1.26
$C_{15}HNO_2$	16.69	1.70
$C_{15}H_3N_2O$	17.06	1.57
$C_{15}H_5N_3$	17.43	1.43
$C_{15}H_{15}O_2$	16.53	1.68
$C_{15}H_{17}NO$	16.90	1.54
$C_{15}H_{19}N_2$	17.28	1.40
$C_{15}H_{31}O$	16.74	1.51
$C_{15}H_{33}N$	17.12	1.38
$C_{16}H_3O_2$	17.42	1.82
$C_{16}H_5NO$	17.79	1.69
$C_{16}H_7N_2$	18.17	1.55
$C_{16}H_{19}O$	17.63	1.66
$C_{16}H_{21}N$	18.01	1.53
$C_{17}H_7O$	18.52	1.82
$C_{17}H_9N$	18.90	1.69
$C_{17}H_{23}$	18.74	1.66
$C_{18}H_{11}$	19.63	1.82

228

	P + 1	P + 2
$C_{10}H_{16}N_2O_4$	11.98	1.46
$C_{10}H_{18}N_3O_3$	12.36	1.30
$C_{10}H_{20}N_4O_2$	12.73	1.15
$C_{11}H_4N_2O_4$	12.87	1.56
$C_{11}H_6N_3O_3$	13.24	1.41
$C_{11}H_8N_4O_2$	13.62	1.26
$C_{11}H_{18}NO_4$	12.71	1.55
$C_{11}H_{20}N_2O_3$	13.09	1.39
$C_{11}H_{22}N_3O_2$	13.46	1.24
$C_{11}H_{24}N_4O$	13.84	1.09
$C_{12}H_6NO_4$	13.60	1.66
$C_{12}H_8N_2O_3$	13.98	1.51
$C_{12}H_{10}N_3O_2$	14.35	1.36
$C_{12}H_{12}N_4O$	14.72	1.21
$C_{12}H_{20}O_4$	13.44	1.64
$C_{12}H_{22}NO_3$	13.82	1.49
$C_{12}H_{24}N_2O_2$	14.19	1.34
$C_{12}H_{26}N_3O$	14.57	1.19
$C_{12}H_{28}N_4$	14.94	1.04
$C_{13}H_8O_4$	14.33	1.75
$C_{13}H_{10}NO_3$	14.71	1.61
$C_{13}H_{12}N_2O_2$	15.08	1.46
$C_{13}H_{14}N_3O$	15.46	1.32
$C_{13}H_{16}N_4$	15.83	1.17
$C_{13}H_{24}O_3$	14.55	1.58
$C_{13}H_{26}NO_2$	14.92	1.44
$C_{13}H_{28}N_2O$	15.30	1.29
$C_{13}H_{30}N_3$	15.67	1.15
$C_{14}H_2N_3O$	16.34	1.45
$C_{14}H_4N_4$	16.72	1.31
$C_{14}H_{12}O_3$	15.44	1.71
$C_{14}H_{14}NO_2$	15.81	1.57
$C_{14}H_{16}N_2O$	16.19	1.43
$C_{14}H_{18}N_3$	16.56	1.29
$C_{14}H_{28}O_2$	15.66	1.54
$C_{14}H_{30}NO$	16.03	1.40
$C_{14}H_{32}N_2$	16.40	1.26
$C_{15}H_2NO_2$	16.70	1.71
$C_{15}H_4N_2O$	17.08	1.57
$C_{15}H_6N_3$	17.45	1.43
$C_{15}H_{16}O_2$	16.54	1.68
$C_{15}H_{18}NO$	16.92	1.54
$C_{15}H_{20}N_2$	17.29	1.41
$C_{15}H_{32}O$	16.76	1.52
$C_{16}H_4O_2$	17.43	1.83
$C_{16}H_6NO$	17.81	1.69
$C_{16}H_8N_2$	18.18	1.56
$C_{16}H_{20}O$	17.65	1.66
$C_{16}H_{22}N$	18.02	1.53
$C_{17}H_8O$	18.54	1.82
$C_{17}H_{10}N$	18.91	1.69
$C_{17}H_{24}$	18.75	1.66
$C_{18}H_{12}$	19.64	1.82

229

	P + 1	P + 2
$C_{10}H_{17}N_2O_4$	12.00	1.46
$C_{10}H_{19}N_3O_3$	12.37	1.31
$C_{10}H_{21}N_4O_2$	12.75	1.15
$C_{11}H_5N_2O_4$	12.89	1.57
$C_{11}H_7N_3O_3$	13.26	1.41
$C_{11}H_9N_4O_2$	13.64	1.26
$C_{11}H_{19}NO_4$	12.73	1.55
$C_{11}H_{21}N_2O_3$	13.10	1.39
$C_{11}H_{23}N_3O_2$	13.48	1.24
$C_{11}H_{25}N_4O$	13.85	1.09
$C_{12}H_7NO_4$	13.62	1.66
$C_{12}H_9N_2O_3$	13.99	1.51

	P + 1	P + 2
$C_{12}H_{11}N_3O_2$	14.37	1.36
$C_{12}H_{13}N_4O$	14.74	1.21
$C_{12}H_{21}O_4$	13.46	1.64
$C_{12}H_{23}NO_3$	13.83	1.49
$C_{12}H_{25}N_2O_2$	14.21	1.34
$C_{12}H_{27}N_3O$	14.58	1.19
$C_{12}H_{29}N_4$	14.96	1.05
$C_{13}HN_4O$	15.63	1.34
$C_{13}H_9O_4$	14.35	1.76
$C_{13}H_{11}NO_3$	14.72	1.61
$C_{13}H_{13}N_2O_2$	15.10	1.46
$C_{13}H_{15}N_3O$	15.47	1.32
$C_{13}H_{17}N_4$	15.85	1.18
$C_{13}H_{25}O_3$	14.57	1.59
$C_{13}H_{27}NO_2$	14.94	1.44
$C_{13}H_{29}N_2O$	15.31	1.30
$C_{13}H_{31}N_3$	15.69	1.15
$C_{14}HN_2O_2$	15.99	1.60
$C_{14}H_3N_3O$	16.36	1.45
$C_{14}H_5N_4$	16.73	1.32
$C_{14}H_{13}O_3$	15.45	1.71
$C_{14}H_{15}NO_2$	15.83	1.57
$C_{14}H_{17}N_2O$	16.20	1.43
$C_{14}H_{19}N_3$	16.58	1.29
$C_{14}H_{29}O_2$	15.67	1.55
$C_{14}H_{31}NO$	16.05	1.41
$C_{15}HO_3$	16.34	1.85
$C_{15}H_3NO_2$	16.72	1.71
$C_{15}H_5N_2O$	17.09	1.57
$C_{15}H_7N_3$	17.47	1.44
$C_{15}H_{17}O_2$	16.56	1.68
$C_{15}H_{19}NO$	16.93	1.55
$C_{15}H_{21}N_2$	17.31	1.41
$C_{16}H_5O_2$	17.45	1.83
$C_{16}H_7NO$	17.82	1.69
$C_{16}H_9N_2$	18.20	1.56
$C_{16}H_{21}O$	17.67	1.67
$C_{16}H_{23}N$	18.04	1.53
$C_{17}H_9O$	18.55	1.82
$C_{17}H_{11}N$	18.93	1.69
$C_{17}H_{25}$	18.77	1.66
$C_{18}H_{13}$	19.66	1.83
$C_{19}H$	20.55	2.00

230

	P + 1	P + 2
$C_{10}H_{18}N_2O_4$	12.01	1.46
$C_{10}H_{20}N_3O_3$	12.39	1.31
$C_{10}H_{22}N_4O_2$	12.76	1.15
$C_{11}H_6N_2O_4$	12.90	1.57
$C_{11}H_8N_3O_3$	13.28	1.42
$C_{11}H_{10}N_4O_2$	13.65	1.27
$C_{11}H_{20}NO_4$	12.74	1.55
$C_{11}H_{22}N_2O_3$	13.12	1.40
$C_{11}H_{24}N_3O_2$	13.49	1.24
$C_{11}H_{26}N_4O$	13.87	1.09
$C_{12}H_8NO_4$	13.63	1.66
$C_{12}H_{10}N_2O_3$	14.01	1.51
$C_{12}H_{12}N_3O_2$	14.38	1.36
$C_{12}H_{14}N_4O$	14.76	1.22
$C_{12}H_{22}O_4$	13.48	1.64
$C_{12}H_{24}NO_3$	13.85	1.49
$C_{12}H_{26}N_2O_2$	14.22	1.34
$C_{12}H_{28}N_3O$	14.60	1.19
$C_{12}H_{30}N_4$	14.97	1.05
$C_{13}H_2N_4O$	15.65	1.35
$C_{13}H_{10}O_4$	14.36	1.76
$C_{13}H_{12}NO_3$	14.74	1.61
$C_{13}H_{14}N_2O_2$	15.11	1.47
$C_{13}H_{16}N_3O$	15.49	1.32
$C_{13}H_{18}N_4$	15.86	1.18
$C_{13}H_{26}O_3$	14.58	1.59
$C_{13}H_{28}NO_2$	14.96	1.44
$C_{13}H_{30}N_2O$	15.33	1.30
$C_{14}H_2N_2O_2$	16.00	1.60
$C_{14}H_4N_3O$	16.38	1.46
$C_{14}H_6N_4$	16.75	1.32
$C_{14}H_{14}O_3$	15.47	1.72
$C_{14}H_{16}NO_2$	15.84	1.57
$C_{14}H_{18}N_2O$	16.22	1.43
$C_{14}H_{20}N_3$	16.59	1.29
$C_{14}H_{30}O_2$	15.69	1.55
$C_{15}H_2O_3$	16.36	1.85
$C_{15}H_4NO_2$	16.73	1.71
$C_{15}H_6N_2O$	17.11	1.57
$C_{15}H_8N_3$	17.48	1.44
$C_{15}H_{18}O_2$	16.58	1.69
$C_{15}H_{20}NO$	16.95	1.55
$C_{15}H_{22}N_2$	17.32	1.41
$C_{16}H_6O_2$	17.46	1.83
$C_{16}H_8NO$	17.84	1.70
$C_{16}H_{10}N_2$	18.21	1.56
$C_{16}H_{22}O$	17.68	1.67
$C_{16}H_{24}N$	18.06	1.54
$C_{17}H_{10}O$	18.57	1.83
$C_{17}H_{12}N$	18.94	1.69
$C_{17}H_{26}$	18.79	1.67
$C_{18}H_{14}$	19.68	1.83
$C_{19}H_2$	20.56	2.00

231

	P + 1	P + 2
$C_{10}H_{19}N_2O_4$	12.03	1.47
$C_{10}H_{21}N_3O_3$	12.40	1.31
$C_{10}H_{23}N_4O_2$	12.78	1.16
$C_{11}H_7N_2O_4$	12.92	1.57
$C_{11}H_9N_3O_3$	13.29	1.42
$C_{11}H_{11}N_4O_2$	13.67	1.27
$C_{11}H_{21}NO_4$	12.76	1.55
$C_{11}H_{23}N_2O_3$	13.14	1.40
$C_{11}H_{25}N_3O_2$	13.51	1.25
$C_{11}H_{27}N_4O$	13.88	1.10
$C_{12}H_9NO_4$	13.65	1.66
$C_{12}H_{11}N_2O_3$	14.02	1.51
$C_{12}H_{13}N_3O_2$	14.40	1.37
$C_{12}H_{15}N_4O$	14.77	1.22
$C_{12}H_{23}O_4$	13.49	1.64
$C_{12}H_{25}NO_3$	13.87	1.49
$C_{12}H_{27}N_2O_2$	14.24	1.34
$C_{12}H_{29}N_3O$	14.62	1.20
$C_{13}HN_3O_2$	15.29	1.49
$C_{13}H_3N_4O$	15.66	1.35
$C_{13}H_{11}O_4$	14.38	1.76
$C_{13}H_{13}NO_3$	14.76	1.61
$C_{13}H_{15}N_2O_2$	15.13	1.47
$C_{13}H_{17}N_3O$	15.50	1.32
$C_{13}H_{19}N_4$	15.88	1.18
$C_{13}H_{27}O_3$	14.60	1.59
$C_{13}H_{29}NO_2$	14.97	1.45
$C_{14}HNO_3$	15.64	1.74
$C_{14}H_3N_2O_2$	16.02	1.60
$C_{14}H_5N_3O$	16.39	1.46
$C_{14}H_7N_4$	16.77	1.32
$C_{14}H_{15}O_3$	15.49	1.72
$C_{14}H_{17}NO_2$	15.86	1.58
$C_{14}H_{19}N_2O$	16.23	1.44
$C_{14}H_{21}N_3$	16.61	1.30
$C_{15}H_3O_3$	16.37	1.85
$C_{15}H_5NO_2$	16.75	1.72
$C_{15}H_7N_2O$	17.12	1.58
$C_{15}H_9N_3$	17.50	1.44
$C_{15}H_{19}O_2$	16.59	1.69
$C_{15}H_{21}NO$	16.97	1.55
$C_{15}H_{23}N_2$	17.34	1.41
$C_{16}H_7O_2$	17.48	1.84
$C_{16}H_9NO$	17.85	1.70
$C_{16}H_{11}N_2$	18.23	1.57
$C_{16}H_{23}O$	17.70	1.67
$C_{16}H_{25}N$	18.07	1.54
$C_{17}H_{11}O$	18.59	1.83
$C_{17}H_{13}N$	18.96	1.70
$C_{17}H_{27}$	18.80	1.67
$C_{18}HN$	19.85	1.86
$C_{18}H_{15}$	19.69	1.83
$C_{19}H_3$	20.58	2.01

232

	P + 1	P + 2
$C_{10}H_{20}N_2O_4$	12.05	1.47
$C_{10}H_{22}N_3O_3$	12.42	1.31
$C_{10}H_{24}N_4O_2$	12.79	1.16
$C_{11}H_8N_2O_4$	12.93	1.57
$C_{11}H_{10}N_3O_3$	13.31	1.42
$C_{11}H_{12}N_4O_2$	13.68	1.27
$C_{11}H_{22}NO_4$	12.78	1.55
$C_{11}H_{24}N_2O_3$	13.15	1.40
$C_{11}H_{26}N_3O_2$	13.53	1.25
$C_{11}H_{28}N_4O$	13.90	1.10
$C_{12}H_{10}NO_4$	13.67	1.66
$C_{12}H_{12}N_2O$	14.04	1.52
$C_{12}H_{14}N_3O_2$	14.41	1.37
$C_{12}H_{16}N_4O$	14.79	1.22
$C_{12}H_{24}O_4$	13.51	1.64
$C_{12}H_{26}NO_3$	13.88	1.49
$C_{12}H_{28}N_2O_2$	14.26	1.35
$C_{13}H_2N_3O_2$	15.30	1.49
$C_{13}H_4N_4O$	15.68	1.35
$C_{13}H_{12}O_4$	14.40	1.76
$C_{13}H_{14}NO_3$	14.77	1.62
$C_{13}H_{16}N_2O_2$	15.15	1.47
$C_{13}H_{18}N_3O$	15.52	1.33
$C_{13}H_{20}N_4$	15.89	1.18
$C_{13}H_{28}O_3$	14.61	1.59
$C_{14}H_2NO_3$	15.66	1.75
$C_{14}H_4N_2O_2$	16.03	1.60
$C_{14}H_6N_3O$	16.41	1.46
$C_{14}H_8N_4$	16.78	1.32
$C_{14}H_{16}O_3$	15.50	1.72
$C_{14}H_{18}NO_2$	15.88	1.58
$C_{14}H_{20}N_2O$	16.25	1.44
$C_{14}H_{22}N_3$	16.63	1.30
$C_{15}H_4O_3$	16.39	1.86
$C_{15}H_6NO_2$	16.77	1.72
$C_{15}H_8N_2O$	17.14	1.58
$C_{15}H_{10}N_3$	17.51	1.44
$C_{15}H_{20}O_2$	16.61	1.69
$C_{15}H_{22}NO$	16.98	1.55
$C_{15}H_{24}N_2$	17.36	1.42
$C_{16}H_8O_2$	17.50	1.84
$C_{16}H_{10}NO$	17.87	1.70
$C_{16}H_{12}N_2$	18.25	1.57
$C_{16}H_{24}O$	17.71	1.68
$C_{16}H_{26}N$	18.09	1.54
$C_{17}H_{12}O$	18.60	1.83
$C_{17}H_{14}N$	18.98	1.70
$C_{17}H_{28}$	18.82	1.67
$C_{18}H_2N$	19.86	1.87
$C_{18}H_{16}$	19.71	1.84
$C_{19}H_4$	20.60	2.01

233

	P + 1	P + 2
$C_{10}H_{21}N_2O_4$	12.06	1.47
$C_{10}H_{23}N_3O_3$	12.44	1.31
$C_{10}H_{25}N_4O_2$	12.81	1.16
$C_{11}H_9N_2O_4$	12.95	1.57
$C_{11}H_{11}N_3O_3$	13.32	1.42
$C_{11}H_{13}N_4O_2$	13.70	1.27
$C_{11}H_{23}NO_4$	12.79	1.56
$C_{11}H_{25}N_2O_3$	13.17	1.40
$C_{11}H_{27}N_3O_2$	13.54	1.25
$C_{12}HN_4O_2$	14.59	1.39
$C_{12}H_{11}NO_4$	13.68	1.67
$C_{12}H_{13}N_2O_3$	14.06	1.52
$C_{12}H_{15}N_3O_2$	14.43	1.37
$C_{12}H_{17}N_4O$	14.80	1.22
$C_{12}H_{25}O_4$	13.52	1.65
$C_{12}H_{27}NO_3$	13.90	1.50
$C_{13}HN_2O_3$	14.94	1.64
$C_{13}H_3N_3O_2$	15.32	1.50
$C_{13}H_5N_4O$	15.69	1.35
$C_{13}H_{13}O_4$	14.41	1.76
$C_{13}H_{15}NO_3$	14.79	1.62
$C_{13}H_{17}N_2O_2$	15.16	1.47
$C_{13}H_{19}N_3O$	15.54	1.33
$C_{13}H_{21}N_4$	15.91	1.19
$C_{14}HO_4$	15.30	1.89
$C_{14}H_3NO_3$	15.68	1.75
$C_{14}H_5N_2O_2$	16.05	1.61
$C_{14}H_7N_3O$	16.42	1.47
$C_{14}H_9N_4$	16.80	1.33
$C_{14}H_{17}O_3$	15.52	1.72
$C_{14}H_{19}NO_2$	15.89	1.58
$C_{14}H_{21}N_2O$	16.27	1.44
$C_{14}H_{23}N_3$	16.64	1.30
$C_{15}H_5O_3$	16.41	1.86
$C_{15}H_7NO_2$	16.78	1.72
$C_{15}H_9N_2O$	17.16	1.58
$C_{15}H_{11}N_3$	17.53	1.45
$C_{15}H_{21}O_2$	16.62	1.70
$C_{15}H_{23}NO$	17.00	1.56
$C_{15}H_{25}N_2$	17.37	1.42
$C_{16}H_9O_2$	17.51	1.84
$C_{16}H_{11}NO$	17.89	1.71
$C_{16}H_{13}N_2$	18.26	1.57
$C_{16}H_{25}O$	17.73	1.68
$C_{16}H_{27}N$	18.10	1.54

	P + 1	P + 2
$C_{17}HN_2$	19.15	1.73
$C_{17}H_{13}O$	18.62	1.83
$C_{17}H_{15}N$	18.99	1.70
$C_{17}H_{29}$	18.83	1.67
$C_{18}HO$	19.51	2.00
$C_{18}H_3N$	19.88	1.87
$C_{18}H_{17}$	19.72	1.84
$C_{19}H_5$	20.61	2.01

234

	P + 1	P + 2
$C_{10}H_{22}N_2O_4$	12.08	1.47
$C_{10}H_{24}N_3O_3$	12.45	1.32
$C_{10}H_{26}N_4O_2$	12.83	1.16
$C_{11}H_{10}N_2O_4$	12.97	1.58
$C_{11}H_{12}N_3O_3$	13.34	1.42
$C_{11}H_{14}N_4O_2$	13.72	1.27
$C_{11}H_{24}NO_4$	12.81	1.56
$C_{11}H_{26}N_2O_3$	13.18	1.40
$C_{12}H_2N_4O_2$	14.60	1.39
$C_{12}H_{12}NO_4$	13.70	1.67
$C_{12}H_{14}N_2O_3$	14.07	1.52
$C_{12}H_{16}N_3O_2$	14.45	1.37
$C_{12}H_{18}N_4O$	14.82	1.23
$C_{12}H_{26}O_4$	13.54	1.65
$C_{13}H_2N_2O_3$	14.96	1.64
$C_{13}H_4N_3O_2$	15.33	1.50
$C_{13}H_6N_4O$	15.71	1.36
$C_{13}H_{14}O_4$	14.43	1.77
$C_{13}H_{16}NO_3$	14.80	1.62
$C_{13}H_{18}N_2O_2$	15.18	1.48
$C_{13}H_{20}N_3O$	15.55	1.33
$C_{13}H_{22}N_4$	15.93	1.19
$C_{14}H_2O_4$	15.32	1.89
$C_{14}H_4NO_3$	15.69	1.75
$C_{14}H_6N_2O_2$	16.07	1.61
$C_{14}H_8N_3O$	16.44	1.47
$C_{14}H_{10}N_4$	16.81	1.33
$C_{14}H_{18}O_3$	15.53	1.73
$C_{14}H_{20}NO_2$	15.91	1.58
$C_{14}H_{22}N_2O$	16.28	1.44
$C_{14}H_{24}N_3$	16.66	1.30
$C_{15}H_6O_3$	16.42	1.86
$C_{15}H_8NO_2$	16.80	1.72
$C_{15}H_{10}N_2O$	17.17	1.59
$C_{15}H_{12}N_3$	17.55	1.45
$C_{15}H_{22}O_2$	16.64	1.70
$C_{15}H_{24}NO$	17.01	1.56
$C_{15}H_{26}N_2$	17.39	1.42
$C_{16}H_{10}O_2$	17.53	1.84
$C_{16}H_{12}NO$	17.90	1.71
$C_{16}H_{14}N_2$	18.28	1.58
$C_{16}H_{26}O$	17.75	1.68
$C_{16}H_{28}N$	18.12	1.55
$C_{17}H_2N_2$	19.17	1.74
$C_{17}H_{14}O$	18.63	1.84
$C_{17}H_{16}N$	19.01	1.71
$C_{17}H_{30}$	18.85	1.68
$C_{18}H_2O$	19.52	2.00
$C_{18}H_4N$	19.90	1.87
$C_{18}H_{18}$	19.74	1.84
$C_{19}H_6$	20.63	2.02

235

	P + 1	P + 2
$C_{10}H_{23}N_2O_4$	12.09	1.47
$C_{10}H_{25}N_3O_3$	12.47	1.32
$C_{11}H_{11}N_2O_4$	12.98	1.58
$C_{11}H_{13}N_3O_3$	13.36	1.43
$C_{11}H_{15}N_4O_2$	13.73	1.28
$C_{11}H_{25}NO_4$	12.82	1.56
$C_{12}HN_3O_3$	14.25	1.54
$C_{12}H_3N_4O_2$	14.62	1.40
$C_{12}H_{13}NO_4$	13.71	1.67
$C_{12}H_{15}N_2O_3$	14.09	1.52
$C_{12}H_{17}N_3O_2$	14.46	1.37
$C_{12}H_{19}N_4O$	14.84	1.23
$C_{13}HNO_4$	14.60	1.79
$C_{13}H_3N_2O_3$	14.98	1.65
$C_{13}H_5N_3O_2$	15.35	1.50
$C_{13}H_7N_4O$	15.73	1.36
$C_{13}H_{15}O_4$	14.44	1.77
$C_{13}H_{17}NO_3$	14.82	1.62
$C_{13}H_{19}N_2O_2$	15.19	1.48
$C_{13}H_{21}N_3O$	15.57	1.33
$C_{13}H_{23}N_4$	15.94	1.19
$C_{14}H_3O_4$	15.33	1.90
$C_{14}H_5NO_3$	15.71	1.75
$C_{14}H_7N_2O_2$	16.08	1.61
$C_{14}H_9N_3O$	16.46	1.47
$C_{14}H_{11}N_4$	16.83	1.33
$C_{14}H_{19}O_3$	15.55	1.73
$C_{14}H_{21}NO_2$	15.92	1.59
$C_{14}H_{23}N_2O$	16.30	1.45
$C_{14}H_{25}N_3$	16.67	1.31
$C_{15}H_7O_3$	16.44	1.86
$C_{15}H_9NO_2$	16.81	1.73
$C_{15}H_{11}N_2O$	17.19	1.59
$C_{15}H_{13}N_3$	17.56	1.44
$C_{15}H_{23}O_2$	16.66	1.70
$C_{15}H_{25}NO$	17.03	1.56
$C_{15}H_{27}N_2$	17.40	1.43
$C_{16}HN_3$	18.45	1.61
$C_{16}H_{11}O_2$	17.54	1.85
$C_{16}H_{13}NO$	17.92	1.71
$C_{16}H_{15}N_2$	18.29	1.58
$C_{16}H_{27}O$	17.76	1.68
$C_{16}H_{29}N$	18.14	1.55
$C_{17}HNO$	18.81	1.87
$C_{17}H_3N_2$	19.18	1.74
$C_{17}H_{15}O$	18.65	1.84
$C_{17}H_{17}N$	19.02	1.71
$C_{17}H_{31}$	18.87	1.68
$C_{18}H_3O$	19.54	2.00
$C_{18}H_3N$	19.91	1.88
$C_{18}H_{19}$	19.76	1.85
$C_{19}H_7$	20.64	2.02

236

	P + 1	P + 2
$C_{10}H_{24}N_2O_4$	12.11	1.48
$C_{11}H_{12}N_2O_4$	13.00	1.58
$C_{11}H_{14}N_3O_3$	13.37	1.43
$C_{11}H_{16}N_4O_2$	13.75	1.28
$C_{12}H_2N_3O_3$	14.26	1.55
$C_{12}H_4N_4O_2$	14.64	1.40
$C_{12}H_{14}NO_4$	13.73	1.67
$C_{12}H_{16}N_2O_3$	14.10	1.52
$C_{12}H_{18}N_3O_2$	14.48	1.38
$C_{12}H_{20}N_4O$	14.85	1.23
$C_{13}H_2NO_4$	14.62	1.79
$C_{13}H_4N_2O_3$	14.99	1.65
$C_{13}H_6N_3O_2$	15.37	1.50
$C_{13}H_8N_4O$	15.74	1.36
$C_{13}H_{16}O_4$	14.46	1.77
$C_{13}H_{18}NO_3$	14.84	1.63
$C_{13}H_{20}N_2O_2$	15.21	1.48
$C_{13}H_{22}N_3O$	15.58	1.34
$C_{13}H_{24}N_4$	15.96	1.19
$C_{14}H_4O_4$	15.35	1.90
$C_{14}H_6NO_3$	15.72	1.76
$C_{14}H_8N_2O_2$	16.10	1.61
$C_{14}H_{10}N_3O$	16.47	1.47
$C_{14}H_{12}N_4$	16.85	1.33
$C_{14}H_{20}O_3$	15.57	1.73
$C_{14}H_{22}NO_2$	15.94	1.59
$C_{14}H_{24}N_2O$	16.31	1.45
$C_{14}H_{26}N_3$	16.69	1.31
$C_{15}H_8O_3$	16.45	1.87
$C_{15}H_{10}NO_2$	16.83	1.73
$C_{15}H_{12}N_2O$	17.20	1.59
$C_{15}H_{14}N_3$	17.58	1.46
$C_{15}H_{24}O_2$	16.67	1.70
$C_{15}H_{26}NO$	17.05	1.56
$C_{15}H_{28}N_2$	17.42	1.43
$C_{16}H_2N_3$	18.47	1.61
$C_{16}H_{12}O_2$	17.56	1.85
$C_{16}H_{14}NO$	17.93	1.71
$C_{16}H_{16}N_2$	18.31	1.58
$C_{16}H_{28}O$	17.78	1.69
$C_{16}H_{30}N$	18.15	1.55
$C_{17}H_2NO$	18.82	1.87
$C_{17}H_4N_2$	19.20	1.74
$C_{17}H_{16}O$	18.67	1.84
$C_{17}H_{18}N$	19.04	1.71
$C_{17}H_{32}$	18.88	1.68
$C_{18}H_4O$	19.55	2.01
$C_{18}H_6N$	19.93	1.88
$C_{18}H_{20}$	19.77	1.85
$C_{19}H_8$	20.66	2.02

237

	P + 1	P + 2
$C_{11}H_{13}N_2O_4$	13.01	1.58
$C_{11}H_{15}N_3O_3$	13.39	1.43
$C_{11}H_{17}N_4O_2$	13.76	1.28
$C_{12}HN_2O_4$	13.90	1.70
$C_{12}H_3N_3O_3$	19.28	1.55
$C_{12}H_5N_4O_2$	14.65	1.40
$C_{12}H_{15}NO_4$	13.75	1.68
$C_{12}H_{17}N_2O_3$	14.12	1.53
$C_{12}H_{19}N_3O_2$	14.49	1.38
$C_{12}H_{21}N_4O$	14.87	1.23
$C_{13}H_3NO_4$	14.63	1.80
$C_{13}H_5N_2O_3$	15.01	1.65
$C_{13}H_7N_3O_2$	15.38	1.51
$C_{13}H_9N_4O$	15.76	1.36
$C_{13}H_{17}O_4$	14.48	1.77
$C_{13}H_{19}NO_3$	14.85	1.63
$C_{13}H_{21}N_2O_2$	15.23	1.48
$C_{13}H_{23}N_3O$	15.60	1.34
$C_{13}H_{25}N_4$	15.97	1.20
$C_{14}H_5O_4$	15.37	1.90
$C_{14}H_7NO_3$	15.74	1.76
$C_{14}H_9N_2O_2$	16.11	1.62
$C_{14}H_{11}N_3O$	16.49	1.48
$C_{14}H_3N_4$	16.86	1.34
$C_{14}H_{21}O_3$	15.58	1.73
$C_{14}H_{23}NO_2$	15.96	1.59
$C_{14}H_{25}N_2O$	16.33	1.45
$C_{14}H_{27}N_3$	16.71	1.31
$C_{15}HN_4$	17.75	1.49
$C_{15}H_9O_3$	16.47	1.87
$C_{15}H_{11}NO_2$	16.85	1.73
$C_{15}H_{13}N_2O$	17.22	1.59
$C_{15}H_{15}N_3$	17.59	1.46
$C_{15}H_{25}O_2$	16.69	1.71
$C_{15}H_{27}NO$	17.06	1.57
$C_{15}H_{29}N_2$	17.44	1.43
$C_{16}HN_2O$	18.11	1.75
$C_{16}H_3N_3$	18.48	1.61
$C_{16}H_{13}O_2$	17.58	1.85
$C_{16}H_{15}NO$	17.95	1.72
$C_{16}H_{17}N_2$	18.33	1.58
$C_{16}H_{29}O$	17.79	1.69
$C_{16}H_{31}N$	18.17	1.56
$C_{17}HO_2$	18.46	2.01
$C_{17}H_3NO$	18.84	1.88
$C_{17}H_5N_2$	19.21	1.75
$C_{17}H_{17}O$	18.68	1.85
$C_{17}H_{19}N$	19.06	1.72
$C_{17}H_{33}$	18.90	1.69
$C_{18}H_5O$	19.57	2.01
$C_{18}H_7N$	19.94	1.88
$C_{18}H_{21}$	19.79	1.85
$C_{19}H_9$	20.68	2.03

238

	P + 1	P + 2
$C_{11}H_{14}N_2O_4$	13.03	1.59
$C_{11}H_{16}N_3O_3$	13.40	1.43
$C_{11}H_{18}N_4O_2$	13.78	1.28
$C_{12}H_2N_2O_4$	13.92	1.70
$C_{12}H_4N_3O_3$	14.29	1.55
$C_{12}H_6N_4O_2$	14.67	1.40
$C_{12}H_{16}NO_4$	13.76	1.68
$C_{12}H_{18}N_2O_3$	14.14	1.53
$C_{12}H_{20}N_3O_2$	14.51	1.38
$C_{12}H_{22}N_4O$	14.88	1.24
$C_{13}H_4NO_4$	14.65	1.80
$C_{13}H_6N_2O_3$	15.02	1.65
$C_{13}H_8N_3O_2$	15.40	1.51
$C_{13}H_{10}N_4O$	15.77	1.37
$C_{13}H_{18}O_4$	14.49	1.78
$C_{13}H_{20}NO_3$	14.87	1.63
$C_{13}H_{22}N_2O_2$	15.24	1.49
$C_{13}H_{24}N_3O$	15.62	1.34
$C_{13}H_{26}N_4$	15.99	1.20
$C_{14}H_6O_4$	15.38	1.90
$C_{14}H_8NO_3$	15.76	1.76
$C_{14}H_{10}N_2O_2$	16.13	1.62
$C_{14}H_{12}N_3O$	16.50	1.48
$C_{14}H_{14}N_4$	16.88	1.34
$C_{14}H_{22}O_3$	15.60	1.74
$C_{14}H_{24}NO_2$	15.97	1.59
$C_{14}H_{26}N_2O$	16.35	1.45
$C_{14}H_{28}N_3$	16.72	1.31
$C_{15}H_2N_4$	17.77	1.49
$C_{15}H_{10}O_3$	16.49	1.87

	P + 1	P + 2
$C_{15}H_{12}NO_2$	16.86	1.73
$C_{15}H_{14}N_2O$	17.24	1.60
$C_{15}H_{16}N_3$	17.61	1.46
$C_{15}H_{26}O_2$	16.70	1.71
$C_{15}H_{28}NO$	17.08	1.57
$C_{15}H_{30}N_2$	17.45	1.43
$C_{16}H_2N_2O$	18.12	1.75
$C_{16}H_4N_3$	18.50	1.62
$C_{16}H_{14}O_2$	17.59	1.85
$C_{16}H_{16}NO$	17.97	1.72
$C_{16}H_{18}N_2$	18.34	1.59
$C_{16}H_{30}O$	17.81	1.69
$C_{16}H_{32}N$	18.18	1.56
$C_{17}H_2O_2$	18.48	2.01
$C_{17}H_4NO$	18.86	1.88
$C_{17}H_6N_2$	19.23	1.75
$C_{17}H_{18}O$	18.70	1.85
$C_{17}H_{20}N$	19.07	1.72
$C_{17}H_{34}$	18.91	1.69
$C_{18}H_6O$	19.59	2.01
$C_{18}H_8N$	19.96	1.89
$C_{18}H_{22}$	19.80	1.86
$C_{19}H_{10}$	20.69	2.03

239

	P + 1	P + 2
$C_{11}H_{15}N_2O_4$	13.05	1.59
$C_{11}H_{17}N_3O_3$	13.42	1.44
$C_{11}H_{19}N_4O_2$	13.80	1.29
$C_{12}H_3N_2O_4$	13.93	1.70
$C_{12}H_5N_3O_3$	14.31	1.55
$C_{12}H_7N_4O_2$	14.68	1.41
$C_{12}H_{17}NO_4$	13.78	1.68
$C_{12}H_{19}N_2O_3$	14.15	1.53
$C_{12}H_{21}N_3O_2$	14.53	1.38
$C_{12}H_{23}N_4O$	14.90	1.24
$C_{13}H_5NO_4$	14.67	1.80
$C_{13}H_7N_2O_3$	15.04	1.66
$C_{13}H_9N_3O_2$	15.41	1.51
$C_{13}H_{11}N_4O$	15.79	1.37
$C_{13}H_{19}O_4$	14.51	1.78
$C_{13}H_{21}NO_3$	14.88	1.63
$C_{13}H_{23}N_2O_2$	15.26	1.49
$C_{13}H_{25}N_3O$	15.63	1.34
$C_{13}H_{27}N_4$	16.01	1.20
$C_{14}H_7O_4$	15.40	1.91
$C_{14}H_9NO_3$	15.77	1.76
$C_{14}H_{11}N_2O_2$	16.15	1.62
$C_{14}H_{13}N_3O$	16.52	1.48
$C_{14}H_{15}N_4$	16.89	1.34
$C_{14}H_{23}O_3$	15.61	1.74
$C_{14}H_{25}NO_2$	15.99	1.60
$C_{14}H_{27}N_2O$	16.36	1.46
$C_{14}H_{29}N_3$	16.74	1.32
$C_{15}HN_3O$	17.41	1.63
$C_{15}H_3N_4$	17.78	1.49
$C_{15}H_{11}O_3$	16.50	1.88
$C_{15}H_{13}NO_2$	16.88	1.74
$C_{15}H_{15}N_2O$	17.25	1.60
$C_{15}H_{17}N_3$	17.63	1.46
$C_{15}H_{27}O_2$	16.72	1.71
$C_{15}H_{29}NO$	17.09	1.57
$C_{15}H_{31}N_2$	17.47	1.44
$C_{16}HNO_2$	17.77	1.88
$C_{16}H_3N_2O$	18.14	1.75
$C_{16}H_5N_3$	18.51	1.62
$C_{16}H_{15}O_2$	17.61	1.86
$C_{16}H_{17}NO$	17.98	1.72
$C_{16}H_{19}N_2$	18.36	1.59
$C_{16}H_{31}O$	17.83	1.70
$C_{16}H_{33}N$	18.20	1.56
$C_{17}H_3O_2$	18.50	2.01
$C_{17}H_5NO$	18.87	1.88
$C_{17}H_7N_2$	19.25	1.75
$C_{17}H_{19}O$	18.71	1.85
$C_{17}H_{21}N$	19.09	1.72
$C_{17}H_{35}$	18.93	1.69
$C_{18}H_7O$	19.60	2.02
$C_{18}H_9N$	19.98	1.89
$C_{18}H_{23}$	19.82	1.86
$C_{19}H_{11}$	20.71	2.03

240

	P + 1	P + 2
$C_{11}H_{16}N_2O_4$	13.06	1.59
$C_{11}H_{18}N_3O_3$	13.44	1.44
$C_{11}H_{20}N_4O_2$	13.81	1.29
$C_{12}H_4N_2O_4$	13.95	1.70
$C_{12}H_6N_3O_3$	14.33	1.56
$C_{12}H_8N_4O_2$	14.70	1.41
$C_{12}H_{18}NO_4$	13.79	1.68
$C_{12}H_{20}N_2O_3$	14.17	1.53
$C_{12}H_{22}N_3O_2$	14.54	1.39
$C_{12}H_{24}N_4O$	14.92	1.24
$C_{13}H_6NO_4$	14.68	1.80
$C_{13}H_8N_2O_3$	15.06	1.66
$C_{13}H_{10}N_3O_2$	15.43	1.51
$C_{13}H_{12}N_4O$	15.81	1.37
$C_{13}H_{20}O_4$	14.52	1.78
$C_{13}H_{22}NO_3$	14.90	1.63
$C_{13}H_{24}N_2O_2$	15.27	1.49
$C_{13}H_{26}N_3O$	15.65	1.35
$C_{13}H_{28}N_4$	16.02	1.20
$C_{14}H_8O_4$	15.41	1.91
$C_{14}H_{10}NO_3$	15.79	1.77
$C_{14}H_{12}N_2O_2$	16.16	1.62
$C_{14}H_{14}N_3O$	16.54	1.48
$C_{14}H_{16}N_4$	16.91	1.35
$C_{14}H_{24}O_3$	15.63	1.74
$C_{14}H_{26}NO_2$	16.00	1.60
$C_{14}H_{28}N_2O$	16.38	1.46
$C_{14}H_{30}N_3$	16.75	1.32
$C_{15}H_2N_3O$	17.42	1.63
$C_{15}H_4N_4$	17.80	1.49
$C_{15}H_{12}O_3$	16.52	1.88
$C_{15}H_{14}NO_2$	16.89	1.74
$C_{15}H_{16}N_2O$	17.27	1.60
$C_{15}H_{18}N_3$	17.64	1.47
$C_{15}H_{28}O_2$	16.74	1.71
$C_{15}H_{30}NO$	17.11	1.58
$C_{15}H_{32}N_2$	17.48	1.44
$C_{16}H_2NO_2$	17.78	1.89
$C_{16}H_4N_2O$	18.16	1.75
$C_{16}H_6N_3$	18.53	1.62
$C_{16}H_{16}O_2$	17.62	1.86
$C_{16}H_{18}NO$	18.00	1.73
$C_{16}H_{20}N_2$	18.37	1.59
$C_{16}H_{32}O$	17.84	1.70
$C_{16}H_{34}N$	18.22	1.56
$C_{17}H_4O_2$	18.51	2.02
$C_{17}H_6NO$	18.89	1.88
$C_{17}H_8N_2$	19.26	1.75
$C_{17}H_{20}O$	18.73	1.86
$C_{17}H_{22}N$	19.10	1.72
$C_{17}H_{36}$	18.95	1.70
$C_{18}H_8O$	19.62	2.02
$C_{18}H_{10}N$	19.99	1.89
$C_{18}H_{24}$	19.84	1.86
$C_{19}H_{12}$	20.72	2.04

241

	P + 1	P + 2
$C_{11}H_{17}N_2O_4$	13.08	1.59
$C_{11}H_{19}N_3O_3$	13.45	1.44
$C_{11}H_{21}N_4O_2$	13.83	1.29
$C_{12}H_5N_2O_4$	13.97	1.71
$C_{12}H_7N_3O_3$	14.34	1.56
$C_{12}H_9N_4O_2$	14.72	1.41
$C_{12}H_{19}NO_4$	13.81	1.68
$C_{12}H_{21}N_2O_3$	14.18	1.54
$C_{12}H_{23}N_3O_2$	14.56	1.39
$C_{12}H_{25}N_4O$	14.93	1.24
$C_{13}H_7NO_4$	14.70	1.81
$C_{13}H_9N_2O_3$	15.07	1.66
$C_{13}H_{11}N_3O_2$	15.45	1.52
$C_{13}H_{13}N_4O$	15.82	1.37
$C_{13}H_{21}O_4$	14.54	1.78
$C_{13}H_{23}NO_3$	14.92	1.64
$C_{13}H_{25}N_2O_2$	15.29	1.49
$C_{13}H_{27}N_3O$	15.66	1.35
$C_{13}H_{29}N_4$	16.04	1.21
$C_{14}HN_4O$	16.71	1.51
$C_{14}H_9O_4$	15.43	1.91
$C_{14}H_{11}NO_3$	15.80	1.77
$C_{14}H_{13}N_2O_2$	16.18	1.63
$C_{14}H_{15}N_3O$	16.55	1.49
$C_{14}H_{17}N_4$	16.93	1.35
$C_{14}H_{25}O_3$	15.65	1.74
$C_{14}H_{27}NO_2$	16.02	1.60
$C_{14}H_{29}N_2O$	16.39	1.46
$C_{14}H_{31}N_3$	16.77	1.32
$C_{15}HN_2O_2$	17.07	1.77
$C_{15}H_3N_3O$	17.44	1.63
$C_{15}H_5N_4$	17.82	1.50
$C_{15}H_{13}O_3$	16.53	1.88
$C_{15}H_{15}NO_2$	16.91	1.74
$C_{15}H_{17}N_2O$	17.28	1.60
$C_{15}H_{19}N_3$	17.66	1.47
$C_{15}H_{29}O_2$	16.75	1.72
$C_{15}H_{31}NO$	17.13	1.58
$C_{15}H_{33}N_2$	17.50	1.44
$C_{16}HO_3$	17.42	2.03
$C_{16}H_3NO_2$	17.80	1.89
$C_{16}H_5N_2O$	18.17	1.76
$C_{16}H_7N_3$	18.55	1.62
$C_{16}H_{17}O_2$	17.64	1.86
$C_{16}H_{19}NO$	18.01	1.73
$C_{16}H_{21}N_2$	18.39	1.60
$C_{16}H_{33}O$	17.86	1.70
$C_{16}H_{35}N$	18.23	1.57
$C_{17}H_5O_2$	18.53	2.02
$C_{17}H_7NO$	18.90	1.89
$C_{17}H_9N_2$	19.28	1.76
$C_{17}H_{21}O$	18.75	1.86
$C_{17}H_{23}N$	19.12	1.73
$C_{18}H_9O$	19.63	2.02
$C_{18}H_{11}N$	20.01	1.90
$C_{18}H_{25}$	19.85	1.87
$C_{19}H_{13}$	20.74	2.04
$C_{20}H$	21.63	2.22

242

	P + 1	P + 2
$C_{11}H_{18}N_2O_4$	13.09	1.59
$C_{11}H_{20}N_3O_3$	13.47	1.44
$C_{11}H_{22}N_4O_2$	13.84	1.29
$C_{12}H_6N_2O_4$	13.98	1.71
$C_{12}H_8N_3O_3$	14.36	1.56
$C_{12}H_{10}N_4O_2$	14.73	1.41
$C_{12}H_{20}NO_4$	13.83	1.69
$C_{12}H_{22}N_2O_3$	14.20	1.54
$C_{12}H_{24}N_3O_2$	14.57	1.39
$C_{12}H_{26}N_4O$	14.95	1.24
$C_{13}H_8NO_4$	14.71	1.81
$C_{13}H_{10}N_2O_3$	15.09	1.66
$C_{13}H_{12}N_3O_2$	15.46	1.52
$C_{13}H_{14}N_4O$	15.84	1.38
$C_{13}H_{22}O_4$	14.56	1.79
$C_{13}H_{24}NO_3$	14.93	1.64
$C_{13}H_{26}N_2O_2$	15.31	1.49
$C_{13}H_{28}N_3O$	15.68	1.35
$C_{13}H_{30}N_4$	16.05	1.21
$C_{14}H_2N_4O$	16.73	1.51
$C_{14}H_{10}O_4$	15.45	1.91
$C_{14}H_{12}NO_3$	15.82	1.77
$C_{14}H_{14}N_2O_2$	16.19	1.63
$C_{14}H_{16}N_3O$	16.57	1.49
$C_{14}H_{18}N_4$	16.94	1.35
$C_{14}H_{26}O_3$	15.66	1.75
$C_{14}H_{28}NO_2$	16.04	1.60
$C_{14}H_{30}N_2O$	16.41	1.46
$C_{14}H_{32}N_3$	16.79	1.32
$C_{15}H_2N_2O_2$	17.08	1.77
$C_{15}H_4N_3O$	17.46	1.63
$C_{15}H_6N_4$	17.83	1.50
$C_{15}H_{14}O_3$	16.55	1.88
$C_{15}H_{16}NO_2$	16.93	1.74
$C_{15}H_{18}N_2O$	17.30	1.61
$C_{15}H_{20}N_3$	17.67	1.47
$C_{15}H_{30}O_2$	16.77	1.72
$C_{15}H_{32}NO$	17.14	1.58
$C_{15}H_{34}N_2$	17.52	1.45
$C_{16}H_2O_3$	17.44	2.03
$C_{16}H_4NO_2$	17.81	1.89
$C_{16}H_6N_2O$	18.19	1.76
$C_{16}H_8N_3$	18.56	1.63
$C_{16}H_{18}O_2$	17.66	1.87
$C_{16}H_{20}NO$	18.03	1.73
$C_{16}H_{22}N_2$	18.41	1.60
$C_{16}H_{34}O$	17.87	1.70
$C_{17}H_6O_2$	18.54	2.02
$C_{17}H_8NO$	18.92	1.89
$C_{17}H_{10}N_2$	19.29	1.76
$C_{17}H_{22}O$	18.76	1.86
$C_{17}H_{24}N$	19.14	1.73
$C_{18}H_{10}O$	19.65	2.03
$C_{18}H_{12}N$	20.02	1.90

	P + 1	P + 2
$C_{18}H_{26}$	19.87	1.87
$C_{19}H_{14}$	20.76	2.04
$C_{20}H_{2}$	21.64	2.23
243		
$C_{11}H_{19}N_{2}O_{4}$	13.11	1.60
$C_{11}H_{21}N_{3}O_{3}$	13.48	1.44
$C_{11}H_{23}N_{4}O_{2}$	13.86	1.29
$C_{12}H_{7}N_{2}O_{4}$	14.00	1.71
$C_{12}H_{9}N_{3}O_{3}$	14.37	1.56
$C_{12}H_{11}N_{4}O_{2}$	14.75	1.42
$C_{12}H_{21}NO_{4}$	13.84	1.69
$C_{12}H_{23}N_{2}O_{3}$	14.22	1.54
$C_{12}H_{25}N_{3}O_{2}$	14.59	1.39
$C_{12}H_{27}N_{4}O$	14.96	1.25
$C_{13}H_{9}NO_{4}$	14.73	1.81
$C_{13}H_{11}N_{2}O_{3}$	15.10	1.66
$C_{13}H_{13}N_{3}O_{2}$	15.48	1.52
$C_{13}H_{15}N_{4}O$	15.85	1.38
$C_{13}H_{23}O_{4}$	14.57	1.79
$C_{13}H_{25}NO_{3}$	14.95	1.64
$C_{13}H_{27}N_{2}O_{2}$	15.32	1.50
$C_{13}H_{29}N_{3}O$	15.70	1.35
$C_{13}H_{31}N_{4}$	16.07	1.21
$C_{14}HN_{3}O_{2}$	16.37	1.66
$C_{14}H_{3}N_{4}O$	16.74	1.52
$C_{14}H_{11}O_{4}$	15.46	1.92
$C_{14}H_{13}NO_{3}$	15.84	1.77
$C_{14}H_{15}N_{2}O_{2}$	16.21	1.63
$C_{14}H_{17}N_{3}O$	16.58	1.49
$C_{14}H_{19}N_{4}$	16.96	1.35
$C_{14}H_{27}O_{3}$	15.68	1.75
$C_{14}H_{29}NO_{2}$	16.05	1.61
$C_{14}H_{31}N_{2}O$	16.43	1.47
$C_{14}H_{33}N_{3}$	16.80	1.33
$C_{15}HNO_{3}$	16.72	1.91
$C_{15}H_{3}N_{2}O_{2}$	17.10	1.77
$C_{15}H_{5}N_{3}O$	17.47	1.64
$C_{15}H_{7}N_{4}$	17.85	1.50
$C_{15}H_{15}O_{3}$	16.57	1.89
$C_{15}H_{17}NO_{2}$	16.94	1.75
$C_{15}H_{19}N_{2}O$	17.32	1.61
$C_{15}H_{21}N_{3}$	17.69	1.47
$C_{15}H_{31}O_{2}$	16.78	1.72
$C_{15}H_{33}NO$	17.16	1.58
$C_{16}H_{3}O_{3}$	17.46	2.03
$C_{16}H_{5}NO_{2}$	17.83	1.90
$C_{16}H_{7}N_{2}O$	18.20	1.76
$C_{16}H_{9}N_{3}$	18.58	1.63
$C_{16}H_{19}O_{2}$	17.67	1.87
$C_{16}H_{21}NO$	18.05	1.73
$C_{16}H_{23}N_{2}$	18.42	1.60
$C_{17}H_{7}O_{2}$	18.56	2.02
$C_{17}H_{9}NO$	18.94	1.89
$C_{17}H_{11}N_{2}$	19.31	1.76
$C_{17}H_{23}O$	18.78	1.86
$C_{17}H_{25}N$	19.15	1.73
$C_{18}H_{11}O$	19.67	2.03
$C_{18}H_{13}N$	20.04	1.90
$C_{18}H_{27}$	19.88	1.87
$C_{19}HN$	20.93	2.08
$C_{19}H_{15}$	20.77	2.05
$C_{20}H_{3}$	21.66	2.23
244		
$C_{11}H_{20}N_{2}O_{4}$	13.13	1.60
$C_{11}H_{22}N_{3}O_{3}$	13.50	1.45
$C_{11}H_{24}N_{4}O_{2}$	13.88	1.30
$C_{12}H_{8}N_{2}O_{4}$	14.01	1.71
$C_{12}H_{10}N_{3}O_{3}$	14.39	1.56
$C_{12}H_{12}N_{4}O_{2}$	14.76	1.42
$C_{12}H_{22}NO_{4}$	13.86	1.69
$C_{12}H_{24}N_{2}O_{3}$	14.23	1.54
$C_{12}H_{26}N_{3}O_{2}$	14.61	1.40
$C_{12}H_{28}N_{4}O$	14.98	1.25
$C_{13}H_{10}NO_{4}$	14.75	1.81
$C_{13}H_{12}N_{2}O_{3}$	15.12	1.67
$C_{13}H_{14}N_{3}O_{2}$	15.49	1.52
$C_{13}H_{16}N_{4}O$	15.87	1.38
$C_{13}H_{24}O_{4}$	14.59	1.79
$C_{13}H_{26}NO_{3}$	14.96	1.64
$C_{13}H_{28}N_{2}O_{2}$	15.34	1.50
$C_{13}H_{30}N_{3}O$	15.71	1.36
$C_{13}H_{32}N_{4}$	16.09	1.21
$C_{14}H_{2}N_{3}O_{2}$	16.38	1.66
$C_{14}H_{4}N_{4}O$	16.76	1.52
$C_{14}H_{12}O_{4}$	15.48	1.92
$C_{14}H_{14}NO_{3}$	15.85	1.78
$C_{14}H_{16}N_{2}O_{2}$	16.23	1.63
$C_{14}H_{18}N_{3}O$	16.60	1.49
$C_{14}H_{20}N_{4}$	16.97	1.36
$C_{14}H_{28}O_{3}$	15.69	1.75
$C_{14}H_{30}NO_{2}$	16.07	1.61
$C_{14}H_{32}N_{2}O$	16.44	1.47
$C_{15}H_{2}NO_{3}$	16.74	1.91
$C_{15}H_{4}N_{2}O_{2}$	17.11	1.78
$C_{15}H_{6}N_{3}O$	17.49	1.64
$C_{15}H_{8}N_{4}$	17.86	1.50
$C_{15}H_{16}O_{3}$	16.58	1.89
$C_{15}H_{18}NO_{2}$	16.96	1.75
$C_{15}H_{20}N_{2}O$	17.33	1.61
$C_{15}H_{22}N_{3}$	17.71	1.48
$C_{15}H_{32}O_{2}$	16.80	1.72
$C_{16}H_{4}O_{3}$	17.47	2.03
$C_{16}H_{6}NO_{2}$	17.85	1.90
$C_{16}H_{8}N_{2}O$	18.22	1.77
$C_{16}H_{10}N_{3}$	18.59	1.63
$C_{16}H_{20}O_{2}$	17.69	1.87
$C_{16}H_{22}NO$	18.06	1.74
$C_{16}H_{24}N_{2}$	18.44	1.60
$C_{17}H_{8}O_{2}$	18.58	2.03
$C_{17}H_{10}NO$	18.95	1.90
$C_{17}H_{12}N_{2}$	19.33	1.77
$C_{17}H_{24}O$	18.79	1.87
$C_{17}H_{26}N$	19.17	1.74
$C_{18}H_{12}O$	19.68	2.03
$C_{18}H_{14}N$	20.06	1.91
$C_{18}H_{28}$	19.90	1.87
$C_{19}H_{2}N$	20.95	2.08
$C_{19}H_{16}$	20.79	2.05
$C_{20}H_{4}$	21.68	2.23
245		
$C_{11}H_{21}N_{2}O_{4}$	13.14	1.60
$C_{11}H_{23}N_{3}O_{3}$	13.52	1.45
$C_{11}H_{25}N_{4}O_{2}$	13.89	1.30
$C_{12}H_{9}N_{2}O_{4}$	14.03	1.71
$C_{12}H_{11}N_{3}O_{3}$	14.41	1.57
$C_{12}H_{13}N_{4}O_{2}$	14.78	1.42
$C_{12}H_{23}NO_{4}$	13.87	1.69
$C_{12}H_{25}N_{2}O_{3}$	14.25	1.54
$C_{12}H_{27}N_{3}O_{2}$	14.62	1.40
$C_{12}H_{29}N_{4}O$	15.00	1.25
$C_{13}HN_{4}O_{2}$	15.67	1.55
$C_{13}H_{11}NO_{4}$	14.76	1.81
$C_{13}H_{13}N_{2}O_{3}$	15.14	1.67
$C_{13}H_{15}N_{3}O_{2}$	15.51	1.53
$C_{13}H_{17}N_{4}O$	15.89	1.38
$C_{13}H_{25}O_{4}$	14.60	1.79
$C_{13}H_{27}NO_{3}$	14.98	1.65
$C_{13}H_{29}N_{2}O_{2}$	15.35	1.50
$C_{13}H_{31}N_{3}O$	15.73	1.36
$C_{14}HN_{2}O_{3}$	16.03	1.80
$C_{14}H_{3}N_{3}O_{2}$	16.40	1.66
$C_{14}H_{5}N_{4}O$	16.77	1.52
$C_{14}H_{13}O_{4}$	15.49	1.92
$C_{14}H_{15}NO_{3}$	15.87	1.78
$C_{14}H_{17}N_{2}O_{2}$	16.24	1.64
$C_{14}H_{19}N_{3}O$	16.62	1.50
$C_{14}H_{21}N_{4}$	16.99	1.36
$C_{14}H_{29}O_{3}$	15.71	1.75
$C_{14}H_{31}NO_{2}$	16.08	1.61
$C_{15}HO_{4}$	16.38	2.06
$C_{15}H_{3}NO_{3}$	16.76	1.92
$C_{15}H_{5}N_{2}O_{2}$	17.13	1.78
$C_{15}H_{7}N_{3}O$	17.50	1.64
$C_{15}H_{9}N_{4}$	17.88	1.51
$C_{15}H_{17}O_{3}$	16.60	1.89
$C_{15}H_{19}NO_{2}$	16.97	1.75
$C_{15}H_{21}N_{2}O$	17.35	1.62
$C_{15}H_{23}N_{3}$	17.72	1.48
$C_{16}H_{5}O_{3}$	17.49	2.04
$C_{16}H_{7}NO_{2}$	17.86	1.90
$C_{16}H_{9}N_{2}O$	18.24	1.77
$C_{16}H_{11}N_{3}$	18.61	1.64
$C_{16}H_{21}O_{2}$	17.70	1.87
$C_{16}H_{23}NO$	18.08	1.74
$C_{16}H_{25}N_{2}$	18.45	1.61
$C_{17}H_{9}O_{2}$	18.59	2.03
$C_{17}H_{11}NO$	18.97	1.90
$C_{17}H_{13}N_{2}$	19.34	1.77
$C_{17}H_{25}O$	18.81	1.87
$C_{17}H_{27}N$	19.18	1.74
$C_{18}HN_{2}$	20.23	1.94
$C_{18}H_{13}O$	19.70	2.04
$C_{18}H_{15}N$	20.07	1.91
$C_{18}H_{29}$	19.92	1.88
$C_{19}H_{17}$	20.80	2.05
$C_{19}HO$	20.59	2.21
$C_{19}H_{3}N$	20.96	2.09
$C_{20}H_{5}$	21.69	2.24
246		
$C_{11}H_{22}N_{2}O_{4}$	13.16	1.60
$C_{11}H_{24}N_{3}O_{3}$	13.53	1.45
$C_{11}H_{26}N_{4}O_{2}$	13.91	1.30
$C_{12}H_{10}N_{2}O_{4}$	14.05	1.72
$C_{12}H_{12}N_{3}O_{3}$	14.42	1.57
$C_{12}H_{14}N_{4}O_{2}$	14.80	1.42
$C_{12}H_{24}NO_{4}$	13.89	1.70
$C_{12}H_{26}N_{2}O_{3}$	14.26	1.55
$C_{12}H_{28}N_{3}O_{2}$	14.64	1.40
$C_{12}H_{30}N_{4}O$	15.01	1.25
$C_{13}H_{2}N_{4}O_{2}$	15.68	1.55
$C_{13}H_{12}NO_{4}$	14.78	1.82
$C_{13}H_{14}N_{2}O_{3}$	15.15	1.67
$C_{13}H_{16}N_{3}O_{2}$	15.53	1.53
$C_{13}H_{18}N_{4}O$	15.90	1.39
$C_{13}H_{26}O_{4}$	14.62	1.79
$C_{13}H_{28}NO_{3}$	15.00	1.65
$C_{13}H_{30}N_{2}O_{2}$	15.37	1.50
$C_{14}H_{2}N_{2}O_{3}$	16.04	1.80
$C_{14}H_{4}N_{3}O_{2}$	16.42	1.66
$C_{14}H_{6}N_{4}O$	16.79	1.53
$C_{14}H_{14}O_{4}$	15.51	1.92
$C_{14}H_{16}NO_{3}$	15.88	1.78
$C_{14}H_{18}N_{2}O_{2}$	16.26	1.64
$C_{14}H_{20}N_{3}O$	16.63	1.50
$C_{14}H_{22}N_{4}$	17.01	1.36
$C_{14}H_{30}O_{3}$	15.73	1.76
$C_{15}H_{2}O_{4}$	16.40	2.06
$C_{15}H_{4}NO_{3}$	16.77	1.92
$C_{15}H_{6}N_{2}O_{2}$	17.15	1.78
$C_{15}H_{8}N_{3}O$	17.52	1.65
$C_{15}H_{10}N_{4}$	17.90	1.51
$C_{15}H_{18}O_{3}$	16.61	1.89
$C_{15}H_{20}NO_{2}$	16.99	1.76
$C_{15}H_{22}N_{2}O$	17.36	1.62
$C_{15}H_{24}N_{3}$	17.74	1.48
$C_{16}H_{6}O_{3}$	17.50	2.04
$C_{16}H_{8}NO_{2}$	17.88	1.90
$C_{16}H_{10}N_{2}O$	18.25	1.77
$C_{16}H_{12}N_{3}$	18.63	1.64
$C_{16}H_{22}O_{2}$	17.72	1.88
$C_{16}H_{24}NO$	18.09	1.74
$C_{16}H_{26}N_{2}$	18.47	1.61
$C_{17}H_{10}O_{2}$	18.61	2.03
$C_{17}H_{12}NO$	18.98	1.90
$C_{17}H_{14}N_{2}$	19.36	1.77
$C_{17}H_{26}O$	18.83	1.87
$C_{17}H_{28}N$	19.20	1.74
$C_{18}H_{2}N_{2}$	20.25	1.94
$C_{18}H_{14}O$	19.71	2.04
$C_{18}H_{16}N$	20.09	1.91
$C_{18}H_{30}$	19.93	1.88
$C_{19}H_{2}O$	20.60	2.21
$C_{19}H_{4}N$	20.98	2.09
$C_{19}H_{18}$	20.82	2.06
$C_{20}H_{6}$	21.71	2.24
247		
$C_{11}H_{23}N_{2}O_{4}$	13.17	1.60
$C_{11}H_{25}N_{3}O_{3}$	13.55	1.45
$C_{11}H_{27}N_{4}O_{2}$	13.92	1.30
$C_{12}H_{11}N_{2}O_{4}$	14.06	1.72
$C_{12}H_{13}N_{3}O_{3}$	14.44	1.57
$C_{12}H_{15}N_{4}O_{2}$	14.81	1.42
$C_{12}H_{25}NO_{4}$	13.91	1.70
$C_{12}H_{27}N_{2}O_{3}$	14.28	1.55
$C_{12}H_{29}N_{3}O_{2}$	14.65	1.40
$C_{13}HN_{3}O_{3}$	15.33	1.70
$C_{13}H_{3}N_{4}O_{2}$	15.70	1.55
$C_{13}H_{13}NO_{4}$	14.79	1.82
$C_{13}H_{15}N_{2}O_{3}$	15.17	1.67

	P + 1	P + 2
$C_{13}H_{17}N_3O_2$	15.54	1.53
$C_{13}H_{19}N_4O$	15.92	1.39
$C_{13}H_{27}O_4$	14.64	1.80
$C_{13}H_{29}NO_3$	15.01	1.65
$C_{14}HNO_4$	15.68	1.95
$C_{14}H_3N_2O_3$	16.06	1.81
$C_{14}H_5N_3O_2$	16.43	1.67
$C_{14}H_7N_4O$	16.81	1.53
$C_{14}H_{15}O_4$	15.53	1.93
$C_{14}H_{17}NO_3$	15.90	1.78
$C_{14}H_{19}N_2O_2$	16.27	1.64
$C_{14}H_{21}N_3O$	16.65	1.50
$C_{14}H_{23}N_4$	17.02	1.36
$C_{15}H_3O_4$	16.41	2.06
$C_{15}H_5NO_3$	16.79	1.92
$C_{15}H_7N_2O_2$	17.16	1.78
$C_{15}H_9N_3O$	17.54	1.65
$C_{15}H_{11}N_4$	17.91	1.51
$C_{15}H_{19}O_3$	16.63	1.90
$C_{15}H_{21}NO_2$	17.01	1.76
$C_{15}H_{23}N_2O$	17.38	1.62
$C_{15}H_{25}N_3$	17.75	1.49
$C_{16}H_7O_3$	17.52	2.04
$C_{16}H_9NO_2$	17.89	1.91
$C_{16}H_{11}N_2O$	18.27	1.77
$C_{16}H_{13}N_3$	18.64	1.64
$C_{16}H_{23}O_2$	17.74	1.88
$C_{16}H_{25}NO$	18.11	1.75
$C_{16}H_{27}N_2$	18.49	1.61
$C_{17}HN_3$	19.53	1.81
$C_{17}H_{11}O_2$	18.62	2.04
$C_{17}H_{13}NO$	19.00	1.91
$C_{17}H_{15}N_2$	19.37	1.78
$C_{17}H_{27}O$	18.84	1.88
$C_{17}H_{29}N$	19.22	1.75
$C_{18}HNO$	19.89	2.07
$C_{18}H_3N_2$	20.26	1.95
$C_{18}H_{15}O$	19.73	2.04
$C_{18}H_{17}N$	20.10	1.92
$C_{18}H_{31}$	19.95	1.88
$C_{19}H_3O$	20.62	2.22
$C_{19}H_5N$	20.99	2.09
$C_{19}H_{19}$	20.84	2.06
$C_{20}H_7$	21.72	2.24
248		
$C_{11}H_{24}N_2O_4$	13.19	1.61
$C_{11}H_{26}N_3O_3$	13.56	1.45
$C_{11}H_{28}N_4O_2$	13.94	1.31
$C_{12}H_{12}N_2O_4$	14.08	1.72
$C_{12}H_{14}N_3O_3$	14.45	1.57
$C_{12}H_{16}N_4O_2$	14.83	1.43
$C_{12}H_{26}NO_4$	13.92	1.70
$C_{12}H_{28}N_2O_3$	14.30	1.55
$C_{13}H_2N_3O_3$	15.34	1.70
$C_{13}H_4N_4O_2$	15.72	1.56
$C_{13}H_{14}NO_4$	14.81	1.82
$C_{13}H_{16}N_2O_3$	15.18	1.68
$C_{13}H_{18}N_3O_2$	15.56	1.53
$C_{13}H_{20}N_4O$	15.93	1.39
$C_{13}H_{28}O_4$	14.65	1.80
$C_{14}H_2NO_4$	15.70	1.95
$C_{14}H_4N_2O_3$	16.07	1.81
$C_{14}H_6N_3O_2$	16.45	1.67
$C_{14}H_8N_4O$	16.82	1.53
$C_{14}H_{16}O_4$	15.54	1.93
$C_{14}H_{18}NO_3$	15.92	1.79
$C_{14}H_{20}N_2O_2$	16.29	1.64
$C_{14}H_{22}N_3O$	16.66	1.51
$C_{14}H_{24}N_4$	17.04	1.37
$C_{15}H_4O_4$	16.43	2.06
$C_{15}H_6NO_3$	16.80	1.92
$C_{15}H_8N_2O_2$	17.18	1.79
$C_{15}H_{10}N_3O$	17.55	1.65
$C_{15}H_{12}N_4$	17.93	1.52
$C_{15}H_{20}O_3$	16.65	1.90
$C_{15}H_{22}NO_2$	17.02	1.76
$C_{15}H_{24}N_2O$	17.40	1.62
$C_{15}H_{26}N_3$	17.77	1.49
$C_{16}H_8O_3$	17.54	2.05
$C_{16}H_{10}NO_2$	17.91	1.91
$C_{16}H_{12}N_2O$	18.28	1.78
$C_{16}H_{14}N_3$	18.66	1.65
$C_{16}H_{24}O_2$	17.75	1.88
$C_{16}H_{26}NO$	18.13	1.75
$C_{16}H_{28}N_2$	18.50	1.62
$C_{17}H_2N_3$	19.55	1.81
$C_{17}H_{12}O_2$	18.64	2.04
$C_{17}H_{14}NO$	19.02	1.91
$C_{17}H_{16}N_2$	19.39	1.78
$C_{17}H_{28}O$	18.86	1.88
$C_{17}H_{30}N$	19.23	1.75
$C_{18}H_2NO$	19.90	2.08
$C_{18}H_4N_2$	20.28	1.95
$C_{18}H_{16}O$	19.75	2.04
$C_{18}H_{18}N$	20.12	1.92
$C_{18}H_{32}$	19.96	1.89
$C_{19}H_4O$	20.64	2.22
$C_{19}H_6N$	21.01	2.10
$C_{19}H_{20}$	20.85	2.06
$C_{20}H_8$	21.74	2.25
249		
$C_{11}H_{25}N_2O_4$	13.21	1.61
$C_{11}H_{27}N_3O_3$	13.58	1.46
$C_{12}H_{13}N_2O_4$	14.10	1.72
$C_{12}H_{15}N_3O_3$	14.47	1.58
$C_{12}H_{17}N_4O_2$	14.84	1.43
$C_{12}H_{27}NO_4$	13.94	1.70
$C_{13}HN_2O_4$	14.98	1.85
$C_{13}H_3N_3O_3$	15.36	1.70
$C_{13}H_5N_4O_2$	15.73	1.56
$C_{13}H_{15}NO_4$	14.83	1.82
$C_{13}H_{17}N_2O_3$	15.20	1.68
$C_{13}H_{19}N_3O_2$	15.57	1.54
$C_{13}H_{21}N_4O$	15.95	1.39
$C_{14}H_3NO_4$	15.71	1.95
$C_{14}H_5N_2O_3$	16.09	1.81
$C_{14}H_7N_3O_2$	16.46	1.67
$C_{14}H_9N_4O$	16.84	1.53
$C_{14}H_{17}O_4$	15.56	1.93
$C_{14}H_{19}NO_3$	15.93	1.79
$C_{14}H_{21}N_2O_2$	16.31	1.65
$C_{14}H_{23}N_3O$	16.68	1.51
$C_{14}H_{25}N_4$	17.05	1.37
$C_{15}H_5O_4$	16.45	2.07
$C_{15}H_7NO_3$	16.82	1.93
$C_{15}H_9N_2O_2$	17.19	1.79
$C_{15}H_{11}N_3O$	17.57	1.65
$C_{15}H_{13}N_4$	17.94	1.52
$C_{15}H_{21}O_3$	16.66	1.90
$C_{15}H_{23}NO_2$	17.04	1.76
$C_{15}H_{25}N_2O$	17.41	1.63
$C_{15}H_{27}N_3$	17.79	1.49
$C_{16}HN_4$	18.83	1.68
$C_{16}H_9O_3$	17.55	2.05
$C_{16}H_{11}NO_2$	17.93	1.91
$C_{16}H_{13}N_2O$	18.30	1.78
$C_{16}H_{15}N_3$	18.67	1.65
$C_{16}H_{25}O_2$	17.77	1.89
$C_{16}H_{27}NO$	18.14	1.75
$C_{16}H_{29}N_2$	18.52	1.62
$C_{17}HN_2O$	19.19	1.94
$C_{17}H_3N_3$	19.56	1.81
$C_{17}H_{13}O_2$	18.66	2.04
$C_{17}H_{15}NO$	19.03	1.91
$C_{17}H_{17}N_2$	19.41	1.78
$C_{17}H_{29}O$	18.87	1.88
$C_{17}H_{31}N$	19.25	1.75
$C_{18}HO_2$	19.55	2.21
$C_{18}H_3NO$	19.92	2.08
$C_{18}H_5N_2$	20.29	1.95
$C_{18}H_{17}O$	19.76	2.05
$C_{18}H_{19}N$	20.14	1.92
$C_{18}H_{33}$	19.98	1.89
$C_{19}H_5O$	20.65	2.22
$C_{19}H_7N$	21.03	2.10
$C_{19}H_{21}$	20.87	2.07
$C_{20}H_9$	21.76	2.25
250		
$C_{11}H_{26}N_2O_4$	13.22	1.61
$C_{12}H_{14}N_2O_4$	14.11	1.73
$C_{12}H_{16}N_3O_3$	14.49	1.58
$C_{12}H_{18}N_4O_2$	14.86	1.43
$C_{13}H_2N_2O_4$	15.00	1.85
$C_{13}H_4N_3O_3$	15.37	1.71
$C_{13}H_6N_4O_2$	15.75	1.56
$C_{13}H_{16}NO_4$	14.84	1.83
$C_{13}H_{18}N_2O_3$	15.22	1.68
$C_{13}H_{20}N_3O_2$	15.59	1.54
$C_{13}H_{22}N_4O$	15.97	1.40
$C_{14}H_4NO_4$	15.73	1.96
$C_{14}H_6N_2O_3$	16.11	1.82
$C_{14}H_8N_3O_2$	16.48	1.67
$C_{14}H_{10}N_4O$	16.85	1.54
$C_{14}H_{18}O_4$	15.57	1.93
$C_{14}H_{20}NO_3$	15.95	1.79
$C_{14}H_{22}N_2O_2$	16.32	1.65
$C_{14}H_{24}N_3O$	16.70	1.51
$C_{14}H_{26}N_4$	17.07	1.37
$C_{15}H_6O_4$	16.46	2.07
$C_{15}H_8NO_3$	16.84	1.93
$C_{15}H_{10}N_2O_2$	17.21	1.79
$C_{15}H_{12}N_3O$	17.58	1.66
$C_{15}H_{14}N_4$	17.96	1.52
$C_{15}H_{22}O_3$	16.68	1.90
$C_{15}H_{24}NO_2$	17.05	1.77
$C_{15}H_{26}N_2O$	17.43	1.63
$C_{15}H_{28}N_3$	17.80	1.49
$C_{16}H_2N_4$	18.85	1.68
$C_{16}H_{10}O_3$	17.57	2.05
$C_{16}H_{12}NO_2$	17.94	1.92
$C_{16}H_{14}N_2O$	18.32	1.78
$C_{16}H_{16}N_3$	18.69	1.65
$C_{16}H_{26}O_2$	17.78	1.89
$C_{16}H_{28}NO$	18.16	1.75
$C_{16}H_{30}N_2$	18.53	1.62
$C_{17}H_2N_2O$	19.20	1.94
$C_{17}H_4N_3$	19.58	1.82
$C_{17}H_{14}O_2$	18.67	2.05
$C_{17}H_{16}NO$	19.05	1.91
$C_{17}H_{18}N_2$	19.42	1.79
$C_{17}H_{30}O$	18.89	1.89
$C_{17}H_{32}N$	19.26	1.76
$C_{18}H_2O_2$	19.56	2.21
$C_{18}H_4NO$	19.94	2.08
$C_{18}H_6N_2$	20.31	1.96
$C_{18}H_{18}O$	19.78	2.05
$C_{18}H_{20}N$	20.15	1.92
$C_{18}H_{34}$	20.00	1.89
$C_{19}H_6O$	20.67	2.23
$C_{19}H_8N$	21.04	2.10
$C_{19}H_{22}$	20.88	2.07
$C_{20}H_{10}$	21.77	2.25

APPENDIX B Common Fragment Ions

Not all members of homologous and isomeric series are given. The list is meant to be suggestive rather than exhaustive. Any such list will vary with the interests of the compiler.

m/e	Ions
14	CH_2
15	CH_3
16	O
17	OH
18	H_2O, NH_4
19	F, H_3O
26	$C{\equiv}N$
27	C_2H_3
28	C_2H_4, CO, N_2 (air), $CH{=}NH$
29	C_2H_5, CHO
30	CH_2NH_2, NO
31	CH_2OH, OCH_3
32	O_2(Air)
33	SH, CH_2F
34	H_2S
35	Cl
36	HCl
39	C_3H_3
40	$CH_2C{\equiv}N$, Ar(Air)
41	C_3H_5, $CH_2C{\equiv}N+H$, C_2H_2NH
42	C_3H_6
43	C_3H_7, $CH_3C{=}O$, C_2H_5N
44	$CH_2C(H){=}O + H$, CH_3CHNH_2, CO_2, $NH_2C{=}O$, $(CH_3)_2N$
45	CH_3CHOH, CH_2CH_2OH, CH_2OCH_3, $C({=}O){-}OH$, $CH_3CH{-}O + H$
46	NO_2
47	CH_2SH, CH_3S
48	$CH_3S + H$
49	CH_2Cl
51	CHF_2
53	C_4H_5
54	$CH_2CH_2C{\equiv}N$
55	C_4H_7, $CH_2{=}CHC{=}O$
56	C_4H_8
57	C_4H_9, $C_2H_5C{=}O$
58	$CH_3{-}C({=}O){-}CH_2 + H$, $C_2H_5CHNH_2$, $(CH_3)_2NCH_2$, $C_2H_5NHCH_2$, C_2H_2S
59	$(CH_3)_2COH$, $CH_2OC_2H_5$, $C({=}O){-}OCH_3$, $NH_2C({=}O){-}CH_2 + H$, CH_3OCHCH_3, CH_3CHCH_2OH
60	$CH_2C({=}O){-}OH + H$, CH_2ONO
61	$C({=}O){-}OCH_3 + 2H$, CH_2CH_2SH, CH_2SCH_3
65	(ring)
67	C_5H_7
68	$CH_2CH_2CH_2C{\equiv}N$
69	C_5H_9, CF_3, $CH_3CH{=}CHC{=}O$, $CH_2{=}C(CH_3)C{=}O$
70	C_5H_{10}
71	C_5H_{11}, $C_3H_7C{=}O$
72	$C_2H_5C({=}O){-}CH_2 + H$, $C_3H_7CHNH_2$, $(CH_3)_2N{=}C{=}O$, $C_2H_5NHCHCH_3$, and isomers
73	Homologs of 59
74	$CH_2{-}C({=}O){-}OCH_3 + H$
75	$C({=}O){-}OC_2H_5 + 2H$, $CH_2SC_2H_5$, $(CH_3)_2CSH$, $(CH_3O)_2CH$
77	C_6H_5
78	$C_6H_5 + H$
79	$C_6H_5 + 2H$, Br
80	(N–H ring)$-CH_2$, CH_3SS+H
81	(O ring)$-CH_2$, C_6H_9, (ring)
82	$CH_2CH_2CH_2CH_2C{\equiv}N$, CCl_2, C_6H_{10}
83	C_6H_{11}, $CHCl_2$, (S ring)
85	C_6H_{13}, $C_4H_9C{=}O$, $CClF_2$
86	$C_3H_7C({=}O){-}CH_2 + H$, $C_4H_9CHNH_2$, and isomers.
87	$C_3H_7C({=}O)$, homologs of 73, $CH_2CH_2C({=}O)OCH_3$

m/e	Ions
88	$CH_2—C(=O)—OC_2H_5$ + H
89	$C(=O)—OC_3H_7$ + 2H, —C
90	CH_3CHONO_2, —CH
91	$—CH_2$, —CH + H, —C + 2H, $(CH_2)_4Cl$, N
92	$—CH_2$ + H, N —CH_2, =O
93	CH_2Br, —OH, C_7H_9, N =C=O, —O, C_7H_9 (terpenes)
94	—O + H, N H —C=O
95	O —C=O
96	$CH_2CH_2CH_2CH_2CH_2C{\equiv}N$
97	C_7H_{13}, S —CH_2
98	O —CH_2O + H
99	C_7H_{15}, $C_6H_{11}O$
100	$C_4H_9C(=O)CH_2$ + H, $C_5H_{11}CHNH_2$
101	$C(=O)—OC_4H_9$
102	$CH_2C(=O)—OC_3H_7$ + H
103	$C(=O)—OC_4H_9$ + 2H, $C_5H_{11}S$, $CH(OCH_2CH_3)_2$
104	$C_2H_5CHONO_2$
105	—C=O, —CH_2CH_2, —$CHCH_3$
106	$NHCH_2$
107	—CH_2O, CH_2 OH, CH_2 —OH
108	—CH_2O + H, N CH_3 —C=O
109	C=O
111	S —C=O
119	CF_3CF_2, CH_3—C—CH_3, CH_3CH —CH_3, C=O —CH_3
120	O C O
121	C=O —OH, OCH_3 —CH_2, N=O NH, C_9H_{13}(terpenes)
123	C=O —F
125	—S → O
127	I
131	C_3F_5, —CH=CH—C(=O)
135	$(CH_2)_4Br$
138	—C(=O)O —OH + H

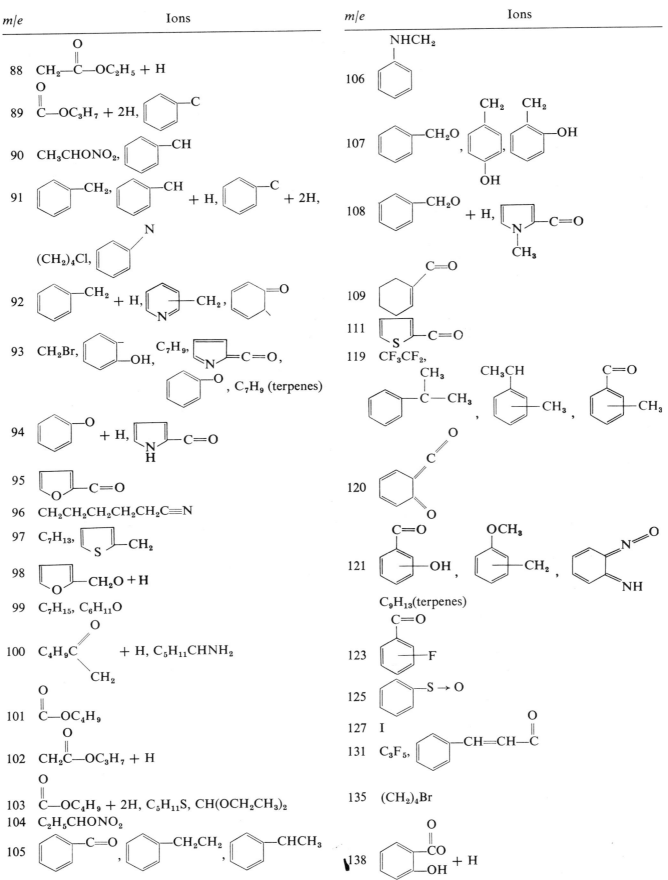

m/e	Ions
139	$ClC_6H_4-C{=}O$ (benzene ring bearing C=O and Cl)
149	$C_6H_4(CO)_2O + H$ (benzene ring fused to C(=O)–O–C(=O))
154	$C_6H_5-C_6H_5$ (biphenyl)

APPENDIX C Common Fragments Lost

This list is suggestive rather than comprehensive. It should be used in conjunction with Appendix B.

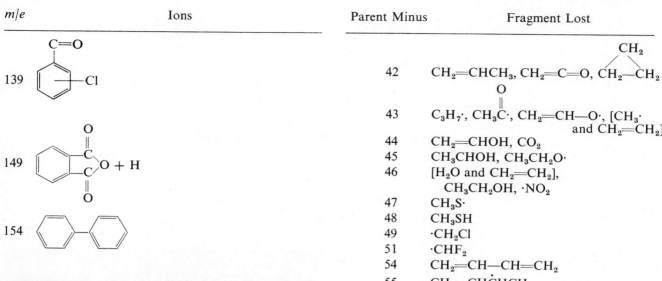

Parent Minus	Fragment Lost
1	$H\cdot$
15	$CH_3\cdot$
17	$HO\cdot$
18	H_2O
19	$F\cdot$
20	HF
26	$CH{\equiv}CH$, $\cdot C{\equiv}N$
27	$CH_2{=}CH\cdot$, $HC{\equiv}N$
28	$CH_2{=}CH_2$, CO, $H_2C{=}N$
29	$CH_3CH_2\cdot$, $\cdot CHO$
30	$NH_2CH_2\cdot$, CH_2O, NO
31	$\cdot OCH_3$, $\cdot CH_2OH$, CH_3NH_2
32	CH_3OH
33	$HS\cdot$, ($\cdot CH_3$ and H_2O)
34	H_2S
35	$Cl\cdot$
36	HCl
37	H_2Cl
40	$CH_3C{\equiv}CH$
41	$CH_2{=}CHCH_2\cdot$
42	$CH_2{=}CHCH_3$, $CH_2{=}C{=}O$, cyclo-$(CH_2CH_2CH_2)$
43	$C_3H_7\cdot$, $CH_3\overset{O}{\overset{\|}{C}}\cdot$, $CH_2{=}CH{-}O\cdot$, [$CH_3\cdot$ and $CH_2{=}CH_2$]
44	$CH_2{=}CHOH$, CO_2
45	CH_3CHOH, $CH_3CH_2O\cdot$
46	[H_2O and $CH_2{=}CH_2$], CH_3CH_2OH, $\cdot NO_2$
47	$CH_3S\cdot$
48	CH_3SH
49	$\cdot CH_2Cl$
51	$\cdot CHF_2$
54	$CH_2{=}CH{-}CH{=}CH_2$
55	$CH_2{=}CH\dot{C}HCH_3$
56	$CH_2{=}CHCH_2CH_3$, $CH_3CH{=}CHCH_3$
57	$C_4H_9\cdot$
58	$\cdot NCS$
59	$CH_3O\overset{O}{\overset{\|}{C}}\cdot$, $CH_3\overset{O}{\overset{\|}{C}}NH_2$
60	C_3H_7OH
61	$CH_3CH_2S\cdot$
62	[H_2S and $CH_2{=}CH_2$]
63	$\cdot CH_2CH_2Cl$
68	$CH_2{=}\overset{CH_3}{\overset{\vert}{C}}{-}CH{=}CH_2$
69	$CF_3\cdot$
71	$C_5H_{11}\cdot$
73	$CH_3CH_2O\overset{O}{\overset{\|}{C}}\cdot$
74	C_4H_9OH
79	$Br\cdot$
80	HBr
85	$\cdot CClF_2$
122	C_6H_5COOH
127	$I\cdot$
128	HI

CHAPTER 3

Infrared Spectrometry

I. INTRODUCTION

Infrared radiation refers broadly to that part of the electromagnetic spectrum between the visible and microwave regions. Of greatest practical use to the organic chemist is the limited portion between 4000 cm^{-1} and 666 cm^{-1} (2.5–15.0 μ). Recently there has been increasing interest in the near infrared region, 16,668–4000 cm^{-1} (0.6–2.5 μ), and the far infrared region, 700–200 cm^{-1} (14.3–50 μ).

From the brief theoretical discussion which follows, it is clear that even a very simple molecule can give an extremely complex spectrum. The organic chemist takes advantage of this complexity when he matches the spectrum of an unknown compound against that of an authentic sample. A peak-by-peak correlation is excellent evidence for identity. It is unlikely that any two compounds, except optical enantiomorphs, give the same infrared spectrum.

Although the infrared spectrum is characteristic of the entire molecule, it turns out that certain groups of atoms give rise to bands at or near the same frequency regardless of the structure of the rest of the molecule. It is the persistence of these characteristic bands that permits the chemist to obtain useful structural information by simple inspection and reference to generalized charts of characteristic group frequencies. We shall rely heavily upon these characteristic group frequencies.

Since we are not solely dependent upon infrared spectra for identification, a detailed analysis of the spectrum will not be required. Following our general plan, we shall present only sufficient theory to accomplish our purpose: utilization of infrared spectra in conjunction with other spectral data to determine molecular structure.

Nearly all academic and industrial laboratories make infrared spectrophotometers available as bench tools for the organic chemist. A simplified infrared spectrophotometer costs about $4000. Precision instruments are available at $11,000 to $15,000. Spectrophotometers covering the range of 667–33 cm^{-1} (15–300 μ) cost approximately $30,000. Since the organic chemist very frequently obtains his own infrared spectra, we shall describe instrumentation and sample preparation in somewhat more detail than is given in the chapters on mass spectrometry and NMR spectrometry.

The increased emphasis on infrared spectrometry, as a tool of the practicing organic chemist, is readily apparent from the number of books devoted wholly or in part to discussions of applications of infrared spectrometry, which have been published in the last three years. There is no lack of reference material covering all aspects of infrared spectrometry.[1–28e] The new text, by Colthup, Daly, and Wiberly,[12] presents a thorough coverage of theory, practice, and spectra-structure correlations. The compact manuals by Cross,[4] Flett,[14] and Nakanishi[13] are convenient sources of concise information. The volumes by Potts[26] and Miller[27] are valuable references for instrument operation and sample handling techniques. There are ten principal compilations of infrared spectra including indices to collections of spectra and to the literature.[29–38]

II. THEORY

Infrared radiation of frequencies less than about 100 cm^{-1} (wavelengths longer than 100 μ) is absorbed and converted by an organic molecule into energy of molecular rotation. This absorption is quantized; thus, a molecular rotation spectrum consists of discrete lines.

Infrared radiation in the range from about 10,000–100 cm^{-1} (1–100 μ) is absorbed and converted by an organic molecule into energy of molecular vibration. This absorption is also quantized, but vibrational spectra appear as bands rather than lines because a single vibrational energy change is accompanied by a number of rotational energy changes. It is with these vibrational-rotational bands, particularly those occurring between 4000 cm^{-1} and 666 cm^{-1} (2.5–15 μ), that we shall be concerned. The frequency or wavelength of absorption depends on the relative masses of the atoms, the force constants of the bonds, and the geometry of the atoms.

Band positions in infrared spectra are presented either as wavelengths or frequencies. The common unit of wavelength in infrared spectrometry is the micron (μ), equal to 10^{-3} mm. Frequencies are usually expressed in terms of wavenumbers (ν) whose unit is the reciprocal centimeter (cm^{-1}). In terms of this unit, the wavenumber is the reciprocal of the wavelength in centimeters. Or, when the wavelength is in microns, the wavenumber is $\frac{1}{\mu} \times 10^4$. The energy of radiation is directly proportional to the frequency.

Band intensities are expressed either as transmittance (T) or absorbance (A). Transmittance is the ratio of the radiant power transmitted by a sample to the radiant power incident on the sample. Absorbance is the logarithm, to the base 10, of the reciprocal of the transmittance, $A = \log_{10} (1/T)$. A concise compilation of approved spectrometry nomenclature has recently been published.[39]

There are two types of molecular vibrations: stretching and bending. A stretching vibration is a rhythmical movement along the bond axis such that the interatomic distance is increasing or decreasing. A bending vibration may consist of a change in bond angles between bonds with a common atom, or the movement of a group of atoms with respect to the remainder of the molecule without movement of the atoms in the group with respect to one another. For example, twisting, rocking, and torsional vibrations involve a change in bond angles with reference to a set of coordinates arbitrarily set up within the molecule.

Only those vibrations that result in a rhythmical change in the dipole moment of the molecule are observed in the infrared. The alternating electric field, produced by the changing charge distribution accompanying a vibration, couples the molecular vibration with the oscillating electric field of the electromagnetic radiation.

A molecule has as many degrees of freedom as the total degrees of freedom of its individual atoms. Each atom has 3 degrees of freedom, corresponding to the Cartesian coordinates (X, Y, Z), necessary to describe its position relative to other atoms in the molecule. A molecule of n atoms therefore has $3n$ degrees of freedom. For nonlinear molecules, three of the degrees of freedom describe rotation and three describe translation; the remaining $3n-6$ degrees of freedom are vibrational degrees of freedom or fundamental vibrations. Linear molecules have $3n-5$ vibrational degrees of freedom, for only two degrees of freedom are required to describe rotation.

The three fundamental vibrations of the nonlinear, triatomic water molecule can be depicted as shown at top of page 66.

Fundamental vibrations involve no change in the center of gravity of the molecule.

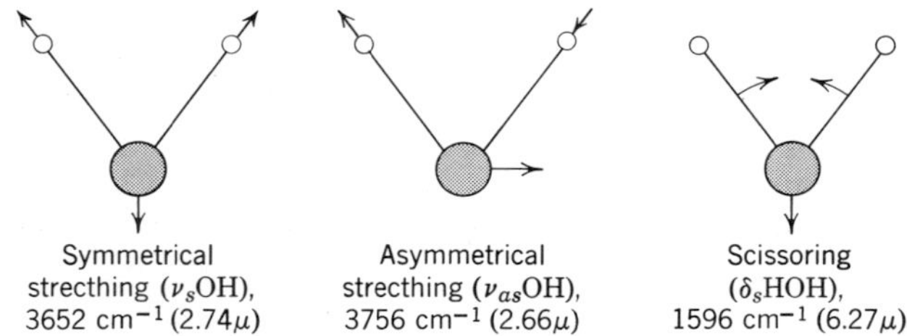

The CO_2 molecule is linear and contains three atoms; therefore it has four fundamental vibrations ((3 × 3)−5).

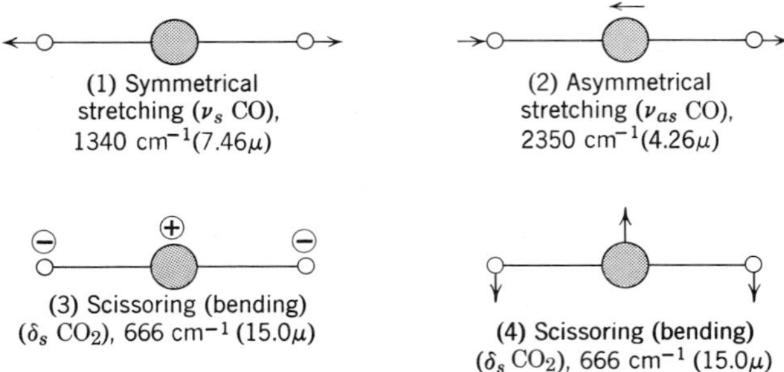

⊕ and ⊖ indicate movement perpendicular to the plane of the page.

The symmetrical stretching vibration (1) is inactive in the infrared since it produces no change in the dipole moment of the molecule. The bending vibrations (3) and (4) are equivalent, and are the resolved components of bending motion oriented at any angle to the internuclear axis; they have the same frequency and are said to be doubly degenerate.

The various stretching and bending modes for an AX_2 group appearing as a portion of a molecule, e.g., the CH_2 group in a hydrocarbon molecule, are shown in Figure 1. The $3n-6$ rule does not apply since the CH_2 represents only a portion of a molecule.

The theoretical number of fundamental vibrations (absorption frequencies) will seldom be observed because overtones and combination tones increase the number of bands, whereas other phenomena reduce the number of bands. The following will reduce the theoretical number of bands.

1. Fundamental frequencies that fall outside of the 2.5–15 μ region.
2. Fundamental bands that are too weak to be observed.
3. Fundamental vibrations that are so close that they coalesce.
4. The occurrence of a degenerate band from several absorptions of the same frequency in highly symmetrical molecules.
5. The failure of certain fundamental vibrations to appear in the infrared because of lack of required .change in dipole character of the molecule.

Assignments for stretching frequencies can be approximated by the application of Hooke's law. In the application of the law, two atoms and their connecting bond are treated as a simple harmonic oscillator composed of two masses joined by a spring. Equation 1, derived from Hooke's law, states the relationship between frequency of oscillation, atomic masses, and the force constant of the bond.

$$\nu = \frac{1}{2\pi c}\left(\frac{f}{\dfrac{MxMy}{Mx + My}}\right)^{1/2}$$

where ν = the vibrational frequency (cm^{-1})
c = velocity of light (cm/sec)
f = force constant of bond (dynes/cm)
Mx and My = mass of atom x and atom y, respectively (g).

The value of f is approximately 5×10^5 dynes per cm for single bonds and approximately two and three times this value for double bonds and triple bonds, respectively.

Application of the formula to C—H stretching, using

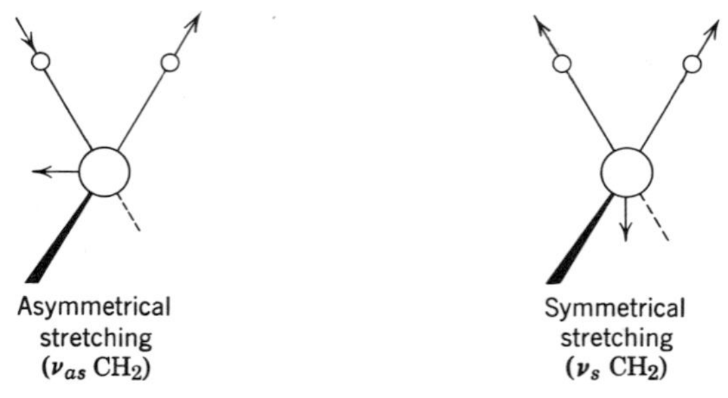

STRETCHING VIBRATIONS

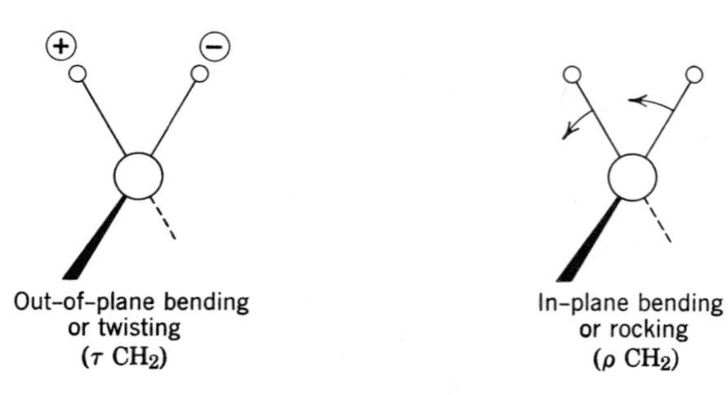

BENDING VIBRATIONS

Fig. 1. Vibrational modes for a CH_2 group. (⊕ and ⊖ indicate movement perpendicular to the plane of the page.)

19.8×10^{-24} g and 1.64×10^{-24} g as mass values for C and H, respectively, places the frequency of the C—H bond vibration at 3040 cm^{-1} (3.30 μ). Actually, C—H stretching vibrations, associated with methyl and methylene groups, are generally observed in the region between 2960–2850 cm^{-1} (3.38–3.51 μ). The calculation is not precise because effects arising from the environment of the C—H within a molecule have been ignored. The frequency of infrared absorption is commonly used to calculate the force constants of bonds.

The shift in absorption frequency following deuteration is often employed in the assignment of C—H stretching frequencies. If the hydrogen in an X—H group is replaced by deuterium, equation 1 indicates that the ratio of the C—H to C—D stretching frequencies should equal $\sqrt{2}$. If the ratio of the frequencies, following deuteration, is much less than $\sqrt{2}$ we can not assume that the vibration is simply a C—H stretching vibration, but rather a mixed vibration involving interaction or coupling with another vibration. The actual mode of vibration is a combination of both.

Calculations place the stretching frequencies of the following bonds in the general absorption regions indicated.

C—C, C—O, C—N	1300–800 cm^{-1} (7.7–12.5 μ)
C=C, C=O, C=N, N=O	1900–1500 cm^{-1} (5.3–6.7 μ)
C≡C, C≡N	2300–2000 cm^{-1} (4.4–5.0 μ)

To approximate the vibrational frequencies of bond stretching by Hooke's law, the relative contributions of bond strengths and atomic masses must be considered. For example, a superficial comparison of the C—H group with the F—H group, on the basis of atomic masses, might lead to the conclusion that the stretching frequency of the F—H bond should occur at a lower frequency than that for the C—H bond. However, the increase in the force constant from left to right across the first two rows of the periodic table has a greater effect than the mass increase. Thus the F—H group absorbs at a higher frequency (4138 cm^{-1}, 2.42 μ) than the C—H group (3040 cm^{-1}, 3.30 μ).

INTERACTION. When two bond oscillators share a common atom they seldom behave as individual oscillators unless the individual oscillation frequencies are widely different. This is because there is mechanical coupling or interaction between the oscillators. For example, the carbon dioxide molecule, which consists of two C=O bonds with a common carbon atom, has two fundamental stretching vibrations: an asymmetrical and a symmetrical stretching mode. The symmetrical stretching mode consists of an in-phase stretching or contracting of the C to O bonds, and absorption occurs at a wavelength longer than that observed for the carbonyl group in an aliphatic ketone. The symmetrical stretching mode produces no change in the dipole moment of the molecule and is therefore "inactive" in the infrared, but is easily observed in the Raman spectrum near 1340 cm^{-1} (7.46 μ). In the asymmetrical stretching mode, the two C to O bonds stretch out of phase; one C—O bond stretches as the other contracts. The asymmetrical stretching mode, since it produces a change in the dipole moment, is infrared active; the absorption (2350 cm^{-1}, 4.26 μ) is at a shorter wavelength (higher frequency) than observed for a carbonyl group in aliphatic ketones.

This difference in carbonyl absorption frequencies, displayed by the carbon dioxide molecule results from strong mechanical coupling or interaction. In contrast, two ketonic carbonyl groups separated by one or more carbon atoms show normal carbonyl absorption near 1715 cm^{-1} (5.83 μ) because appreciable coupling is prevented by the intervening carbon atom or atoms.

Coupling accounts for the two N—H stretching bands in the 3497–3077 cm^{-1} (2.86–3.25 μ) region in primary amine and primary amide spectra, for the two C=O stretching bands in the 1818–1720 cm^{-1} (5.50–5.81 μ) region in carboxylic anhydrides and imide spectra, and for the two C—H stretching bands in the 3000–2760 cm^{-1} (3.33–3.62 μ) region for both methylene and methyl groups.

Useful characteristic group frequency bands often involve coupled vibrations. The spectra of alcohols have a strong band in the region between 1212 and 1000 cm^{-1} (8.25–10.00 μ) which is usually designated as the "C—O stretching band." In the spectrum of methanol this band is at 1034 cm^{-1} (9.67 μ); in the spectrum of ethanol it occurs at 1053 cm^{-1} (9.50 μ). Branching and unsaturation produce absorption characteristic of these structures[40] (see discussion of alcohols). It is evident that we are not dealing with an isolated C—O stretching vibration, but rather a coupled asymmetric vibration involving C—C—O stretching.

Vibrations resulting from bond angle bending frequently couple in a manner similar to stretching vibrations. Thus, the ring C—H out-of-plane bending frequencies of aromatic molecules depend on the number of adjacent hydrogen atoms on the ring; coupling between the hydrogen atoms is effected by the bending of the C—C bond in the ring to which the hydrogen atoms are attached.

Interaction arising from coupling of stretching and bending vibrations is illustrated by the absorption of secondary acyclic amides. Secondary acyclic amides, which exist predominantly in the *trans* configuration, show strong absorption in the 1563–1515 cm^{-1} (6.40–6.60 μ) region; this absorption involves coupling of the N—H bending and C—N stretching vibrations.

The requirements for effective interaction may be summarized as follows:

1. The vibrations must be of the same symmetry species if interaction is to occur.

2. Strong coupling between stretching vibrations requires a common atom between the groups.
3. Interaction is greatest when the coupled groups absorb, individually, near the same frequency.
4. Coupling between bending and stretching vibrations can occur if the stretching bond forms one side of the changing angle.
5. A common bond is required for coupling of bending vibrations.
6. Little or no interaction occurs between groups separated by two or more bonds.

HYDROGEN BONDING. Hydrogen bonding can occur in any system containing a proton donor group (X—H) and a proton acceptor Y if the s orbital of the proton can effectively overlap the p or π orbital of the acceptor group. Atoms X and Y are electronegative with Y possessing lone pair electrons. The common proton donor groups in organic molecules are carboxyl, hydroxyl, amine, or amide groups. Common proton acceptor atoms are oxygen, nitrogen, and the halogens. Unsaturated groups, such as the ethylenic linkage, can also act as proton acceptors.

The strength of the hydrogen bond is at a maximum when the proton donor group and the axis of the lone pair orbital are collinear. The strength of the bond is inversely proportional to the distance between X and Y.

Hydrogen bonding alters the force constant of both groups; thus, the frequencies of both stretching and bending vibrations are altered. The X—H stretching bands move to longer wavelengths (lower frequencies) usually with increased intensity and band widening. The stretching frequency of the acceptor group, e.g., C=O, is also reduced but to a lesser degree than the proton donor group. The H—X bending vibration usually shifts to a shorter wavelength when bonding occurs; this shift is less pronounced than that of the stretching frequency.

*Inter*molecular hydrogen bonding involves association of two or more molecules of the same or different compounds. Intermolecular bonding may result in dimer molecules (as observed for carboxylic acids) or in polymer molecules, which exist in neat samples or concentrated solutions of monohydric alcohols. *Intra*molecular hydrogen bonds are formed when the proton donor and acceptor are present in a single molecule under spacial conditions that allow the required overlap of orbitals, for example, the formation of a 5- or 6-membered ring. The extent of both inter- and intramolecular bonding is temperature dependent. The effect of concentration on intermolecular and intramolecular hydrogen bonding is markedly different. The bands that result from intermolecular bonding generally disappear at low concentrations (less than about 0.01M in nonpolar solvents). Intramolecular hydrogen bonding is an internal effect and persists at very low concentrations.

The change in frequency between "free" OH absorption and bonded OH absorption is a measure of the strength of the hydrogen bond. Ring strain, molecular geometry, and the relative acidity and basicity of the proton donor and acceptor groups affect the strength of bonding. Intramolecular bonding involving the same bonding groups is stronger when a 6-membered ring is formed than when a smaller ring results from bonding. Hydrogen bonding is strongest when the bonded structure is stabilized by resonance.

The effects of hydrogen bonding on the stretching frequencies of hydroxyl and carbonyl groups are summarized in Table I.

An important aspect of hydrogen bonding involves interaction between functional groups of solvent and solute. If the solute is polar, then it is necessary to specify the solvent used and the solute concentration.

FERMI RESONANCE. As we have seen in our discussion of interaction, coupling of two fundamental vibrational modes will produce two new modes of vibration, with frequencies higher and lower than that observed when interaction is absent. Interaction can also occur between fundamental vibrations and overtones or combination-tone vibrations. Such interaction is known as Fermi resonance. One example of Fermi resonance is afforded by the absorption pattern of carbon dioxide. In our discussion of interaction, we indicated that the symmetrical stretching band of CO_2 appears in the Raman spectrum near 1340 cm^{-1} (7.46 μ). Actually two bands are observed; one at 1286 cm^{-1} (7.78 μ), one at 1388 cm^{-1} (7.20 μ). The splitting results from coupling between the fundamental C=O stretching vibration, near 1340 cm^{-1} (7.46 μ), and the first overtone of the bending vibration. The fundamental bending vibration occurs near 666 cm^{-1} (15.00 μ), the first overtone near 1334 cm^{-1} (7.55 μ).

Fermi resonance is a common phenomenon in infrared and Raman spectra. It requires that the vibrational levels be of the same symmetry species and that the interacting groups be located in the molecule so that mechanical coupling is appreciable.

III. INSTRUMENTATION

The modern double-beam infrared spectrophotometer consists of five principal sections: radiation source, sampling area, photometer, monochromator, and detector. A diagram of the optical system of a double-beam infrared spectrophotometer is shown in Figure 2.

RADIATION SOURCE. Infrared radiation is produced by electrically heating a source, usually a Nernst filament or a Globar to 1000–1800°C. The Nernst filament is fabricated from a binder and oxides of zirconium, thorium, and cerium. The Globar is a small rod of silicon carbide. The image of the source must be wider

Table I Stretching Frequencies in Hydrogen Bonding

	INTERMOLECULAR BONDING			INTRAMOLECULAR BONDING		
X—H...Y Strength	Freq. Reduction (cm^{-1})* νOH	νC=O†	Compound Class	Freq. Reduction (cm^{-1})* νOH	νC=O†	Compound Class
Weak	300	15	Alcohols, phenols, and intermolecular hydroxyl to carbonyl bonding.	<100	10	1, 2-diols; α- and most β-hydroxy ketones; α-substituted phenols
Medium				100–300	50	1, 3-diols; some β-hydroxy ketones; β-hydroxy amino compounds; β-hydroxy nitro compounds
Strong	>500	50	RCOOH dimers	>300	100	o-hydroxy aryl ketones; o-hydroxy aryl acids; o-hydroxy aryl esters; β-diketones; tropolones.

* Frequency shift referred to "free" stretching frequencies. † Carbonyl stretching only where applicable.

than the maximum width of the slits (vide infra). The maximum radiation for the Globar occurs in the 5500–5000 cm^{-1} (1.8–2.0 μ) region and drops off by a factor of about 600 as the 600 cm^{-1} (16.7 μ) region is approached. The Nernst filament furnishes maximum radiation energy at about 7100 cm^{-1} (1.4 μ) and drops by a factor of about 1000 as the lower frequency region is approached.

The radiation from the source is divided into two beams by mirrors *M*1 and *M*2. The two beams, reference beam and sample beam, are focused into the sample area by mirrors *M*3 and *M*4.

SAMPLING AREA. Reference and sample beams enter the sampling area and pass through the reference cell and sampling cell, respectively. Opaque shutters, mounted on the source housing, permit blocking of either beam independently. The sampling area of a precision spectrophotometer accommodates a wide variety of sampling accessories varying from gas cells of 40 m effective path to microcells.

PHOTOMETER. The reference beam passes through the attenuator (vide infra) and is reflected by mirrors *M*6 and *M*8 to the rotating sector mirror *M*7, which alternately reflects the reference beam out of the optical system and transmits the beam to mirror *M*9. The reference beam is now an intermittent beam with a "frequency" of from 8 to 13 cycles per second depending on the particular instrument. This beam is focused by mirror *M*10 on the slit *S*1. The sample beam passes through the comb (vide infra) and is reflected by mirror *M*5 to the rotating sector mirror *M*7, which alternately transmits the beam out of the optical system and reflects it to mirror *M*9, thence to mirror *M*10 and slit *S*1.

At any given moment, the beam focused on slit *S*1 is either the reference beam, which was transmitted by the

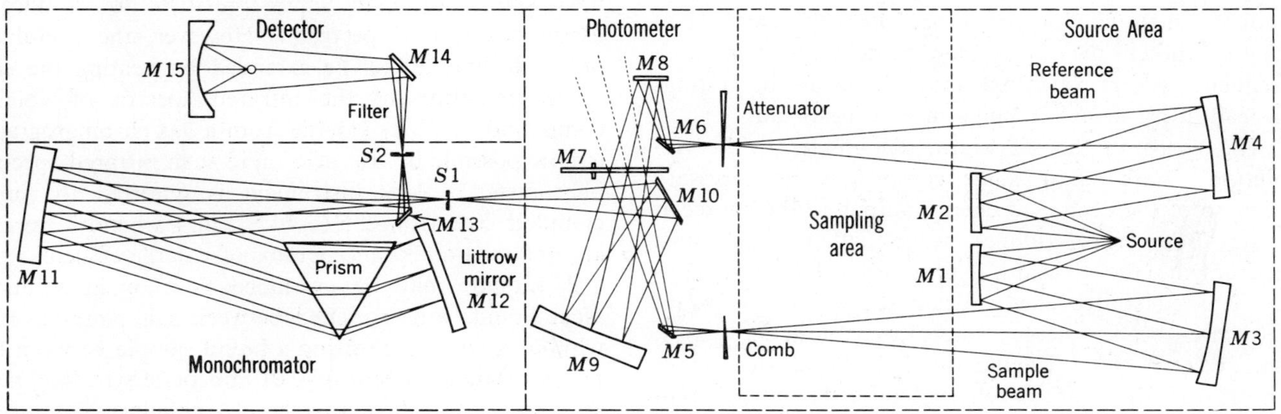

Fig. 2. Optical system of double-beam infrared spectrophotometer.

rotating sector mirror *M*7, or the sample beam, which was reflected by *M*7. In other words, the reference beam and the sample beam have been combined into a single beam of alternating segments; this establishes a switching frequency at the detector equal to the speed of rotation of *M*7.

When the beams are of equal intensity, the instrument is at an optical null. The comb in the sample beam permits balancing the beams. The recording pen is then at 100% transmittance when no sample is present.

The attenuator is driven in and out of the reference beam in response to the signal created at the detector by the sample beam. Thus, when the sample beam is absorbed by the sample, the attenuator is driven into the reference beam until its intensity matches that of the sample beam.

MONOCHROMATOR. The combined beam passes through the monochromator entrance slit *S*1 to the mirror *M*11, which reflects it through the prism to the Littrow mirror *M*12. At this point, the beam is dispersed by the prism over a range of frequencies (wavelengths). The dispersed beam is reflected back through the prism (to increase its dispersion) to mirror *M*11, thence to mirror *M*13, which focuses the beam on the exit slit *S*2. The width of the frequency range focused on the exit slit *S*2 is determined by the width of the entrance slit *S*1 and the dispersing power of the prism. The frequency range (that is, the region of the dispersed beam) focused on *S*2 at any one moment is determined by the angle of the Littrow mirror *M*12 at that moment. Thus rotating *M*12 produces a scan of frequency ranges at the exit slit *S*2 and, consequently, at the detector.

Maximum resolution is obtained by using prism materials only in their range of greatest dispersing effectiveness. Each material has only a rather narrow effective range, and several materials should be used for greatest resolution over a spectral range. For example, calcium fluoride is most useful from 4200–1300 cm^{-1} (2.4–7.7 μ), whereas potassium or cesium bromide is most effective in the range 1100–385 cm^{-1} (9.1–26.0 μ). Sodium chloride prisms are widely accepted as a compromise material for the range 4000–650 cm^{-1} (2.5–15.4 μ), though they are somewhat deficient at the high frequency (short wavelength) end. The use of gratings instead of prisms is becoming more widespread.

The narrower the slit width, the greater is the resolution. Here again, some compromise is necessary because of the decreased energy output of the source at lower frequencies (longer wavelengths). On most instruments, the slit width is programmed to increase as the emitted source energy decreases, so that constant reference beam energy enters the monochromator.

DETECTOR. After leaving the exit slit of the monochromator, the beam is reflected by a flat mirror *M*14 to an ellipsoidal mirror *M*15. The foci of the ellipsoidal mirror are the exit slit *S*2 and the detector.

The detector is a device that measures radiant energy by means of its heating effect. Two common types of detectors are the thermocouple and bolometer. In the thermocouple detector, the radiant energy heats one of two bimetallic junctions, and an emf is produced between the two junctions proportional to the degree of heating. The bolometer changes its resistance upon heating. It serves as one arm of a bridge so that a change in temperature will cause an unbalanced signal across the circuit. The unbalanced signal can be amplified and recorded or used to activate a servomechanism to re-establish a balance.

Since the detector sees alternately the reference and the sample beam at a switching frequency determined by the rotation of the sector mirror, any change in the intensity of the radiation due to absorption is detected as an off-null signal.

The amplified off-null signal of the detector is used to position the optical attenuator so that the radiation from the reference and sample beam are kept at equal intensity. The amount of attenuation required is a direct measure of the absorption by the sample. The movement of the attenuator is recorded by the recording chart pen.

IV. SAMPLE HANDLING

Infrared spectra may be obtained for gases, liquids, or solids.

1. The spectra of gases or low boiling liquids may be obtained by expansion of the sample into an evacuated cell. Cells equipped with freeze-out tips are used for sample concentration and cell evacuation prior to expansion of the sample into the cell. Gas cells are available in lengths of a few centimeters to 40 meters. The sampling area of a standard infrared spectrophotometer will not accommodate cells much longer than 10 cm; long paths are achieved by multiple reflection optics.

The vapor phase technique is limited because of the relatively large percentage of compounds that do not have sufficiently high vapor pressures to produce a useful absorption spectrum. However, the usefulness of the technique can be extended by heating the cell.

Determination of the infrared spectra of volatile compounds, as they emerge from a gas chromatograph, is now possible by use of a rapid scan infrared spectrophotometer.* This instrument is reported to run a complete scan from 2.5 to 14.5 μ in 4 seconds. Spectra are obtained on 30 micrograms of volatile effluent.

2. Liquids may be examined neat or in solution. Neat liquids are examined between salt plates usually without a spacer. Pressing a liquid sample between flat plates produces a film of 0.01 mm or less in thickness, the plates being held together by capillarity. Samples

* Beckman Instruments, Inc., Fullerton, Calif. Model IR-102.

of 1–10 mg are required. Thick samples of neat liquids usually absorb too strongly to produce a satisfactory spectrum. Volatile liquids are examined in sealed cells with very thin spacers. Silver chloride or KRS-5 plates may be used for samples that dissolve sodium chloride plates.

Solutions are handled in cells of 0.1–1 mm thickness. Volumes of 0.1–1 ml of 0.05–10% solutions are required for readily available demountable cells. A compensating cell, containing pure solvent, is placed in the reference beam. The spectrum thus obtained is that of the solute except in those regions in which the solvent absorbs strongly. For example, thick samples of carbon tetrachloride absorb strongly near 800 cm^{-1} (12.50 μ); compensation for this band is ineffective since strong absorption prevents any radiation from reaching the detector.

The solvent selected must be dry and reasonably transparent in the region of interest. When the entire spectrum is of interest, several solvents must be used. A common pair of solvents is carbon tetrachloride and carbon disulfide. Carbon tetrachloride is relatively free of absorption at frequencies above 1333 cm^{-1} (shorter than 7.50 μ), whereas carbon disulfide shows little absorption below 1333 cm^{-1} (longer than 7.50 μ). Solvent and solute combinations that react must be avoided. For example, carbon disulfide cannot be used as a solvent for primary or secondary amines. Amino alcohols react slowly with carbon disulfide and carbon tetrachloride.

When only very small samples are available, ultramicro cavity cells are used in conjunction with a beam condenser. The smallest commercially available cell has a path length of approximately 0.05 mm and a capacity of about 0.8 microliter.* A spectrum can thus be obtained on a few micrograms of sample in solution. When volatility permits, the solute can be recovered for examination by other spectrometric techniques.

The absorption pattern of selected solvents and mulling oils are presented in Figure 3.

3. Solids are usually examined as a mull, a pressed disc, or as a deposited glassy film.

Mulls are prepared by thoroughly grinding 2–5 mg of a solid in a smooth agate mortar. Grinding is continued after the addition of a drop or two of the mulling oil. The suspended particles must be less than 2 μ to avoid excessive scattering of radiation. The mull is examined as a thin film between flat salt plates. Nujol (a high-boiling petroleum oil) is commonly used as a mulling agent. When hydrocarbon bands interfere with the spectrum, Fluorolube (a completely halogenated polymer containing F and Cl), or hexachlorobutadiene may be used. The use of both Nujol and Fluorolube mulls makes possible a scan, essentially free of interfering bands, over the 4000 cm^{-1}–666 cm^{-1} (2.5–15.0 μ) region.

The pressed-disc technique depends upon the fact that dry, powdered potassium bromide (or other alkali metal

* Barnes Engineering Co., Instrument Division, Stamford, Conn.

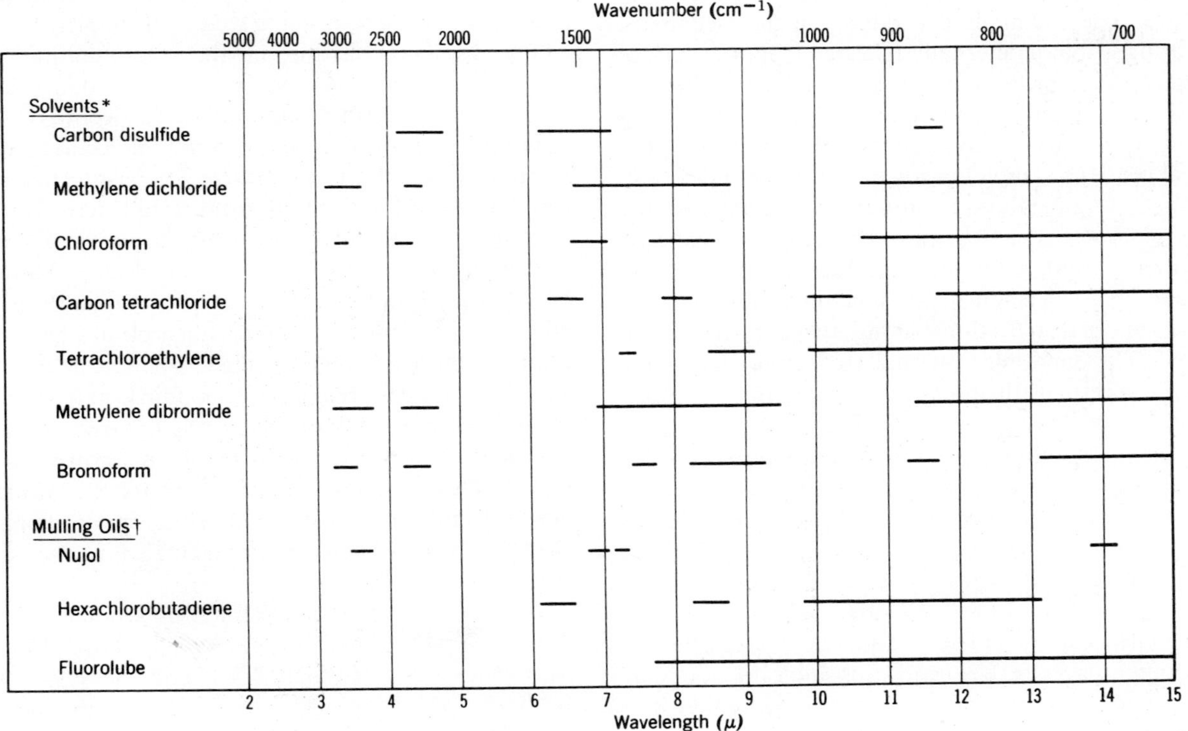

Fig. 3. Transparent regions of solvents and mulling oils. * The open regions are those in which the solvent transmits more than 25% of the incident light at 1 mm thickness. † The open regions for mulling oils indicate transparency of thin films.

halides) can be pressed under pressure *in vacuo* to form transparent discs. The sample (0.5–1.0 mg) is intimately mixed with approximately 100 mg of dry, powdered potassium bromide. Mixing can be effected by thorough grinding in a smooth agate mortar or, more efficiently, with a small vibrating ball mill, or by lyophilization. The mixture is pressed into a transparent disc, with special dies, under a pressure of 10,000–15,000 pounds per square inch. The quality of the spectrum depends upon the intimacy of mixing and the reduction of the suspended particles to 2 μ or less. Micro-discs, 0.5 to 1.5 mm in diameter, can be used with a beam condenser. The micro-disc technique permits examination of samples as small as 1 microgram. Bands near 3448 cm^{-1} and 1639 cm^{-1} (2.9 and 6.1 μ), due to moisture, frequently appear in spectra obtained by the pressed disc technique.

Deposited films are useful only when the material can be deposited from solution or cooled from a melt as micro-crystals or as a glassy film. Crystalline films generally lead to excessive light scattering. Specific crystal orientation may lead to spectra differing from those observed for randomly oriented particles such as exist in a mull or halide disc. The deposited film technique is particularly useful for obtaining spectra of resins and plastics. Care must be taken to free the sample of solvent by vacuum treatment or gentle heating.

A new technique, known as attenuated total reflection or internal reflection spectroscopy is available for obtaining qualitative spectra of solids regardless of thickness. The technique depends upon the fact that a beam of light that is internally reflected from the surface of a transmitting medium passes a short distance beyond the reflecting boundry and returns to the transmitting medium as a part of the process of reflection. If a material (i.e., the sample) of lower refraction index than the transmitting medium, is brought in contact with the reflecting surface, the light passes through the material to the depth of a few microns, producing an absorption spectrum. An extension of the technique, provides for multiple internal reflections along the surface of the sample. The multiple internal reflection technique results in spectra with intensities comparable to transmission spectra.*

In general, a dilute solution in a nonpolar solvent furnishes the best (that is, least distorted) spectrum. Nonpolar compounds give essentially the same spectra in the condensed phase (that is, neat liquid, a mull, a KBr disc, or a film) as they give in nonpolar solvents. Polar compounds, however, often show hydrogen bonding effects in the condensed phase. Unfortunately, polar compounds are frequently insoluble in nonpolar solvents, and the spectrum must be obtained either in a condensed phase, or in a polar solvent; the latter introduces the possibility of solute-solvent hydrogen bonding.

Reasonable care must be taken in handling salt cells and plates. Moisture-free samples should be used. Fingers should not come in contact with the optical surfaces. Care should be taken to prevent contamination with silicones, which are hard to remove and have strong absorption patterns.

* Wilks Scientific Corp., South Norwalk, Conn.

V. INTERPRETATION OF SPECTRA

There are no rigid rules for interpreting an infrared spectrum. Certain requirements, however, must be met before an attempt is made to interpret a spectrum.

1. The spectrum must be adequately resolved and of adequate intensity.
2. The spectrum should be that of a reasonably pure compound.
3. The spectrophotometer should be calibrated so that the bands are observed at their proper frequencies or wavelengths. Proper calibration can be made with reliable standards such as polystyrene film.
4. The method of sample handling must be specified. If a solvent is employed, the solvent, concentration, and the cell thickness should be indicated.

A precise treatment of the vibrations of a complex molecule is not feasible; thus the infrared spectrum must be interpreted from empirical comparison of spectra, and extrapolation of studies of simpler molecules. Many questions arising in the interpretation of an infrared spectrum can be answered by data obtained from the mass, ultraviolet, and NMR spectra.

Infrared absorption of organic molecules is summarized in the chart of characteristic group frequencies (see Fig. 4). Many of the group frequencies vary over a wide range because the bands arise from complex interacting vibrations within the molecule. Absorption bands may, however, represent predominantly a single vibrational mode. Certain absorption bands, for example, those arising from the C—H, O—H, and C=O stretching modes, remain within fairly narrow regions of the spectrum. Important details of structure may be revealed by the exact position of an absorption band within these narrow regions. Shifts in absorption position and changes in band contours, accompanying changes in molecular environment, may also suggest important structural details.

The two important areas for a preliminary examination of a spectrum are the region above 1300 cm^{-1} (wavelengths shorter than 7.7 μ) and the 909–650 cm^{-1} (11.0–15.4 μ) region. The short-wavelength portion of the spectrum is called the functional group region. The characteristic stretching frequencies for important functional groups such as OH, NH, and C=O occur in this

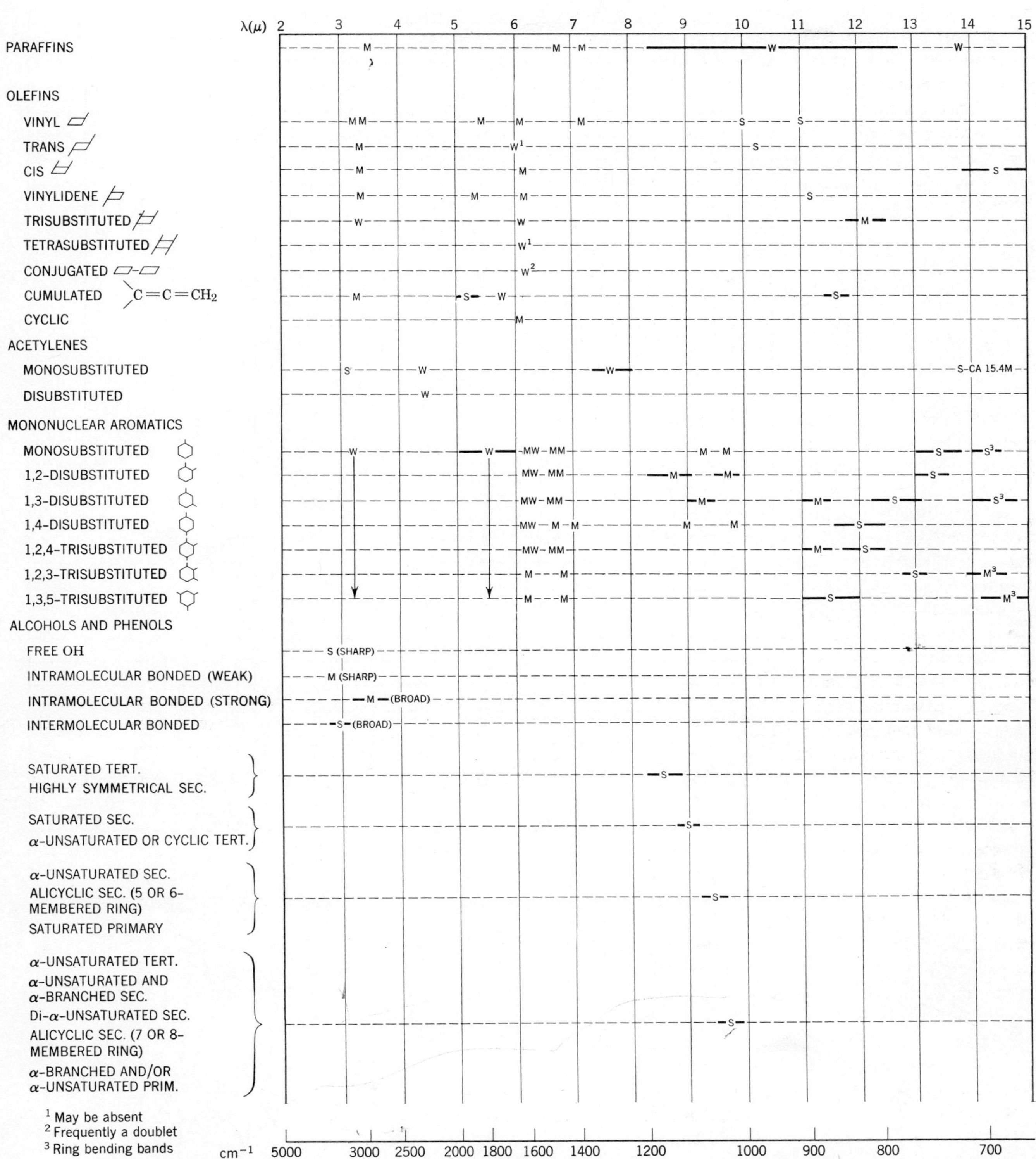

Fig. 4. Characteristic group frequencies. The position of narrow absorption ranges is covered by a single letter indicating an average intensity. Broader absorption regions are indicated by a heavy bar. For example, a monosubstituted mononuclear aromatic may have four bands between 6 and 7 μ, three of medium intensity, and one weak.

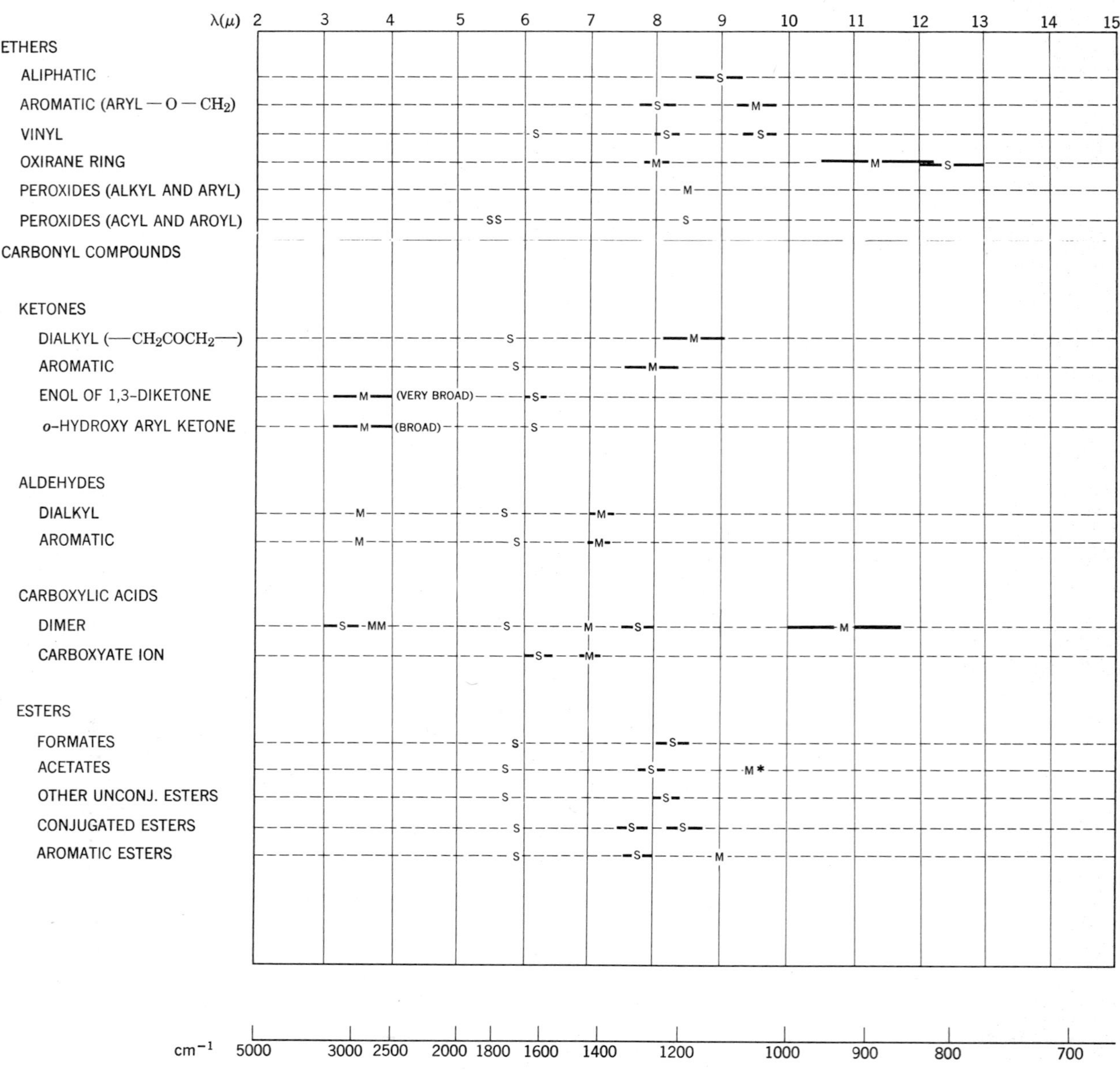
λ(μ) 2 3 4 5 6 7 8 9 10 11 12 13 14 15
ETHERS
ALIPHATIC
AROMATIC (ARYL — O — CH_2)
VINYL
OXIRANE RING
PEROXIDES (ALKYL AND ARYL)
PEROXIDES (ACYL AND AROYL)
CARBONYL COMPOUNDS
KETONES
DIALKYL (—CH_2COCH_2—)
AROMATIC
ENOL OF 1,3-DIKETONE
(VERY BROAD)
o-HYDROXY ARYL KETONE
(BROAD)
ALDEHYDES
DIALKYL
AROMATIC
CARBOXYLIC ACIDS
DIMER
CARBOXYATE ION
ESTERS
FORMATES
ACETATES
OTHER UNCONJ. ESTERS
CONJUGATED ESTERS
AROMATIC ESTERS
cm^{-1} 5000 3000 2500 2000 1800 1600 1400 1200 1000 900 800 700

* ACETATES OF PRIMARY ALCOHOLS.

Fig. 4. (*Continued*)

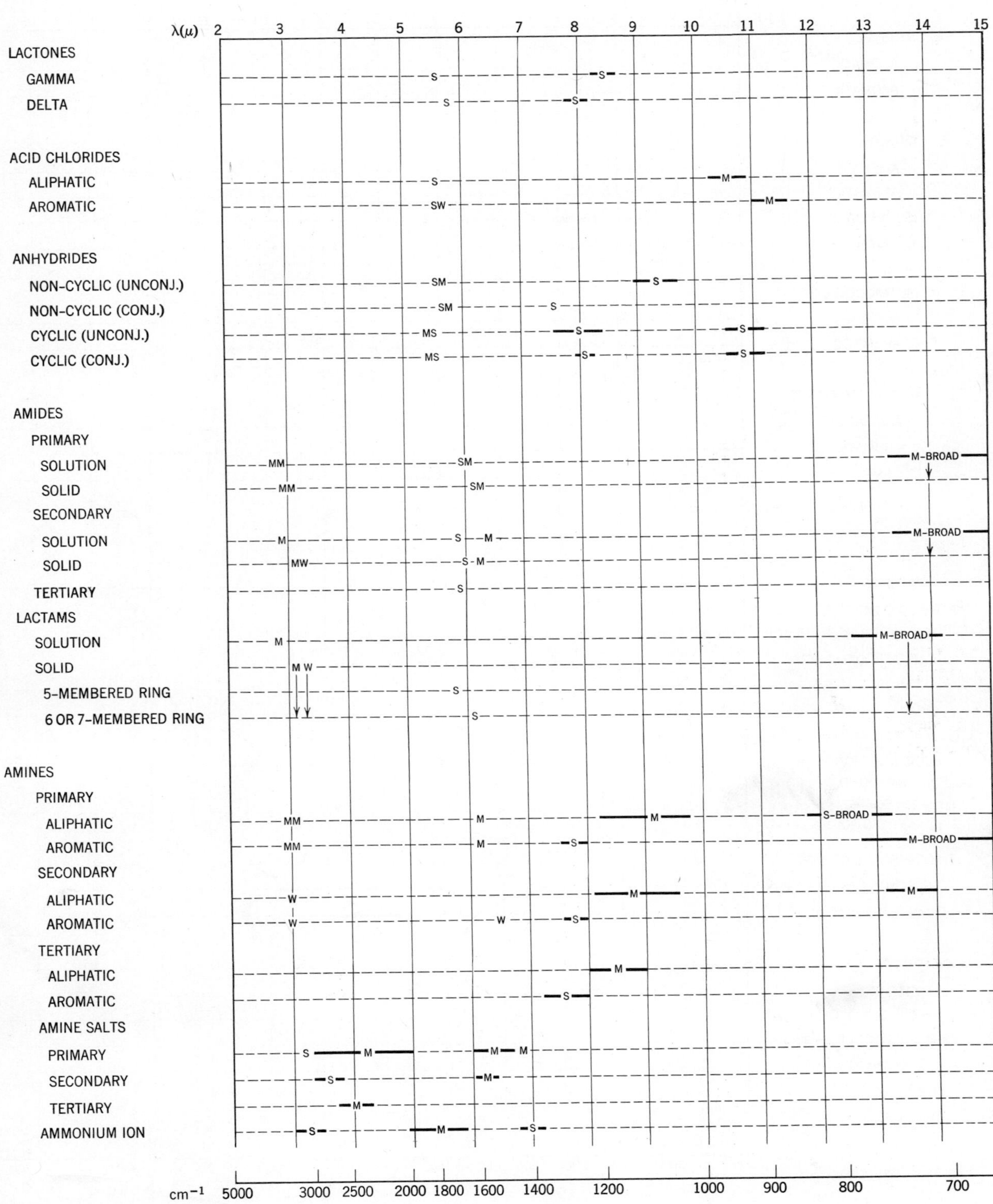

Fig. 4. (*Continued*)

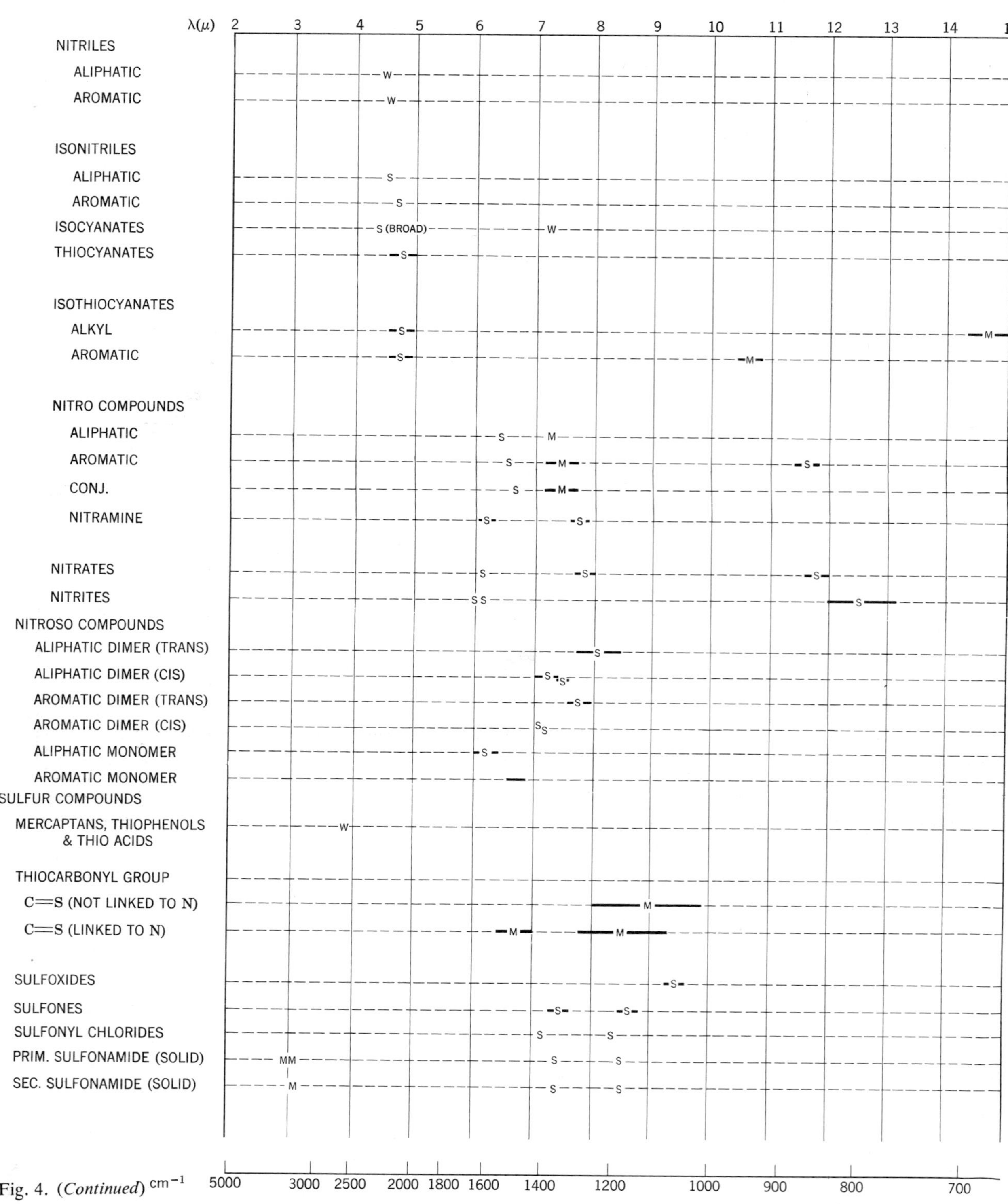

λ(μ) 2 3 4 5 6 7 8 9 10 11 12 13 14 15
NITRILES
ALIPHATIC
AROMATIC
ISONITRILES
ALIPHATIC
AROMATIC
ISOCYANATES
S (BROAD)
THIOCYANATES
ISOTHIOCYANATES
ALKYL
AROMATIC
NITRO COMPOUNDS
ALIPHATIC
AROMATIC
CONJ.
NITRAMINE
NITRATES
NITRITES
NITROSO COMPOUNDS
ALIPHATIC DIMER (TRANS)
ALIPHATIC DIMER (CIS)
AROMATIC DIMER (TRANS)
AROMATIC DIMER (CIS)
ALIPHATIC MONOMER
AROMATIC MONOMER
SULFUR COMPOUNDS
MERCAPTANS, THIOPHENOLS & THIO ACIDS
THIOCARBONYL GROUP
C=S (NOT LINKED TO N)
C=S (LINKED TO N)
SULFOXIDES
SULFONES
SULFONYL CHLORIDES
PRIM. SULFONAMIDE (SOLID)
SEC. SULFONAMIDE (SOLID)
cm⁻¹ 5000 3000 2500 2000 1800 1600 1400 1200 1000 900 800 700

Fig. 4. (*Continued*)

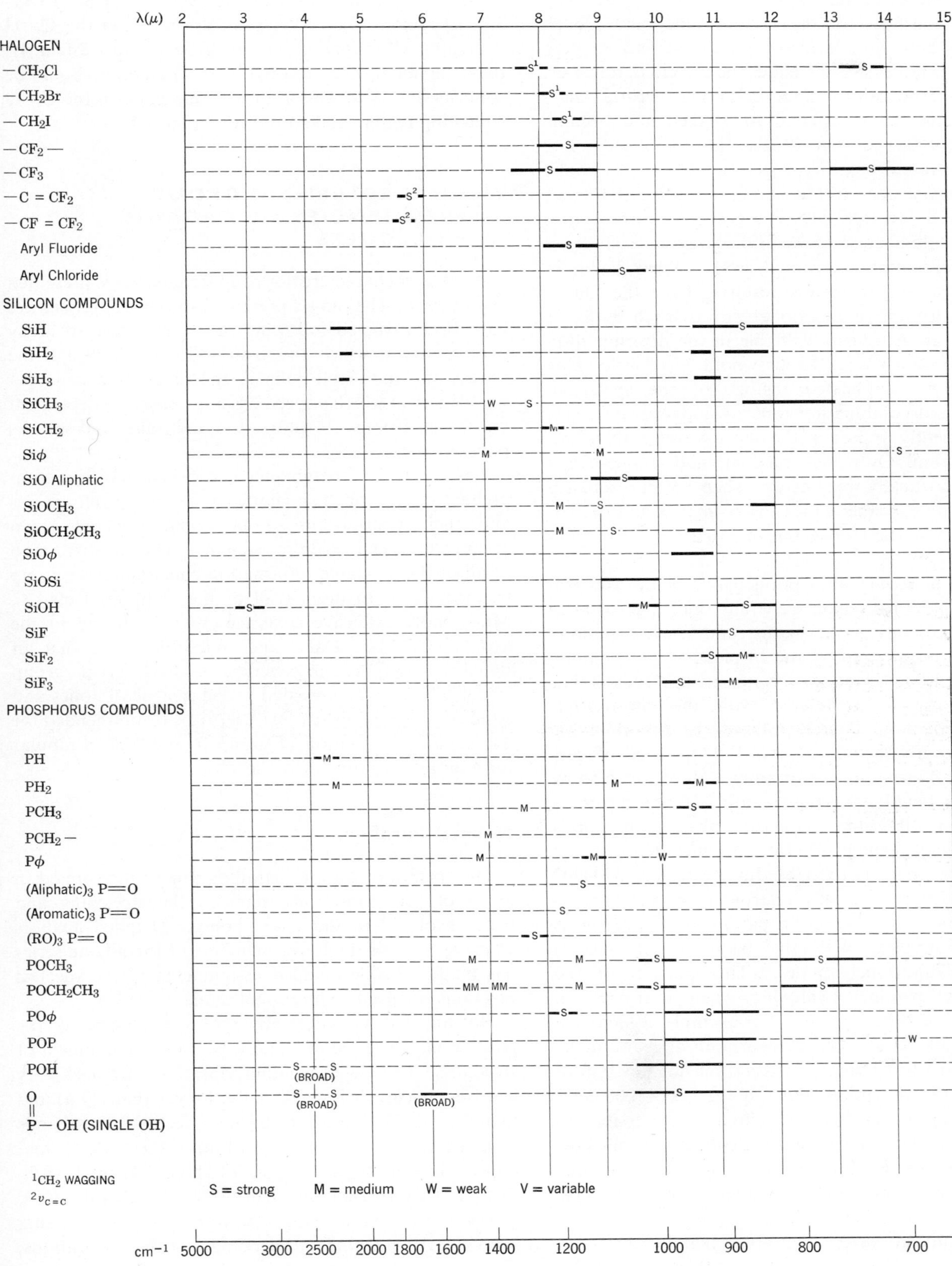

Fig. 4. (*Continued*)

portion of the spectrum. The absence of absorption in the assigned ranges for the various functional groups can usually be used as evidence for the absence of such groups in the molecule. Care must be exercised, however, in such interpretations since certain structural characteristics may cause a band to weaken and become extremely broad so that it may go unnoticed. For example, intramolecular hydrogen bonding in the enolic form of acetylacetone results in a broad, weak OH band, which may be overlooked. The absence of absorption in the 1850–1540 cm^{-1} (5.40–6.50 μ) region excludes a structure containing a carbonyl group. Weak bands in the short wavelength region, resulting from the fundamental absorption of functional groups such as S—H and C≡C, are extremely valuable in the determination of structure. Such weak bands would be of little value in the more complicated regions of the spectrum. Overtones and combination tones of longer wavelength bands frequently appear in the short wavelength region of the spectrum. Overtone- and combination tone-bands are characteristically weak except when Fermi resonance occurs. Strong skeletal bands for aromatics and heteroaromatics fall in the 1600–1300 cm^{-1} (6.25–7.70 μ) region of the spectrum.

The lack of strong absorption bands in the 909–650 cm^{-1} (11.0–15.4 μ) region generally indicates a nonaromatic structure. Aromatic and heteroaromatic compounds display strong out-of-plane C—H bending and ring bending absorption bands in this region that can frequently be correlated with the substitution pattern. Broad, moderately intense absorption in the long wavelength region suggests the presence of carboxylic acid dimers, amines or amides all of which show out-of-plane bending in this region. If the region is extended to 1000 cm^{-1} (10.0 μ), absorption bands characteristic of olefinic structures are included.

The intermediate portion of the spectrum, 1300–909 cm^{-1} (7.7–11.0 μ) is usually referred to as the "fingerprint" region. The absorption pattern in this region is frequently complex, with the bands originating in interacting vibrational modes. This portion of the spectrum is extremely valuable when examined in reference to the other regions. For example, if alcoholic or phenolic O—H stretching absorption appears in the short-wavelength region of the spectrum, the position of the C—C—O absorption band in the 1260–1000 cm^{-1} (7.93–10.00 μ) region frequently makes it possible to assign the O—H absorption to alcohols and phenols with highly specific structures. Absorption in this intermediate region is probably unique for every molecular species.

Any conclusions arrived at after examination of a particular band should be confirmed where possible by examination of other portions of the spectrum. For example, the assignment of a carbonyl band to an aldehyde should be confirmed by the appearance of a band or a pair of bands in the 2900–2695 cm^{-1} (3.45–3.71 μ) region of the spectrum, arising from the C—H stretching vibration of the aldehyde group. Similarly, the assignment of a carbonyl band to an ester should be confirmed by observation of a strong band in the C—O stretching region, 1300–1100 cm^{-1} (7.6–9.1 μ).

VI. CHARACTERISTIC GROUP FREQUENCIES OF ORGANIC MOLECULES

A table of characteristic group frequencies is presented as Figure 4. The ranges presented for group frequencies have been assigned following the examination of many compounds in which the groups occur. Although the ranges are quite well defined, the precise frequency of wavelength at which a specific group absorbs is dependent on its environment within the molecule and on its physical state.

This section of the chapter is concerned with a comprehensive look at these characteristic group frequencies and their relationship to molecular structure. No attempt has been made to present a detailed discussion of all of the available information concerning the group frequencies or to discuss all of the compound classes. Much more extensive coverages may be found in the text of Colthup, Daly, and Wiberley[12] and that of Bellamy.[3] A thorough coverage of characteristic group frequencies is also presented in the treatise of Jones and Sandorfy.[1] Nakanishi's text[13] is to be recommended for its concise presentation of group frequencies in tabular form along with illustrative spectra.

Normal Paraffins

The spectra of normal paraffins can be interpreted in terms of four vibrations, namely, the stretching and bending of C—H and C—C bonds. Detailed analysis of the spectra of the lower members of the alkane series has made possible detailed assignments of the spectral positions of specific vibrational modes.

Not all of the possible absorption frequencies of the paraffin molecule are of equal value in the assignment of structure. The C—C bending vibrations occur at very low frequencies (below 500 cm^{-1}, longer than 20 μ) and therefore do not appear in our spectra. The bands assigned to C—C stretching vibrations are weak, and appear in the broad region of 1200–800 cm^{-1} (8.3–12.5 μ); they are generally of little value for identification.

The most characteristic vibrations are those arising from C—H stretching and bending. Of these vibrations, those arising from methylene twisting and wagging are usually of limited diagnostic value because of their weakness and instability; this instability is a result of strong coupling to the remainder of the molecule.

The vibrational modes of paraffins are common to many organic molecules. Although the positions of C—H stretching and bending frequencies of methyl and methylene groups remain nearly constant in hydrocarbons, the attachment of CH_3 or CH_2 to atoms other than carbon, or to a carbonyl group or aromatic ring, may result in appreciable shifts of the C—H stretching and bending frequencies. These shifts are summarized in Tables I and II of the Appendix to this chapter.

C—H *Stretching Vibrations*

Absorption arising from C—H stretching in the alkanes occurs in the general region of 3000–2840 cm^{-1} (3.3–3.5 μ). The positions of the C—H stretching vibrations are among the most stable in the spectrum. When a spectrum is obtained with an instrument using a sodium chloride prism, the bands in this region are frequently unresolved. Resolution is achieved through the use of a fluoride prism or a grating instrument.

METHYL GROUPS. An examination of a large number of saturated hydrocarbons containing methyl groups showed, in all cases, two distinct bands occurring at 2962 cm^{-1} (3.38 μ) and at 2872 cm^{-1} (3.48 μ). The first of these results from the asymmetrical stretching mode in which two C—H bonds of the methyl group are extending while the third one is contracting ($\nu_{as}CH_3$). The second arises from symmetrical stretching ($\nu_{s}CH_3$) in which all three of the C—H bonds extend and contract in phase. The presence of several methyl groups in a molecule results in strong absorption at these positions.

METHYLENE GROUPS. The asymmetrical stretching ($\nu_{as}CH_2$) and symmetrical stretching ($\nu_{s}CH_2$) occur, respectively, near 2926 cm^{-1} (3.43 μ) and 2853 cm^{-1} (3.51 μ). The positions of these bands do not vary more than ± 10 cm^{-1} in the aliphatic and nonstrained cyclic hydrocarbons. The frequency of methylene stretching is increased when the methylene group is part of a strained ring.

C—H *Bending Vibrations*

METHYL GROUPS. Two bending vibrations can occur within a methyl group. The first of these, the symmetrical bending vibration, involves the in-phase bending of the C—H bonds (I). The second, the asymmetrical bending vibration, involves out-of-phase bending of the C—H bonds (II).

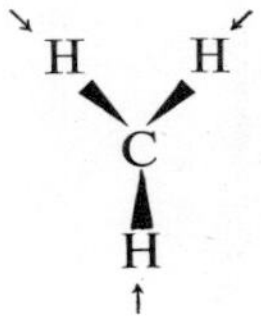

H H
C (I) 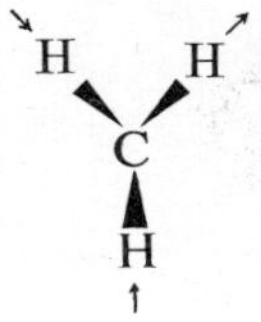
H

H H
C (II)
H

In the above diagrams, the carbon atom is behind the plane of the page with the hydrogen atoms lying and moving essentially in the plane of the page. The symmetrical bending vibration ($\delta_s CH_3$) occurs near 1375 cm^{-1} (7.28 μ), the asymmetrical bending vibration ($\delta_{as}CH_3$) near 1450 cm^{-1} (6.90 μ).

The asymmetrical vibration generally overlaps the scissoring vibration of the methylene group (vide infra). Two distinct bands are observed, however, in compounds such as diethyl ketone, in which the methylene scissoring band has been shifted to a lower frequency, 1439–1399 cm^{-1} (6.95–7.15 μ), and increased in intensity because of its proximity to the carbonyl group.

The absorption band near 1375 cm^{-1} (7.28 μ), arising from the symmetrical bending of the methyl C—H bonds, is very stable in position when the methyl group is attached to another carbon atom. The intensity of this band is greater for each methyl group in the compound than that for the asymmetrical methyl bending vibration or the methylene scissoring vibration.

METHYLENE GROUPS. The bending vibrations of the C—H bonds in the methylene group have already been shown schematically in Figure 1. The four bending vibrations are referred to as scissoring, rocking, wagging, and twisting.

The scissoring band ($\delta_s CH_2$) in the spectra of hydrocarbons occurs at a nearly constant position near 1465 cm^{-1} (6.83 μ).

The band resulting from the methylene rocking vibration (ρ CH_2), in which all of the methylene groups rock in phase, appears near 720 cm^{-1} (13.9 μ) for straight chain paraffins of seven or more carbons. This band may appear as a doublet in the spectra of solid samples. In the lower members of the *n*-paraffin series, the band appears at somewhat higher frequencies.

Absorption of hydrocarbons, due to methylene twisting and wagging vibrations, is observed in the 1350–1150 cm^{-1} (7.4–8.7 μ) region. These bands are generally appreciably weaker than those resulting from methylene scissoring. A series of bands in this region, arising from the methylene group, is characteristic of the spectra of solid samples of long-chain acids, amides, and esters.

Branched Chain Hydrocarbons

In general, the changes brought about in the spectrum of a hydrocarbon by branching result from changes in skeletal stretching vibrations and methyl bending vibrations; these occur below 1500 cm^{-1} (longer than 6.7 μ).

C—H *Stretching Vibrations*

TERTIARY C—H GROUPS. Absorption resulting from this vibrational mode is very weak and is usually lost in other aliphatic C—H absorption. Absorption in hydrocarbons occurs near 2890 cm^{-1} (3.46 μ).

C—H *Bending Vibrations*

GEM-DIMETHYL GROUPS. Configurations in which two methyl groups are attached to the same carbon atom exhibit distinctive absorption in the C—H bending region. The isopropyl group shows a strong doublet, with peaks of almost equal intensity, at 1385–1380 cm^{-1} (7.22–7.25 μ) and at 1370–1365 cm^{-1} (7.30–7.33 μ). The tertiary butyl group gives rise to two C—H bending bands, one in the 1395–1385 cm^{-1} (7.17–7.22 μ) region and one near 1370 cm^{-1} (7.30 μ). In the *t*-butyl doublet, the long wavelength band is more intense. When the gem-dimethyl group occurs at an internal position, a doublet is observed in essentially the same region where absorption occurs for the isopropyl and *t*-butyl groups. Doublets are observed for gem-dimethyl groups because of interaction between the in-phase and out-of-phase symmetrical CH_3 bending of the two methyl groups attached to a common carbon atom.

Weak bands result from methyl rocking vibrations in isopropyl and *t*-butyl groups. These vibrations are sensitive to mass and interaction with skeletal stretching modes and are generally less reliable than the C—H bending vibrations. The following assignments have been made: isopropyl group, 922–919 cm^{-1} (10.85–10.88 μ), and *t*-butyl group, 932–926 cm^{-1} (10.73–10.80 μ).

Cycloparaffins

C—H *Stretching Vibrations*

The methylene stretching vibrations of unstrained cyclic polymethylene structures are much the same as those observed for acyclic paraffins. Increasing ring strain moves the C—H stretching bands progressively to higher frequencies. The ring CH_2 and CH groups in a monoalkyl cyclopropane ring absorb in the region of 3100–2990 cm^{-1} (3.23 to 3.34 μ).

C—H *Bending Vibrations*

Cyclization decreases the frequency of the CH_2 scissoring vibration. Cyclohexane absorbs at 1452 cm^{-1} (6.89 μ), whereas *n*-hexane absorbs at 1468 cm^{-1} (6.81 μ). Cyclopentane absorbs at 1455 cm^{-1} (6.87 μ), cyclopropane at 1442 cm^{-1} (6.94 μ). This shift frequently makes it possible to observe distinct bands for methylene and methyl absorption in this region.

Olefinic Hydrocarbons

Olefinic structure introduces several new modes of vibration into a hydrocarbon molecule: a C═C stretching vibration, C—H stretching vibrations in which the carbon atom is present in the olefinic linkage, and in-plane and out-of-plane bending of the olefinic C—H bond.

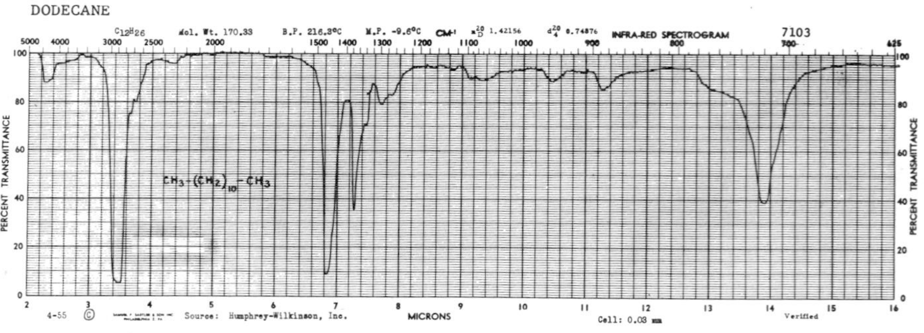

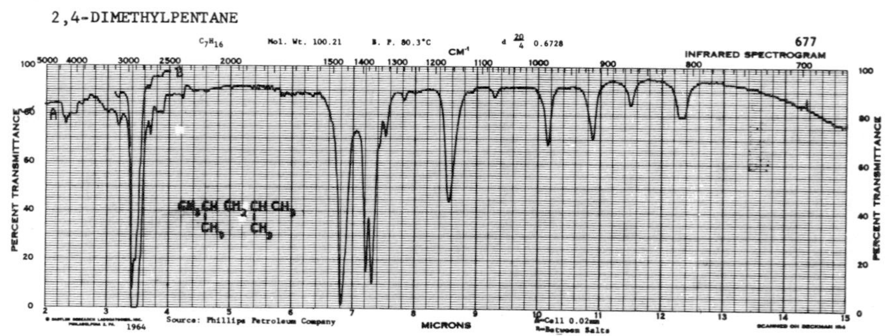

C═C *Stretching Vibrations*

UNCONJUGATED LINEAR OLEFINS. The C═C stretching mode of unconjugated olefins usually shows moderate to weak absorption at 1660–1640 cm^{-1} (6.00–6.10 μ). Monosubstituted olefins, i.e., vinyl groups, absorb near 1640 cm^{-1} (6.10 μ) with moderate intensity. Disubstituted *trans*-olefins, tri-, and tetra-alkyl substituted olefins absorb at or near 1670 cm^{-1} (5.99 μ); disubstituted *cis*-olefins and vinylidene olefins absorb near 1650 cm^{-1} (6.06 μ).

The absorption of symmetrical disubstituted *trans*-olefins or tetrasubstituted olefins may be extremely weak or absent. *Cis*-olefins, which lack the symmetry of the *trans* structure, absorb more strongly than *trans*-olefins. Internal double bonds generally absorb more weakly than terminal double bonds because of pseudosymmetry.

Abnormally high frequency absorption is observed for —CH═CF_2 and —CF═CF_2 groups. The former absorbs near 1754 cm^{-1} (5.70 μ), the latter near 1786 cm^{-1} (5.60 μ). In contrast, the absorption frequency is reduced by the attachment of chlorine, bromine, or iodine.

CYCLOOLEFINS. Absorption of the internal double bond in the unstrained cyclohexene system is essentially the same as that of a *cis* isomer in an acyclic system. The C═C stretch vibration is coupled with the C—C stretching of the adjacent bonds. As the angle α (C—C(α)═C) becomes smaller the interaction becomes less until it is at a minimum at 90° in cyclobutene, (1566 cm^{-1}, 6.39 μ). In the cyclopropene structure, interaction again becomes appreciable and the absorption frequency increases, (1641 cm^{-1}, 6.09 μ).

The substitution of alkyl groups for an α-hydrogen atom in strained ring systems serves to increase the frequency of C═C absorption. Cyclobutene absorbs at 1566 cm^{-1} (6.39 μ), 1-methylcyclobutene at 1641 cm^{-1} (6.09 μ).

The absorption frequency of external (exo) olefinic bonds increases with decreasing ring size. Methylenecyclohexane absorbs at 1650 cm^{-1} (6.06 μ), methylenecyclopropane at 1781 cm^{-1} (5.62 μ).

CONJUGATED SYSTEMS. The olefinic bond stretching vibrations in conjugated dienes without a center of symmetry interact to produce two C═C stretching bands. The spectrum of an unsymmetrical conjugated diene, such as 1,3 pentadiene, shows absorption near 1650 cm^{-1} (6.06 μ) and near 1600 cm^{-1} (6.25 μ). The symmetrical molecule, 1,3 butadiene, shows only one band near 1600 cm^{-1} (6.25 μ), resulting from asymmetric stretching; the symmetrical stretching band is inactive in the infrared.

Conjugation of an olefinic double bond with an aromatic ring produces enhanced olefinic absorption near 1625 cm^{-1} (6.15 μ).

The absorption frequency of the olefinic bond in conjugation with a carbonyl group is lowered by about 30 cm^{-1} (ca 0.11 μ); the intensity of absorption is increased. In *s-cis* structures, the olefinic absorption may be as intense as that of the carbonyl group. *s-Trans* structures absorb more weakly than *s-cis* structures.

CUMULATED OLEFINS. A cumulated double bond system, as occurs in the allenes (>C═C═CH_2), absorbs near 2000–1900 cm^{-1} (5.00–5.26 μ). The absorption results from asymmetric C═C═C stretching. The absorption may be considered an extreme case of exocyclic C═C absorption.

Olefinic C—H *Stretching Vibrations*

In general, any C—H stretching bands above 3000 cm^{-1} (below 3.33 μ) result from aromatic, heteroaromatic, acetylenic, or olefinic C—H stretching. Also found in the same region, are the C—H stretching in small rings such as cyclopropane, and the C—H in halogenated alkyl groups. The frequency and intensity of olefinic C—H stretching absorption are influenced by the pattern of substitution. With proper resolution, multiple bands are observed for structures in which stretching interaction may occur. For example, the vinyl group produces three closely spaced C—H stretching bands. Two of these result from symmetrical and asymmetrical stretching of the terminal C—H groups, and the third from the stretching of the remaining single C—H.

Olefinic C—H *Bending Vibrations*

Olefinic C—H bonds can undergo bending either in the same plane as the C═C bond, or perpendicular to it; the bending vibrations can be either in-phase or out-of-phase with respect to each other.

Assignments have been made for a few of the more prominent and reliable in-plane bending vibrations. The vinyl group absorbs near 1416 cm^{-1} (7.06 μ), due to a scissoring vibration of the terminal methylene. The C—H rocking vibration of a *cis*-disubstituted olefin occurs in the same general region.

The most characteristic vibrational modes of olefins are the out-of-plane C—H bending vibrations between 1000 and 650 cm^{-1} (10.0 and 15.4 μ). These bands are usually the strongest in the spectra of olefins. The most reliable bands are those of the vinyl group, the vinylidene group, and the trans disubstituted olefins. Olefinic absorption is summarized in Table III of the Appendix.

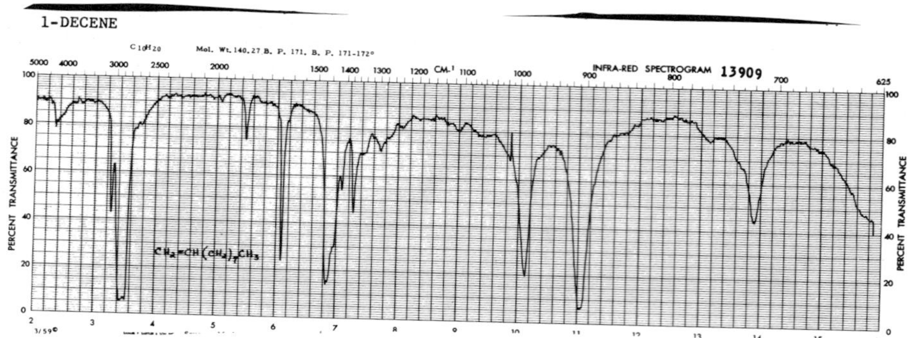

In allene structures, strong absorption is observed near 850 cm^{-1} (11.76 μ), arising from $=CH_2$ wagging. The first overtone of this band may also be seen.

Acetylenic Hydrocarbons

The two stretching vibrations in acetylenic molecules involve C≡C and C—H stretching. Absorption due to C—H bending is characteristic of acetylene and monosubstituted acetylenes.

C≡C *Stretching Vibrations*

The weak C≡C stretching band of acetylenic molecules occurs in the region of 2260–2100 cm^{-1} (4.43–4.76 μ). Because of symmetry, no C≡C band is observed in the infrared for acetylene and symmetrically substituted acetylenes. In the infrared spectra of monosubstituted acetylenes, the band appears at 2140–2100 cm^{-1} (4.67–4.76 μ). Disubstituted acetylenes, in which the substituents are different, absorb near 2260–2190 cm^{-1} (4.43–4.57 μ). When the substituents are similar in mass, or produce similar inductive and mesomeric effects, the band may be so weak as to be unobserved in the infrared spectrum. For reasons of symmetry, a terminal C≡C produces a stronger band than an internal C≡C (pseudosymmetry). The intensity of the C≡C stretching band is increased by conjugation with a carbonyl group.

C—H *Stretching Vibrations*

The C—H stretching band of monosubstituted acetylenes occurs in the general region of 3333–3267 cm^{-1} (3.00–3.06 μ). This is a strong band and is narrower than the bonded OH and NH bands occurring in the same region.

C—H *Bending Vibrations*

The C—H bending vibration of acetylene or monosubstituted acetylenes leads to strong, broad absorption in the 700–610 cm^{-1} (14.29–16.39 μ) region. The first overtone of the C—H bending vibration appears as a weak, broad band in the 1370–1220 cm^{-1} (7.30–8.20 μ) region.

Mononuclear Aromatic Hydrocarbons

The most prominent and most informative bands in the spectra of aromatic compounds occur in the low-frequency range between 900 and 675 cm^{-1} (11.11 and 14.82 μ). These strong absorption bands result from the out-of-plane bending of the ring C—H bonds. In-plane bending bands appear in the 1300—1000 cm^{-1} (7.70–10.00 μ) region. Skeletal vibrations, involving carbon to carbon stretching within the ring, absorb in the 1600–1585 cm^{-1} (6.25–6.31 μ) and in the 1500–1400

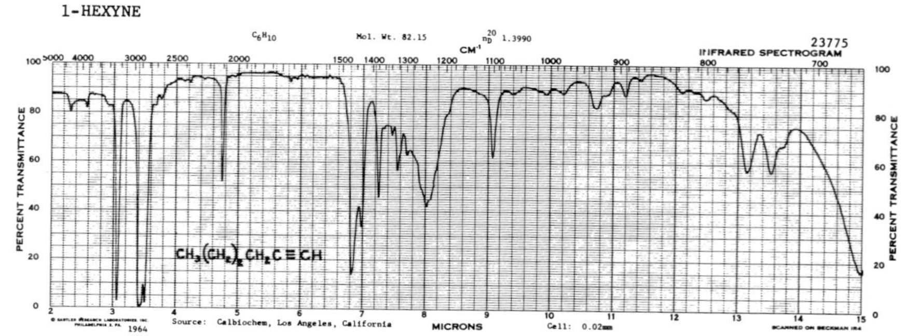

cm^{-1} (6.67–7.14 μ) regions. The skeletal bands frequently appear as doublets, depending upon the nature of the ring substituents.

Aromatic C—H stretching bands occur between 3100 and 3000 cm^{-1} (3.23–3.33 μ).

Weak combination and overtone bands appear in the 2000–1650 cm^{-1} (5.00–6.06 μ) region. The pattern of the overtone bands is characteristic of the substitution pattern of the ring. Because they are weak, the overtone and combination bands are most readily observed in spectra obtained from thick samples.

Out-of-Plane C—H *Bending Vibrations*

The in-phase, out-of-plane bending of a ring hydrogen atom is strongly coupled to adjacent hydrogen atoms. The position of absorption of the out-of-plane bending bands is, therefore, characteristic of the number of adjacent hydrogen atoms on the ring. The bands are frequently intense, and may be used for the quantitative determination of the relative concentrations of isomers in mixtures.

Assignments for C—H out-of-plane bending bands in the spectra of substituted benzenes appear in the chart of characteristic group frequencies (Fig. 4). These assignments are usually reliable for alkyl substituted benzenes, but caution must be observed in the interpretation of spectra when polar groups are attached directly to the ring, e.g., nitrobenzenes, aromatic acids, and esters or amides of aromatic acids.

The absorption band that frequently appears in the spectra of substituted benzenes near 710–675 cm^{-1} (14.08–14.81 μ) is attributed to out-of-plane ring bending.

Polynuclear Aromatic Compounds

Polynuclear aromatic compounds, like the mononuclear aromatics, show characteristic absorption in three regions of the spectrum.

The aromatic C—H stretching and the skeletal vibrations absorb in the same regions as observed for the mononuclear aromatics. The most characteristic absorption of polynuclear aromatics results from C—H out-of-plane bending in the 900–675 cm^{-1} (11.11–14.81 μ) region. These bands can be correlated with the number of adjacent hydrogen atoms on the rings. Most β-substituted naphthalenes, for example, show three absorption bands due to out-of-plane C—H bending; these correspond to an isolated hydrogen atom and 2 adjacent hydrogen atoms on one ring and 4 adjacent hydrogen atoms on the other ring.

C—H *Out-of-Plane Bending Vibrations of a β-Substituted Naphthalene*

Isolated hydrogen	862–835 cm^{-1} (11.60–11.98 μ)
2 Adjacent hydrogens	835–805 cm^{-1} (11.98–12.42 μ)
4 Adjacent hydrogens	760–735 cm^{-1} (13.16–13.61 μ)

In the spectra of α-substituted naphthalenes the bands for the isolated hydrogen and the two adjacent hydrogens of β-naphthalenes are replaced by a band for three adjacent hydrogens. This band is near 810–785 cm^{-1} (12.34–12.74 μ).

Additional bands may appear due to ring bending vibrations. The position of absorption bands for more highly substituted naphthalenes and other polynuclear aromatics are summarized by Colthup.[12]

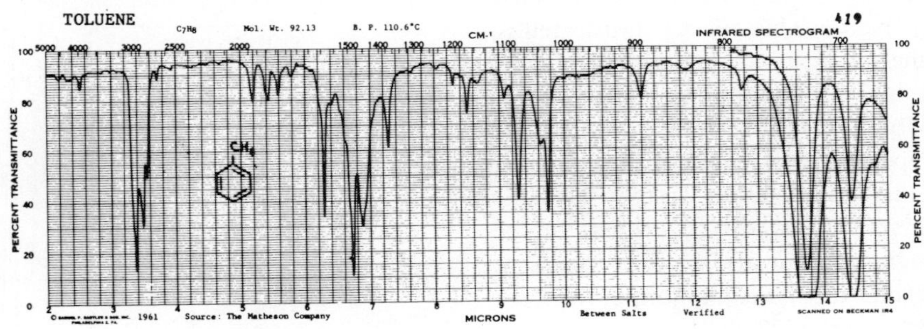

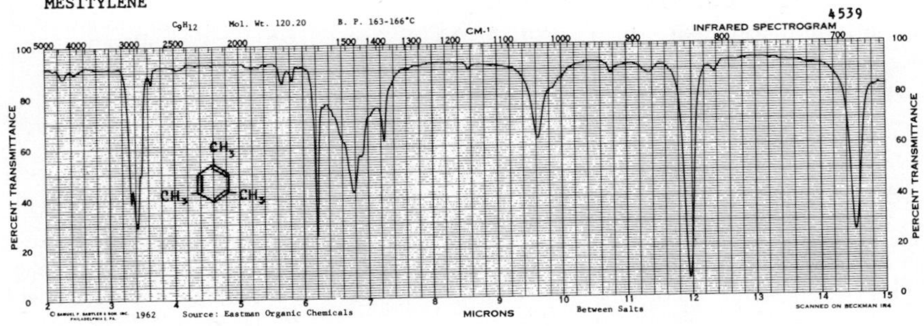

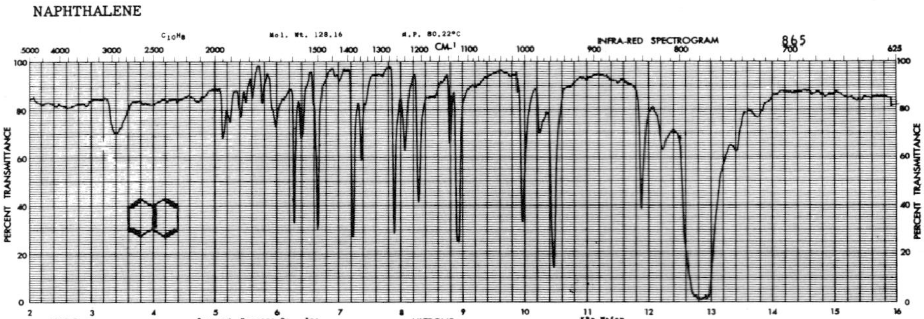

Alcohols and Phenols

The characteristic bands observed in the spectra of alcohols and phenols result from O—H stretching, C—O stretching, and O—H bending vibrations. All of these vibrations are sensitive to hydrogen bonding. The C—O stretching and O—H bending modes are not independent vibrational modes because they couple with the vibrations of adjacent groups.

O—H *Stretching Vibrations*

The unbonded or "free" hydroxyl group of alcohols and phenols absorbs strongly in the 3650–3584 cu^{-1} (2.74–2.79 μ) region. Sharp, "free" hydroxyl bands are observed only in the vapor phase or in very dilute solution in nonpolar solvents. Intermolecular hydrogen bonding increases as the concentration of the solution increases, and additional bands start to appear at lower frequencies, 3550–3200 cm^{-1} (2.82–3.13 μ), at the expense of the "free" hydroxyl band. This effect is illustrated in Figure 5, in which the absorption bands in the O—H stretching region are shown for two different concentrations of cyclohexyl carbinol in carbon tetrachloride. For comparisons of this type, the path length of the cell must be altered with changing concentration, so that the same number of absorbing molecules will be present in the infrared beam at each concentration. The band at 3623 cm^{-1} (2.76 μ) results from the monomer, whereas the broad absorption near 3333 cm^{-1} (3.00 μ) arises from "polymeric" structures.

Weak intramolecular bonding frequently occurs when a hydroxyl group is situated adjacent to a proton acceptor group (X).

X···HO | | H_2C—CH_2

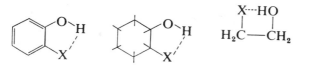

The acceptor group may be a heteroatom or a group containing π-electrons such as a double bond. Intramolecular bonding of this type causes a slight shift of absorption to longer wavelengths, 3600–3450 cm^{-1} (2.78–2.91 μ), compared with "free" OH absorption. The band is generally sharp but may undergo slight broadening. Intramolecular bonding is essentially independent of concentration. Studies to detect intramolecular hydrogen bonding, free from interference from intermolecular hydrogen bonding, are usually carried out in carbon tetrachloride at concentrations less than 0.005 molar. High resolution is necessary.

In the spectra of compounds such as methyl salicylate or *o*-hydroxyacetophenone, in which strong intramolecular bonding exists, a broad, medium to strong band is observed near 3077 cm^{-1} (3.25 μ).

In structures such as 2,6-di-*t*-butylphenol, in which steric hindrance prevents hydrogen bonding, no bonded O—H band is observed even in the spectra of neat samples.

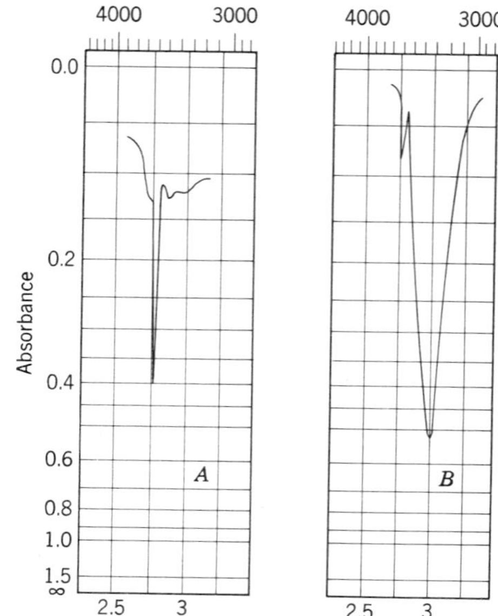

Fig. 5. Infrared spectrum of the O—H stretching region of cyclohexyl carbinol in CCl_4. *A* 0.03 *M* (0.406 mm cell); *B* 1.00 *M* (0.014 mm cell).

C—O *Stretching Vibrations*

The C—O stretching vibrations in alcohols and phenols produce a strong band in the 1260–1000 cm^{-1} (7.93–10.00 μ) region of the spectrum. The C—O stretching mode is coupled with the adjacent C—C stretching vibration; thus in primary alcohols the vibration might better be described as an asymmetric C—C—O stretching vibration. The vibrational mode is further complicated by branching and α, β-unsaturation. These effects are summarized as follows for a series of secondary alcohols (neat samples):

Methylethylcarbinol	1105 cm^{-1} (9.05 μ)
Methylisopropylcarbinol	1091 cm^{-1} (9.17 μ)
Methylphenylcarbinol	1073 cm^{-1} (9.32 μ)
Methylvinylcarbinol	1058 cm^{-1} (9.45 μ)
Diphenylcarbinol	1014 cm^{-1} (9.86 μ)

The absorption ranges of the various types of alcohols appear in Table II. These values are for neat samples of the alcohols.

Solid samples of phenols absorb at 1390–1330 cm^{-1} (7.20–7.52 μ) and 1260–1180 cm^{-1} (7.93–8.48 μ). These bands apparently result from interaction between O—H bending and C—O stretching. The long wavelength band is the stronger and both bands appear at longer wavelengths in spectra observed in solution.

O—H *Bending Vibrations*

The O—H in-plane bending vibration occurs in the general region of 1420–1330 cm^{-1} (7.04–7.52 μ). In primary and secondary alcohols the O—H in-plane bending couples with the C—H wagging vibrations to produce two bands; the first near 1420 cm^{-1} (7.04 μ), the second near 1330 cm^{-1} (7.52 μ). These bands are of little diagnostic value. Tertiary alcohols, in which no coupling can occur, show a single band in this region, the position depending upon the degree of hydrogen bonding.

The spectra of alcohols and phenols determined in the liquid state, show a broad absorption band in the 769–650 cm^{-1} (13.00–15.40 μ) region because of out-of-plane bending of the bonded O—H group.

Ethers, Epoxides, and Peroxides

C—O *Stretching Vibrations*

The characteristic response of ethers in the infrared is associated with the stretching vibration of the C—O—C system. Since the vibrational characteristics of this system would not be expected to differ greatly from the C—C—C system, it is not surprising to find the response to C—O—C stretching in the same general region. However, since vibrations involving oxygen atoms result in greater dipole moment changes than those involving carbon atoms, more intense infrared bands are observed for ethers. The C—O—C stretching bands of ethers, as is the case with the C—O stretching bands of alcohols, involve coupling with other vibrations within the molecule.

In the spectra of aliphatic ethers, the most characteristic absorption is a strong band in the 1150–1085 cm^{-1} (8.70–9.23 μ) region due to asymmetrical C—O—C stretching; this band usually occurs near 1125 cm^{-1} (8.89 μ). The symmetrical stretching band is usually weak and is more readily observed in the Raman spectrum.

The C—O—C group in a six-membered ring absorbs at the same frequency as in an acyclic ether. As the ring

***Table II** Alcoholic C—O Absorption*[28c,40]

ALCOHOL TYPE	ABSORPTION RANGE
(1) Saturated tertiary (2) Secondary, highly symmetrical	1205–1124 cm^{-1} (8.30–8.90 μ)
(1) Saturated secondary (2) α-Unsaturated or cyclic tert.	1124–1087 cm^{-1} (8.90–9.20 μ)
(1) Secondary, α-unsaturated (2) Secondary, alicyclic 5- or 6-membered ring (3) Saturated primary	1085–1050 cm^{-1} (9.22–9.52 μ)
(1) Tertiary, highly α-unsaturated (2) Secondary, di-α-unsaturated (3) Secondary, α-unsaturated and α-branched (4) Secondary, alicyclic 7- or 8-membered ring (5) Primary, α-unsaturated and/or α-branched	>1050 cm^{-1} (9.52 μ)

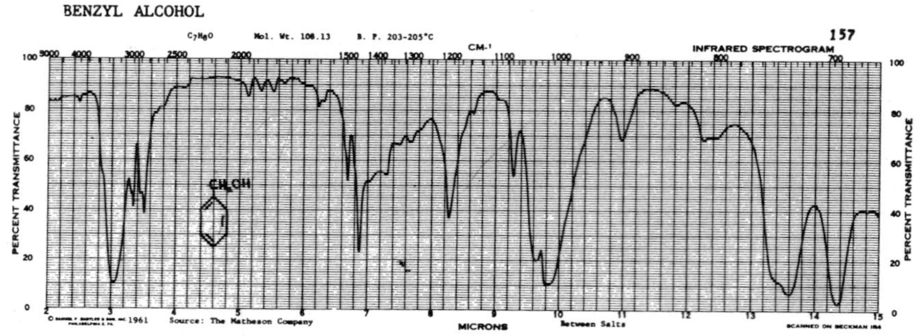

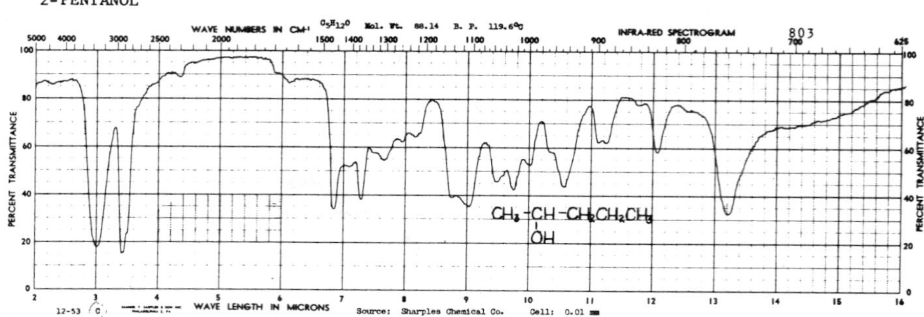

becomes smaller, the asymmetrical C—O—C stretching vibration moves progressively to longer wavelengths, whereas the symmetrical C—O—C stretching vibration (ring breathing frequency) moves to shorter wavelengths.

Branching on the carbon atoms adjacent to the oxygen usually leads to splitting of the C—O—C band. Diisopropyl ether shows a triplet structure in the 1170–1114 cm^{-1} (8.55–8.98 μ) region, the principal band occurring at 1114 cm^{-1} (8.98 μ).

Spectra of aralkyl ethers display an asymmetrical C–O–C stretching band at 1275–1200 cm^{-1} (7.84–8.33 μ) with symmetrical stretching near 1075–1020 cm^{-1} (9.30–9.80 μ). Strong absorption due to asymmetrical C–O–C stretching in vinyl ethers occurs in the 1225–1200 cm^{-1} (8.16–8.33 μ) region with a strong symmetrical band at 1075–1020 cm^{-1} (9.30–9.80 μ). Resonance, which results in strengthening of the C–O bond, is responsible for the shift in the asymmetric absorption band of aralkyl and vinyl ethers.

The C═C stretching band of vinyl ethers occurs in the 1660–1610 cm^{-1} (6.02–6.21 μ) region. This olefinic band is characterized by its higher intensity compared with the C═C stretching band in olefinic hydrocarbons. This band frequently appears as a doublet resulting from absorption of rotational isomers.

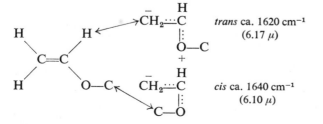

$$
\begin{array}{c}
\text{H}_2\text{C}{=}\text{CH}{-}\text{O}{-}\text{C} \;\longleftrightarrow\; \overset{-}{\text{C}}\text{H}_2{\cdots}\text{CH}{\cdots}\overset{+}{\text{O}}{-}\text{C}
\end{array}
$$

trans ca. 1620 cm^{-1} (6.17 μ)

cis ca. 1640 cm^{-1} (6.10 μ)

Coplanarity in the *trans* isomer allows maximum resonance, thus more effectively reducing the double-bond character of the olefinic linkage. Steric hindrance reduces resonance in the *cis* isomer.

The two bands arising from C—H wagging in terminal olefins occur near 1000 cm^{-1} (10.00 μ) and near 909 cm^{-1} (11.00 μ). In the spectra of vinyl ethers, these bands are shifted to longer wavelengths because of resonance.

$$\text{R—O—C(H)═CH}_2$$

terminal CH_2 wag, 813 cm^{-1} (12.30 μ)
trans CH wag, 960 cm^{-1} (10.42 μ)

Alkyl and aryl peroxides display C—C—O absorption in the 1198–1176 cm^{-1} (8.35–8.50 μ) region. Acyl and aroyl peroxides display two carbonyl absorption bands in the 1818–1754 cm^{-1} (5.50–5.70 μ) region. Two bands are observed because of mechanical interaction between the stretching modes of the two carbonyl groups.

The symmetrical stretching, or ring breathing frequency, of the epoxy ring, all ring bonds stretching and contracting in phase, occurs near 1250 cm^{-1} (8.00 μ). Another band appears in the 950–810 cm^{-1} (10.53–12.35 μ) region attributed to asymmetrical ring stretching in which the C—C bond is stretching during contraction of the C—O bond. A third band, referred to as the "12 μ band," appears in the 840–750 cm^{-1} (11.90–13.33 μ) region. The C—H stretching vibrations of epoxy rings occur in the 3050–2990 cm^{-1} (3.28–3.34 μ) region of the spectrum.

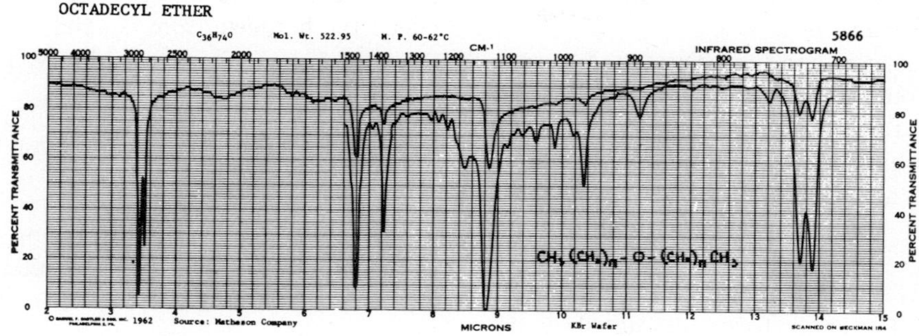

Ketones

C═O *Stretching Vibrations*

Ketones, aldehydes, carboxylic acids, carboxylic esters, lactones, acid halides, anhydrides, amides, and lactams show a strong C═O stretching absorption band in the region of 1870–1540 cm^{-1} (5.35–6.50 μ) Its relatively constant position, high intensity, and relative freedom from interfering bands make this one of the easiest bands to recognize in infrared spectra.

Within its given range, the position of the C═O stretching band is determined by the following factors: (1) the physical state, (2) electrical and mass effects of neighboring substituents, (3) conjugation, (4) hydrogen bonding (intermolecular and intramolecular), and (5) ring strain. Consideration of these factors leads to a considerable amount of information about the environment of the C═O group.

In a discussion of these effects, it is customary to refer to the absorption frequency of a neat sample of a saturated aliphatic ketone, 1715 cm^{-1} (5.83 μ), as "normal." Changes in the environment of the carbonyl can either lower or raise the absorption frequency from this "normal" value.

The absorption frequency observed for a neat sample is increased when absorption is observed in non-polar solvents. Polar solvents reduce the frequency of absorption. The over-all range of solvent effects doesn't exceed 25 cm^{-1}.

Replacement of an alkyl group of a saturated aliphatic ketone by a heteroatom (X) shifts the carbonyl absorption. The direction of the shift depends on whether the inductive effect (a) or resonance effect (b) predominates.

X — C═O — R (a) X$^+$ ═ C—O$^-$ — R (b)

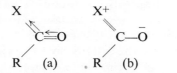

The inductive effect reduces the length of the C═O bond and thus increases its force constant and the frequency of absorption. The resonance effect increases the C═O bond length and reduces the frequency of absorption.

The absorption of several carbonyl compound classes is summarized as follows:

PREDOMINANTLY INDUCTIVE

X	ν C═O
Cl	1815–1785 cm^{-1} (5.51–5.60 μ)
F	ca. 1869 cm^{-1} (5.35 μ)
Br	1812 cm^{-1} (5.52 μ)
OH (monomer)	1760 cm^{-1} (5.68 μ)
OR	1750–1735 cm^{-1} (5.71–5.76 μ)

PREDOMINANTLY RESONANCE

X	ν C═O
NH_2	1695–1650 cm^{-1} (5.90–6.06 μ)
S	1720–1690 cm^{-1} (5.82–5.92 μ)

Conjugation with a C═C bond results in delocalization of the π electrons of both unsaturated groups. Delocalization of the π electrons of the C═O group reduces the double bond character of the C to O bond, causing absorption at longer wavelengths. Conjugation with an olefinic or phenyl group causes absorption in the 1685–1666 cm^{-1} (5.93–6.00 μ) region. Additional conjugation may cause a slight further reduction in frequency.

Steric effects, which reduce the coplanarity of the conjugated system, reduce the effect of conjugation. In the absence of steric hindrance, a conjugated system will tend toward a planar conformation. Thus, α,β-unsaturated ketones may exist in *s-cis* and *s-trans* conformations. When both forms are present, absorption for each of the forms is observed. The absorption of benzalacetone in carbon disulfide, serves as an example; both the *s-cis* and *s-trans* form are present at room temperature.

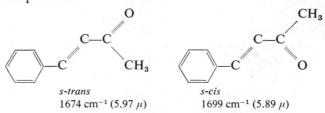

s-trans
1674 cm^{-1} (5.97 μ)

s-cis
1699 cm^{-1} (5.89 μ)

The absorption of the olefinic bond in conjugation with the carbonyl group occurs at a lower frequency and with higher intensity than an isolated olefinic bond; 1626–1600 cm^{-1} (6.15–6.25 μ).

Intermolecular hydrogen bonding between a ketone and a hydroxylic solvent such as methyl alcohol causes a slight decrease in the absorption frequency of the carbonyl group. For example, a neat sample of methyl ethyl ketone absorbs at 1715 cm^{-1} (5.83 μ), whereas a 10% solution of the ketone in methanol absorbs at 1706 cm^{-1} (5.86 μ).

β-Diketones usually exist as mixtures of tautomeric keto and enol forms. The enolic form does not show the normal absorption of conjugated ketones. Instead, a broad band appears in the 1640–1580 cm^{-1} (6.10–6.33 μ) region, many times more intense than normal carbonyl absorption. The intense and displaced absorption results from intramolecular hydrogen bonding, the bonded structure being stabilized by resonance.

```
 OH--------O              +           −
 |         ||             OH--------O
R—C═CR'—C—R"    ↔         ||         |
                        R—C—CR'═C—R"
```

Acetylacetone as a liquid at 40°C exists to the extent of 64% in the enolic form that absorbs at 1613 cm^{-1} (6.20 μ). The keto form and a small amount of unbonded enolic form may be responsible for two bands centering near 1725 cm^{-1} (5.80 μ). Interaction between the two carbonyl groups in the keto form has also been suggested as a cause for this doublet. The enolic O—H stretching absorption is seen as a broad shallow band at 3000–2700 cm^{-1} (3.33–3.70 μ).

α-Diketones, in which carbonyl groups exist in formal conjugation, show a single absorption band near the frequency observed for the corresponding monoketone. Biacetyl absorbs at 1718 cm^{-1} (5.82 μ), dibenzoyl at 1681 cm^{-1} (5.92 μ). Conjugation is ineffective because there is no tendency to form structures with opposite formal charges ($\overset{+}{O}$⋯C⋯C⋯$\overset{-}{O}$) since the oxygen atoms are of equal electronegativity.

Quinones, which have both carbonyl groups in the same ring, absorb in the 1690–1655 cm^{-1} (5.92–6.04 μ) region. With extended conjugation, in which the carbonyl groups appear in different rings, the absorption shifts to the 1655–1635 cm^{-1} (6.04–6.12 μ) region.

Acyclic α-chloro ketones absorb at two frequencies due to rotational isomerism. When the chlorine atom is near the oxygen, its negative field repels the nonbonding electrons of the oxygen atom, thus increasing the force constant of the C═O bond. This conformation absorbs at a higher frequency (1745 cm^{-1}, 5.73 μ) than that in which the carbonyl oxygen and chlorine atom are widely separated (1725 cm^{-1}, 5.80 μ). In rigid molecules such as the monoketo-steroids, α-halogenation results in equatorial or axial substitution. In the equatorial orientation, the halogen atom is near the carbonyl group and the "field effect" causes an increase in the C═O stretching frequency. In the isomer in which the halogen atom is axial to the ring, and distant from the C═O, no shift is observed.

In cyclic ketones, the bond angle of the

```
C
 \
  C═O
 /
C
```

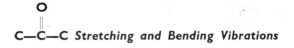

group influences the absorption frequency of the carbonyl group. The C═O stretching undoubtedly is affected by adjacent C—C stretching. In noncyclic ketones and in ketones with a 6-membered ring, the angle is near 120°. In strained rings in which the angle is less than 120° interaction with C—C bond stretching increases the energy required to produce C═O stretching and thus increases the stretching frequency. Cyclohexanone absorbs at 1715 cm^{-1} (5.83 μ); cyclobutanone absorbs at 1775 cm^{-1} (5.63 μ).

C—C(═O)—C *Stretching and Bending Vibrations*

Ketones show moderate absorption in the 1300–1100 cm^{-1} (7.70–9.09 μ) region as a result of C—C(═O)—C stretching and bending in the C—C(═O)—C group. The absorption may consist of multiple bands. Aliphatic ketones absorb in the 1230–1100 cm^{-1} (8.13–9.09 μ) region; aromatic ketones absorb at the higher frequency end of the general absorption region.

The absorption frequencies of methyl and methylene groups, attached to a carbonyl, are summarized in Tables I and II of the Appendix.

Aldehydes

C═O *Stretching Vibrations*

The carbonyl group of aldehydes absorb at slightly higher frequencies than that of the corresponding methyl ketones. Aliphatic aldehydes absorb near 1740–1720 cm^{-1} (5.75–5.82 μ). Aldehydic carbonyl absorption responds to structural changes in the same manner as ketones. Electronegative substitution on the α-carbon increases the frequency of carbonyl absorption. Acetaldehyde absorbs at 1730 cm^{-1} (5.78 μ); trichloroacetaldehyde absorbs at 1768 cm^{-1} (5.65 μ). Conjugate unsaturation, as occurs in α,β-unsaturated and aryl aldehydes, reduces the frequency of carbonyl absorption. α,β-Unsaturated aldehydes and aromatic aldehydes absorb in the region of 1710–1685 cm^{-1} (5.85–5.94 μ). Internal hydrogen bonding, such as occurs in salicylaldehyde, shifts the absorption to 1666 cm^{-1} (6.00 μ).

2-PENTANONE

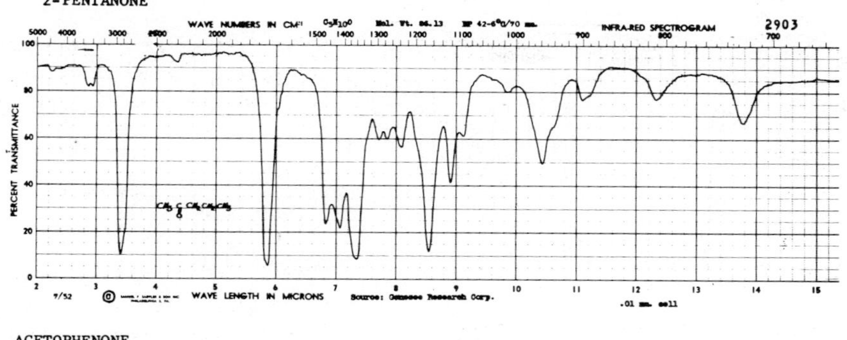

ACETOPHENONE

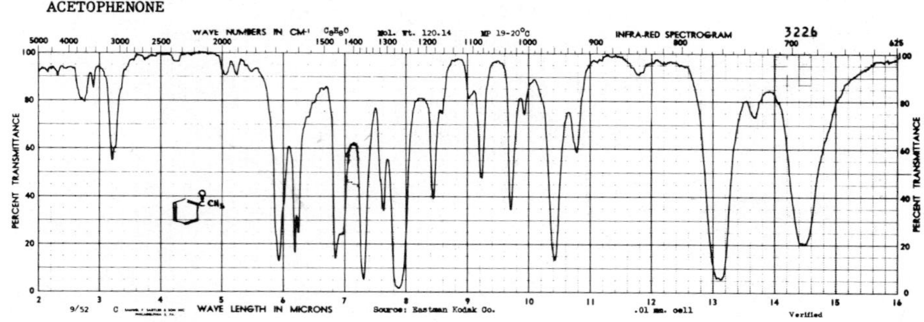

2,4-PENTANEDIONE

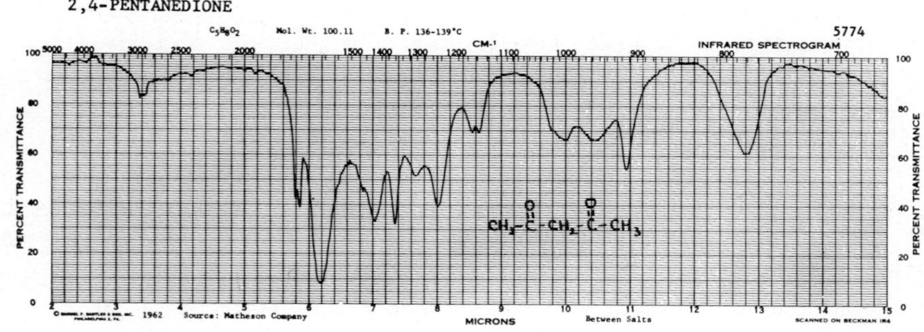

α-Dialdehydes, like the α-diketones, show only one carbonyl absorption peak with no shift from the normal absorption position of mono-aldehydic absorption.

C—H *Stretching Vibrations*

The majority of aldehydes show aldehydic C—H stretching absorption in the 2830–2695 cm^{-1} (3.53–3.71 μ) region. Two moderately intense bands are frequently observed in this region. The appearance of two bands is attributed to Fermi resonance between the fundamental C—H stretch and the first overtone of the C—H bending vibration that usually appears near 1390 cm^{-1} (7.20 μ). Only one C—H stretching band is observed for aldehydes whose C—H bending band has been shifted appreciably from 1390 cm^{-1} (7.20 μ).

Some aromatic aldehydes with strongly electronegative groups in the ortho position may absorb as high as 2900 cm^{-1} (3.45 μ).

Medium intense absorption near 2720 cm^{-1} (3.68 μ) accompanied by a carbonyl absorption band is good evidence for the presence of an aldehyde group.

Carboxylic Acids

O—H *Stretching Vibrations*

In the liquid or solid state, and in carbon tetrachloride solution at concentrations much over 0.01 *M*, carboxylic acids exist as dimers due to strong hydrogen bonding.

```
                                        −       +
     OH------O                          O------HO
    /         \\                       /         \\
R—C             C—R  ←→  R—C                       C—R
    \\         /                       \\         /
     O------HO                          OH------O
                                        +       −
```

The exceptional strength of the hydrogen bonding is explained on the basis of the large contribution of the ionic resonance structure. Because of the strong bonding, a free hydroxyl stretching vibration (near 3520 cm^{-1}, 2.84 μ) is observed only in very dilute solution in nonpolar solvents or in the vapor phase. In each case, however, there is a mixture of monomer and dimer.

Carboxylic acid dimers display very broad, intense O—H stretching absorption in the region of 3300–2500 cm^{-1} (3.03–4.00 μ). The band usually centers near

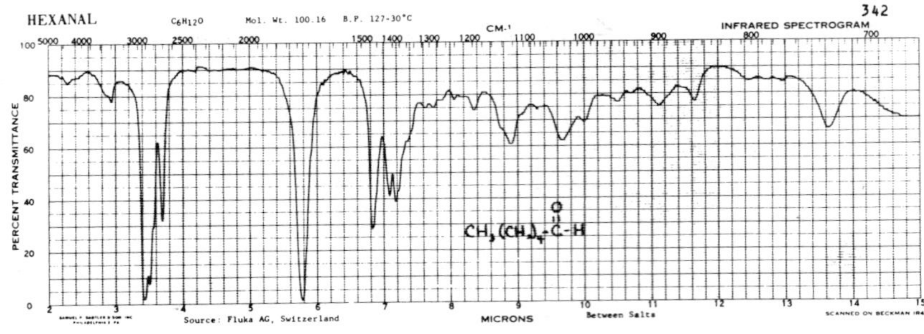

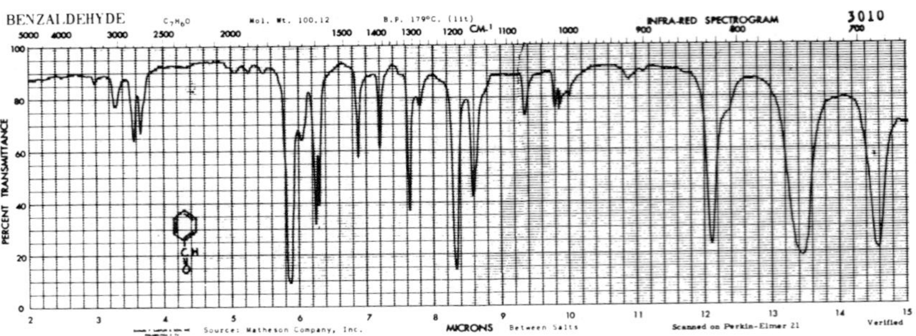

3000 cm^{-1} (3.33 μ). The weaker C—H stretching bands are generally seen superimposed upon the broad O—H band. Fine structure observed on the long wavelength side of the broad O—H band represents overtones and combination tones of fundamental bands occurring at longer wavelengths.

Other structures with strong hydrogen bonding, such as β-diketones, also absorb in the 3300–2500 cm^{-1} (3.03–4.00 μ) region, but the absorption is usually less intense. Also, the C=O stretching vibrations of structures such as β-diketones are shifted to lower frequencies than those observed for carboxylic acids.

Carboxylic acids can bond intermolecularly with ethers such as dioxane and tetrahydrofuran or with other solvents that can act as proton acceptors. Spectra determined in such solvents show bonded O—H absorption near 3100 cm^{-1} (3.23 μ).

C=O *Stretching Vibrations*

The C=O stretching bands of acids are considerably more intense than ketonic C=O stretching bands. The monomers of saturated aliphatic acids absorb near 1760 cm^{-1} (5.68 μ).

The carboxylic dimer has a center of symmetry; only the asymmetrical C=O stretching mode absorbs in the infrared. Hydrogen bonding and resonance weaken the C=O bond, resulting in absorption at a lower frequency than the monomer. The C=O group in dimerized saturated aliphatic acids absorbs in the region of 1720–1706 cm^{-1} (5.81–5.86 μ).

Internal hydrogen bonding reduces the frequency of the carbonyl stretching absorption to a greater degree than does intermolecular hydrogen bonding. For example, salicylic acid absorbs at 1665 cm^{-1} (6.01 μ), whereas *p*-hydroxybenzoic acid absorbs at 1680 cm^{-1} (5.95 μ).

Unsaturation in conjugation with the carboxylic carbonyl group decreases the frequency (increases the wavelength) of absorption of both the monomer and dimer forms only slightly. In general, α,β-unsaturated and aryl conjugated acids show absorption for the dimer in the 1710–1680 cm^{-1} (5.85–5.95 μ) region. Extension of conjugation beyond the α,β-position results in very little additional shifting of the C=O absorption.

Substitution in the α-position with electronegative groups, such as the halogens, brings about a slight increase in the C=O absorption frequency (10–20 cm^{-1}; 0.03–0.07 μ). The spectra of acids with halogens in the α-position, determined in the liquid state or in solution, show dual carbonyl bands due to rotational isomerism (field effect). The higher frequency (shorter wavelength) band corresponds to the conformation in which the halogen is in proximity to the carbonyl group.

C—O *Stretching and* O—H *Bending Vibrations*

Two bands arising from C—O stretching and O—H bending appear in the spectra of carboxylic acids near 1320–1210 cm^{-1} (7.58–8.26 μ) and near 1440–1395 cm^{-1} (6.95–7.17 μ), respectively. Both of these bands involve some interaction between C—O stretching and in-plane C—O—H bending. The more intense band, near 1315–1280 cm^{-1} (7.60–7.81 μ) for dimers, is generally referred to as the C—O stretching band, and usually appears as a doublet in the spectra of long-chain fatty

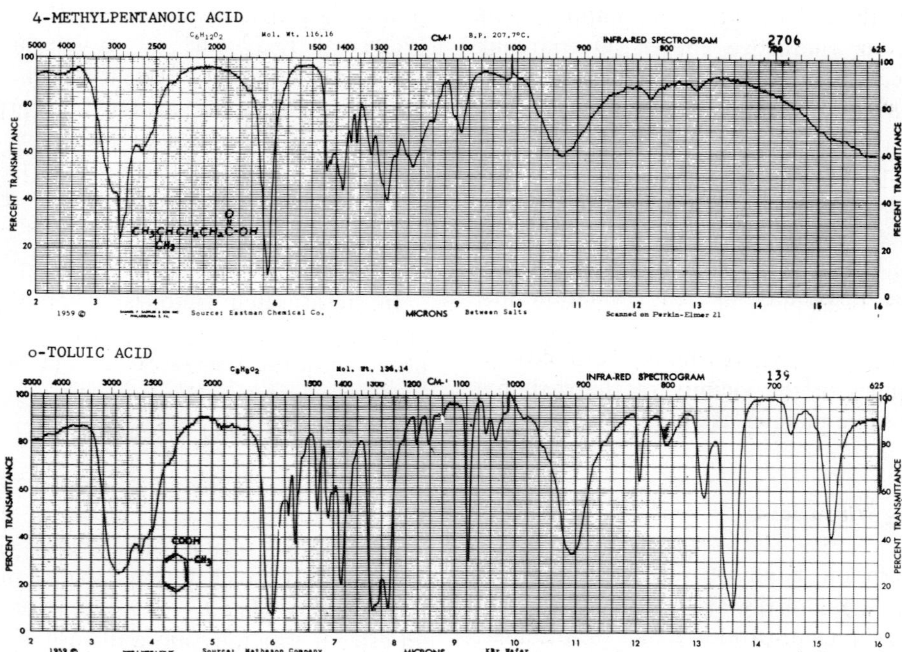

acids. The C—O—H bending band near 1440–1395 cm^{-1} (6.95–7.17 μ) is weak and occurs in the same region as the CH_2 scissoring vibration of the CH_2 group adjacent to the carbonyl.

One of the characteristic bands in the spectra of dimeric carboxylic acids results from the out-of-plane bending of the bonded O—H. The band appears near 920 cm^{-1} (10.87 μ) and is characteristically broad with medium intensity.

Carboxylate Anion

The carboxylate anion has two strongly coupled carbon to oxygen bonds with bond strengths intermediate between C═O and C—O.

$$-C\!\!\begin{array}{l}\nearrow O\\ \searrow O\end{array}\;^{-}$$

The carboxylate ion gives rise to two bands: a strong asymmetrical stretching band near 1650–1550 cm^{-1} (6.06–6.45 μ), and a weaker, symmetrical stretching band near 1400 cm^{-1} (7.15 μ).

The conversion of a carboxylic acid to a salt can serve as confirmation of the acid structure. This is conveniently done by the addition of a tertiary, aliphatic amine, such as triethylamine, to a solution of the carboxylic acid in chloroform (no reaction occurs in carbon tetrachloride). The carboxylate ion, thus formed, shows the two characteristic carbonyl absorption bands in addition to an "ammonium" band in the 2700–2200 cm^{-1} (3.70–4.55 μ) region. The O—H stretching band, of course, disappears.

Esters and Lactones

Esters and lactones have two characteristically strong absorption bands arising from C═O and C—O stretching. The intense C═O stretching vibration occurs at higher frequencies (shorter wavelength) than that of normal ketones. The force constant of the carbonyl

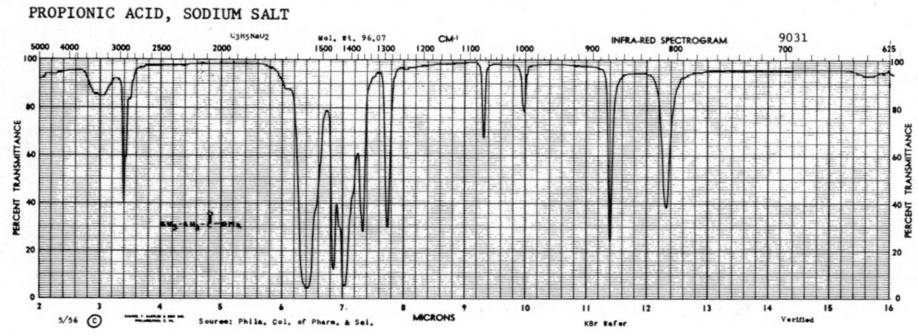

bond is increased by the electron attracting nature of the adjacent oxygen atom (inductive effect). Overlapping occurs between esters in which the carbonyl frequency is lowered, and ketones in which the normal ketone frequency is raised. A distinguishing feature of esters and lactones, however, is the strong C—O stretching band in the region where a weaker band occurs for ketones. There is overlapping in the C═O frequency of esters or lactones and acids, but the OH stretching and bending vibrations, and the possibility of salt formation distinguish the acids.

The frequency of the ester carbonyl responds to environmental changes in the vicinity of the carbonyl group in much the same manner as ketones.

C═O *Stretching Vibrations*

The C═O absorption band of saturated aliphatic esters (except formates) is in the 1750–1735 cm^{-1} (5.71–5.76 μ) region. The C═O absorption bands of formates, α,β-unsaturated, and aryl esters are in the region of 1730–1715 cm^{-1} (5.78–5.83 μ). Further conjugation has little or no additional effect upon the frequency of the carbonyl absorption.

In the spectra of vinyl or phenyl esters, with unsaturation adjacent to the C—O— group, a marked rise in the carbonyl frequency is observed along with a lowering of the C—O frequency. Vinyl acetate has a carbonyl band at 1776 cm^{-1} (5.63 μ); phenyl acetate absorbs at 1770 cm^{-1} (5.65 μ).

α-Halogen substitution results in a rise in the C═O stretching frequency. Ethyl trichloroacetate absorbs at 1770 cm^{-1} (5.65 μ).

In α-diesters and α-keto esters, as in α-diketones, there appears to be little or no interaction between the two carbonyl groups so that normal absorption occurs in the region of 1755–1740 cm^{-1} (5.70–5.75 μ). In the spectra of β-keto esters, however, where enolization can occur, a band is observed near 1650 cm^{-1} (6.06 μ) that results from bonding between the ester C═O and the enolic hydroxyl group.

The carbonyl absorption of saturated δ-lactones (six membered ring) occurs in the same region as straight-chain, unconjugated esters. Unsaturation α to the C═O reduces the C═O absorption frequency. Unsaturation, α- to the —O— group, increases it.

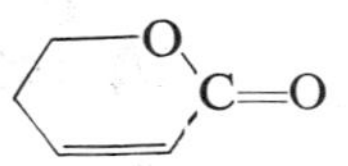

1720 cm^{-1} (5.81 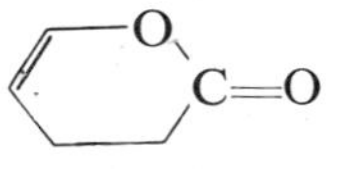 μ) 1760 cm^{-1} (5.68 μ)

α-Pyrones frequently display two carbonyl absorption bands in the 1775–1715 cm^{-1} (5.63–5.83 μ) region, probably due to Fermi resonance.

Saturated γ-lactones (five membered ring) absorb at shorter wavelengths than esters or δ-lactones: 1795-1760 cm^{-1} (5.57–5.68 μ). γ-Valerolactone absorbs at 1770 cm^{-1} (5.65 μ). Unsaturation in the γ-lactone molecule affects the carbonyl absorption in the same manner as unsaturation in δ-lactones.

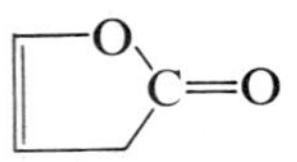

1800 cm^{-1} (5.56 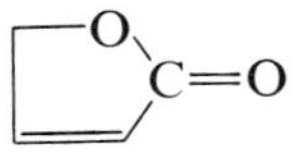 μ) 1750 cm^{-1} (5.71 μ)

In unsaturated lactones, when the double bond is adjacent to the —O—, a strong C═C absorption is observed in the 1685–1660 cm^{-1} (5.94–6.02 μ) region.

C—O *Stretching Vibrations*

The C—O stretching mode of esters, ethers, acids, and alcohols give rise to bands in the 1300–1000 cm^{-1} (7.70–10.00 μ) region. The frequencies of these bands are generally much less reliable than those of the carbonyl bands. The C—O asymmetric stretching band of an ester is generally more intense and broader than the carbonyl band and undoubtedly involves coupling between C—O and C—C stretching vibrations. Saturated esters, with the exception of acetates, show a strong asymmetrical C—$\overset{\mathrm{O}}{\overset{\|}{\mathrm{C}}}$—O stretching band in the 1210–1163 cm^{-1} (8.26–8.60 μ) region. Acetates absorb strongly near 1240 cm^{-1} (8.07 μ). Unsaturation, such as occurs in vinyl acetate, reduces the frequency of the "acetate band" by approximately 20 cm^{-1}.

The symmetrical C—O bands are weaker than the asymmetrical C—O bands and are of little diagnostic value. Acetates of primary alcohols show a second band in the 1064–1031 cm^{-1} (9.40–9.70 μ) region. This vibration appears to involve coupling between C—O and C—C stretching in the alcoholic portion of the molecule, since the position changes for acetates of secondary alcohols (near 1100 cm^{-1}, 9.09 μ).

The methyl esters of long-chain fatty acids present a three-band pattern with bands near 1250 cm^{-1} (8.00 μ), 1205 cm^{-1} (8.30 μ), and 1175 cm^{-1} (8.51 μ). The band near 1175 cm^{-1} (8.51 μ) is the strongest.

Esters of α,β-unsaturated acids show multiple bands in the C—O stretching region, 1300–1160 cm^{-1} (7.69–8.62 μ). Esters of aromatic acids absorb strongly in the 1310–1250 cm^{-1} (7.63–8.00 μ) region. Aromatic esters of primary alcohols absorb near 1111 cm^{-1} (9.00 μ) due to asymmetrical —O—CH_2—C absorption. Absorption due to C—O stretching in lactones is observed in the 1250–1111 cm^{-1} (8.00–9.00 μ) region.

The influence of the —$\overset{\mathrm{O}}{\overset{\|}{\mathrm{C}}}$—O group upon adjacent CH_2 and CH_3 groups is summarized in the Appendix, Tables I and II.

ACETIC ACID, OCTYL ESTER

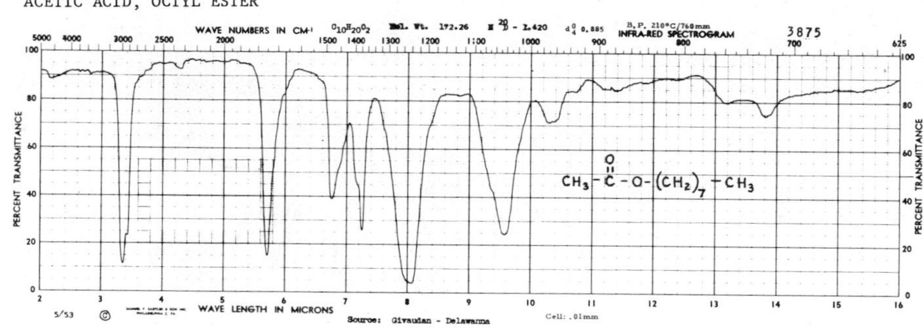

BENZOIC ACID, ISOPROPYL ESTER

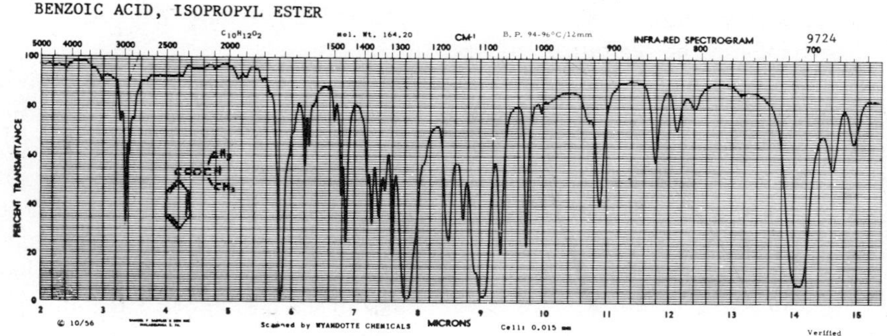

Acid Halides

C═O *Stretching Vibrations*

Acid halides show strong absorption in the C═O stretching region. Unconjugated acid chlorides absorb in the 1815–1785 cm^{-1} (5.51–5.60 μ) region. Acetyl fluoride in the gas phase absorbs near 1869 cm^{-1} (5.35 μ). Conjugated acid halides absorb at a slightly lower frequency because resonance reduces the force constant of the C═O bond; aromatic acid chlorides absorb strongly at 1800–1770 cm^{-1} (5.56–5.65 μ). A weak band near 1750–1735 cm^{-1} (5.71–5.76 μ) appearing in the spectra of aroyl chlorides probably results from Fermi resonance between the C═O band and the overtone of a longer wavelength band near 875 cm^{-1} (11.43 μ).

Carboxylic Acid Anhydrides

C═O *Stretching Vibrations*

Anhydrides display two stretching bands in the carbonyl region. The two bands result from asymmetrical and symmetrical C═O stretching modes. Saturated noncyclic anhydrides absorb near 1818 cm^{-1} (5.50 μ), and near 1750 cm^{-1} (5.71 μ). Conjugated noncyclic anhydrides show absorption near 1775 cm^{-1} (5.63 μ) and near 1720 cm^{-1} (5.81 μ); the decrease in the frequency of absorption is due to resonance. The higher frequency band is the more intense.

Cyclic anhydrides with five-membered rings show absorption at higher frequencies than noncyclic anhydrides because of ring strain; succinic anhydride absorbs at 1865 cm^{-1} (5.37 μ) and at 1782 cm^{-1} (5.62 μ). The longer wavelength C═O band is the stronger of the two carbonyl bands in five-membered-ring cyclic anhydrides.

C—O *Stretching Vibrations*

Other strong bands appear in the spectra of anhydrides as a result of $\text{C—}\overset{\text{O}}{\overset{\|}{\text{C}}}\text{—O—}\overset{\text{O}}{\overset{\|}{\text{C}}}\text{—C}$ stretching vibrations. Unconjugated straight chain anhydrides absorb near 1047 cm^{-1} (9.55 μ). Cyclic anhydrides display bands near 952–909 cm^{-1} (10.50–11.00 μ) and near 1299–1176 cm^{-1} (7.70–8.50 μ). The C—O stretching band for acetic anhydride is at 1125 cm^{-1} (8.89 μ).

Amides

All amides show a carbonyl absorption band known as the Amide I band. Its position depends upon the degree of hydrogen bonding, and thus on the physical state of the compound.

Primary amides show two N—H stretching bands resulting from symmetrical and asymmetrical N—H stretching. Secondary amides and lactams show only one N—H stretching band. As in the case of O—H stretching, the frequency of the N—H stretching is reduced by hydrogen bonding, though to a lesser degree. Overlapping occurs in the observed position of N—H and O—H stretching frequencies so that an unequivocal differentiation in structure is sometimes impossible.

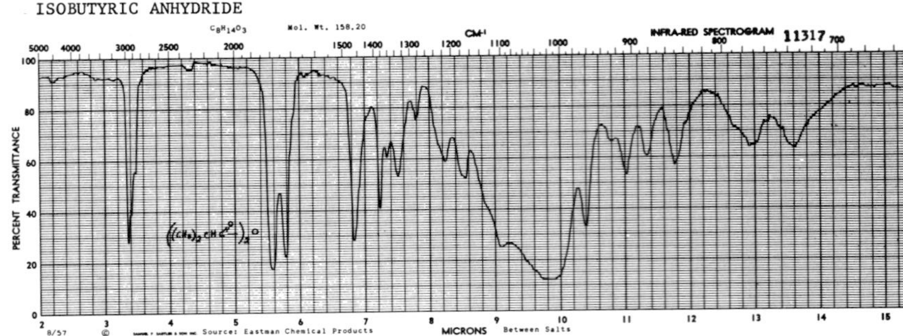

Primary amides and secondary amides, and a few lactams, display a band or bands in the region of 1650–1515 cm^{-1} (6.06–6.60 μ) due primarily to NH_2 or NH bending; the amide II band. This absorption involves coupling between N—H bending and other fundamental vibrations and requires a *trans* configuration.

Out-of-plane NH wagging is responsible for a broad band of medium intensity in the 800–666 cm^{-1} (12.5–15.0 μ) region.

N—H *Stretching Vibrations*

In dilute solution in nonpolar solvents, primary amides show two moderately intense NH stretching frequencies corresponding to the asymmetrical and symmetrical NH stretching vibrations. These bands occur near 3520 cm^{-1} (2.84 μ) and 3400 cm^{-1} (2.94 μ), respectively. In the spectra of solid samples, these bands are observed near 3350 cm^{-1} (2.99 μ) and 3180 cm^{-1} (3.15 μ) because of hydrogen bonding.

In infrared spectra of secondary amides, which exist mainly in the trans configuration, the free NH stretching vibration observed in dilute solutions occurs near 3500–3400 cm^{-1} (2.86–2.94 μ). In more concentrated solutions and in solid samples, the free NH band is replaced by multiple bands in the 3330–3060 cm^{-1} (3.00–3.27 μ) region. Multiple bands are observed since the amide group can bond to produce dimers, with a cis configuration, and polymers, with a *trans* configuration.

```
R      O------H      R'
 \   //        \    /
   C             N
   |             |
   N             C
 /   \        //   \
R'     H------O      R
```

cis

```
   R'                 R
     \              /
      NH------O=C
                    \
----O=C              N—H----
        \          /
         R        R'
```

trans

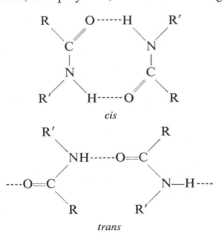

C=O *Stretching Vibrations (Amide I Band)*

The C=O absorption of amides occurs at longer wavelengths than "normal" carbonyl absorption due to the resonance effect. (see p. 87) The position of absorption depends upon the same environmental factors as the carbonyl absorption of other compounds.

Primary amides (except acetamide, whose C=O bond absorbs at 1694 cm^{-1} (5.90 μ)), have a strong amide I band in the region of 1650 cm^{-1} (6.06 μ) when examined in the solid phase. When the amide is examined in dilute solution, the absorption is observed at a higher frequency, near 1690 cm^{-1} (5.92 μ). In more concentrated solutions, the C=O frequency is observed at some intermediate value, depending on the degree of hydrogen bonding.

Simple, open chain, secondary amides absorb near 1640 cm^{-1} (6.10 μ) when examined in the solid state. In dilute solution, the frequency of the amide I band may be raised to 1680 cm^{-1} (5.95 μ) and even to 1700 cm^{-1} (5.88 μ) in the case of the anilides. In the anilide structure there is competition between the ring and the C=O for the nonbonded electron pair of the nitrogen.

The carbonyl frequency of tertiary amides is independent of the physical state, since hydrogen bonding with another tertiary amide group is impossible. The C=O absorption occurs in the range of 1680 to 1630 cm^{-1} (5.95 to 6.13 μ). The absorption range of tertiary amides in solution is influenced by hydrogen bonding with the solvent. N,N-Diethylacetamide absorbs at 1647 cm^{-1} (6.07 μ) in dioxane and at 1615 cm^{-1} (6.20 μ) in methanol.

Electron attracting groups attached to the nitrogen increase the frequency of absorption since they effectively compete with the carbonyl oxygen for the electrons of the nitrogen, thus increasing the force constant of the C=O bond.

N—H *Bending Vibrations (Amide II Band)*

All primary amides show a sharp absorption band (amide II band) resulting from NH_2 bending at a somewhat lower frequency than the C=O band. This band has an intensity of one-half to one-third of the C=O absorption band. In solid samples, the band usually appears as a doublet near 1655–1620 cm^{-1} (6.04–6.17 μ). In dilute solution, the band appears at lower frequencies, near 1620–1590 cm^{-1} (6.17–6.29 μ). Multiple bands may appear in the spectra of concentrated solutions, arising from the free and associated states. The nature of the R group ($R{-}C({=}O){-}NH_2$) has little effect upon the amide II band.

Secondary acyclic amides in the solid state display an amide II band in the region of 1570–1515 cm^{-1} (6.37–6.60 μ). In dilute solution, the band occurs in the 1550–1510 cm^{-1} (6.45–6.62 μ) region. This band results from interaction between the N—H bending and the C—N stretching of the C—N—H group. A second, weaker band near 1250 cm^{-1} (8.00 μ) also results from interaction between the N—H bending and C—N stretching.

Other Vibration Bands

The C—N stretching band of primary amides occurs near 1400 cm^{-1} (7.14 μ). A broad, medium band in the 800–666 cm^{-1} (12.5–15.0 μ) region in the spectra of primary and secondary amides results from out-of-plane N—H wagging.

Lactams

In lactams of medium ring size, the amide group is forced into the *cis* configuration. Solid lactams absorb strongly near 3200 cm^{-1} (3.12 μ) due to the N—H stretching vibration. This band does not shift appreciably with dilution since the *cis* form remains associated at relatively low concentrations.

C=O *Stretching Vibrations*

The C=O absorption of lactams with six-membered rings or larger is near 1650 cm^{-1} (6.06 μ). Five-membered ring (γ) lactams absorb in the 1750–1700 cm^{-1} (5.71–5.88 μ) region. Four-membered ring (β) lactams, unfused, absorb at 1760–1730 cm^{-1} (5.68–5.78 μ). Fusion of the lactam ring to another ring generally increases the frequency by 20–50 cm^{-1} (0.07–0.17 μ).

Most lactams do not show a band near 1550 cm^{-1} (6.45 μ) that is characteristic of *trans* non-cyclic secondary amides. The N—H out-of-plane wagging in lactams causes broad absorption in the 800–700 cm^{-1} (12.5–14.3 μ) region.

Amines

N—H *Stretching Vibrations*

Primary amines, examined in dilute solution, display two weak absorption bands: one near 3500 cm^{-1} (2.86 μ) the other near 3400 cm^{-1} (2.94 μ). These bands represent, respectively, the "free" asymmetrical and symmetrical N—H stretching modes. Secondary amines show a single weak band in the 3350–3310 cm^{-1} (2.98–3.02 μ) region. These bands are shifted to longer wavelengths by hydrogen bonding. The shift is less than that observed for O—H groups (less than 100 cm^{-1}), and the associated N—H bands are weaker and frequently sharper. Aliphatic primary amines (neat) absorb at 3400–3330 cm^{-1} (2.94–3.00 μ) and at 3330–3250 cm^{-1} (3.00–3.08 μ). Aromatic primary amines absorb at slightly shorter wavelengths. In the spectra of liquid primary and secondary amines, a shoulder usually appears on the long wavelength side of the N—H stretching band, arising from the overtone of the NH bending band intensified by Fermi resonance. Tertiary amines do not absorb in this region of the spectrum.

N—H *Bending Vibrations*

The N—H bending (scissoring) vibration of primary amines is observed in the 1650–1580 cm^{-1} (6.06–6.33 μ) region of the spectrum. The band is medium to strong in intensity and is moved to slightly higher frequencies

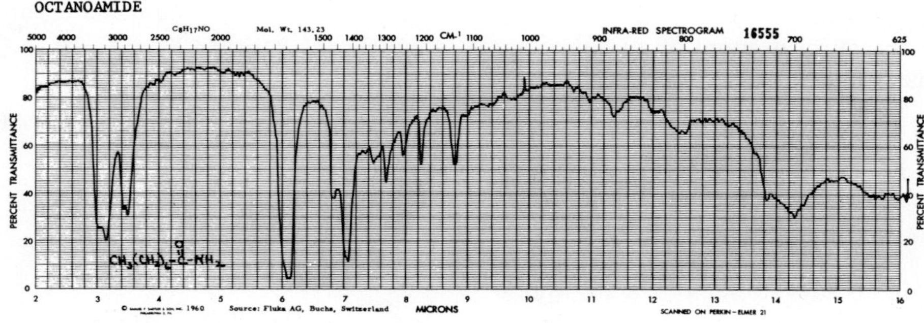

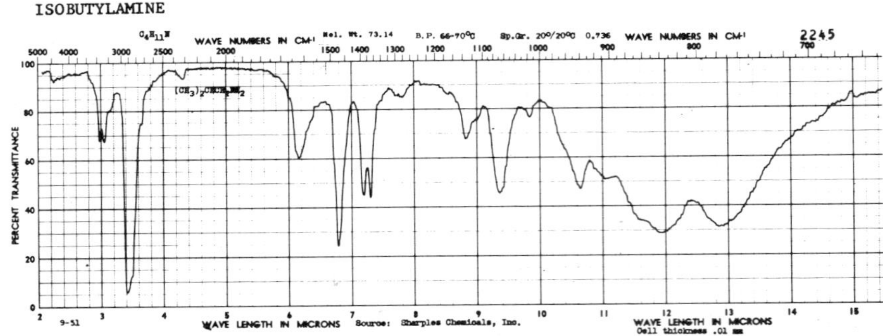

when the compound is associated. The N—H bending band is seldom detectable in the spectra of aliphatic secondary amines, whereas secondary aromatic amines absorb near 1515 cm^{-1} (6.60 μ).

Liquid samples of primary and secondary amines display medium-to-strong broad absorption in the 909–666 cm^{-1} (11.00–15.00 μ) region of the spectrum arising from NH wagging. The position of this band depends on the degree of hydrogen bonding.

C—N *Stretching Vibrations*

Medium-to-weak absorption bands for the unconjugated C—N linkage in primary and secondary aliphatic amines appear in the region of 1250–1020 cm^{-1} (8.00–9.80 μ). The vibrations responsible for these bands involve C—N stretching coupled with the stretching of adjacent bonds in the molecule. The position of absorption in this region depends on the class of the amine and the pattern of substitution on the α-carbon.

Aromatic amines display strong C—N stretching absorption in the 1342–1266 cm^{-1} (7.45–7.90 μ) region. The absorption appears at higher frequencies than the corresponding absorption of aliphatic amines because the force constant of the C—N bond is increased by resonance with the ring.

Characteristic strong C—N stretching bands in the spectra of aromatic amines have been assigned as follows:

Primary	1340–1250 cm^{-1} (7.46–8.00 μ)
Secondary	1350–1280 cm^{-1} (7.41–7.81 μ)
Tertiary	1360–1310 cm^{-1} (7.35–7.63 μ)

The absorption frequencies of methyl and methylene groups attached to the nitrogen atom of an amine are summarized in Tables I and II of the Appendix.

Amine Salts

N—H *Stretching Vibrations*

The ammonium ion displays strong, broad absorption in the 3300–3030 cm^{-1} (3.03–3.30 μ) region due to N—H stretching vibrations. There is also a combination band in the 2000–1709 cm^{-1} (5.00–5.85 μ) region.

Salts of primary amines show strong, broad absorption between 3000 and 2800 cm^{-1} (3.33–3.57 μ) arising from asymmetrical and symmetrical stretching in the NH_3^+ group. In addition, multiple combination bands of medium intensity occur in the 2800–2000 cm^{-1} (3.57–5.00 μ) region, the most prominent being the band near 2000 cm^{-1} (5.00 μ). Salts of secondary amines absorb strongly in the 3000–2700 cm^{-1} (3.33–3.70 μ) region with multiple bands extending to 2273 cm^{-1} (4.00 μ). A medium band near 2000 cm^{-1} (5.00 μ) may be observed. Tertiary amine salts absorb at longer wavelengths than the salts of primary and secondary amines; 2700–2250 cm^{-1} (3.70–4.44 μ). Quaternary ammonium salts have no N—H stretching vibrations.

N—H *Bending Vibrations*

The ammonium ion displays a strong, broad NH_4^+ bending band near 1429 cm^{-1} (7.00 μ). The NH_3^+ group of the salt of a primary amine absorbs near 1600–1575 cm^{-1} (6.25–6.35 μ) and near 1550–1504 cm^{-1} (6.45–6.65 μ). These bands originate in asymmetrical and symmetrical NH_3^+ bending, analogous to the corresponding bands of the CH_3 group. Salts of secondary amines absorb near 1620–1560 cm^{-1} (6.17–6.41 μ). The N—H bending band of the salts of tertiary amines is weak and of no practical value.

Amino Acids and Salts of Amino Acids

Amino acids are encountered in three forms: the free amino acid (zwitterion)

$$-\overset{|}{\underset{\underset{NH_3^+}{|}}{C}}-COO^-$$

the hydrochloride (or other acid) salt,

$$-\overset{|}{\underset{\underset{NH_3^+\ Cl^-}{|}}{C}}-COOH$$

the sodium (or other cation) salt,

$$-\underset{\underset{NH_2}{|}}{\overset{|}{C}}-COO^- \ Na^+$$

Free primary amino acids are characterized by the following absorption (most of the work has been done with α-amino acids, but the relative positions of the amino and carboxyl groups seem to have little effect):

1. A broad strong NH_3^+ stretching band in the 3100–2600 cm^{-1} (3.23–3.85 μ) region. Multiple combination and overtone bands extend the absorption to about 2000 cm^{-1} (5.00 μ). This overtone region usually contains a prominent band near 2222–2000 cm^{-1} (4.50–5.00 μ) assigned to a combination of the asymmetrical NH_3^+ bending vibration and the torsional oscillation of the NH_3^+ group. The torsional oscillation occurs near 500 cm^{-1} (20.00 μ). The 2000 cm^{-1} (5.00 μ) band is absent if the nitrogen atom of the amino acid is substituted.

2. A weak asymmetric NH_3^+ bending band near 1660–1610 cm^{-1} (6.03–6.21 μ); a fairly strong symmetrical bending band near 1550–1485 cm^{-1} (6.45–6.73 μ).

3. The carboxylate ion group $\left(-C\begin{smallmatrix} \nearrow O \\ \searrow O \end{smallmatrix}\ -\right)$ absorbs strongly near 1600–1590 cm^{-1} (6.25–6.29 μ) and more weakly near 1400 cm^{-1} (7.15 μ). These bands result, respectively, from asymmetrical and symmetrical C—O stretching.

Hydrochlorides of amino acids present the following patterns:

1. Broad strong absorption in the 3333–2380 cm^{-1} (3.00–4.20 μ) region resulting from superimposed O—H and NH_3^+ stretching bands. Absorption in this region is characterized by multiple fine structure on the long wavelength side of the band.

2. A weak, asymmetrical $\overset{+}{N}H_3$ bending band near 1610–1590 cm^{-1} (6.21–6.29 μ); a relatively strong, symmetrical, $\overset{+}{N}H_3$ bending band at 1550–1481 cm^{-1} (6.45–6.75 μ).

3. A strong band at 1220–1190 cm^{-1} (8.20–8.40 μ) arising from $C-\overset{\overset{O}{\|}}{C}-O$ stretching.

4. Strong carbonyl absorption at 1755–1730 cm^{-1} (5.70–5.78 μ) for α-amino acid hydrochlorides, and at 1730–1700 cm^{-1} (5.78–5.88 μ) for other amino acid hydrochlorides.

Sodium salts of amino acids show the normal N—H stretching vibrations at 3400–3200 cm^{-1} (2.94–3.13 μ) common to other amines. The characteristic carboxylate ion bands appear near 1600–1590 cm^{-1} (6.25–6.29 μ) and near 1400 cm^{-1} (7.15 μ).

Nitriles

The spectra of nitriles (R—C≡N) are characterized by weak to medium absorption in the triple-bond stretching region of the spectrum. Aliphatic nitriles absorb near 2260–2240 cm^{-1} (4.42–4.46 μ). Electron attracting atoms, such as oxygen or chlorine, attached to the carbon atom alpha to the C≡N group reduce the intensity of absorption. Conjugation, such as occurs in aromatic nitriles, reduces the frequency of absorption to 2240–2222 cm^{-1} (4.46 to 4.50 μ) and enhances the intensity.

Isocyanides (Isonitriles)

Isocyanides (R—N$^+$≡C$^-$) display strong absorption in the 2185 to 2105 cm^{-1} (4.58–4.75 μ) region resulting from C to N stretching. Aliphatic isocyanides absorb at the short wavelength end of the general region, whereas aromatic isocyanides absorb near 2127–2105 cm^{-1} (4.70–4.75 μ).

Isocyanates

Of the two isomers (R—O—C≡N and R—N=C=O), the latter is the more stable arrangement. Isocyanates (R—N=C=O) show strong, broad absorption in the 2275–2240 cm^{-1} (4.40–4.46 μ) region due to asymmetrical N=C=O stretching. The symmetrical stretching mode produces very weak absorption in the 1399–1370 cm^{-1} (7.15–7.30 μ) region of the spectrum that is of little diagnostic value.

Thiocyanates and Isothiocyanates

Organic thiocyanates (R—S—C≡N) display strong C≡N-stretching absorption in the 2174–2004 cm^{-1} (4.60–4.99 μ) region of the spectrum. Isothiocyanates (R—N=C=S) absorb intensely in the 2174–2041 cm^{-1} (4.60–4.90 μ) region as a result of asymmetrical N=C=S stretching. The symmetrical N=C=S stretching vibration occurs near 945–925 cm^{-1} (10.58–10.81 μ) for aryl isothiocyanates and in the 700–650 cm^{-1} (14.29–15.39 μ) region for alkyl isothiocyanates.

Compounds Containing the —C=N— Group

All compounds containing the C=N group show a C=N stretching band in the 1689–1471 cm^{-1} (5.92–6.80 μ) region of the spectrum. These compounds include Schiff's bases (RCH=N—R), oximes, thiazoles, iminocarbonates ([RO]$_2$C=NH), guanidines, etc.

The absorption intensities are variable. Frequently it

BENZONITRILE

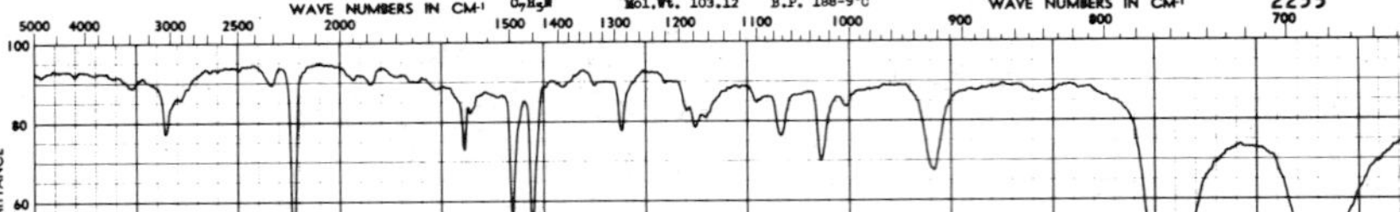

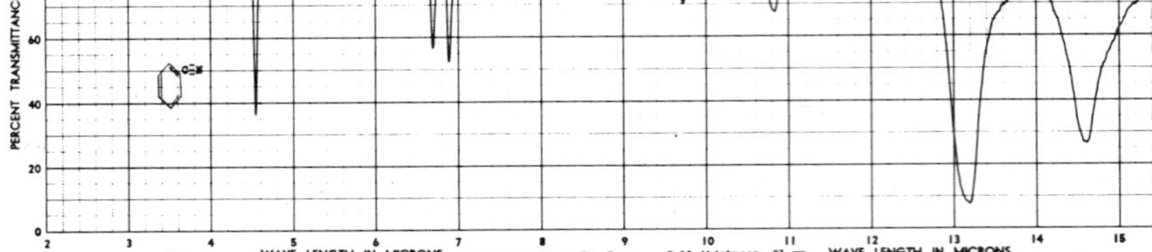

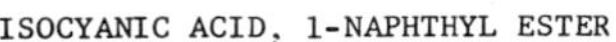

ISOCYANIC ACID, 1-NAPHTHYL ESTER

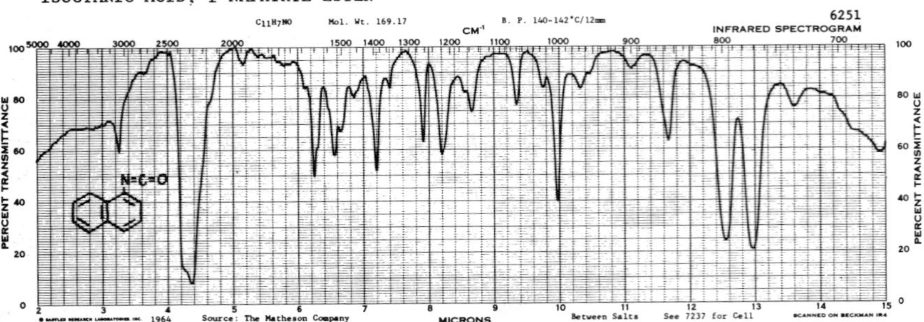

THIOCYANIC ACID, BENZYL ESTER

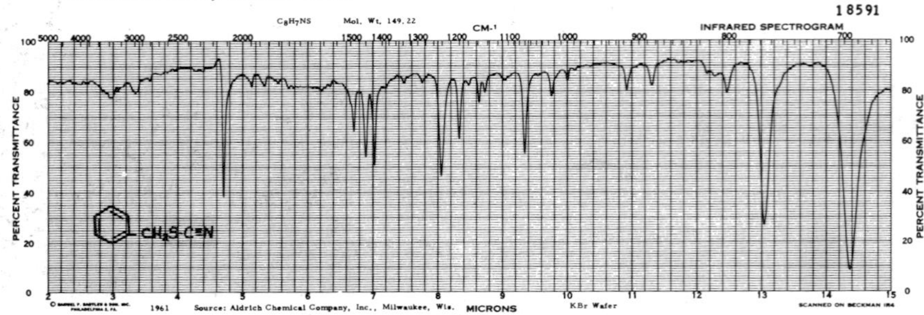

BENZOPHENONE, OXIME

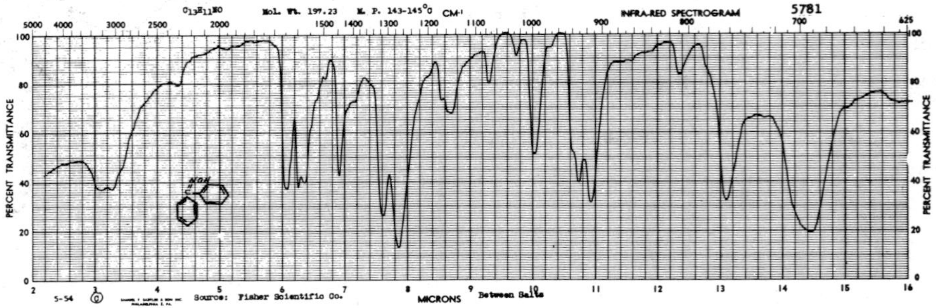

AZOBENZENE

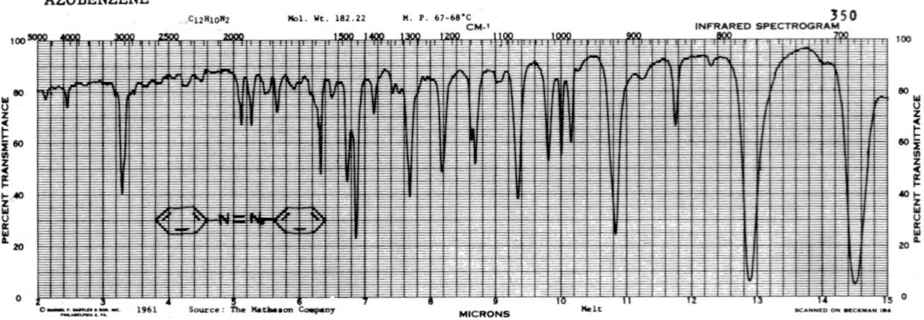

is stronger than C═C absorption because of the polar nature of the bond.

Compounds Containing —N═N—Group

The N═N stretching vibration of a symmetrical trans azo compound is forbidden in the infrared but absorbs in the 1576 cm^{-1} (6.35 μ) region of the Raman spectrum. Unsymmetrical para-substituted azobenzenes in which the substituent is an electron donating group absorb near 1429 cm^{-1} (7.00 μ). The bands are weak because of the nonpolar nature of the bond.

Covalent Compounds Containing Nitrogen—Oxygen Bonds

Nitro compounds, nitrates, and nitramines contain an NO_2 group. Each of these classes shows absorption due to asymmetrical and symmetrical stretching of the NO_2 group. Asymmetrical absorption results in a strong band in the 1661–1499 cm^{-1} (6.02–6.67 μ) region; symmetrical absorption occurs in the region between 1389 and 1259 cm^{-1} (7.20 and 7.94 μ). The exact position of the bands is dependent on substitution and unsaturation in the vicinity of the NO_2 group.

NITRO COMPOUNDS. In the nitroparaffins, the bands occur near 1550 cm^{-1} (6.45 μ) and near 1372 cm^{-1} (7.29 μ). Conjugation lowers the frequency of both bands, resulting in absorption near 1550–1500 cm^{-1} (6.45–6.67 μ) and near 1360–1290 cm^{-1} (7.36–7.75 μ). Attachment of electronegative groups to the α-carbon of a nitro compound causes an increase in the frequency of the asymmetrical NO_2 band and a reduction in the frequency of the symmetrical band; chloropicrin absorbs at 1610 cm^{-1} (6.21 μ) and at 1307 cm^{-1} (7.65 μ).

Aromatic nitro groups absorb near the same frequencies as observed for conjugated aliphatic nitro compounds. Interaction between the NO_2 out-of-plane bending and ring C—H out-of-plane bending frequencies destroys the reliability of the substitution pattern observed for nitro-aromatics in the long wavelength region of the spectrum. Nitroaromatic compounds show a C—N stretching vibration near 870 cm^{-1} (11.49 μ).

Because of strong resonance in aromatic systems containing NO_2 groups and electron-donating groups such as the amino group ortho or para to one another, the symmetrical NO_2 vibration is shifted to lower frequencies and increases in intensity. *p*-Nitroaniline absorbs at 1475 cm^{-1} (6.78 μ) and 1310 cm^{-1} (7.64 μ).

Nitramines $\left(\gt N—NO_2\right)$ commonly show an asymmetric NO_2 stretching band in the 1585–1530 cm^{-1} (6.31–6.54 μ) region; the symmetrical stretching band occurs at 1300–1260 cm^{-1} (7.69–7.94 μ).

NITRATES. Organic nitrates show absorption for N—O stretching vibrations of the NO_2 group and for the O—N linkage. Asymmetrical stretching in the NO_2 group results in strong absorption in the 1660–1625 cm^{-1} (6.02–6.15 μ) region; the symmetrical vibration absorbs strongly near 1300–1255 cm^{-1} (7.69–7.97 μ). Stretching of the single bond of the N—O linkage produces absorption near 870–833 cm^{-1} (11.50–12.00 μ). Absorption observed at longer wavelengths, near 763–690 cm^{-1} (13.10–14.50 μ), likely results from NO_2 bending vibrations.

NITRITES. Nitrites display two strong N═O stretching bands. The band near 1680–1650 cm^{-1} (5.95–6.06 μ) is attributed to the *trans* isomer; the *cis* isomer absorbs in the 1625–1610 cm^{-1} (6.16–6.21 μ) region. The N—O stretching band appears in the region between 850 and 750 cm^{-1} (11.76 and 13.33 μ). The nitrite absorption bands are among the strongest observed in infrared spectra.

NITROSO COMPOUNDS. Primary and secondary aliphatic nitroso compounds are usually unstable and rearrange to oximes or dimerize. Tertiary and aromatic nitroso compounds are reasonably stable, existing as monomers in the gaseous phase or in dilute solution and as dimers in neat samples. Monomeric, tertiary, aliphatic nitroso compounds show N═O absorption in the 1585–1539 cm^{-1} (6.31–6.50 μ) region; aromatic monomers absorb between 1511 and 1495 cm^{-1} (6.62 and 6.69 μ).

The N→O stretching absorption of the dimeric species is summarized as follows:

Aliphatic compounds:

Trans	1290–1176 cm^{-1} (7.75–8.50 μ).
Cis	1344–1323 cm^{-1} (7.44–7.56 μ).
	1426–1389 cm^{-1} (7.01–7.20 μ).

Aromatic compounds:

Trans	1299–1253 cm^{-1} (7.70–7.98 μ).
Cis	1397–1389 cm^{-1} (7.16–7.20 μ).
	near 1409 cm^{-1} (7.10 μ).

Nitrosoamines, in the vapor state, absorb near 1490 cm^{-1} (6.71 μ). In the liquid state, absorption occurs near 1448 cm^{-1} (6.90 μ).

Organic Sulfur Compounds

MERCAPTANS. Aliphatic mercaptans and thiophenols, as liquids or in solution, show S—H stretching absorption in the range of 2600–2550 cm^{-1} (3.85–3.92 μ). The S—H stretching band is characteristically weak and may go undetected in the spectra of dilute solutions or thin films. However, since few other groups show absorption in this region, it is useful in detecting S—H groups.

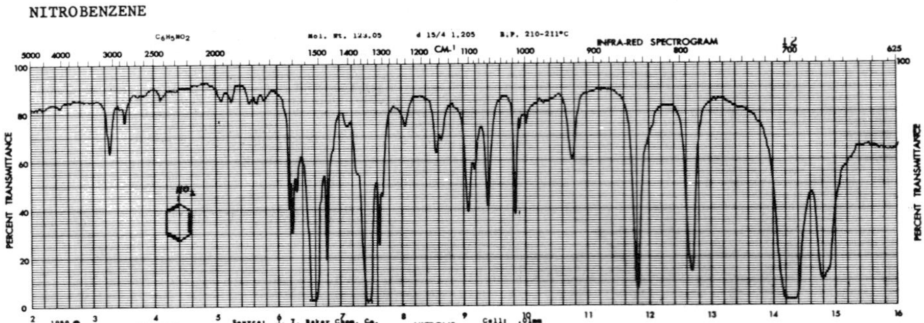

The band may be obscured by strong carboxyl absorption in the same region. Hydrogen bonding is much weaker for S—H groups than for O—H and N—H groups.

The S—H group of thiol acids absorbs in the same region as mercaptans and thiophenols.

SULFIDES. The stretching vibrations assigned to the C—S linkage occur in the region of 700–600 cm^{-1} (14.30–16.70 μ). The weakness of absorption and variability of position make this band of little value in structural determination.

DISULFIDES. The S—S stretching vibration is very weak and falls between 500 and 400 cm^{-1} (20–25 μ), outside the range of sodium chloride optics. The characteristic absorptions of methyl and methylene groups attached to sulfur are summarized in Tables I and II in the Appendix.

THIOCARBONYL COMPOUNDS. Aliphatic thials or thiones exist as trimeric, cyclic sulfides. Aralkyl thiones may exist either as monomers or trimers, whereas diaryl thiones, such as thiobenzophenone, exist only as monomers.

Compounds that contain a thiocarbonyl group show absorption in the 1250–1020 cm^{-1} (8.00–9.80 μ) region. Thiobenzophenone and its derivatives absorb moderately near 1217 cm^{-1} (8.22 μ). Since the absorption occurs in the same general region as C—O and C—N stretching, considerable interaction can occur between these vibrations within a single molecule.

Spectra of compounds in which the C═S group is attached to a nitrogen atom show an absorption band in the general C═S stretching region. In addition, several other bands in the broad region of 1563–700 cm^{-1} (6.40–14.30 μ) can be attributed to vibrations involving interaction between C═S and stretching and C—N stretching.

Thioketo compounds that can undergo enolization exist as thioketo-thioenol tautomeric systems; such systems show S—H stretching absorption. The thioenol tautomer of ethyl thiobenzoylacetate,

$$\begin{array}{c} \text{H} \\ C_6H_5\text{—C═C—C—}OC_2H_5 \\ \quad\;\; | \qquad\; \| \\ \text{SH------O} \end{array}$$

absorbs broadly at 2415 cm^{-1} (4.14 μ) due to bonded S—H stretching absorption.[41]

Compounds Containing Sulfur—Oxygen Bonds

SULFOXIDES. Alkyl and aryl sulfoxides as liquids or in solution show strong absorption in the 1070–1030 cm^{-1} (9.35–9.71 μ) region. Conjugation brings about a small change (10–20 cm^{-1}) in the observed frequency in contrast to the marked reduction in frequency of the C═O bond accompanying conjugation. Diallylsulfoxide absorbs at 1047 cm^{-1} (9.55 μ). Phenylmethylsulfoxide and cyclohexylmethylsulfoxide absorb at 1055 cm^{-1} (9.48 μ) in dilute solution in carbon tetrachloride. The sulfoxide group is susceptible to hydrogen bonding, the absorption shifting to slightly lower frequencies in methanol or chloroform solutions, or on passing from dilute solution to the liquid phase. The frequency of S═O absorption is increased by electronegative substitution.

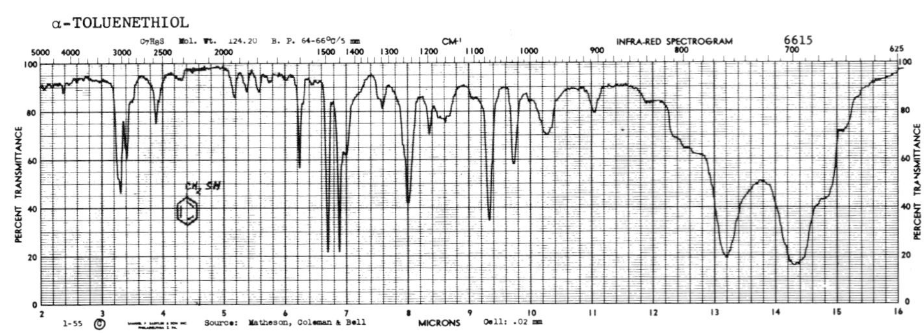

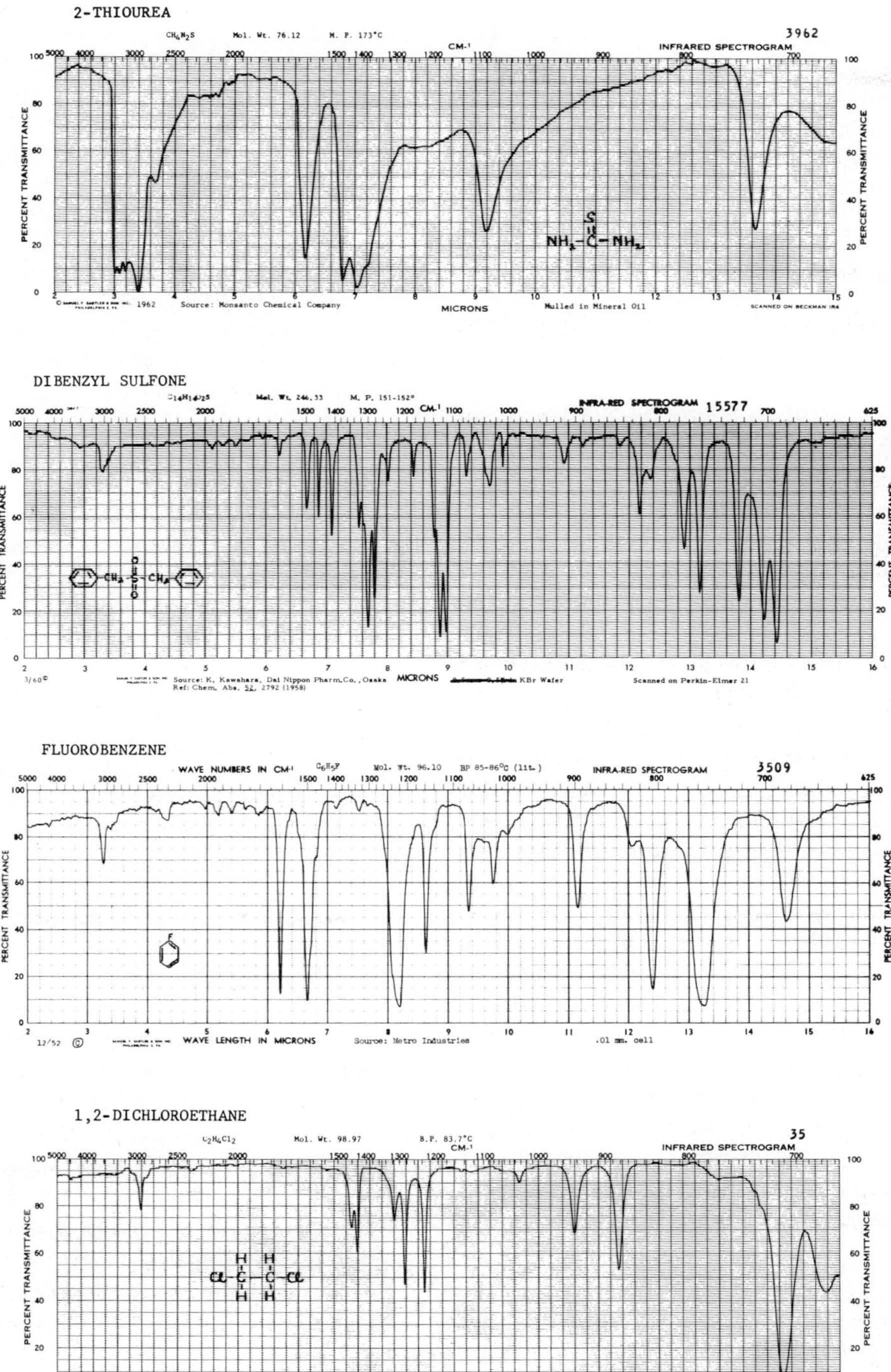

SULFONES. Spectra of sulfones show strong absorption bands at 1350–1300 cm^{-1} (7.41–7.70 μ) and at 1160–1120 cm^{-1} (8.62–8.93 μ). These bands arise, respectively, from asymmetric and symmetric SO_2 stretching. Hydrogen bonding results in absorption near 1300 cm^{-1} (7.70 μ) and near 1125 cm^{-1} (8.90 μ). Splitting of the high frequency band often occurs in carbon tetrachloride solution or in the solid state.

SULFONYL CHLORIDES. Sulfonyl chlorides absorb strongly in the regions of 1410–1380 cm^{-1} (7.09–7.25 μ) and 1204–1177 cm^{-1} (8.31–8.49 μ). This increase in frequency, compared with the sulfones, results from the electronegativity of the chlorine atom.

SULFONAMIDES. Solutions of sulfonamides absorb strongly at 1370–1335 cm^{-1} (7.30–7.49 μ) and at 1170–1155 cm^{-1} (8.55–8.66 μ). In the solid phase, these frequencies are lowered by 10–20 cm^{-1}. In solid samples, the high frequency band is broadened and several sub-maxima usually appear.

Primary sulfonamides show strong N—H stretching bands at 3390–3330 cm^{-1} (2.95–3.00 μ) and at 3300–3247 cm^{-1} (3.03–3.08 μ) in the solid state; secondary sulfonamides absorb near 3265 cm^{-1} (3.06 μ).

Organic Halogen Compounds

The strong absorption of halogenated hydrocarbons arises from the stretching vibrations of the carbon to halogen bond.

Aliphatic C—Cl absorption is observed in the broad region between 850 and 550 cm^{-1} (11.76–18.18 μ). When several chlorine atoms are attached to one carbon atom, the band is usually more intense and at the high frequency end of the assigned limits. Carbon tetrachloride shows an intense band at 797 cm^{-1} (12.55 μ). The first overtones of the intense fundamental bands are frequently observed. Brominated compounds absorb in the 690–515 cm^{-1} (14.49–19.42 μ) region, iodo-compounds in the 600–500 cm^{-1} (16.67–20.00 μ) region. A strong CH_2 wagging band is observed for the CH_2Cl (—Br, —I) group in the 1300–1150 cm^{-1} (7.69–8.70 μ) region.

Fluorine-containing compounds absorb strongly over a wide range between 1400–730 cm^{-1} (7.15–13.70 μ) due to C—F stretching modes. A monofluoro-alkane shows a strong band in the 1100–1000 cm^{-1} (9.09–10.00 μ) region. As the number of fluorine atoms in an aliphatic molecule increases, the band pattern becomes more complex, with multiple strong bands appearing over the broad region of C—F absorption. The CF_3 and CF_2 groups absorb strongly in the 1350–1120 cm^{-1} (7.41–8.93 μ) region.

Chlorobenzenes absorb in the 1096–1089 cm^{-1} (9.12–9.18 μ) region. The position within this region depends on the substitution pattern.[12] Aryl fluorides absorb in the 1250–1100 cm^{-1} (8.00–9.10 μ) region of the spectrum. A monofluorinated-benzene ring displays a strong narrow absorption band near 1230 cm^{-1} (8.13 μ).

Silicon Compounds

Si—H *Stretching Vibrations*

Medium to strong stretching vibrations for the Si—H bond occur in the 2250–2100 cm^{-1} (4.44–4.76 μ) region. The Si—H stretching frequencies are increased by the attachment of an electronegative group to the silicon.

Si—H *Bending Vibrations*

The $\rangle SiH_2$ group shows a scissoring vibration near 942–923 cm^{-1} (10.62–10.83 μ).

The —SiH_3 group displays two bands in the 959–900 cm^{-1} (10.43–11.11 μ) region, resulting from asymmetrical and symmetrical bending. These vibrational modes are analogous to those for the methyl group. The wagging vibrations of the $\rangle SiH_2$ group appear in the 900–840 cm^{-1} (11.11–11.90 μ) region of the spectrum. $\equiv$Si—H bending vibrations occur at lower frequencies, 950–800 cm^{-1} (10.53–12.50 μ).

The absorption bands of methylene and methyl groups attached to silicon are summarized in the Appendix (Tables I and II).

Si—O *Stretching Vibration*

The Si—O stretching vibrations are summarized in Table III.

Table III* Si—O *Stretching Vibrations

GROUP	ν_{Si-O} BANDS
Si—O—R (aliphatic)	1110–1000 cm^{-1} (9.01–10.00 μ)s
Si—O—Si	1110–1000 cm^{-1} (9.01–10.00 μ)s
Si—O—R (aromatic)	970–920 cm^{-1} (10.31–10.87 μ)s
Si—OH	910–830 cm^{-1} (11.00–12.05 μ)s

s = strong

The OH stretching vibrations of the SiOH group absorb in the same region as the alcohols, 3700–3200 cm^{-1} (2.70–3.12 μ). As in alcohols, the absorption characteristics depend on the degree of hydrogen bonding.

Silicon-Halogen Stretching Vibrations

The absorption of groups containing Si—F bonds is summarized in Table IV.

Bands resulting from Si—Cl stretching occur at frequencies below 666 cm^{-1} (wavelengths longer than 15 μ).

Phosphorus Compounds

P—H *Stretching*

The P—H group absorbs in the region of 2440–2275 cm^{-1} (4.10–4.40 μ). The absorption is of medium intensity and the band is sharp. Alkyl and aryl phosphines absorb between 2326 and 2275 cm^{-1} (4.30 and 4.40 μ).

Table IV Absorption of Si—F Bonds

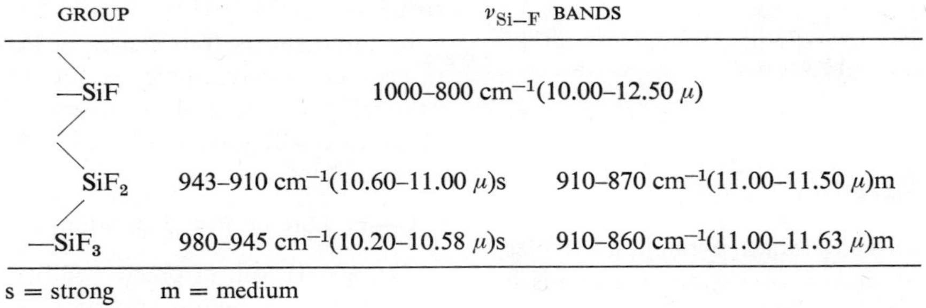

GROUP	ν_{Si-F} BANDS	
—SiF (with two further bonds on Si)	1000–800 cm^{-1}(10.00–12.50 μ)	
SiF$_2$ (with two further bonds on Si)	943–910 cm^{-1}(10.60–11.00 μ)s	910–870 cm^{-1}(11.00–11.50 μ)m
—SiF$_3$	980–945 cm^{-1}(10.20–10.58 μ)s	910–860 cm^{-1}(11.00–11.63 μ)m

s = strong m = medium

Table V P—O Stretching Vibrations

GROUP	ν_{P-O} BANDS	
P—OH	1040–910 cm^{-1}(9.62–11.00 μ)s	
P—O—P	1000–870 cm^{-1}(10.00–11.50 μ)s	ca. 700 cm^{-1}(14.30 μ)w
P—O—C (aliph.)	1050–970 cm^{-1}(9.52–10.30 μ)s*	830–740 cm^{-1}(12.05–13.51 μ)s†
P—O—C (arom.)	1260–1160 cm^{-1}(7.94–8.62 μ)s	994–855 cm^{-1}(10.06–11.70 μ)s

* May be a doublet. † May be absent. s = strong w = weak

PH_2 *Bending Vibrations*

The scissoring vibration of the PH_2 group produces a band of medium intensity near 1090–1080 cm^{-1} (9.19–9.26 μ). A PH_2 wagging band appears in the region of 940–909 cm^{-1} (10.64–11.00 μ).

P=O *Stretching Vibrations*

The P=O bond of aliphatic phosphine oxides absorbs near 1150 cm^{-1} (8.70 μ); aromatic phosphine oxides absorb near 1190 cm^{-1} (8.40 μ). Phosphate esters display P=O stretching between 1299 and 1250 cm^{-1} (between 7.70 and 8.00 μ). The increase in P=O stretching frequency of the ester, results from the electronegativity of the attached alkoxyl groups.

P—O *Stretching Vibrations*

Absorption characteristics of P—O stretching vibrations are summarized in Table V.

The absorption of methylene and methyl groups attached to a phosphorus atom are summarized in Tables I and II of the Appendix.

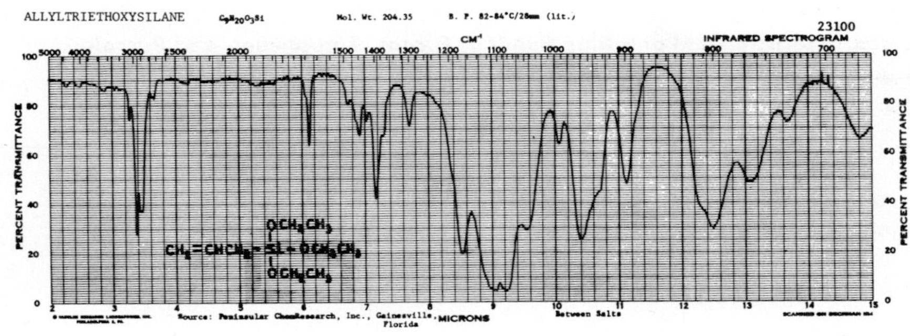

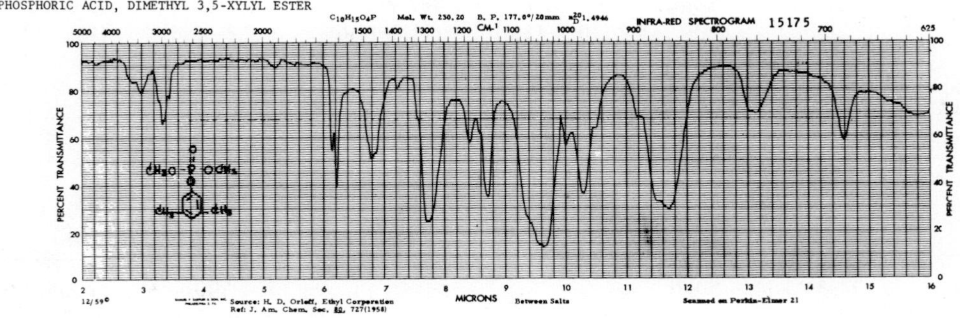

Heteroaromatic Compounds

The spectra of heteroaromatic compounds result primarily from the same vibrational modes as observed for the aromatics.

C—H *Stretching Vibrations*

Heteroaromatics such as pyridines, pyrazines, pyrroles, furans, and thiophenes show C—H stretching bands in the 3077–3003 cm^{-1} (3.25–3.33 μ) region.

N—H *Stretching Frequencies*

Heteroaromatics containing an N—H group show N—H stretching absorption in the region of 3500–3220 cm^{-1} (2.86–3.11 μ). The position of absorption within this general region depends upon the degree of hydrogen bonding, and hence upon the physical state of the sample or the polarity of the solvent. Pyrrole and indole in dilute solution in nonpolar solvents show a sharp band near 3495 cm^{-1} (2.86 μ); concentrated solutions show a widened band near 3400 cm^{-1} (2.94 μ).

Ring-Stretching Vibrations (Skeletal Bands)

Ring stretching vibrations occur in the general region between 1600–1300 cm^{-1} (6.25–7.69 μ). The absorption involves stretching and contraction of all of the bonds in the ring and interaction between these stretching modes. The band pattern and the relative intensities depend on the substitution pattern and the nature of the substituents.

Pyridine shows four bands in this region and in this respect closely resembles a monosubstituted benzene. Furans, pyrroles, and thiophenes display two to four bands in this region.

C—H *Out of Plane Bending*

The C—H out-of-plane bending (γCH) absorption pattern of the heteroaromatics is determined by the number of adjacent hydrogen atoms bending in phase. The C—H out-of-plane and ring bending (β ring) absorption of the alkyl pyridines are summarized in Table VI.

***Table VI** γCH and Ring Bending Bands (β Ring) of Pyridines*[20]

SUBSTITUTION	NO. ADJACENT H's	γCH	β RING
2-	4	781–740 cm^{-1} (12.80–13.50 μ)	752–746 cm^{-1} (13.30–13.40 μ)
3-	3	810–789 cm^{-1} (12.35–12.67 μ)	715–712 cm^{-1} (13.99–14.04 μ)
4-	2	820–794 cm^{-1} (12.19–12.60 μ)	775–709 cm^{-1} (12.90–14.10 μ)

Absorption data for the out-of-plane C—H bending (γCH), and ring bending (β ring) modes of three common five-membered heteroaromatic rings are presented in Table VII.

The ranges in Table VII include polar as well as nonpolar substituents on the ring.

***Table VII** Characteristic γCH or β Ring Bands of Furans, Thiophenes, and Pyrroles*[20]

NUCLEUS	POS. OF SUBSTITUTION	PHASE	γCH OR β RING MODES cm^{-1} (μ)	cm^{-1} (μ)	cm^{-1} (μ)	cm^{-1} (μ)
Furan	2-	$CHCl_3$	ca 925 (10.8)	ca 884 (11.3)	835–780 (12.0–12.8)	
	2-	liq.	960–915 (10.4–10.9)	890–875 (11.2–11.4)		780–725 (12.8–13.8)
	2-	Solid	955–906 (10.5–11.0)	887–860 (11.3–11.6)	821–793 (12.2–12.6)	750–723 (13.3–13.8)
	3-	liq.		885–870 (11.3–11.5)	741 (13.5)	
Thiophene	2-	$CHCl_3$	ca 925 (10.8)	ca 853 (11.7)	843–803 (11.9–12.5)	
	3-	liq.				755 (13.2)
Pyrrole	2-Acyl	Solid			774–740 (12.9–13.5)	ca 755 (13.2)

2-METHYLFURAN

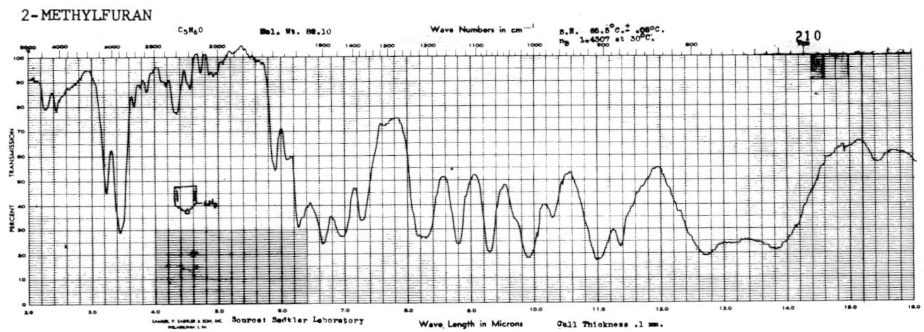

2-ACETYLTHIOPHENE

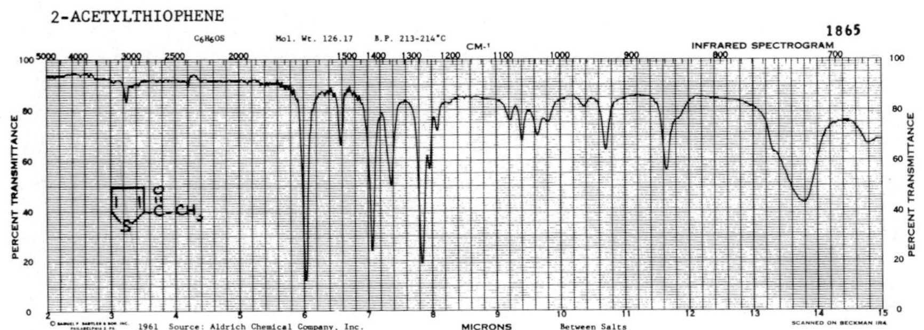

PYRIDINE

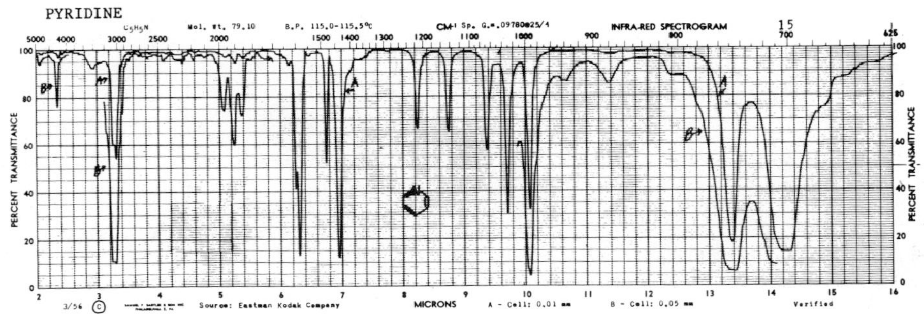

PYRAZINE

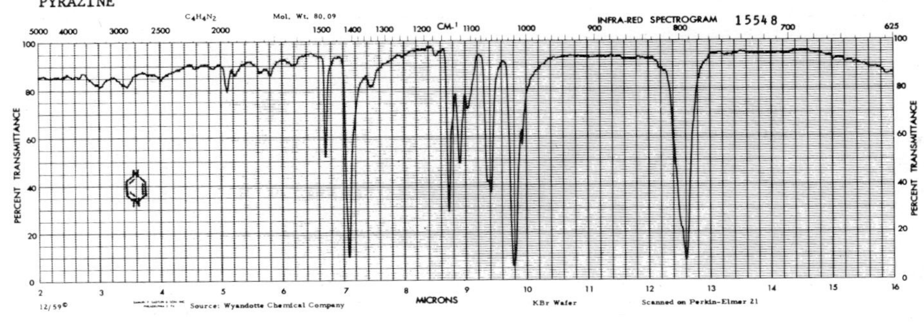

PYRIMIDINE

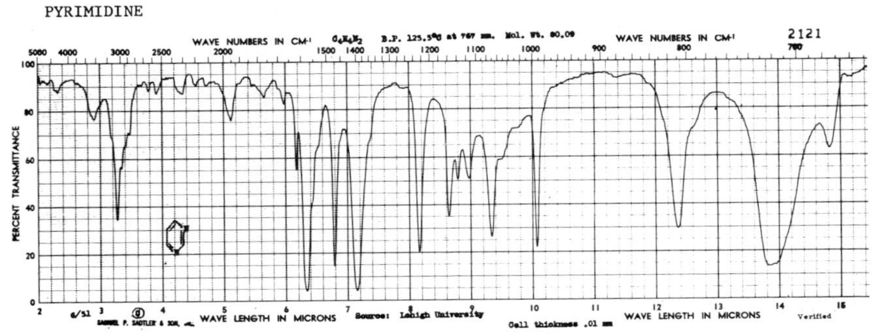

APPENDIX

Table I CH_3 *Group Absorption*

STRUCTURE	$\nu_s CH_3$ cm^{-1} (μ)	$\delta_{as} CH_3$ cm^{-1} (μ)	$\delta_s CH_3$ cm^{-1} (μ)
$CH_3—C(=O)—$ (ketone)	...	1450–1400 (6.90–7.15)	1375–1350 (7.28–7.41)
$CH_3—O—R$	2832–2815* (3.53–3.55)	1470–1440 (6.80–6.95)	1470–1440 (6.80–6.95)
$CH_3—C(=O)—O—$	...	1450–1400 (6.90–7.15)	1400–1340 (7.15–7.46)
$CH_3—N<$ (amines and imines)	2820–2760 (3.55–3.62)	...	1440–1390 (6.95–7.20)
$CH_3—N<$ (amides)	...	1500–1450 (6.67–6.90)	1420–1405 (7.04–7.11)
$CH_3—X$ (X = halogen)	...	...	1500–1250 (6.67–8.00)
$CH_3—S—$	...	1440–1415 (6.95–7.07)	1330–1290 (7.52–7.75)
$CH_3—Si≡$	...	1429–1389 (7.00–7.20)	1280–1255 (7.81–7.97)
$CH_3—P<$	...	...	1310–1280 (7.64–7.81)

* Overtone of CH_3 bending band.

Table II* CH_2 *Group Absorption

STRUCTURE	$\nu_s CH_2$ cm^{-1} (μ)	$\delta_s CH_2$ (scissoring) cm^{-1} (μ)	ωCH_2 (wagging) cm^{-1} (μ)
$-CH_2-C(=O)-$ (acyclic)	...	1435–1405 (6.97–7.11)	...
$-CH_2-C(=O)-$ (small ring)	...	1475–1425* (6.78–7.02)	...
$-CH_2-O-$ (acyclic)	...	1470–1435 (6.80–6.97)	...
$-CH_2-O-$ (small ring)	...	1500–1470* (6.67–6.80)	...
$-CH_2-N-$ (sec. and tert. amines)	2820–2760 (3.55–3.62)	1475–1445 (6.78–6.92)	...
$-CH_2-N<$ (amides)	...	1450–1405 (6.89–7.11)	...
$-CH_2-O-C(=O)$	...	1475–1460 (6.78–6.85)	...
$-CH_2-S-$	...	1440–1415 (6.94–7.06)	...
$-CH_2-$halogen	...	1460–1430 (6.85–7.00)	1275–1170 (7.85–8.55)
$-CH_2NO_2$	...	1425–1415 (7.02–7.06)	...
$-CH_2-CN$	...	1425 (7.02)	...
$-CH_2-N=C=S$	...	...	1351–1316 (7.40–7.60)
$-Si-CH_2-$	...	near 1410 (7.09)	1250–1200 (8.00–8.33)
$-CH_2-P<$	...	1440–1405 (6.95–7.11)	...

* Multiple bands

***Table III* Olefinic Absorption**

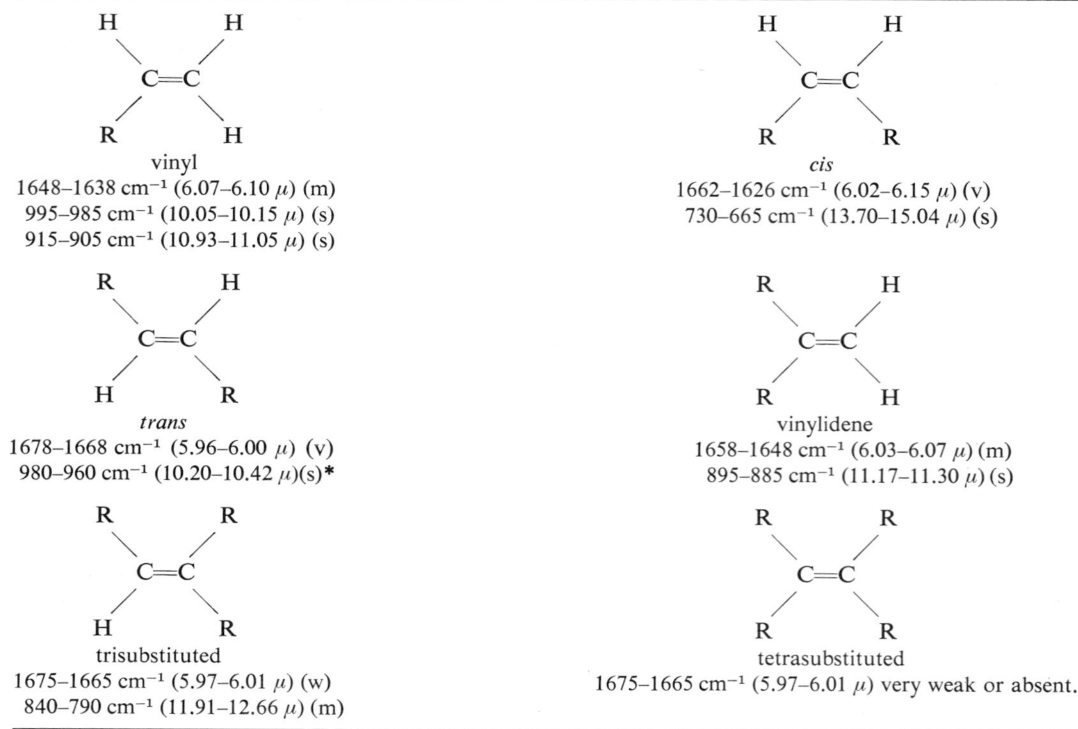

vinyl (RHC=CH₂)	1648–1638 cm^{-1} (6.07–6.10 μ) (m) 995–985 cm^{-1} (10.05–10.15 μ) (s) 915–905 cm^{-1} (10.93–11.05 μ) (s)
cis	1662–1626 cm^{-1} (6.02–6.15 μ) (v) 730–665 cm^{-1} (13.70–15.04 μ) (s)
trans	1678–1668 cm^{-1} (5.96–6.00 μ) (v) 980–960 cm^{-1} (10.20–10.42 μ)(s)*
vinylidene	1658–1648 cm^{-1} (6.03–6.07 μ) (m) 895–885 cm^{-1} (11.17–11.30 μ) (s)
trisubstituted	1675–1665 cm^{-1} (5.97–6.01 μ) (w) 840–790 cm^{-1} (11.91–12.66 μ) (m)
tetrasubstituted	1675–1665 cm^{-1} (5.97–6.01 μ) very weak or absent.

s = strong m = medium w = weak v = variable

* This band occurs near 1000 cm^{-1} (10.00 μ) in conjugated *trans-trans* systems such as the esters of sorbic acid.

References

1. Jones, R. N., and C. Sandorfy, "The Application of Infrared and Raman Spectrometry to the Elucidation of Molecular Structure," Chapter IV, Vol. IX, in A. Weissberger, *Technique of Organic Chemistry*, Interscience, New York, 1956, pp. 247–580.
2. Miller, F. A., "Applications of Infrared and Ultraviolet Spectra to Organic Chemistry," Vol. III, in H. Gilman, *Organic Chemistry, An Advance Treatise*, John Wiley, New York, 1953, pp. 122–77.
3. Bellamy, L. J., *The Infra-red Spectra of Complex Organic Molecules*, John Wiley, 2nd ed., New York, 1958.
4. Cross, A. D., *Introduction to Practical Infra-red Spectroscopy*, Butterworths Scientific Publications, London, 1960.
5. Randall, H. M., R. G. Fowler, N. Fuson, and J. R. Dangl, *Infrared Determination of Organic Structures*, D. Van Nostrand, New York, 1949.
6. Williams, V. Z., "Infrared Instrumentation and Techniques," *Rev. Sci. Instruments*, **19**, 135–78 (1948).
7. Herzberg, G., *Infrared and Raman Spectrum of Polyatomic Molecules*, D. Van Nostrand, New York, 1945. Theory.
8. Barnes, R. B., R. C. Gore, U. Liddel, and V. Z. Williams, *Infrared Spectroscopy*, Reinhold, New York, 1944.
9. Sutherland, G. B. B. M., *Infrared and Raman spectra*, Methuen, London, 1935. Theory.
10. Bauman, R. P., *Absorption Spectroscopy*, John Wiley, New York, 1962.
11. Randall, H. M., R. G. Fowler, N. Fuson, and J. R. Dangl, *Infrared Determination of Organic Structures*, D. Van Nostrand, New York, 1943.
12. Colthup, N. B., L. H. Daly, and S. E. Wiberley, *Introduction to Infrared and Raman Spectroscopy*, Academic Press, New York and London, 1964.
13. Nakanishi, Koji, *Infrared Absorption Spectroscopy—Practical*, Holden-Day, San Francisco and Nankodo Company Ltd. Tokyo, 1962.
14. Flett, M. St. C., *Physical Aids to the Organic Chemist*, Elsevier, Amsterdam, 1962.
15. Flett, M. St. C., *Characteristic Frequencies of Chemical Groups in the Infra-Red*, Elsevier, Amsterdam, 1963.
16. Brand, J. C. D., and G. Eglinton, *Applications of Spectroscopy to Organic Chemistry*, Oldbourne Press, London, 1965.
17. Schwartz, J. C. P., Ed., *Physical Methods in Organic Chemistry*, Oliver and Boyd, Edinburgh and London, 1964.
18. Strouts, C. N. R., H. N. Wilson, and R. T. Parry-Jones, *Chemical Analysis—The Working Tools*, Vol. II., Clarendon Press, Oxford, 1962.
19. Dyer, J. R., *Applications of Absorption Spectroscopy of Organic Compounds*, Prentice-Hall, Englewood Cliffs, N.J., 1965.
20. Katritzky, A. R., Ed., *Physical Methods in Heterocyclic Chemistry*, Vol. II, Academic Press, New York and London, 1963.
21. Szymanski, H. A., *IR Theory and Practice of Infrared Spectroscopy*, Plenum Press, New York, 1964.
22. Syzmanski, H. A., *Interpreted Infrared Spectra*, Vol. I, Plenum Press, New York, 1964.
23. Davies, Mansel, Editor, *Infrared Spectroscopy and Molecular Structure—An Outline of Principles*, Elsevier, Amsterdam and London, 1963.
24. Rao, C. N. R., *Chemical Applications of Infrared Spectroscopy*, Academic Press, New York and London, 1963.
25. Phillips, J. P., *Spectra-Structure Correlation*, Academic Press, New York and London, 1964.

26. Potts, W. J., Jr., *Chemical Infrared Spectroscopy, Vol. I, Techniques*, John Wiley, New York, 1963.
27. Miller, R. G. J., Editor, *Laboratory Methods in Infrared Spectroscopy*, Heyden and Sons Ltd., London, 1965.
28. Meloan, C. E., *Elementary Infrared Spectroscopy*, Macmillan, New York, 1963.
28a. Cole, A. R. H., "Applications of Infrared Spectroscopy," Vol. XI (Part I), pp. 133–173, in *Technique of Organic Chemistry*, A. Weissberger, Ed., Interscience, New York, 1963.
28b. Tichy, M. "The Determination of Intramolecular Hydrogen Bonding by Infrared Spectroscopy and Its Applications in Stereochemistry," Vol. 5, pp. 115–299, in *Advances in Organic Chemistry: Methods and Results*, R. R. Raphael, ed., Interscience, New York, 1964.
28c. Gianturco, Maurizio, Chap. II in, *Interpretive Spectroscopy*, S. K. Freeman, Ed., Reinhold, New York, 1965.
28d. Conley, R. T., *Infrared Spectroscopy*, Allyn and Bacon, Boston, 1966.
28e. Kendall, D. N., Editor, *Applied Infrared Spectroscopy*, Reinhold, New York, 1966.
29. *Catalog of Infrared Spectrograms*, Sadtler Research Laboratories, 3314–20 Spring Garden St., Philadelphia, Penn., Spectra indexed by name and by major bands in each micron interval. Trade name: Spec-Finder.
30. *Catalog of Infrared Spectrograms*, American Petroleum Institute Research Project 44, Carnegie Institute of Technology, Pittsburgh, Pa.
31. *Catalog of Infrared Spectral Data*, Manufacturing Chemists Association Research Project, Chemical and Petroleum Research Laboratories, Carnegie Institute of Technology, Pittsburgh, Pa., to June 30, 1960; Chemical Thermodynamics Properties Center, Agriculture and Mechanical College of Texas, College Station, Tex., from July 1, 1960.
32. *ASTM-Wyandotte Index, Molecular Formula List of Compounds, Names and References to Published Infrared Spectra.* ASTM Special Technical Publications 131 (1962) and 131-A (1963), ASTM, 1916 Race St., Philadelphia 3, Pa. Lists about 57,000 compounds. Covers infrared, near infrared, and far infrared spectra.
33. Hershenson, H. H., *Infrared Absorption Spectra Index*, Academic Press, New York and London, 1959 and 1964. Two volumes cover 1945–1962.
34. *An Index of Published Infra-Red Spectra*, M. B. B. Thomas, Ed., Vols. I and II, British Information Service, New York, 1960. Complete to 1957. Gives literature references to spectra, lists state, absorption range, and optics.
35. *Documentation of Molecular Spectroscopy (DMS)*, Butterworths Scientific Publications, London; and Verlag Chemie GMBH, Weinheim/Bergstrasse, West Germany, in cooperation with the infrared Absorption Data Joint Committee, London, and the Institut für Spectrochemie und Angewandte Spectroskopie, Dortmund. Spectra are presented on coded cards. Coded cards containing abstracts of articles relating to infrared spectrometry are also issued.
36. Szymanski, H. A., *Infrared Band Handbook*, Plenum, New York, 1962. Supp. 1 and 2 cover 200–600 cm^{-1} region.
37. IRDC Cards: *Infrared Data Committee of Japan* (S. Mizushima). Handled by Nankodo Co., Haruki-cho, Tokyo.
38. *The NRC–NBS (Creitz) File of Spectrograms*, issued by National Research Council–National Bureau of Standards Committee on Spectral Absorption Data, National Bureau of Standards, Washington 25, D.C. Spectra presented on edge-punched cards.
39. "Spectrometry Nomenclature," *Anal. Chem.*, **37**, 1814 (1965).
40. Zeiss, H. H., and Minoru Tsutsui, *J. Am. Chem. Soc.*, **75**, 897 (1953).
41. Reyes, Z., and R. M. Silverstein, *J. Am. Chem. Soc.*, **80**, 6367 (1958).

CHAPTER 4

Nuclear Magnetic Resonance Spectrometry

I. INTRODUCTION AND THEORY

Nuclear magnetic resonance (NMR) spectrometry is basically another form of absorption spectrometry, akin to infrared or ultraviolet spectrometry. Under appropriate conditions, a sample can absorb electromagnetic radiation in the radio-frequency region at frequencies governed by the characteristics of the sample. Absorption is a function of certain nuclei in the molecule. A plot of the frequencies of the absorption peaks versus peak intensities constitutes an NMR spectrum. This discussion will be limited to proton NMR spectra.

With some mastery of basic theory, interpretation of NMR spectra merely by inspection, is usually feasible in greater detail than is the case for infrared or ultraviolet spectra. To supplement the material presented here, several lucid nonmathematical introductions to nuclear magnetic resonance are recommended.[1–11,11a,11b] For greater depth, the classic treatise by Pople, Schneider, and Bernstein[12] and the more recent work by Emsley, Feeney, and Sutcliffe[12a] are available. Two volumes of NMR spectra have been published by Varian Associates.[13] These volumes are indexed by a unique code that shows the type of proton, nearest neighbor functional group, and next nearest neighbor. Recently the well-known Sadtler IR spectra have been supplemented by NMR spectra.[14]

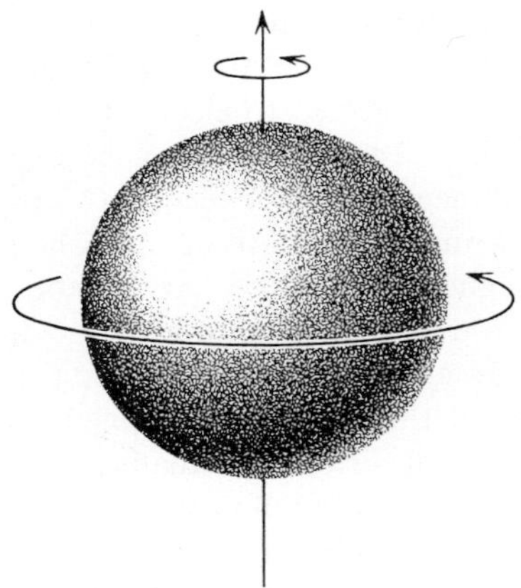

Fig. 1. Spinning charge in proton generates magnetic dipole.

Sets of spectra are also issued by the American Petroleum Institute.[15] Indexes to the NMR literature have been published.[16,16a,16b]

The present account will suffice for the immediate limited objective: identification of organic compounds in conjunction with other spectrometric information.

We begin by describing some magnetic properties of nuclei. All nuclei carry a charge. In some nuclei this charge "spins" on the nuclear axis, and this circulation of nuclear charge generates a magnetic dipole along the axis (Figure 1). The angular momentum of the spinning charge can be described in terms of spin numbers I; these numbers have values of 0, 1/2, 1, 3/2, and so forth. ($I = 0$ denotes no spin). The intrinsic magnitude of the generated dipole is expressed in terms of nuclear magnetic moment, μ.

Each proton and neutron has its own spin, and I is a resultant of these spins. If the sum of protons and neutrons is even, I is zero or integral (0, 1, 2, . . .); if the sum is odd, I is half-integral (1/2, 3/2, 5/2, . . .); if both protons and neutrons are even-numbered, I is zero. Both ^{12}C and ^{16}O fall in the latter category and give no NMR signal.

Several nuclei (^{1}H, ^{19}F, ^{13}C, and ^{31}P) have a spin number I of 1/2 and a uniform spherical charge distribution (Figure 1). Nuclei with a spin number I of 1 or higher have a nonspherical charge distribution. This asymmetry is described by an electrical quadrupole moment which, as we shall see later, affects the relaxation time and, consequently, the coupling with neighboring nuclei. ^{14}N and ^{2}H have a spin number I of 1. ^{11}B, ^{35}Cl, ^{37}Cl, ^{79}Br, and ^{81}Br are examples of nuclei with $I = 3/2$.

The spin number I determines the number of orientations a nucleus may assume in an external uniform magnetic field in accordance with the formula $2I + 1$. We shall be concerned primarily with the proton whose spin number I is 1/2. Thus the proton has two orientations in an applied uniform magnetic field: parallel with the applied field (aligned with the field) or antiparallel (aligned against the field). The former is the low-energy (stable) state, the latter, the high-energy (unstable) state (Figure 2). The energy levels are a function of the magnitude of the nuclear magnetic moment μ, and the strength of the applied external magnetic field H_0.

Two energy levels for the proton having been established, it should now be possible to introduce quanta of energy $h\nu$ (h is Planck's constant; ν is the frequency of electromagnetic radiation) such that the parallel orientation (low-energy state) can be flipped to the antiparallel orientation (high-energy state) in a magnetic field of given strength H_0. The fundamental NMR equation correlating electromagnetic frequency with magnetic field strength is

$$\nu = \frac{\gamma H_0}{2\pi}$$

The constant γ is called the magnetogyric (or more commonly but less properly, gyromagnetic) ratio and is a fundamental nuclear constant; it is the proportionality constant between the magnetic moment μ and the spin number I

$$\gamma = \frac{2\pi\mu}{hI}$$

where h is Planck's constant.

The bald statement made earlier that nuclear magnetic resonance spectrometry is akin to other forms of absorption spectrometry may now seem somewhat more plausible. The problem is how to inject electromagnetic energy into protons aligned in a magnetic field so as to flip the proton spin into a higher energy level, and how to measure the energy thus absorbed. Before we describe the instrumentation, we have to consider one peculiarity of a small magnet spinning in an external magnetic field: The axis of the small magnet (the proton) will precess about the axis of the external magnetic field in the same manner in which a spinning gyroscope precesses under the influence of gravity (Figure 3). The precessional angular velocity, ω_0 is equal to the product

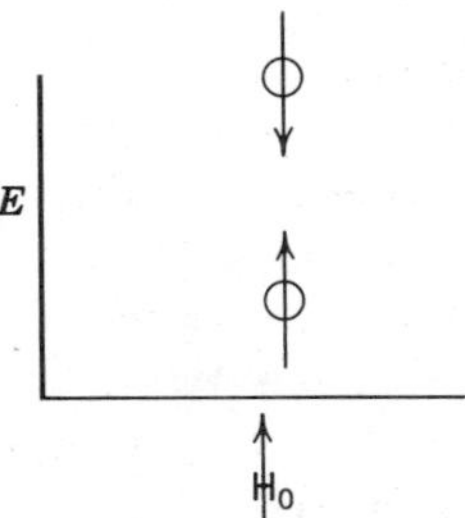

Fig. 2. Energy Levels of a Proton.

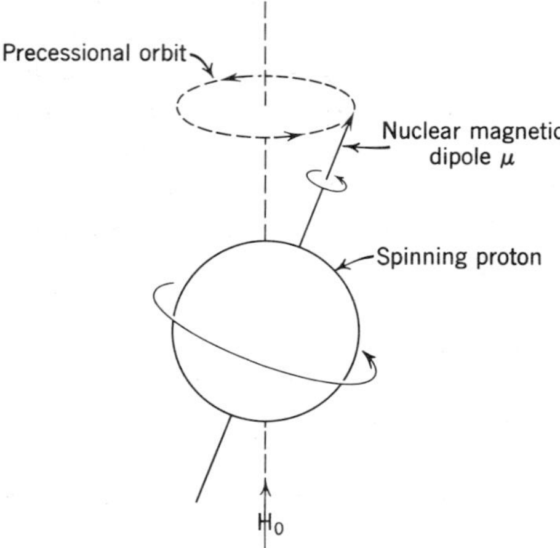

Fig. 3. Proton precessing in a magnetic field H_0.

of the magnetogyric ratio, γ and the strength of the applied magnetic field H_0.

$$\omega_0 = \gamma H_0$$

We recall from the fundamental NMR equation that

$$\gamma H_0 = 2\pi\nu$$

Therefore,

$$\omega_0 = 2\pi\nu$$

This means that if we can introduce the proper frequency, we shall be precisely attuned to the precessional angular velocity. Or to put it another way, the inserted frequency will be *in resonance* with the precessional frequency. The energy of the inserted frequency can thus be absorbed by the nucleus and, given the proper geometry, the nucleus can be caused to flip. This involves a frequency of 60 megacycles per second at a magnetic field H_0 of 14,092 gauss for the proton (or any other desired combination in the same ratio.) Note that when a proton in a magnetic field is subjected to electromagnetic radiation, a field strength of 14,092 gauss can be expressed as its equivalent, 60 megacycles per second (Mcps).

We are now in a position to arrange the geometry for a nuclear magnetic resonance experiment. We subject the protons to a powerful uniform magnetic field. The protons are now aligned with and against the field and are precessing about the axis of the applied magnetic field. Because of thermal disorder, actually only a small fraction of the total population of protons is properly aligned, but this fraction is sufficient. The electromagnetic frequency is applied in such a way that its magnetic component H_1 is at right angles to the main magnetic field H_0 and is rotating with the precessing proton. An oscillator coil whose axis is at right angles to the axis of the main magnetic field H_0 will generate a linear oscillating magnetic field H_1 along the direction of the coil axis as shown in Figure 4. A linear oscillating magnetic field can be resolved into two components rotating in opposite directions. One of these components is rotating in the same direction as the precessional orbit of the nuclear magnetic dipole (the proton); the oppositely rotating component of H_1 is disregarded. If H_0 is held constant and the oscillator frequency is varied, the angular velocity of the component of rotating magnetic field H_1 will vary until it is equal to (in resonance with) the angular velocity ω_0 of the precessing proton. At this point, energy is absorbed, the nucleus flips to its higher energy level, and the recorder shows a peak. In actual practice, the oscillator frequency is held constant, and H_0 is swept over a narrow range.

There is one further complication. We need some mechanism to return the nucleus to its lower-energy state. In the absence of such a mechanism, all of the

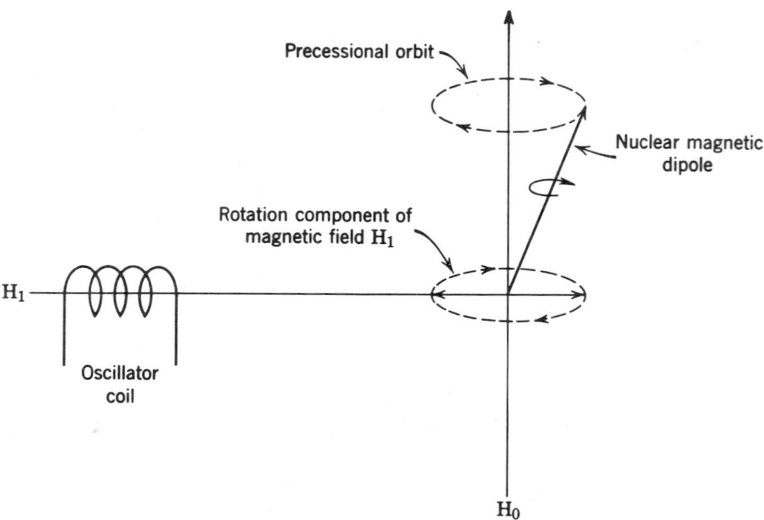

Fig. 4. Oscillator generates rotating component of magnetic field H_1.

small excess population of nuclei in the lower-energy state will be raised to the higher-energy state, and no more energy will be absorbed. Fortunately, there exists a mechanism whereby the nucleus in the higher energy state can lose energy to its environment and thus return to its lower energy state. The mechanism is called a spin-lattice or longitudinal relaxation process and involves transfer of energy from the nucleus in its high-energy state to the molecular lattice. Its efficiency is described as the time T_1 taken for the transfer. An efficient relaxation process involves a short time T_1 and results in broadening of the absorption peak. The line width is inversely proportional to the lifetime of the excited state. In neat liquids, solutions, and gases, the time T_1 is of the proper duration to produce a peak of usable width. In solids, this mechanism is not effective; T_1 is therefore very long, and in the absence of any other effects, a crystalline solid would show extremely narrow lines. There is another effect, called spin-spin or transverse relaxation, operative in solids. This involves transfer of energy from one high-energy nucleus to another. There is no net loss of energy, but the spread of energy among the nuclei concerned results in line broadening. In fact, this latter mechanism causes line broadening of such magnitude as to render NMR spectra of solids of little interest to the organic chemist.

We can now consider very briefly the instrumentation necessary to obtain a nuclear magnetic resonance spectrum.

II. APPARATUS AND SAMPLE HANDLING

A high resolution (defined later) nuclear magnetic resonance spectrometer is commercially available from Varian Associates, Palo Alto, Cal. [these instruments are also marketed by Perkin-Elmer and Jeolco (USA)]. Instruments fitted with permanent magnets with field strengths of about 14,000 gauss give proton spectra at 60 megacycles per second (Mcps). Electromagnets permit greater flexibility so that proton spectra can be obtained at various frequencies up to 100 Mcps (23,500 gauss). In addition, ^{19}F, ^{11}B, ^{13}C, and ^{31}P nuclei can be examined at appropriate combinations of frequencies and magnetic field strengths.

A schematic diagram of an NMR spectrometer is shown in Figure 5. The instrument can be described in terms of the following components:

1. A strong magnet whose homogeneous field can be varied continuously and precisely over a relatively narrow range. This is accomplished by means of the sweep generator.
2. A radio-frequency oscillator.
3. A radio-frequency receiver.
4. A recorder, calibrator, and integrator.
5. A sample holder that positions the sample relative to the main magnetic field, the transmitter coil and the receiver coil. The sample holder also spins the sample to increase the apparent homogeneity of the magnetic field. A variable-temperature sample holder is also available.

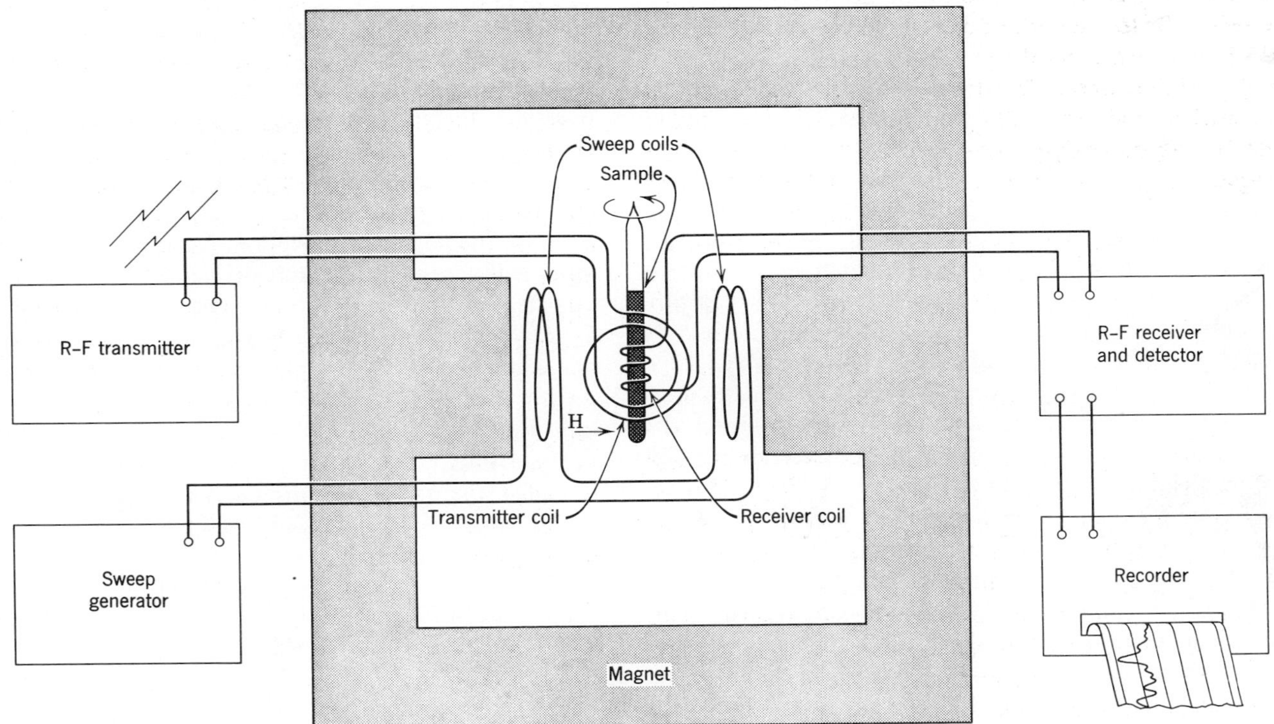

Fig. 5. Schematic diagram of an NMR Spectrometer. (Courtesy of Varian Associates Palo Alto, Calif.)

Operational details will not be described. Suffice to say, the desired frequency and field strength are selected, and the sweep generator sweeps the magnetic field over a narrow range near the field strength selected. Proton spectra are usually run at 60 Mcps or 100 Mcps, and the usual range of field sweep is equivalent to about 1,000 cycles per second, (cps) at 60 Mcps or about 1700 cps at 100 Mcps. By measuring frequency shifts from a reference marker, an accuracy of ± 1 cps can be achieved. The recording is presented as a series of peaks, the peak areas being proportional to the number of protons they represent. Peak areas are measured by the electronic integrator that traces a series of steps whose heights are proportional to the peak areas. The steps can be superimposed on the peaks. As will be obvious in Chapter 6, proton counting with the integrator is extremely useful. Peaks hidden under other peaks can thus be detected. Proton counting is often useful for determining sample purity and, of course, for quantitative analytical work.

The sample, a liquid or a solution in a suitable solvent, is contained in a 5-mm O.D. glass tube. Ordinarily about 0.4 ml of a neat liquid or somewhere between 10 to 50 mg of a liquid or a solid dissolved in 0.4 ml of a solvent is used. By using nylon plugs to cut down on dead space—that is, by restricting the sample to the region of the receiver coil—the volume of liquid or solution can be reduced to about 0.025 ml.

A microtube (Nuclear Magnetic Resonance Specialties, New Kensington, Pa.) consisting of a thick-wall capillary leading to a 25-μl spherical cavity allows usable spectra to be obtained on about 1 mg of sample. To overcome the lack of inherent sensitivity of NMR spectrometry, repetitive scans can be used. Signals can thus be accumulated and noise averaged out. A small computer attachment (computer of average transients, CAT) is available as an accessory for this purpose. Usable spectra can be obtained on samples of the order of 50 μg.

The ideal solvent should contain no protons, be inexpensive, low-boiling, nonpolar, and inert. Carbon tetrachloride is ideal when the sample is sufficiently soluble in it. The most widely used solvent, despite its relatively high cost, is deuterated chloroform ($CDCl_3$). The small sharp proton peak from the $CHCl_3$ impurity present rarely interferes seriously. Almost all of the common solvents are available in the deuterated form with an isotopic purity (atom %D) of 98–99.8% (Merck Sharp and Dohme of Canada, Ltd., Montreal). A list of these solvents and the positions of their proton impurity peaks are given in Appendix A.

Small "spinning side bands" are often seen, symmetrically disposed on both sides of a strong absorption peak; these result from inhomogeneities in the magnetic field and in the spinning tube. They are readily recognized because of their symmetrical appearance and because their separation from the absorption peak is proportional to the rate of spinning. The oscillations often seen at the high-field end of a strong sharp peak are called "ringing."

Traces of ferromagnetic impurities cause severe broadening of absorption peaks. Common sources are tap water, steel wool, Raney nickel, and particles from metal spatulas or fittings. These impurities can be removed by dipping a thin bar magnet into the NMR tube.

III. CHEMICAL SHIFT

Thus far, we have obtained a single peak from the interaction of radio frequency and a strong magnetic field on a proton in accordance with the basic NMR equation in which γ, the magnetogyric ratio, is an intrinsic property of the nucleus. The peak area (measured by the integrator) is proportional to the number of protons it represents. Fortunately, the situation is not quite so simple. The nucleus is shielded to a small extent by its electron cloud whose density varies with the environment. This variation gives rise to different absorption positions within the range of about 1000 cps or so in a magnetic field corresponding to 60 Mcps, or about 1700 cps in a field corresponding to 100 Mcps. The ability to discriminate among the chemical shifts describes high resolution NMR spectrometry.

Electrons under the influence of a magnetic field will circulate, and, in circulating, will generate their own magnetic field opposing the applied field; hence, the shielding effect (Figure 6). This effect accounts for the diamagnetism exhibited by all organic materials. In the case of materials with an unpaired electron, the paramagnetism associated with the net electron spin far overrides the diamagnetism of the circulating, paired electrons.

The degree of shielding depends on the density of the circulating electrons, and as a first, very rough approximation, the degree of shielding of a proton on a carbon atom will depend on the inductive effect of other groups attached to the carbon atom. These are small effects; as we pointed out, we are talking about shifts of parts per million (i.e., cycles per second in a 60- or 100-megacycle field) in relation to a standard reference. The difference in the absorption position of a particular proton from the absorption position of a reference proton is called the *chemical shift* of the particular proton.

The most generally useful reference compound is tetramethylsilane (TMS).

$$\begin{array}{c} CH_3 \\ | \\ CH_3-Si-CH_3 \\ | \\ CH_3 \end{array}$$

It has several advantages: it is chemically inert, magnetically isotropic, volatile (b.p. 27°), and soluble in most

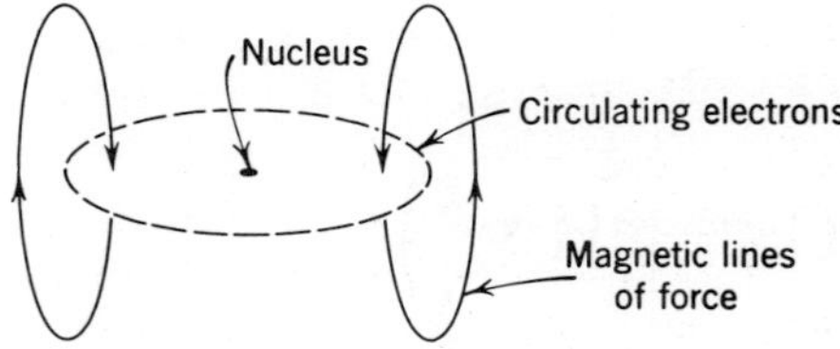

Fig. 6. Diamagnetic shielding of nucleus by circulating electrons.

organic solvents; it gives a single sharp absorption peak, and absorbs at higher field than almost all organic protons. When water or deuterium oxide is the solvent, TMS can be used as an "external reference," i.e., sealed in a capillary immersed in the solution. The methyl protons of sodium 2,2-dimethyl-2-silapentane-5-sulfonate (DSS)

$$(CH_3)_3SiCH_2CH_2CH_2SO_3Na$$

are often used as an internal reference in aqueous solution. Since only enough is used to give a small methyl peak, the diffuse pattern of the CH_2 peaks barely shows on the base line. Unless hydrogen-bonding effects are involved, a proton peak referenced to TMS in deuterochloroform will be within 0.01 to 0.03 ppm of the same peak referenced to DSS in water or deuterium oxide.

Let us set up an NMR scale (Figure 7) and set the TMS peak at 0 cps at the right-hand edge. The magnetic field increases toward the right. When chemicals shifts are given in cps (designated ν), the applied frequency must be specified. Chemical shifts can be expressed in dimensionless units (δ), independent of the applied frequency, by dividing ν by the applied frequency and multiplying by 10^6. Thus a peak at 60 cps (ν 60) from TMS at an applied frequency of 60 Mcps would be at δ 1.00 or 1.00 ppm.

$$\delta \text{ or ppm} = \frac{60 \times 10^6}{60 \times 10^6} = 1.00$$

Since δ units are expressed in parts per million, the expression ppm is often used. The same peak at an applied frequency of 100 Mcps would be at ν 100, but would still be at δ 1.00.

$$\delta \text{ or ppm} = \frac{100 \times 10^6}{100 \times 10^6} = 1.00$$

This scheme has been criticized because δ values increase in the downfield direction; the rejoinder is that these are really negative numbers. The other commonly used system assigns a value of 10.00 for tetramethylsilane, and describes chemical shifts in terms of τ values

$$\tau = 10.00 - \delta$$

It should be noted that δ is treated as a positive number. We shall make our assignments in both δ and τ values. Shifts at higher field than TMS will be encountered very rarely; δ values are then shown with a negative sign, and τ values merely increase numerically.

It is important to realize that the chemical shift in cps is directly proportional to the strength of the applied field H_0, and therefore to the applied frequency. This is understandable because the chemical shift is dependent on the diamagnetic shielding induced by H_0. The strongest magnetic field consistent with field homogeneity should be used to spread out the chemical shifts.

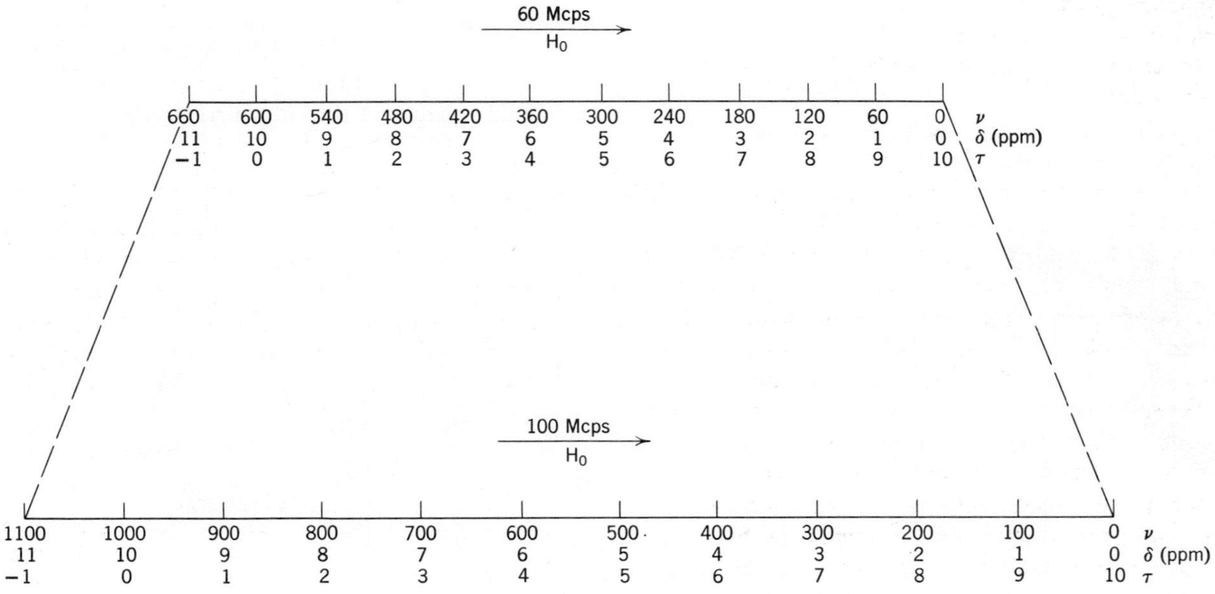

Fig. 7. NMR Scale at 60 Mcps and at 100 Mcps.

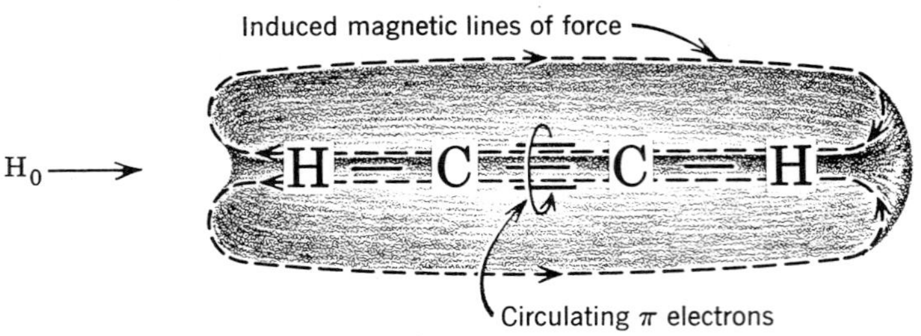

Fig. 8. Shielding of acetylenic protons.

Chemical intuition is a dependable guide, up to a point, to chemical shifts. It tells us that the electron density around the protons of TMS is high (silicon is electropositive relative to carbon), and these protons will therefore be highly shielded and their peak will be found at high field. We could make a number of good guesses as to chemical shifts, using concepts of electronegativity and proton acidity. For example, the following values are reasonable on these grounds:

	δ	τ
$(CH_3)_2O$	3.27	6.73
CH_3F	4.30	5.70
RCOOH	10.8 approx.	−0.8 approx.

But finding the protons of acetylene at δ 2.35, τ 7.65, that is, more shielded than ethylene protons (δ 4.60, τ 5.40) is unsettling. And finding the aldehydic proton of acetaldehyde at δ 9.97, τ 0.03 definitely calls for some augmentation of chemical intuition. We shall use diamagnetic anisotropy to explain these and other apparent anomalies, such as the unexpectedly large deshielding effect of the benzene ring (benzene protons δ 7.27, τ 2.73).

Let us begin with acetylene. The molecule is linear, and the triple bond is symmetrical about the axis. If this axis is aligned with the applied magnetic field, the π-electrons of the bond can circulate at right angles to the applied field, thus inducing their own magnetic field opposing the applied field. Since the protons lie along the magnetic axis, the magnetic lines of force induced by the circulating electrons act to shield the protons (Figure 8), and the NMR peak is found further upfield than chemical intuition would predict.

This effect is called diamagnetic anisotropy, and it depends on the orientation of the molecule with respect to the applied magnetic field. Similar arguments can be adduced to rationalize the unexpected low field position of the aldehydic proton. In this case, the effect of the applied magnetic field is greatest along the transverse axis of the C=O bond (that is, in the plane of the page in Figure 9). The geometry is such that the aldehydic proton, which lies in front of the page, is in the deshielding portion of the induced magnetic field. The same argument can be used to account for at least part of the rather large amount of deshielding of olefinic protons.

The so-called "ring-current effect" is another example of diamagnetic anisotropy and accounts for the large deshielding of benzene ring protons. Figure 10 shows this effect. It also indicates that a proton held directly above or below the ring should be shielded. This has actually been found to be the case for some of the methylene protons in 1,4-polymethylenebenzenes.

All the ring protons of acetophenone are found downfield because of the ring current effect. Moreover,

Circulating electrons

Induced magnetic lines of force

H_0

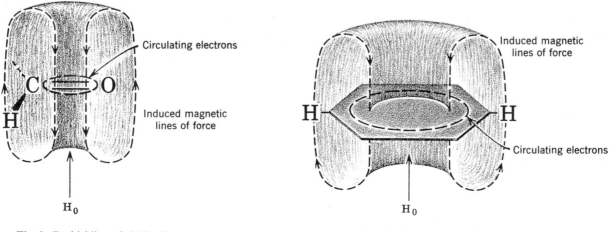

Fig. 9. Deshielding of aldehydic proton.

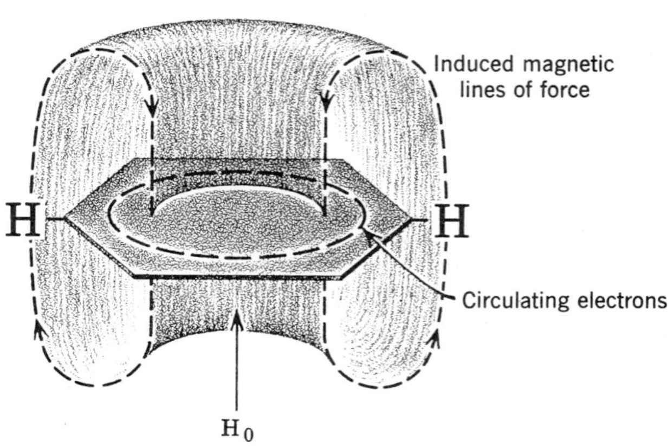

Fig. 10. Ring current effects in benzene.

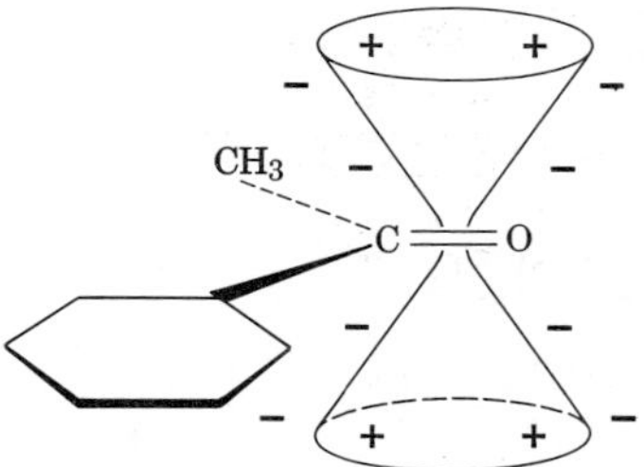

Fig. 11. Shielding (+) and deshielding (−) zones of acetophenone.

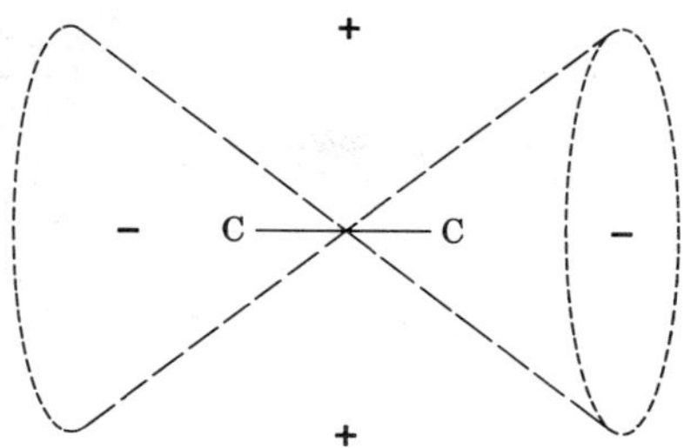

Fig. 12. Shielding (+) and deshielding (−) zones of C—C.

the ortho protons are shifted slightly further downfield (meta, para $\delta \sim 7.40$, τ 2.60; ortho $\delta \sim 7.85$, τ 2.15) because of the additional deshielding effect of the carbonyl group. In Figure 11, the carbonyl bond and the benzene ring are coplanar. If the molecule is oriented so that the applied magnetic field H_0 is perpendicular to the plane of the molecule, the circulating π electrons of the C=O bond shield the conical zones above and below them, and deshield the lateral zones in which the ortho proton is located. Both ortho protons, of course, are equally deshielded.

A spectacular example of shielding and deshielding by ring currents is furnished by some of the annulenes.[17] The protons outside the ring of [18] annulene are strongly deshielded (δ 8.9, τ 1.1), and those inside are strongly shielded (δ −1.8, τ 11.8).

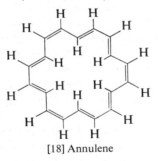

[18] Annulene

Demonstration of such a ring current is probably the best evidence available for aromaticity.

In contrast with the striking anisotropic effects of circulating π electrons, the σ electrons of a C—C bond produce a small effect. The axis of the C—C bond is the axis of the deshielding cone (Figure 12).

This figure accounts for the deshielding effect of successive alkyl substituents on a proton attached to a carbon atom. Thus the protons are found progressively downfield in the sequence RCH_3, R_2CH_2, and R_3CH. The observation that an equatorial proton is consistently found further downfield by 0.1–0.7 ppm than the axial proton on the same carbon atom in a rigid six-membered ring can also be rationalized (Figure 13). The axial and equatorial proton on C_1 are oriented similarly with respect to C_1—C_2 and C_1—C_6, but the equatorial proton is within the deshielding cone of the C_2—C_3 bond (and C_5—C_6).

Chemical shifts of protons bound to carbon and near a single functional group are shown in chart form in Appendix B. Values assigned (δ and τ) are rough averages designed to indicate a region rather than an exact number. Except where otherwise specified, the shifts shown are for aliphatic compounds in deuterochloroform or carbon tetrachloride. Variations due to changes in concentration are usually small in the absence of hydrogen bonding effects. Solvent changes often cause appreciable changes in shift position. A separate value is given for methyl, methylene, and methine protons. Inspection of these charts gives the very useful general impression that chemical shifts of protons in organic compounds fall roughly into eight regions as summarized in Figure 14.

Appendix C gives shift positions for methylene protons carrying two functional groups. The calculated values were obtained from the set of Shoolery's constants,[18] also presented in Appendix C.

IV. SIMPLE SPIN-SPIN COUPLING

We have obtained a series of absorption peaks representing protons in different chemical environments; each absorption area is proportional to the number of protons it represents. This achievement alone furnishes considerable information. We have now to consider one further refinement, spin-spin coupling. This can be described as the indirect coupling of proton spins through the intervening bonding electrons. Very briefly, it occurs

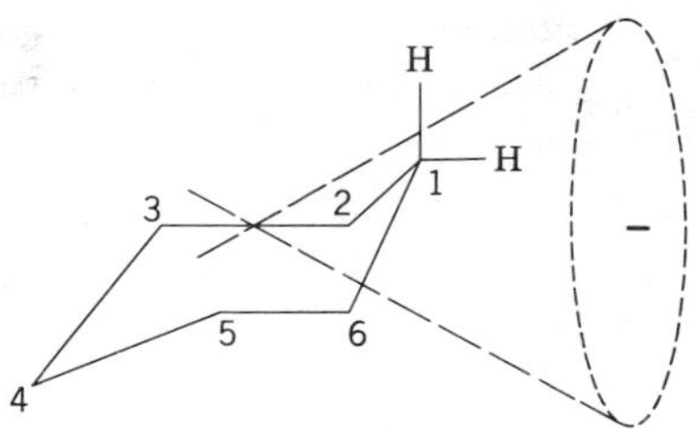

Fig. 13. Deshielding of equatorial proton of a rigid six-membered ring.

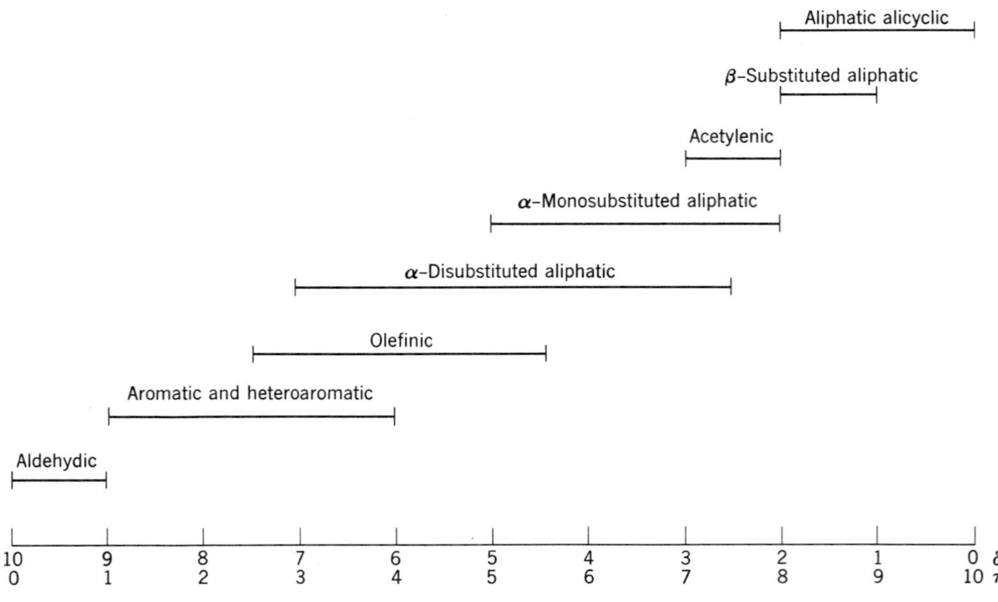

Fig. 14. General regions of chemical shifts.

because there is some tendency for a bonding electron to pair its spin with the spin of the nearest proton; the spin of a bonding electron, having been thus influenced, the electron will affect the spin of the other bonding electron and so on through to the next proton. Coupling is ordinarily not important beyond three bonds unless there is ring strain as in small rings or bridged systems, or bond delocalization as in aromatic or unsaturated systems.

Suppose the two protons shown in Figure 15 are in very different chemical environments from one another as in the compound RO—CH(OR)—CH(C(CH$_3$)$_3$)—C(CH$_3$)$_3$. Each proton will give rise to an absorption, and the absorptions will be quite widely separated. But the spin of each proton is affected slightly by the two orientations of the other proton through the intervening electrons so that each absorption appears as a doublet (Figure 15). The distance between the component peaks of a doublet is proportional to the effectiveness of the coupling, and is denoted by a coupling constant J, which is independent of the applied magnetic field H_0. Whereas chemical shifts can range over about 1700 cps at 100 Mcps, coupling constants between protons rarely exceed 20 cps (see Appendix E). So long as the chemical shift difference in cps is much larger than the coupling constant ($\Delta\nu/J$ is greater than about 6 or 7), the simple pattern of two doublets appears. As $\Delta\nu/J$ becomes smaller, the doublets approach one another, the inner two peaks increase in intensity, and the outer two peaks decrease (Figure 16). The shift position of each proton is no longer midway between its two peaks as was the case in Figure 15, but is at the "center of gravity"; it can be estimated with fair accuracy by inspection, or determined precisely by the following formula in which the peak positions (1, 2, 3, and 4 from left to right) are given in cycles per

Fig. 15. Spin-spin coupling between two protons with very different chemical shifts.

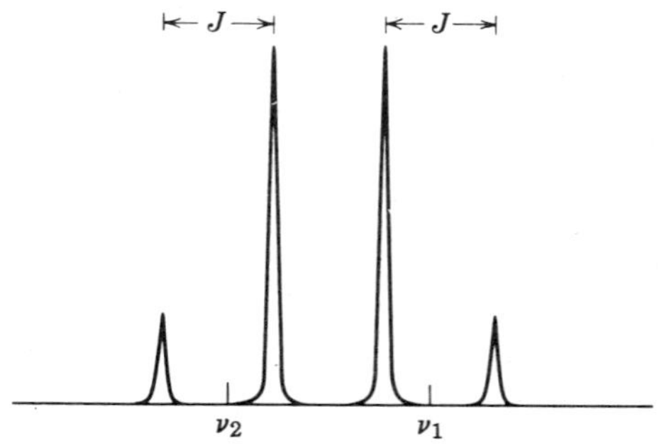

Fig. 16. Spin-spin coupling between protons with a smaller difference in chemical shifts and a larger J value.

second from the reference.

$$(1\text{–}3) = (2\text{–}4) = \sqrt{(\Delta\nu)^2 + J^2}$$

The shift position of each proton is $\Delta\nu/2$ from the midpoint of the pattern. When $\Delta\nu = J\sqrt{3}$, the two pairs resemble a quartet resulting from splitting by three equivalent vicinal protons. Failure to note the small outer peaks (i.e. 1 and 4) may lead to mistaking the two large inner peaks for a doublet. When the chemical shift difference becomes zero, the middle peaks coalesce to give a single peak and the end peaks vanish—that is, the protons are equivalent. (Equivalent protons may spin-spin couple with one another, but splitting is not observed). A further point to be noted is the obvious one that the spacing between the peaks of two coupled multiplets is the same. The dependence of chemical shift on the applied magnetic field and the independence of the spin-spin coupling afford a method of distinguishing between them. The spectrum is merely run at two different applied magnetic fields. Chemical shifts are also solvent dependent, but J values are only very slightly affected by change of solvent.

Look at the next stage in complexity of spin-spin coupling (Figure 17). Consider the system $—\text{HC}—\text{CH}_2—$ (with OR on the HC)

in the compound $\text{RO}—\underset{|}{\text{CH}}—\text{CH}_2—\text{C(CH}_3)_3$ in which the single methine proton is in a very different chemical environment from the two methylene protons. As before, we see two sets of absorptions widely separated, and now the absorption areas are in the ratio of 1:2. The methine proton couples with the methylene protons and splits the methylene proton absorption into a symmetrical doublet, as explained above. The two

Fig. 17. Spin-spin coupling between CH and CH_2 with very different chemical shifts.

methylene protons split the methine proton absorption into a triplet because three combinations of proton spins exist in the two methylene protons (a and b) of Figure 18. Pairs 2 and 3 are equivalent, and the intensities of each peak of the triplet are therefore in the ratio 1:2:1.

$\vec{H}_0$

1	2	3	4
← b	← b	→ b	→ b
← a	→ a	← a	→ a

Fig. 18. Three spin states of a methylene group (protons a and b).

When the methine and methylene protons in the system $—\text{CH}—\text{CH}_2—$ are in similar environments (i.e. $\Delta\nu/J$ is small), the simple doublet-triplet pattern degenerates to a complex pattern of from seven to nine lines as a result of second-order splitting; analysis by inspection is no longer possible.

The use thus far of the term "equivalent" in describing protons on the same carbon atom in aliphatic compounds is intuitively obvious to the organic chemist. However, it is necessary to define two kinds of equivalence: chemical and magnetic. Nuclei are chemically equivalent to one another if they all have the same chemical shift. Magnetically equivalent nuclei not only have the same chemical shift, but must also couple in the same way with any other selected nucleus in the molecule; that is, magnetically equivalent nuclei have the same set of coupling constants. The protons on a carbon atom in the aliphatic compounds considered in this section are magnetically equivalent. Note that in these compounds, there is no appreciable barrier to rotation around the C—C bonds, and that there are no nearby centers of asymmetry. Sets of protons that are chemically, but not magnetically, equivalent to each other will be discussed in Section VIII.

A generalized set of rules can now be formulated on the basis of what we have just observed. Thus far, we have assumed all protons on the same carbon atom to be magnetically equivalent. This is true only if there is no appreciable barrier to rotation around the C—C bonds, and if there is no nearby center of asymmetry. Further, $\Delta\nu/J$ must be large. The following rules then apply.

1. Splitting of a proton absorption is done by neighboring protons, and the multiplicity of the split is determined by the number of these protons. Thus, one proton causes a doublet, and two equivalent protons cause a triplet. The multiplicity then is $n + 1$, n being the number of neighboring equivalent protons. The general formula, which covers all equivalent nuclei is $2nI + 1$, I being the spin number.
2. The relative intensities of the peaks of a multiplet also depend on n. We have seen that doublet ($n = 1$) peaks are in the ratio 1:1, and triplet peaks are in the ratio 1:2:1. Quartets are in the ratio 1:3:3:1. The

general formula is $(a + b)^n$; when this is expanded to the desired value of n, the coefficients give the relative intensities.

Following Pople,[12] we designate sets of protons separated by a small chemical shift with the letters A, B, and C, and sets separated by a large chemical shift ($\Delta\nu/J > 6$ or 7) with the letters A, M, and X. The number of protons in each set is denoted by a subscript number. Members of a set must be magnetically equivalent. Thus the first case we examined (Figure 15) is an AX system. The second case (Figure 16) is an AB system, and the third case (Figure 17) is an A_2X system. As $\Delta\nu/J$ decreases, the A_2X system approaches an A_2B system, and the simple first-order splitting of the A_2X system becomes more complex (see Section VII).

Thus far, we have dealt with two sets of protons. The protons in each set are magnetically as well as chemically equivalent to each other; every proton in each set is equally coupled to every proton in the other set, i.e. a single coupling constant is involved. Given these conditions and the condition that $\Delta\nu/J$ be large (at least 6), the two rules (above) apply, and we obtain a first-order pattern (except for "virtual coupling," Section X). In general, these are the A_aX_x systems (a and x are the number of protons in each set); the first order rules apply only to these systems, but as we have seen, there is a gradual change in the appearances of spectra changing from an AX to an AB pattern. In a similar way, it is frequently possible to relate complex patterns back to first-order patterns in more complex systems. With practice, a fair amount of deviation from first-order may be tolerated.

A system of three sets of protons, each set separated by a large chemical shift, can be designated $A_aM_mX_x$. If two sets are separated from each other by a small chemical shift, and the third set is widely separated from the other two, we use an $A_aB_bX_x$ designation. And if all shift positions are close, the system is $A_aB_bC_c$. Both end sets are coupled to the middle set with the same or different coupling constants, whereas the end sets may or may not be coupled to one another. Thus there may be one, two, or three coupling constants. AMX systems with two or three coupling constants are first-order. ABX systems approximate first-order, but ABC systems cannot be analyzed by inspection. These more compex patterns are treated in Section VII.

We can now appreciate the three main features of an NMR spectrum: chemical shifts, peak intensities, and spin-spin couplings that are first-order or that approximate first-order patterns. We can now analyze first-order NMR spectra.

The NMR spectrum of 1,3-dichloropropane in $CDCl_3$ is shown as Figure 19.

$$Cl{-}CH_2{-}CH_2{-}CH_2{-}Cl$$

The peak at δ 10, τ 0 is the reference tetramethylsilane, that at δ 7.25, τ 2.75 is $CHCl_3$ impurity. The terminal methylene groups are equivalent, and since these four protons are deshielded by the chlorine atoms, their shift position is downfield from that of the two equivalent

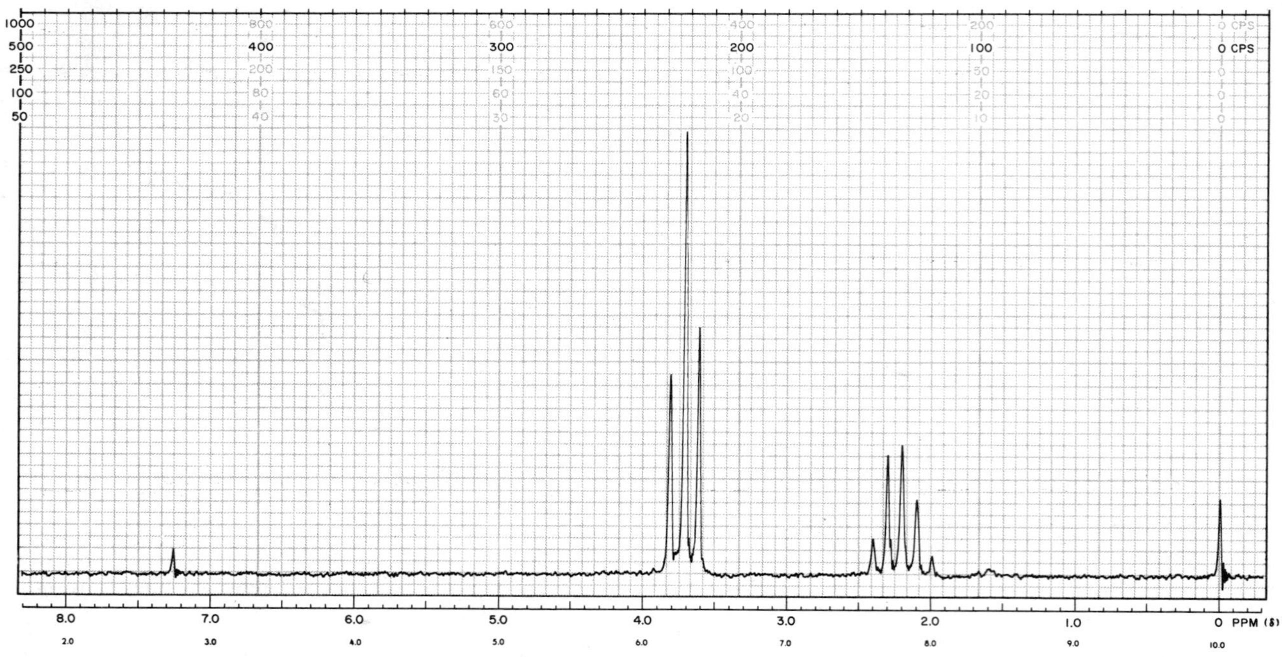

Fig. 19. 1,3-Dichloropropane in $CDCl_3$. 60 Mcps.

$Cl{-}CH_2{-}CH_2{-}CH_2{-}Cl$

$X_2A_2X_2$ or A_2X_4

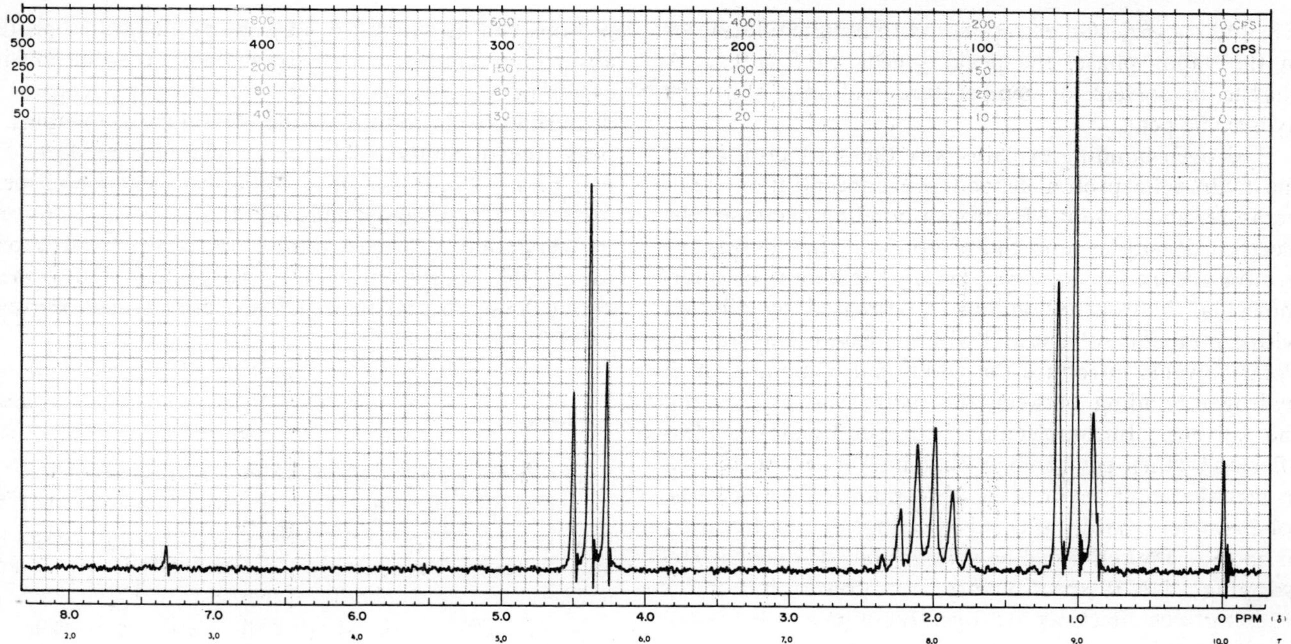

Fig. 20. 1-Nitropropane in $CDCl_3$. 60 Mcps.
$CH_3—CH_2—CH_2—NO_2$
$A_3M_2X_2$

protons on the central methylene group. The system is A_2X_4, and we see a triplet and a quintet. Note that even at a $\Delta\nu/J$ value of about 13, the inner peak of each multiplet is slightly increased in intensity. Actually this common distortion is of some help in determining which multiplets couple; they "slant" toward each other. The splitting and relative intensities can be diagrammed as follows:

1 1
1 2 1

1 1
1 2 1
1 3 3 1
1 4 6 4 1

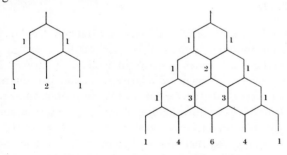

Note that the line intensities are simply the sums of the intensities of the coinciding lines.

The spectrum of 1-nitropropane (Figure 20) is an example of an $A_3M_2X_2$ system with two coupling constants that are almost equal. The protons in each set are magnetically equivalent. The A protons are coupled to the M protons ($J_{AM} \sim 7$ cps), the M protons are coupled to the X protons ($J_{MX} \sim 7$ cps), and the A protons are not coupled to the X protons ($J_{AX} = 0$). The fact that J_{AM} is approximately equal to J_{MX} is fortuitous because the A and the X protons are not chemically identical. However nearly identical coupling constants of aliphatic protons are fairly common. The downfield triplet (X) represents the protons on the same carbon atom as the nitro group split by the adjacent methylene group (M). The upfield triplet represents the CH_3 group (A) split by the adjacent methylene group (M). The sextet (M) centered at δ 2.07, τ 7.93 results from splitting by five adjacent protons that have, fortuitously, nearly the same coupling constant. The slight difference in coupling constants, J_{AM} and J_{MX}, accounts for the slight broadening of the sextet peaks which are almost in the theoretical ratio 1:5:10:10:5:1.

V. PROTONS ON HETEROATOMS

Protons on a heteroatom differ from protons on a carbon atom in that: (1) they are exchangeable, (2) they are subject to hydrogen-bonding, and (3) they are subject to partial or complete decoupling by electrical quadrupole effects of some heteroatoms. Shift ranges for protons on heteroatoms are given in Appendix D.

Protons on Oxygen

Alcohols

Unless special precautions are taken (see below), the spectrum of neat ethanol usually shows the hydroxylic proton as a sharp peak at δ 5.35, τ 4.65. At the commonly used concentration of about 5 to 20% in a nonpolar solvent (e.g., carbon tetrachloride or deuterochloroform), the hydroxylic peak is found between δ 2,

τ 8, and δ 4, τ 6. On extrapolation to infinite dilution or in the vapor phase, the peak is near δ 0.5, τ 9.5. A change in solvent or temperature will also shift the hydroxylic peak.

Hydrogen bonding explains why the shift position of the hydroxylic proton depends on concentration, temperature, and solvent. Hydrogen bonding decreases the electron density around the proton and thus moves the proton absorption to lower field. The extent of intermolecular hydrogen bonding is decreased by dilution with a nonpolar solvent and with increased temperature. Polar solvents introduce the additional complication of hydrogen bonding between the hydroxylic proton and the solvent. Intramolecular hydrogen bonds are less affected by their environment than intermolecular bonds; in fact the enolic hydroxylic absorption of β-diketones, for example, is hardly affected by change of concentration or solvent, though it can be shifted upfield somewhat by warming. NMR spectrometry is a powerful tool for studying such effects as hydrogen bonding and keto-enol tautomerism.

Exchangeability explains why the hydroxylic peak of ethanol is usually seen as a sharp singlet. Under ordinary conditions, enough acidic impurities are present in solution to catalyze rapid exchange of the hydroxylic proton. The proton is not on the oxygen atom long enough for it to "see" the three states of the methylene protons, and there is no coupling. The rate of exchange can be decreased by treating the solution or the solvent with anhydrous sodium carbonate, alumina, or molecular sieves immediately before obtaining the spectrum.[19,20] Purified deuterated dimethyl sulfoxide or acetone, in addition to allowing a slower rate of exchange, shifts the hydroxylic proton to lower field, even in dilute solution, by hydrogen-bonding between solute and solvent.[21,22] Since the hydroxylic proton can now "see" the protons on the α-carbon, a primary alcohol will show a triplet, a secondary alcohol a doublet, and a tertiary alcohol a singlet. Several exceptions have been reported[23] so that due caution is warranted. At intermediate rates of exchange, the multiplet merges into a broad absorption band; at this point, the exchange rate in cycles per second is equal to $\pi J/\sqrt{2}$.

A dihydroxy alcohol may show separate absorption peaks for each hydroxylic proton; in this case, the rate of exchange in cps is much less than the difference in cps between the separate absorptions. As the rate increases, the two absorption peaks broaden, then merge to form a single broad peak; at this point, the exchange rate in cycles per second is equal to the original separation in cycles per second. The relative position of each peak depends on the extent of hydrogen bonding of each hydroxylic proton; steric hindrance to hydrogen bonding frequently accounts for a relative upfield absorption.

The spectrum of a compound containing exchangeable protons can be simplified, and the exchangeable proton absorption removed, simply by shaking the solution with excess deuterium oxide or by obtaining a spectrum in deuterium oxide solution if the compound is soluble. A peak due to HOD will appear, generally between δ 5, τ 5, and δ 4.5, τ 5.5 in nonpolar solvents, and near δ 3.3, τ 6.7 in dimethyl sulfoxide.

Acetylation or benzoylation of a hydroxyl group moves the α protons of a primary alcohol downfield about 0.5 ppm, and that of a secondary alcohol about 1.0–1.2 ppm.

Phenols

The behavior of a phenolic proton resembles that of an alcoholic proton. The phenolic proton peak is usually a sharp singlet (rapid exchange, no coupling) and its range, depending on concentration, solvent and temperature, is generally downfield (δ ~7.5, τ 2.5 to δ ~4.0, τ 6.0) compared with the alcoholic proton. A carbonyl group in the ortho position shifts the phenolic proton absorption downfield to the range of about δ 12.0, τ −2.0 to δ 10.0, τ 0.0 because of intramolecular hydrogen bonding. Thus *o*-hydroxyacetophenone shows a peak at about δ 12.05, τ −2.05 almost completely invariant with concentration. The much weaker intramolecular hydrogen bonding in *o*-chlorophenol explains its shift range (δ ~6.3, τ 3.7 at 1 molar concentration to δ ~5.6, τ 4.4 at infinite dilution) which is broad compared with that of *o*-hydroxyacetophenone, but narrow compared with that of phenol.

Enols

Enols are usually stabilized by intramolecular hydrogen-bonding, which varies from very strong in aliphatic β-diketones to weak in cyclic α-diketones. The enolic proton is downfield relative to alcohol protons and, in the case of the enolic form of some β-diketones, may be found as far downfield as δ 16.6, τ −6.6 (the enolic proton of acetylacetone absorbs at δ 15.0, τ −5.0, and that of dibenzoylmethane at δ 16.6, τ −6.6). The enolic proton peak is frequently broad at room temperature because of slow exchange. Furthermore, the keto-enol conversion is slow enough so that absorption peaks of both forms can be observed, and the equilibrium measured.

When strong intramolecular bonding is not involved, the enolic proton absorbs in about the same range as the phenolic proton.

Carboxylic Acids

Carboxylic acids exist as stable hydrogen-bonded dimers in nonpolar solvents even at high dilution. The carboxylic proton therefore absorbs in a characteristically narrow range, δ ~13.2, τ −3.2 to δ ~10.0, τ 0.0, and is affected only slightly by concentration. Polar solvents partially disrupt the dimer and shift the peak accordingly.

The peak width at room temperature ranges from sharp to broad, depending on the exchange rate of the particular acid. The carboxylic proton exchanges quite rapidly with protons of water and alcohols (or hydroxy groups of hydroxyacids) to give a single peak whose position depends on concentration. Sulfhydryl or enolic protons do not exchange rapidly with carboxylic protons, and individual peaks are observed.

Protons on Nitrogen

The ^{14}N nucleus has a spin number $I = 1$ and, in accordance with the formula $2I + 1$, should cause a proton attached to it and a proton on an adjacent carbon atom to show three equally intense peaks. There are two factors, however, that complicate the picture: the rate of exchange of the proton on the nitrogen atom, and the electrical quadrupole moment of the ^{14}N nucleus.

The proton on a nitrogen atom may undergo rapid, intermediate, or slow exchange. If the exchange is rapid, the NH proton(s) is decoupled from the N atom and from protons on adjacent carbon atoms. The NH peak is therefore a sharp singlet, and the adjacent CH protons are not split by NH. Such is the case for most aliphatic amines. At an intermediate rate of exchange, the NH proton is partially decoupled, and a broad NH peak results. The adjacent CH protons are not split by the NH proton. Such is the case for N-methyl-*p*-nitroaniline. If the NH exchange rate is slow, the NH peak is still broad because the electrical quadrupole moment of the nitrogen nucleus induces a moderately efficient spin relaxation and thus an intermediate lifetime for the spin states of the nitrogen nucleus. The proton thus sees three spin states of the nitrogen nucleus (spin number = 1) which are changing at a moderate rate, and the proton responds by giving a broad peak. In this case, coupling of the NH proton to the adjacent protons is observed. Such is the case for pyrroles, indoles, secondary and tertiary amides and carbamates (Figure 21). Note that H̲—N—C—H̲ coupling takes place through the C—H, C—N, and N—H bonds, but coupling between nitrogen and protons on adjacent carbons is negligible. In the spectrum of ethyl N-methyl carbamate (Figure 21) $CH_3NH\overset{\overset{\displaystyle O}{\|}}{C}OCH_2CH_3$, the NH proton shows a broad absorption centered about δ 5.16, τ 4.84, and the N—CH_3 absorption at δ 2.78, τ 7.22 is split into a doublet (J ~5 cps) by the NH proton. The ethoxy protons are represented by the triplet at δ 1.23, τ 8.77, and the quartet at δ 4.14, τ 5.86. The small peak at δ 2.67, τ 7.33 is an impurity.

Aliphatic and cyclic amine NH protons absorb from δ ~3.0, τ 7.0 to δ ~0.5, τ 9.5; aromatic amines absorb from δ ~5.0, τ 5.0 to δ ~3.0, τ 7.0. Because amines are subject to hydrogen bonding, the shift position depends

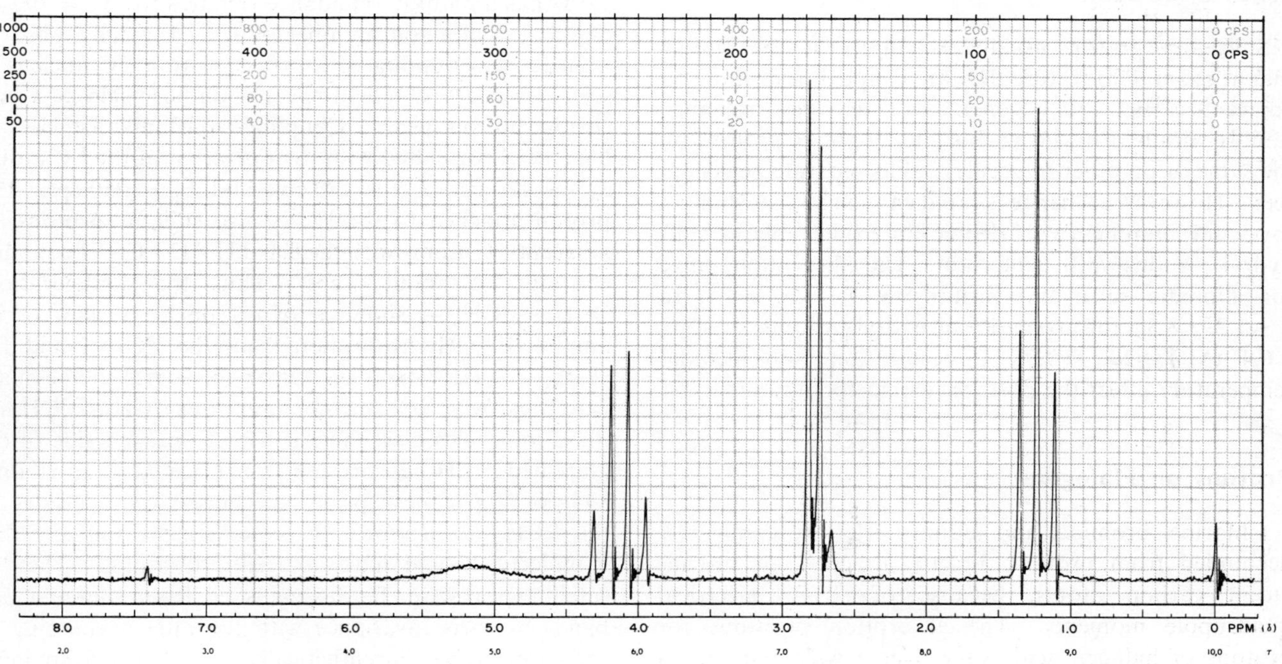

Fig. 21. Ethyl N-methyl carbamate $CH_3NH\overset{\overset{\displaystyle O}{\|}}{C}OCH_2CH_3$, 60 Mcps.

on concentration, solvent, and temperature. Amides, pyrroles, and indoles absorb from $\delta \sim 8.5$, τ 1.5 to $\delta \sim 5.0$, τ 5.0; the effect on the absorption position of concentration, solvent, and temperature is generally smaller than in the case of amines. The nonequivalence of the protons on the nitrogen atom of a primary amide and of the methyl groups of N,N-dimethylamides is caused by hindered rotation around the C—N bond (C=O) because of the contribution of the canonical form $^{-}$O—C=N^{+}.

Protons on the nitrogen atom of an amine salt exchange at a slow rate; they are seen as a broad peak downfield ($\delta \sim 8.5$, τ 1.5 to $\delta \sim 6.0$, τ 4.0), and they are coupled to protons on adjacent carbon atoms ($J \sim 7$ cps); the α-protons are recognized by their downfield position in the salt compared with that in the free amine. The use of trifluoroacetic acid as both a protonating agent and a solvent frequently allows classification of amines as primary, secondary, or tertiary.[24] Sometimes the broad $N^{+}H$, $N^{+}H_2$, or $N^{+}H_3$ absorption can be seen to consist of three broad humps. These humps represent splitting by the nitrogen nucleus ($J \sim 50$ cps). With good resolution, it is sometimes possible to observe splitting of each of the humps by the protons on adjacent carbon atoms ($J \sim 7$ cps).

Protons on Sulfur

Sulfhydryl protons usually exchange at a slow rate so that at room temperature they are coupled to protons on adjacent carbons ($J \sim 8$ cps). Nor do they exchange rapidly with hydroxylic, carboxylic, or enolic protons on the same or on other molecules; thus separate peaks are seen. However, exchange is rapid enough so that shaking for a few minutes with deuterium oxide replaces sulfhydryl protons with deuterium. The absorption range for aliphatic sulfhydryl protons is $\delta \sim 1.6$, τ 8.4, to $\delta \sim 1.2$, τ 8.8; for aromatic sulfhydryl protons, $\delta \sim 3.6$, τ 6.4 to $\delta \sim 2.8$, τ 7.2. Concentration, solvent, and temperature affect the position within these ranges.

Protons on Halogens

Chlorine, bromine, and iodine nuclei are completely decoupled from protons directly attached, or on adjacent carbon atoms, because of strong electrical quadrupole moments. The absorption positions for protons of halogen acids vary over a wide range as a function of concentration, solvent, and temperature (in the vapor phase, for example HF absorbs at δ 2.7, τ 7.3, and HI absorbs at δ −13, τ 23).

The ^{19}F atom has a spin number of 1/2 and couples strongly with protons (see Appendix E). The rules for coupling of protons with fluorine are the same as proton-proton coupling; in general, the proton-fluorine coupling constants are somewhat larger, and long-range effects are frequently found. The ^{19}F nucleus can be observed at 56.4 Mcps at 14,092 gauss. Of course, its spin is split by proton and fluorine spins, and the multiplicity rules are the same as those observed in proton spectra.

VI. COUPLING OF PROTONS TO OTHER NUCLEI

The organic chemist may encounter proton coupling with such other nuclei (besides ^{1}H, ^{19}F, and ^{14}N) as ^{31}P, ^{13}C, ^{2}H, and ^{29}Si. Three factors must be considered: natural abundance, spin number, and electrical quadrupole moment; the nuclear magnetic moment and relative sensitivity are important when a spectrum of the particular nucleus is considered. These properties are listed for a number of nuclei in Appendix F.

^{31}P has a natural abundance of 100% and a spin number of 1/2 (therefore no electrical quadrupole moment). The multiplicity rules for proton-phosphorus splitting are the same as those for proton-proton splitting. The coupling constants are large ($J_{H-P} \sim$ 200 to 700 cps and J_{HC-P} is $\sim$20 cps) and are observable through at least four bonds. The ^{31}P nucleus can be observed at the appropriate frequency and magnetic field.

^{13}C has a natural abundance (relative to ^{12}C = 100%) of 1.1%, and a spin number of 1/2. Typically, absorption due to coupling of a proton with a ^{13}C nucleus is seen as weak "^{13}C satellite peaks" on both sides of a very strong proton peak. Coupling constants for H—^{13}C have been correlated with hybridization of the ^{13}C atom: $J_{sp^3} \sim 120$ cps, $J_{sp^2} \sim 170$ cps, and $J_{sp} \sim 250$ cps. The proton attached to the ^{13}C is also split by protons on adjacent ^{12}C atoms with the usual H—C—C—H coupling constant of about 7 cps. Thus the configuration, $^{13}CH_3$—$^{12}CH_2$—, shows a triplet on both sides of an amplified $^{12}CH_3$ absorption from the ^{13}C—H and the $^{13}CH_3$—$^{12}CH_2$ couplings. Other molecules in the magnetic field will have the configuration $^{12}CH_3$—$^{13}CH_2$—; these molecules also show a triplet on each side of the amplified $^{12}CH_3$ absorption, but since $J_{CH_3-{}^{13}C}$ is only $\sim$4 to 7 cps, these peaks are buried on the sides of the $^{12}CH_3$ absorption. It is statistically unlikely that a molecule would have adjacent ^{13}C atoms. The ^{13}C satellite peaks can be distinguished from spinning side bands by their invariance with the rate of spinning of the sample tube. Parenthetically, note that each spinning side band has the same multiplicity as its "parent."

Deuterium (^{2}H or D) is introduced into a molecule usually to detect a group or to simplify a spectrum.

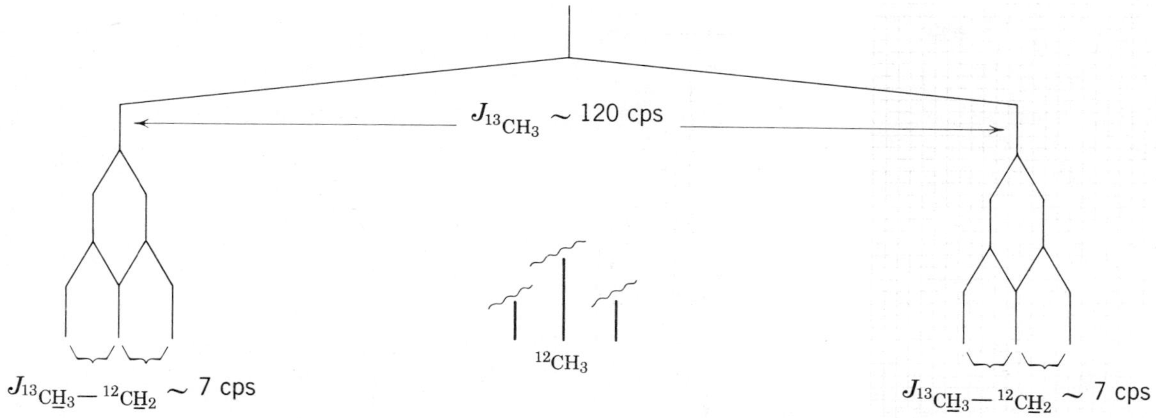

$J_{^{13}CH_3} \sim 120$ cps

$^{12}CH_3$

$J_{^{13}C\underline{H}_3-{}^{12}C\underline{H}_2} \sim 7$ cps

$J_{^{13}C\underline{H}_3-{}^{12}C\underline{H}_2} \sim 7$ cps

^2H has a spin number of 1, a small coupling constant with protons, and a small electrical quadrupole moment. A proton-deuterium coupling constant is approximately 1/7 of the corresponding proton-proton constant. Suppose the protons on the α-carbon atom of a ketone

$$\overset{\gamma}{\text{X—CH}_2}\text{—}\overset{\beta}{\text{CH}_2}\text{—}\overset{\alpha}{\text{CH}_2}\text{—}\overset{\text{O}}{\overset{\|}{\text{C}}}\text{—}$$

were replaced by deuterium

$$\overset{\gamma}{\text{X—CH}_2}\text{—}\overset{\beta}{\text{CH}_2}\text{—}\overset{\alpha}{\text{CD}_2}\text{—}\overset{\text{O}}{\overset{\|}{\text{C}}}\text{—}$$

The original spectrum would consist of a triplet for the α protons, a quintet (assuming equal coupling) for the β-protons, and a triplet for the γ protons. In the deuterated compound, the α-proton absorption would be absent, the β-protons would appear as a slightly broadened triplet, and the γ protons would be unaffected. Actually, each peak of the β-proton triplet is a very closely spaced triplet ($J_{CH-CD} \sim 1$ cps or less), but the effect under ordinary resolution is peak broadening. Most deuterated solvents have residual protonated impurities; the CHD_2 group in deuterated acetone or dimethyl sulfoxide, for example, is frequently encountered as a closely spaced quintet ($J \sim 2$ cps, intensities 1:2:3:2:1).

^{29}Si has a natural abundance of 5.1% (based on $^{28}Si = 100\%$), and a spin number of 1/2. $J_{^{29}Si-CH}$ is about 6 cps. The small doublet caused by the $^{29}Si—CH_3$ coupling can often be seen straddling (±3 cps) an amplified peak of tetramethylsilane; the $^{13}C—H_3$ doublet can also be seen at ±59 cps.[25]

VII. MORE COMPLEX SPIN—SPIN COUPLING

As was pointed out in Section IV, only A_aX_x and $A_aM_mX_x$ systems are first order. The deviations from a first-order spectrum as an AX pattern moves through an AB to an A_2 pattern were traced; the AB pattern could still be analyzed by inspection. But more complex changes occur as an A_2X becomes an A_2B pattern, and a complete analysis by inspection is no longer possible; the ratios of peak intensities are not those predicted by first-order calculation, additional splitting occurs, and the spacings are not necessarily equal to the coupling constants. Most spectra encountered are not first-order spectra. On the other hand, the resemblance of many spectra to first-order spectra can be recognized because there is a gradual transition from A_aX_x to A_aB_b types; Wiberg's collection of calculated spectra[25a] can be used for matching fairly complex splitting patterns.

A_aX_x and A_aB_b Systems

In tracing the distortions that occur as A_aX_x approaches A_aB_b in aliphatic compounds, we remind the reader that all protons in each set are considered magnetically equivalent to each other; this implies no appreciable barrier to rotation around the C—C bonds and no nearby centers of asymmetry. This is a practical approach to most aliphatic systems.

Compounds of the type $Z_2CH—CH_2Y$ show A_2X or A_2B patterns, depending on the relative deshielding effects of Y and Z. These patterns are not encountered very often because the geminal substituents must be identical to avoid setting up an asymmetric center that would destroy the chemical equivalence of the CH_2 protons (see Section IX).

A_2X_2 and A_2B_2 patterns are very common. Figure 22 shows the progressive distortions as $A_2X_2 \rightarrow A_2B_2$ in compounds of the type $ZCH_2—CH_2Y$ when Z and Y are varied. As $\Delta\nu/J$ decreases and the triplets merge, the inner peaks increase in intensity, the middle and the outer peaks undergo additional splitting and some of the outer peaks may disappear in the baseline noise. The general appearance of symmetry throughout aids recognition. When the shift positions of both sets of protons are identical, a single A_4 peak is seen.

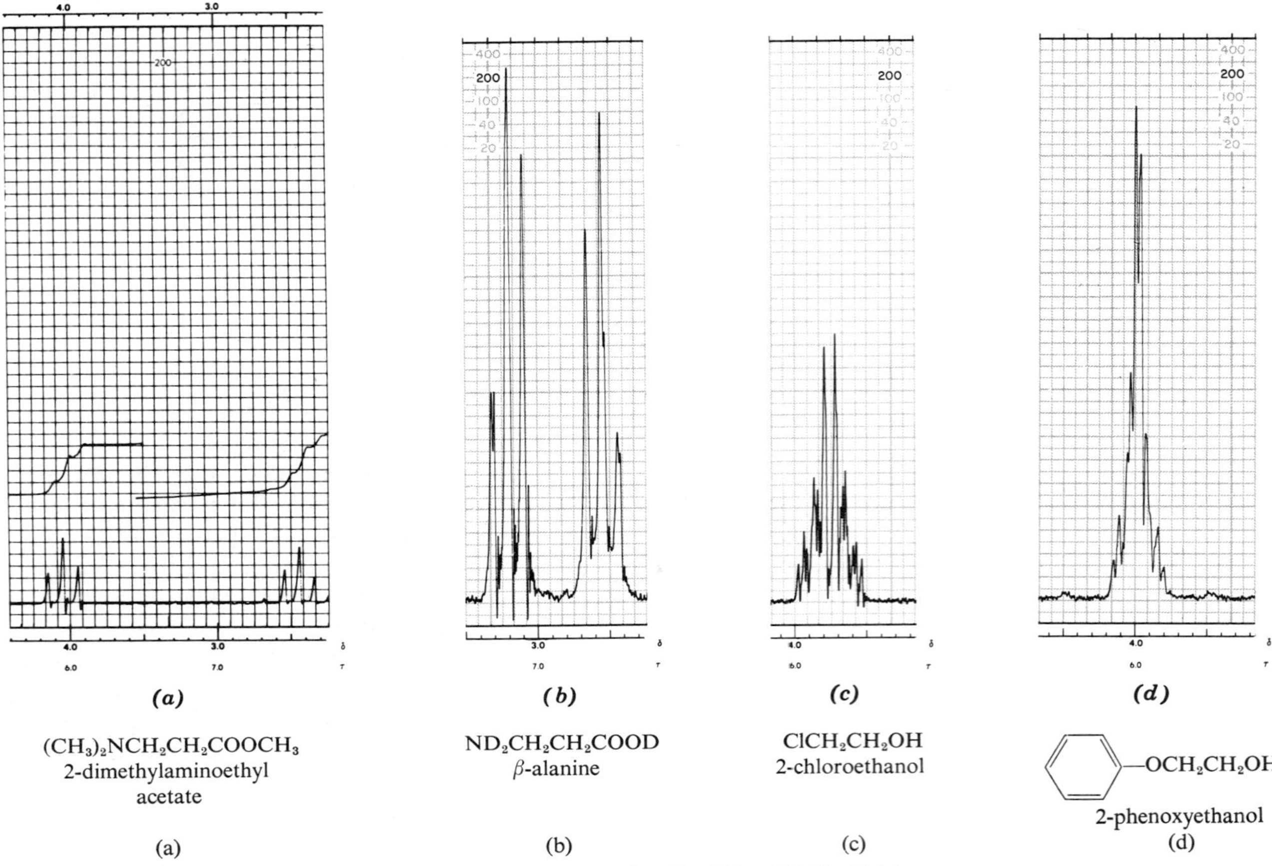

(a) (b) (c) (d)

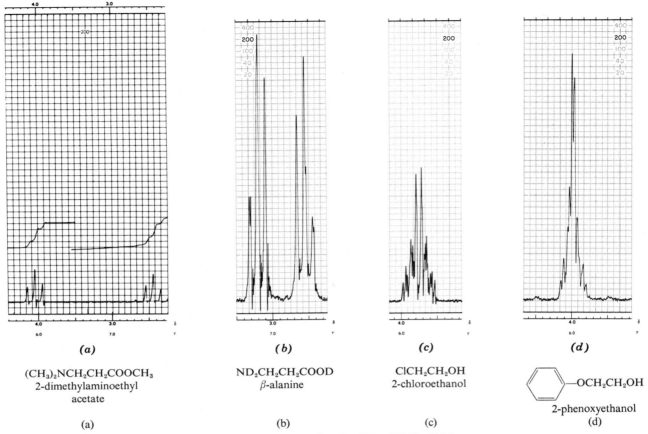

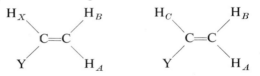

Fig. 22. Progressive distortions as $A_2X_2 \rightarrow A_2B_2$ in the configuration Z—CH_2—CH_2Y. 60 Mcps.

The isolated CH_3CH system gives A_3X or A_3B spectra, and the isolated CH_3CH_2 system, A_3X_2 or A_3B_2 spectra. As $\Delta\nu/J$ decreases, the peak ratios are distorted, extra splitting develops, and the spacing does not correspond to the J values. Very complex unsymmetrical absorptions result, and because of the small spacings of the numerous peaks, the bands are broad and unresolved. Extreme distortion results when the systems are not isolated (see Section X).

AMX, *ABX*, and *ABC* Systems with Three Coupling Constants

The spectrum of methyl-2-furoate (Chapter 6, compound 4) represents a nearly first-order *AMX* System with three coupling constants. Each proton is represented by a pair of doublets.

Although *ABX* systems with three coupling constants are not first-order, the patterns are frequently recognized if the distortions are not too severe. The degree of distortion depends on the ratios of the separation of the *A* and *B* protons to their coupling constants. The vinylic structure gives an *ABX* or an *ABC* system depending on the nature of the substituent Y, which determines the shift positions of the protons.

H_X H_B C=C Y H_A $\qquad$ H_C H_B C=C Y H_A

p-Chlorostyrene (Figure 23) shows an *ABX* spectrum that can readily be related to an *AMX* pattern. The following analysis, though not rigorous, is useful.

H_X H_B C=C H_A Cl

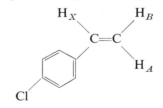

Protons *A* and *B* are not chemically equivalent. Proton *A* (δ ~5.70, τ 4.30) is deshielded about 25 cps, compared with proton *B*, because of its relative proximity to the ring. Proton *X* (δ ~6.70, τ 3.30) is strongly deshielded by the ring, and is split by proton *A* ($J \sim$ 18 cps) and by proton *B* ($J \sim$ 11 cps). The *A* proton is split by the *X* proton ($J \sim$ 18 cps) and by the *B* proton ($J \sim$ 2 cps). The *B* proton is split by the *X* proton ($J \sim$ 11 cps) and by the *A* proton ($J \sim$ 2 cps).

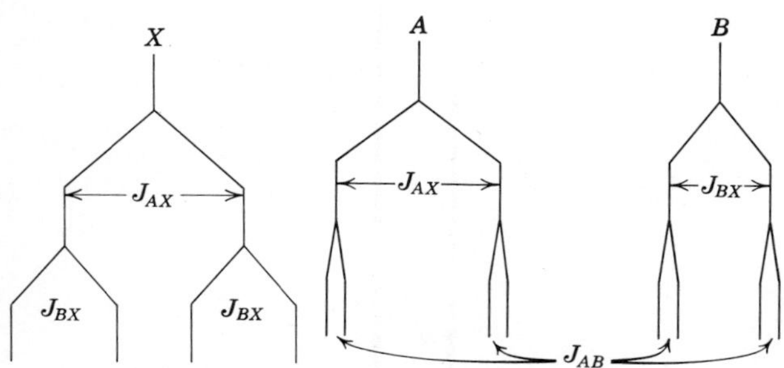

The coupling constants for a vinylic system are characteristic: the *trans* coupling is larger than the *cis*, and the geminal coupling is very small.

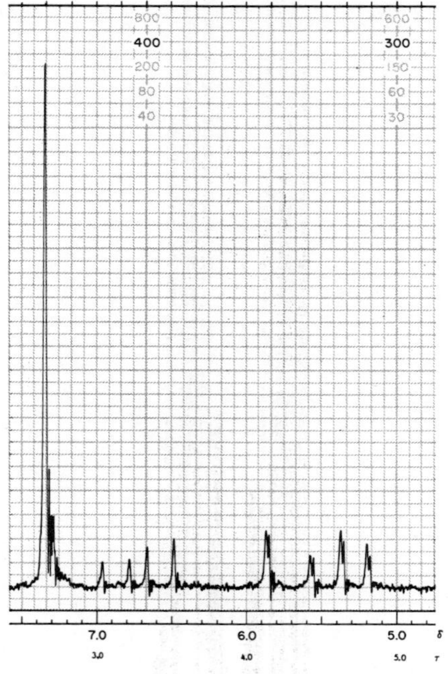

Fig. 23. *p*-Chlorostyrene, 60 Mcps.

The preceding analysis lacks rigor in several details. The splittings in proton X do not correspond exactly to J_{BX} and J_{AX}, although this is a good approximation when $\Delta\nu$ is greater than about 10 for protons AB. The only exact information obtainable from the X pattern is that the spread between the outside peaks is equal to $J_{AX} + J_{BX}$. The distortions in peak intensities from an AMX pattern are obvious. The pattern of two closely spaced pairs should not be confused with the quartet resulting from splitting by three equivalent protons.

As the shift positions of protons A and B approach each other so that $\Delta\nu$ becomes much smaller than 10, the deviations from a first-order spectrum become severe; the A and B patterns overlap, and the middle peaks of the X pattern merge. In the extreme case that $\nu_A = \nu_B$ and $J_{AX} = J_{BX}$, protons A and B are magnetically equivalent, the spectrum is simply A_2X, and the X proton absorption is a triplet. As the shift position of the X proton approaches the A and B absorptions, the spectrum degenerates to a very complex ABC pattern.

An equatorial and an axial proton on the same carbon of a fused 6-membered ring may form the AB part of an ABX or an ABC pattern, depending on the nature of Y on an adjacent carbon. Typically, H_A (equatorial) is deshielded relative to H_B (axial) by about 0.1 to 0.7 ppm (Section III), J_{AB} is about 12 to 15 cps, $J_{\text{ax.-ax.}}$ is about 8 to 10 cps, and $J_{\text{eq.-ax.}}$ is about 2 to 3 cps (Section XI).

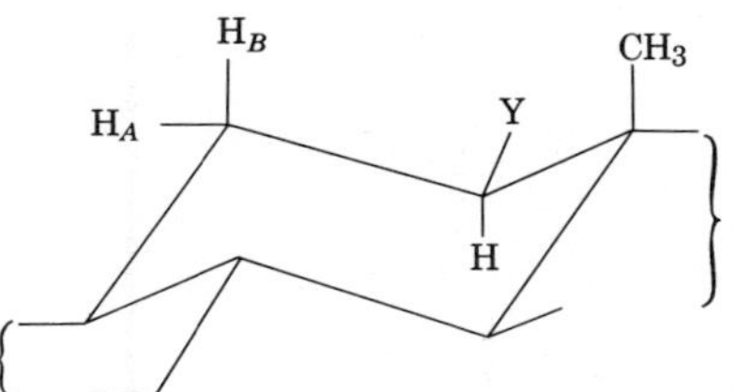

The protons of a methylene group adjacent to an asymmetric center are not necessarily chemically equivalent (Section IX). They frequently split each other to form an AB pattern, and couple individually to an adjacent proton to form an ABX or ABC pattern.

VIII. CHEMICALLY, BUT NOT MAGNETICALLY, EQUIVALENT PROTONS

The distinction between chemical and magnetical equivalence was pointed out in Section IV. First-order coupling rules apply to sets of protons only if all the protons in each set are magnetically equivalent to one another and the shift differences are large compared with the coupling constants. Protons can be chemically equivalent in a trivial sense; coincidence of absorption position may be fortuitous. For example, the spectrum of methylacetylene, $CH_3—C{\equiv}CH$, consists of a single sharp peak when run in deuterochloroform, whereas an A_3B pattern appears in carbon tetrachloride solution.

Thus far, all protons in a set have been magnetically equivalent. It is possible, however, for protons to be chemically equivalent in the sense that the organic chemist understands—they are interchangeable because of elements of symmetry—and yet not be magnetically equivalent. For example, in *p*-chloronitrobenzene,

NO_2
H_A H_A'
H_X H_X'
Cl

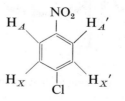

the protons ortho to the nitro group (H_A and $H_{A'}$) are chemically equivalent to each other, and the protons ortho to the chlorine group (H_X and $H_{X'}$) are chemically equivalent to each other. J_{AX} and $J_{A'X'}$ are the same, approximately 7 to 10 cps, and $J_{A'X}$ and $J_{AX'}$ are also the same but much smaller, approximately 0 to 1 cps. Since H_A and $H_{A'}$ couple differently to another specific proton, they are not magnetically equivalent, and first-order rules do not apply. (Similarly, H_X is not magnetically equivalent to $H_{X'}$). In fact for calculations,

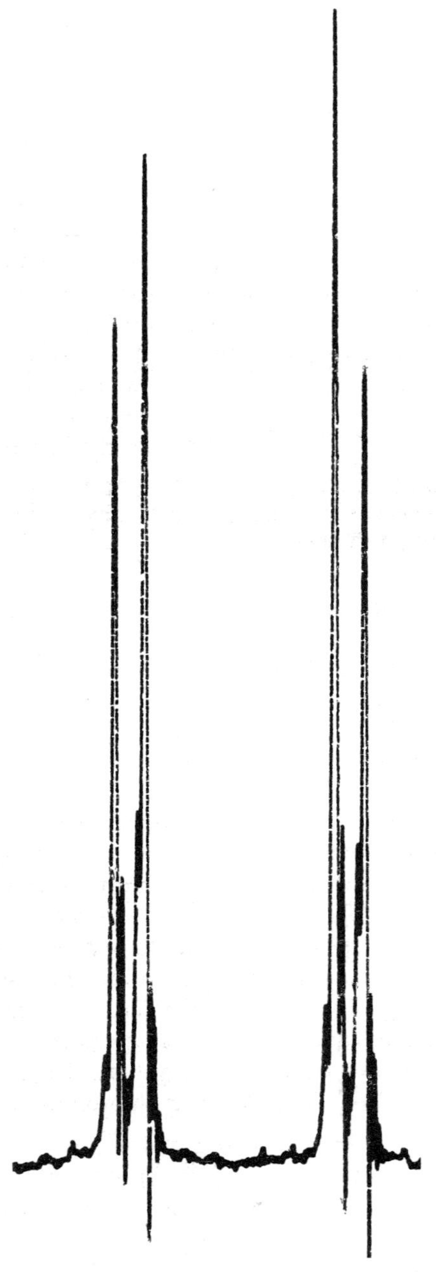

Fig. 24a. *p*-Chloronitrobenzene, 100 Mcps, CCl_4.

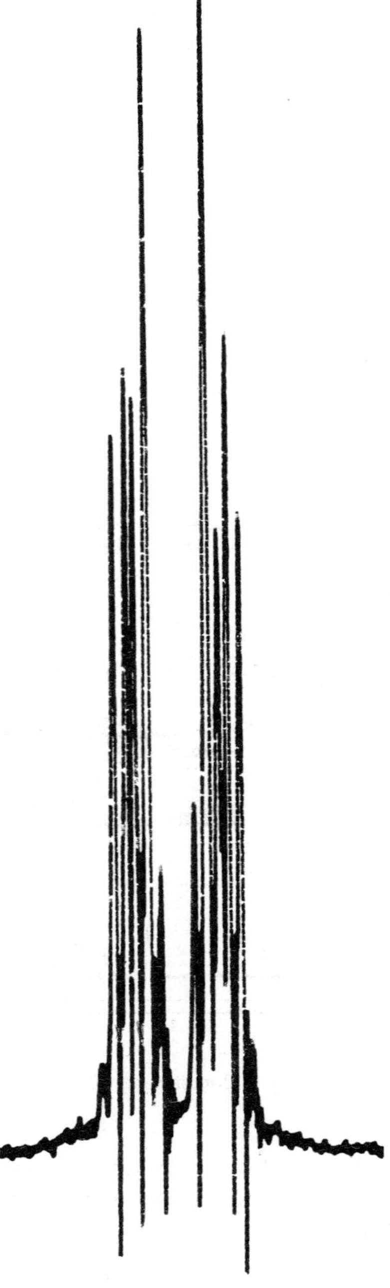

Fig. 24b. *o*-Dichlorobenzene, 100 Mcps, CCl_4.

H_A and $H_{A'}$, and H_X and $H_{X'}$ are also coupled ($J \sim 3$ cps). The system is described as $AA'XX'$, and the spectrum is actually very complex. Fortunately, the pattern is readily recognized because of its symmetry and *apparent* simplicity; under ordinary resolution it resembles an *AB* pattern of two distorted doublets. (Closer inspection reveals many additional splittings (Figure 24a).) As the para substituents become more similar to each other, in their shielding properties, the system tends toward *AA′BB′*; even these absorptions resemble *AB* patterns until they overlap.

The aromatic protons of symmetrically *o*-disubstituted benzenes also give *AA′BB′* spectra. An example is *o*-dichlorobenzene (Figure 24b).

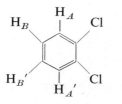

H_A, H_B, Cl, H_B', $H_{A'}$, Cl

IX. EFFECTS OF AN ASYMMETRIC CENTER

The protons of a methylene group near an asymmetric center may not be chemically equivalent. They frequently couple with each other and each may have a different coupling to a vicinal proton. This is a fairly common occurrence that often confounds the organic chemist, secure in his tacit assumption of equivalence of the protons of an acyclic methylene group. Even assuming fast rotation around the C—C bond, the methylene protons of a compound R—C(H_a)(H_b)—C(M)(S)—L may show an *AB* pattern; i.e., they are "intrinsically" nonequivalent because no two conformers are mirror images. However, a large part of the nonequivalence may result from unequal populations of conformers even at fast rotation. The spectrum may be further complicated by slow rotation caused by low temperature or bulky substituents. Nonequivalence of the methylene protons may persist in a compound R—C(H_a)(H_b)—C(M)(S)—C(H_a)(H_b)—R. The middle carbon atom is unsymmetrical with respect to rotation around the C—C bond.

The methylene group may display nonequivalence even though it is once removed from the asymmetric center. Examples of the type R—C(H_a)(H_b)—O—C(M)(S)—L have been reported. Nor need the asymmetric center be a carbon atom. The phenomenon has been reported for the methylene protons in quarternary ammonium salts, sulfites, sulfoxides, diethyl sulfide-borane complexes, and thiophosphonates.[26]

Nonequivalence of the methyl groups of an isopropyl moiety near an asymmetric center is frequently observed; the effect has been measured through as many as seven bonds between the asymmetric center and the methyl protons.[26b]

A single asymmetric center in a terpene alcohol[27]

CH_2=C(CH_2—CHOH—CH_2—CH(CH_3)CH_3)—CH=CH_2

2-Methyl-6-methylene-7-octen-4-ol

effected nonequivalence of the protons of the adjacent methylene groups and of the methyl groups (Figure 25). The shift positions of the methyl groups are δ 0.92, τ 9.08, and δ 0.90, τ 9.10; each absorption is split by the vicinal CH, giving rise to two overlapping doublets ($J = 7$ cps). The nonequivalent protons of the CH_2 between the CH_2=C and CHOH groups absorb at δ 2.47, τ 7.53 and δ 2.18, τ 7.82. Each proton is split by the other ($J_{gem} = 14$ cps) and unequally by the neighboring proton ($J_{vic} = 9$ cps and 4 cps). The protons of the other CH_2 groups are also nonequivalent; additional splitting by the adjacent methine proton results in a partially resolved multiplet.

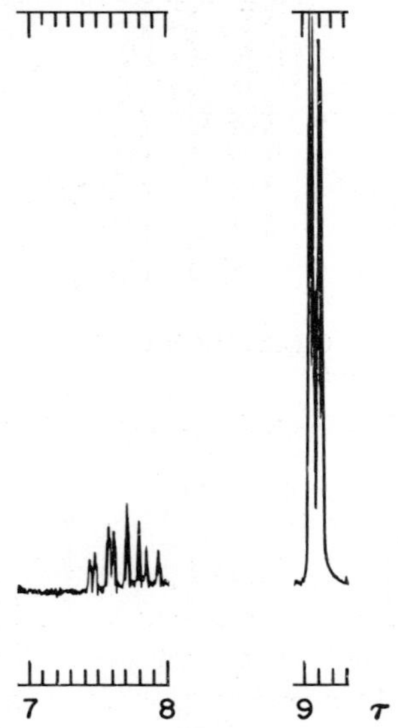

Fig. 25. 5-Methylene and methyl protons of 2-methyl-6-methylene-7-octen-4-ol, 100 Mcps.

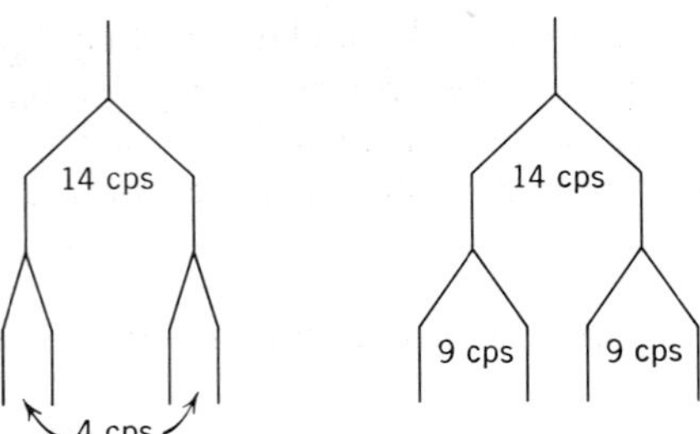

The methylene protons in aspartic acid (Figure 26) (in D_2O) are nonequivalent, and the shift difference between

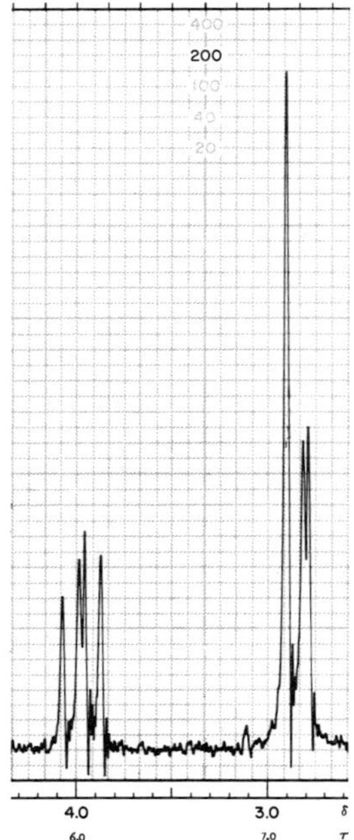

Fig. 26. Aspartic acid in D_2O, 60 Mcps.

them is small compared with the geminal coupling constant. Thus the AB pattern from the geminal coupling

```
    O  ND2  H  O
    ‖   |   |  ‖
DO—C—C———C—C—OD
        |   |
        H   H
```

is quite distorted; the inner peaks are strong, the outer peaks weak. Each methylene proton is also split by the vicinal proton with coupling constants of ~7.5 cps and ~5.5 cps, respectively. Two of the peaks coincide, the end peaks are lost in the baseline noise, and the net result is three peaks. The methine proton absorption consists of two pairs.

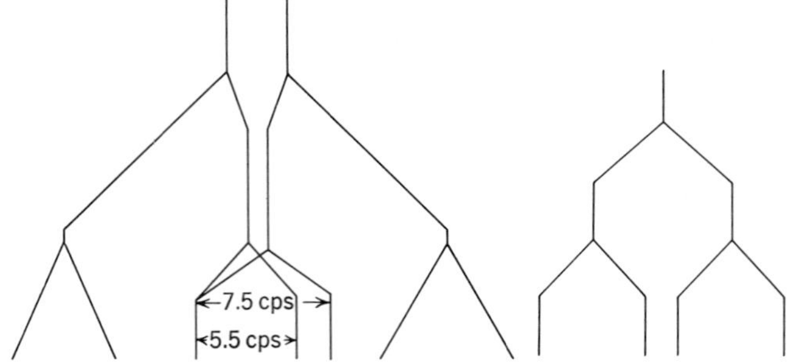

X. VIRTUAL COUPLING

Virtual coupling is a common phenomenon. It occurs when a proton is coupled to a second proton that, in turn, is coupled to a third proton whose chemical shift is similar to that of the second proton. Even though the coupling constant between the first and third protons is zero, the effect of such "strong coupling" between the second and third protons (i.e., $\Delta\nu/J$ for the second and third protons is small) is that they "mix their spins" and both influence the splitting of the first proton. An *ABX* pattern in which J_{AX} is zero and $\Delta\nu/J$ for *AB* is small shows virtual coupling; thus the *X* absorption has additional peaks so that the *X* "doublet" shows a "filled in" appearance. Such would be the case in the following molecule in which the R groups have no protons that would couple with H_A, H_B, or H_X.

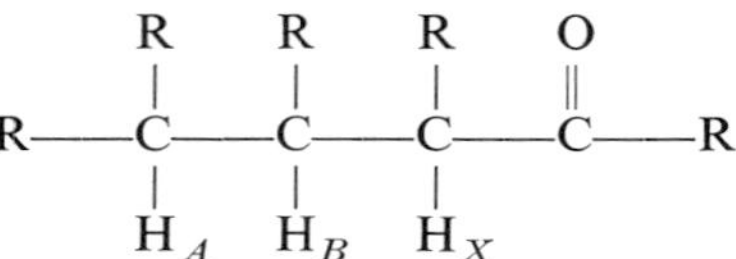

In the extreme case that protons *A* and *B* are chemically

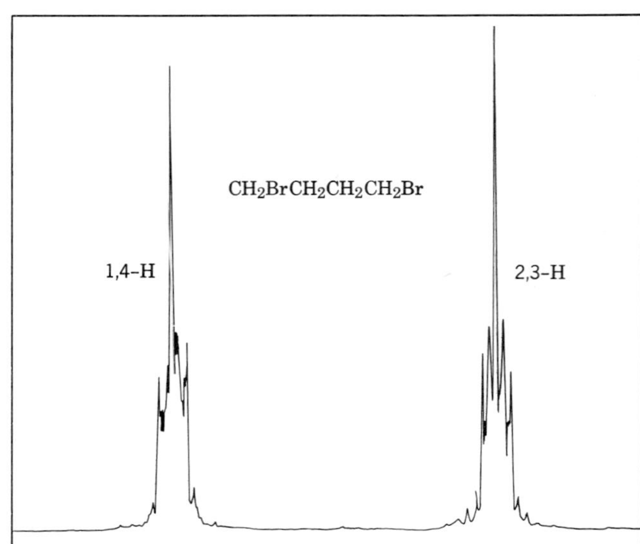

Fig. 27. Proton resonance spectra (100 Mc) of 1,4-dibromobutane.

(but not magnetically) equivalent, the middle peaks of the "filled in" doublet of proton X merge, and the absorption may resemble a "triplet."

Such an isolated system of three linear protons is rare, but the argument is applicable to sets of protons in a ring or an alkyl chain; and these examples are common. The spectrum of 1,4-dibromobutane (Figure 27) should consist of two triplets by first-order reasoning. Instead two complex multiplets are seen that somewhat resemble triplets in general outline.

$$\mathrm{Br{-}\overset{1}{C}H_2{-}\overset{2}{C}H_2{-}\overset{3}{C}H_2{-}\overset{4}{C}H_2{-}Br}$$
$$X_2 \quad A_2 \quad A_2' \quad X_2'$$

The difficulty here is that the 2- and 3-methylene sets are chemically, but not magnetically, equivalent, and they are strongly coupled to each other ($\Delta\nu = 0, J \sim 7$). The 1- and 4-methylene sets are also chemically, but not magnetically, equivalent; they are obviously not coupled to each other. The net result is that the 2- and 3-methylene protons behave as a strongly coupled group and cause complex splitting of the downfield 1- and 4-methylene protons. The pattern of the 2- and 3-methylene protons is also complex. The over-all pattern is $A_2A_2'X_2X_2'$.

The grossly distorted absorption pattern of a methyl group at the end of an alkyl chain is the result of two factors. If coupling to the vicinal CH_2 group alone is considered, the spectrum would be A_3B_2, and the usual deviation from an A_3X_2 methyl triplet would be expected.

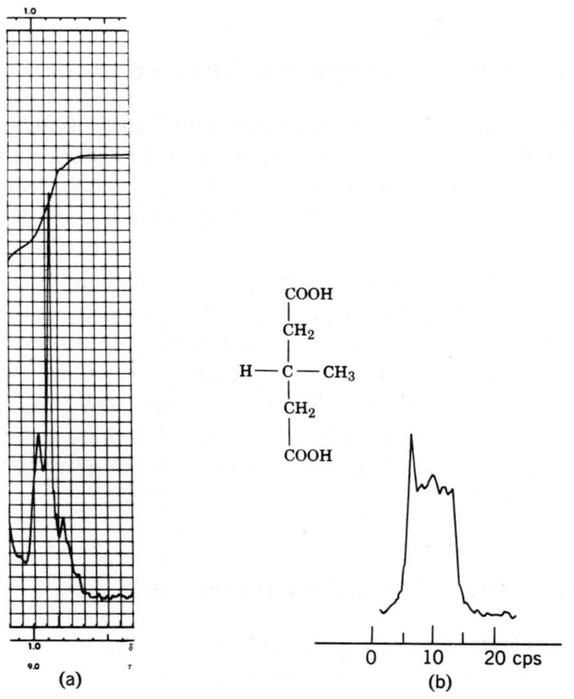

Fig. 28. (a) Methyl group of heptaldehyde, 60 Mcps. (b) Methyl group of β-methylglutaric acid, 60 Mcps., expanded.

The situation is further complicated by virtual coupling to the other methylene groups. The total result is a severely distorted "triplet" for the $RCH_2CH_2CH_3$ case, and a "filled in doublet" for the $RCH_2CH(CH_3)_2$ (A_6B) or the RCH_2CHRCH_3 (A_3B) case. Figure 28 shows the distorted methyl "triplet" of heptaldehyde and the "filled in" and "distorted" methyl doublet of β-methylglutaric acid.

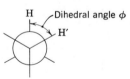

$$\mathrm{HOOC{-}CH_2{-}\underset{}{\overset{\displaystyle CH_3}{\overset{|}{C}}}H{-}CH_2COOH}$$

In the latter compound, the methylene protons and the methine proton have almost exactly the same shift value and are strongly coupled, and virtual coupling distorts the methyl absorption even though the shift difference between the methyl and methine groups is fairly large. Note again the requirements for a first-order methyl triplet or doublet: the shift difference between the methyl group and the adjacent group, and the shift difference between the adjacent group and the group next removed must both be large relative to the coupling constants. In practice, this means that $\Delta\nu/J$ in both cases should be larger than two or three.

XI. VICINAL AND GEMINAL COUPLING IN RIGID SYSTEMS

Coupling between protons on vicinal carbon atoms in rigid systems depends primarily on the dihedral angle ϕ between the H—C—C′ and the C—C′—H′ planes. This angle can be visualized by an end-on view of the

H Dihedral angle ϕ H′

bond between the vicinal carbon atoms and by the perspective in Figure 29 in which the calculated relationship between dihedral angle and vicinal coupling constant[28] is graphed. Karplus emphasized[29] that his calculations are approximations and do not take into account such factors as electronegative substituents, the bond angles θ ($\angle$H—C—C′ and $\angle$C—C′—H′), and bond lengths. Deductions of dihedral angles from measured coupling constants are safely made only by comparison with closely related compounds. The correlation has been very useful in cyclopentanes and cyclohexanes. In cyclopentanes, the observed values of about 8 cps for vicinal *cis* protons and about 0 cps for vicinal *trans* protons are in accord with the corresponding angles of about 0° and about 90°, respectively. In substituted or

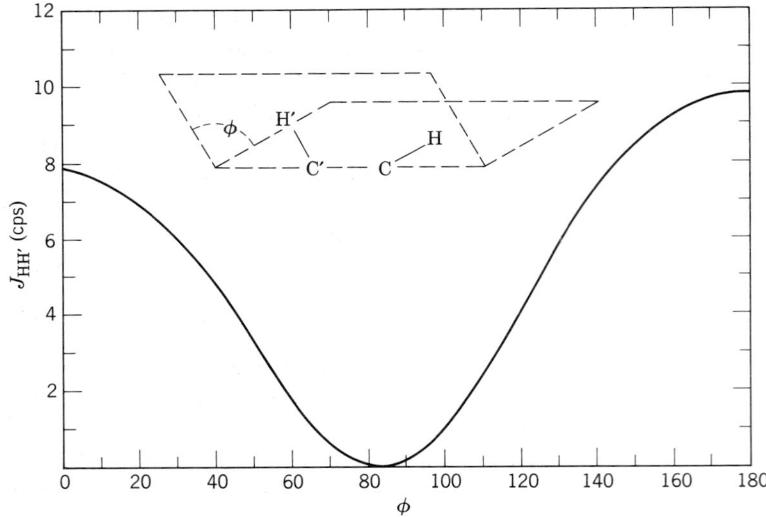

Fig. 29. Relationship between dihedral angle and coupling constant for vicinal protons.

fused cyclohexane rings, the following relations obtain:

	CALC. J	OBSERVED J
axial-axial	9	8–14 (usually 8–10)
axial-equatorial	1.8	1–7 (usually 2–3)
equatorial-equatorial	1.8	1–7 (usually 2–3)

A modified Karplus equation[30] can be applied to vicinal coupling in olefins. The prediction of a larger *trans* coupling ($\varphi = 180°$) than *cis* coupling ($\varphi = 0°$) is borne out. The *cis* coupling in unsaturated rings decreases with increasing bond angle θ (i.e., with decreasing ring size) as follows: cyclohexenes $J = 8.8$ to 10.5, cyclopentenes $J = 5.1$ to 7.0, cyclobutenes $J = 2.5$ to 4.0, and cyclopropenes $J = 0.5$ to 2.0.[31]

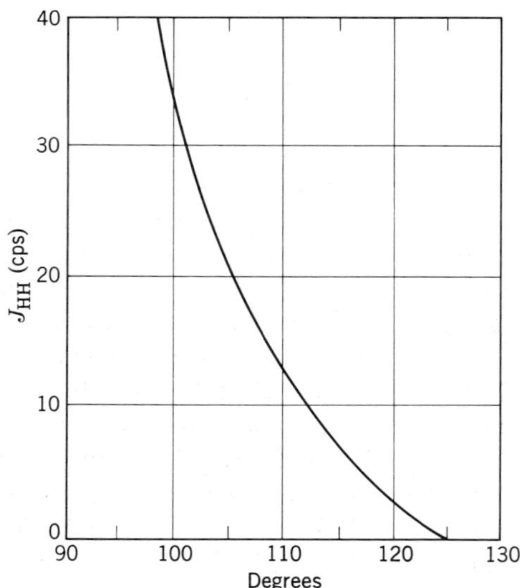

Fig. 30. J_{HH} for CH_2 groups as function of ∠H—C—H.

The calculated relationship[32] between the H—C—H angle of geminal protons is shown in Figure 30. This relationship is quite susceptible to other influences and should be used with due caution. However, it is useful for characterizing methylene groups in a fused cyclohexane ring (approximately tetrahedral, $J \sim 12$ to 18), methylene groups of a cyclopropane ring ($J \sim 5$), or a terminal methylene group ($J \sim 0$ to 3). Geminal coupling constants are actually negative numbers, but this can be ignored except for calculations.

XII. LONG—RANGE COUPLING

Proton-proton coupling beyond three bonds may occur in olefins, acetylenes, aromatics, and heteroaromatics, and in strained ring systems (small or bridged rings). Allylic (H—C—C═C—H) coupling constants are about 0 to 3 cps. Homoallylic (H—C—C═C—CH) couplings are usually negligible but may be as much as 1.6 cps. Coupling through conjugated polyacetylenic chains may occur through as many as nine bonds. Meta coupling in a benzene ring is 1 to 3 cps, and para, 0 to 1 cps. In five-membered heteroaromatic rings, coupling between the 2, 4 protons is 0 to 2 cps. Coupling through four sigma bonds in bicyclo [2.1.1] hexanes up to ~7 cps has been reported.

XIII. SPIN—SPIN DECOUPLING

Spin-spin decoupling (double irradiation or double resonance) is a remarkably powerful tool for simplifying a spectrum, for determining the relative positions of protons in a molecule, or for locating a buried absorption. The other two methods of simplifying a complex

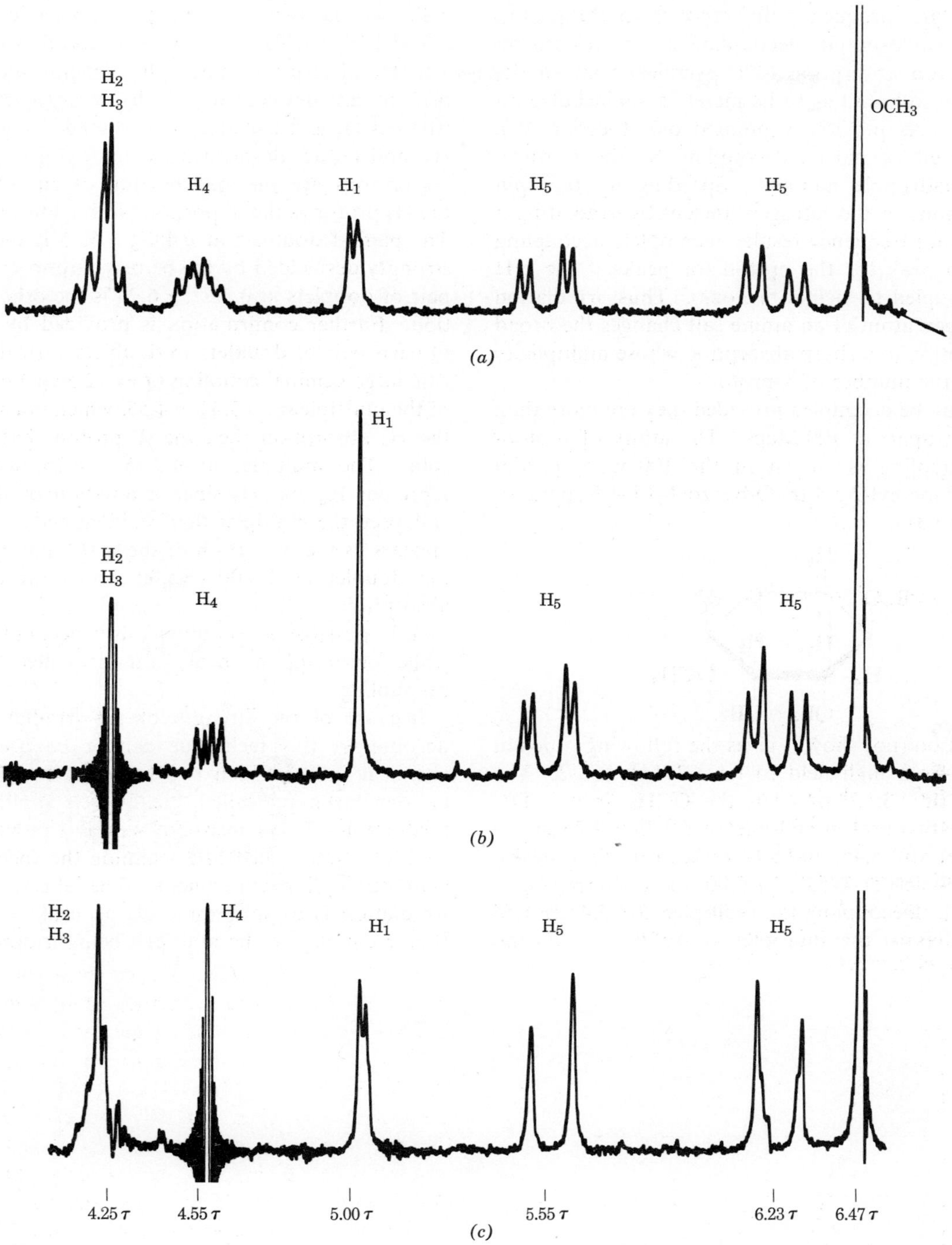

(a)

(b)

(c)

Fig. 31. (a) Partial spectrum of methyl-2,3,4-tri-O-benzoyl-β-L-lyxopyranoside, 100 Mcps, $CDCl_3$. (b) H_2 and H_3 decoupled. (c) H_4 decoupled.

spectrum—deuteration and the use of higher field strengths—were mentioned previously.

A proton whose spin is being split must "see" distinct spin states of the proton to which it is coupled. If the spin states of the latter proton can be made to change rapidly, the former proton "sees" an average state and gives a single peak; i.e., it is decoupled. Spin-spin decoupling is simply a technique for irradiating a nucleus with a strong radiofrequency signal at its resonance frequency, thus artificially "stirring up" its spin states, while scanning other nuclei to detect which ones are affected by decoupling from the irradiated nucleus. The early experiments in spin-spin decoupling were limited to irradiation of other nuclei such as ^{14}N, ^{31}P, or ^{19}F because of the very large frequency difference from the proton resonance. For example, decoupling has been used on the NH proton absorption of a pyrrole or an amide, which can be so broad as to be merely a slight bulge on the baseline. As previously pointed out (Section V), this is a result of partial decoupling by the nitrogen electrical quadrupole moment. Speeding up the spin state transitions of the nitrogen nucleus by irradiating it at its resonance frequency results in complete decoupling and a sharp peak for the proton (or peaks if the NH proton is coupled to vicinal protons). Thus, irradiation of the nitrogen atom of an amine salt changes the broad $^{+}$NH absorption to a sharp absorption whose multiplicity depends on the number of α-protons.

Protons can be decoupled provided they are more than about 20 cps apart at 100 Mcps. The utility of proton-proton decoupling is shown in the 100 Mcps partial spectrum of methyl-2,3,4-tri-O-benzoyl-β-L-lyxopyranoside[33] (Figure 31).

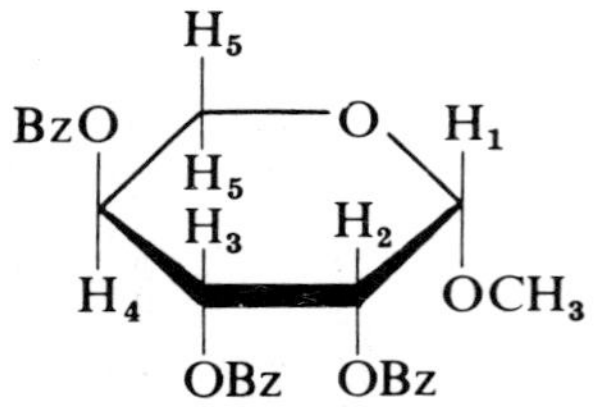

H_5
BzO O H_1
H_5
H_3 H_2
H_4 OCH_3
OBz OBz

The integration (not shown) gives the following ratios in Figure 31a from high field to low: 3:1:1:1:1:2. The sharp peak at δ 3.53, τ 6.47 is the OCH_3 group. Decoupling the two-proton multiplet at δ 5.75, τ 4.25 causes the multiplet at δ 5.45, τ4.55 to collapse to four peaks, and the doublet at δ 5.00, τ 5.00 to a sharp singlet (Figure 31b). Decoupling the multiplet at δ 5.45, τ 4.55 partially collapses the multiplet at δ 5.75, τ 4.25, and collapses the two upfield pairs of doublets (at δ 4.45, τ 5.55 and δ 3.77, τ 6.23) to two doublets (Figure 31c). The H_5 absorption should be upfield since these two protons are deshielded only by a single ether oxygen, whereas H_1 is deshielded by two ether oxygens, and H_2, H_3, and H_4 are deshielded by benzoyl groups. The two H_5 protons are the *AM* portion of an *AMX* pattern; the H_4 proton is the *X* portion (with additional splitting). The pair of doublets at δ 4.45, τ 5.55 is one H_5 proton strongly deshielded by the benzoyl group on C_4, and the pair of doublets at δ 3.77, τ 6.23 is the other H_5 absorption. Further confirmation is provided by the collapse of each pair of doublets to doublets with the characteristic large geminal coupling ($J = 12.5$ cps) on irradiation of the multiplet at δ 5.45, τ 4.55, which must therefore be the H_4 absorption (i.e., the *X* proton that was further split. The multiplet at δ 5.75, τ 4.25 must therefore represent H_2 and H_3 since irradiation of this multiplet collapsed the multiplet that we identified as H_4 (this now appears as the *X* portion of the *AMX* pattern), and also the doublet at δ 5.00, τ 5.00 which must be the H_1 absorption.

It is possible to simultaneously decouple two nuclei while observing a third; this is called double spin decoupling.

Because of the strength of the irradiation used for decoupling, this technique cannot be used when the chemical shift between two protons is small. However, another technique called "tickling" is applicable in such a situation. This consists of weakly irradiating a single peak of a multiplet while scanning the spectrum as in a spin decoupling experiment. The effect of this weak irradiation is to split some of the peaks of a multiplet that is coupled to the multiplet being irradiated.[34]

APPENDIX A Shift Positions of Residual Protons in Commercially Available Deuterated Solvents. Data Furnished by Merck Sharp and Dohme of Canada, Ltd.

SOLVENT	ISOTOPIC PURITY ATOM % D	POSITIONS OF RESIDUAL PROTONS (τ VALUES)					
		Group	τ	Group	τ	Group	τ
Acetic Acid-d_4	99.5	methyl	7.95	hydroxyl	−1.53*		
Acetone-d_6	99.5	methyl	7.95				
Acetonitrile-d_3	98	methyl	8.05				
Benzene-d_6	99.5	methine	2.80				
Chloroform-d	99.8	methine	2.75				
Cyclohexane-d_{12}	99	methylene	8.60				
Deuterium Oxide	99.8	hydroxyl	5.25*				
1,2-Dichloroethane-d_4	99	methylene	6.31				
Diethyl-d_{10} Ether	98	methyl	8.84	methylene	6.64		
Dimethylformamide-d_7	98	methyl	7.24	methyl	7.06	formyl	1.95
Dimethyl-d_6 Sulfoxide	99.5	methyl	7.50				
p-Dioxane-d_8	98	methylene	6.45				
Ethyl Alcohol-d_6 (anh.)	98	methyl	8.83	methylene	6.41	hydroxyl	7.40*
Hexafluoroacetone Deuterate	99.5	hydroxyl	1.0*				
Methyl Alcohol-d_4	99	methyl	6.65	hydroxyl	5.16*		
Methylcyclohexane-d_{14}	99	methyl	9.08	methylene	8.46	methine	8.35
Methylene-d_2 Chloride	99	methylene	4.65				
Pyridine-d_5	99	alpha	1.30	beta	2.80	gamma	2.42
Silanar‡-C ($CDCl_3$ + 1% TMS)	99.8	methyl	10.00†	methine	2.75		
Tetrahydrofuran-d_8	98	α-methylene	6.40	β-methylene	8.25		
Tetramethylene-d_8 Sulfone	98	α-methylene	7.08	β-methylene	7.84		

* This value may vary considerably, depending upon the solute. † By definition. ‡ Trademark.

APPENDIX B Shift Positions of Protons Bound to Carbon, and near a Single Functional Group or in a Ring.

There are two thought processes involved in examining an NMR spectrum with the object of identifying an organic compound. These are exemplified by the following questions:

1. What can we expect to find in the vicinity of δ 3.0, τ 7.0?
2. Where would we expect to find the peak of a proton on a carbon atom to which a chlorine atom is attached?

The following charts are designed to answer such questions. The shift values shown are average values for ranges that are usually less than about 0.5 ppm wide. The exact shift position will vary with changes in solvent or concentration, but, in general, these variations are small in the absence of hydrogen bonding.

A separate value is given for methyl, methylene, and methine protons. In a hydrocarbon, these protons are found, respectively, at about δ 0.9, τ 9.1; δ 1.25, τ 8.75; and δ 1.5, τ 8.5. The first line of the second chart, for example, shows that the protons of CH_3Br absorb near δ 2.7, τ 7.3; the α-protons of RCH_2Br near δ 3.4, τ 6.6; and the α-proton of R_2CHBr near δ 4.1, τ 5.9.

The shift values assigned have been gathered from a variety of sources. Two privately circulated collections are very useful: NMR Summary prepared by G. V. D. Tiers, Minnesota Mining and Manufacturing Company, St. Paul 6, Minn.; and Nuclear Magnetic Resonance by N. F. Chamberlain et al., Esso Research and Engineering Company, P. O. Box 4255, Baytown, Texas. A large number of values have been published by K. Nukada et al., *Anal. Chem.*, **35**, 1892 (1963).

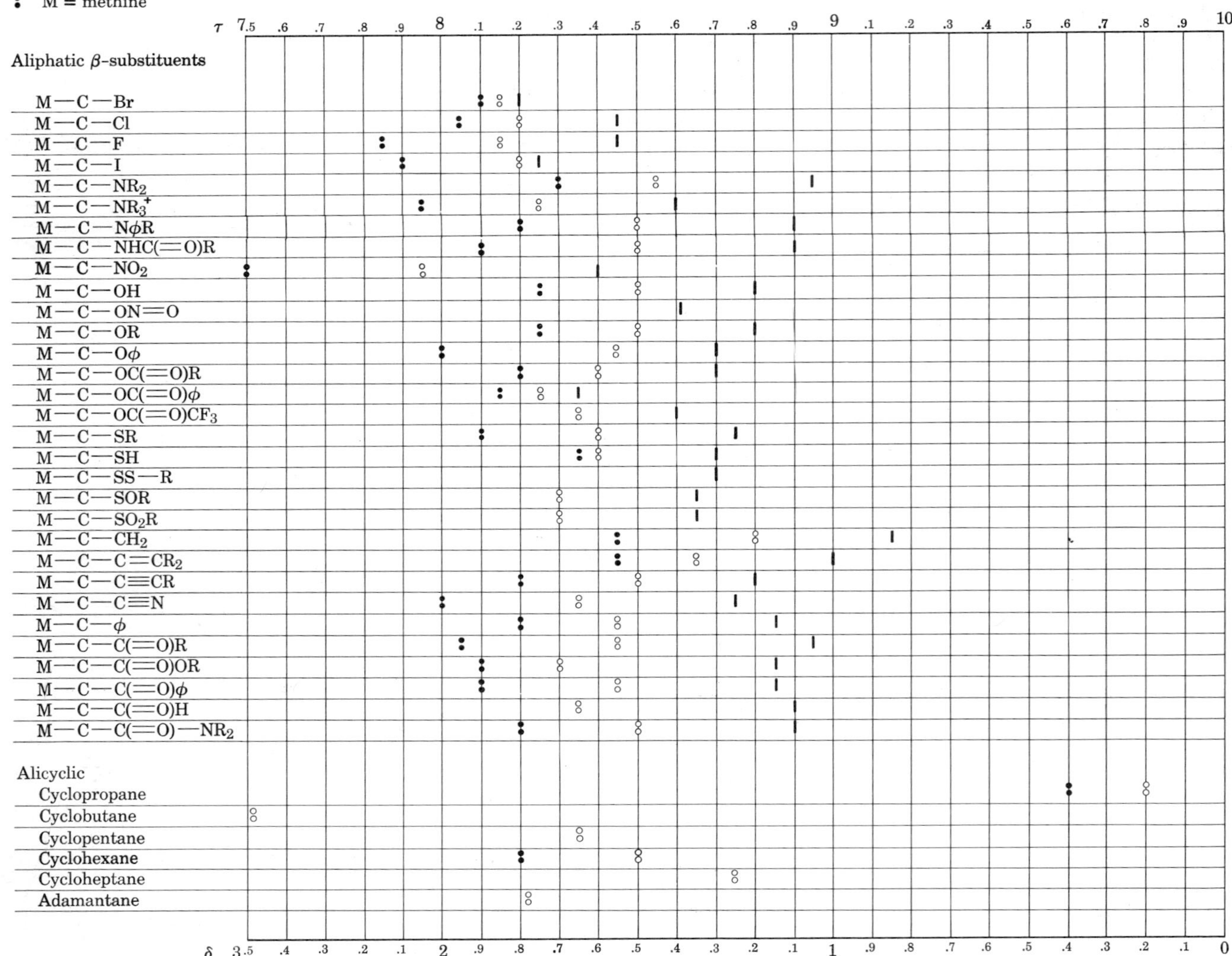

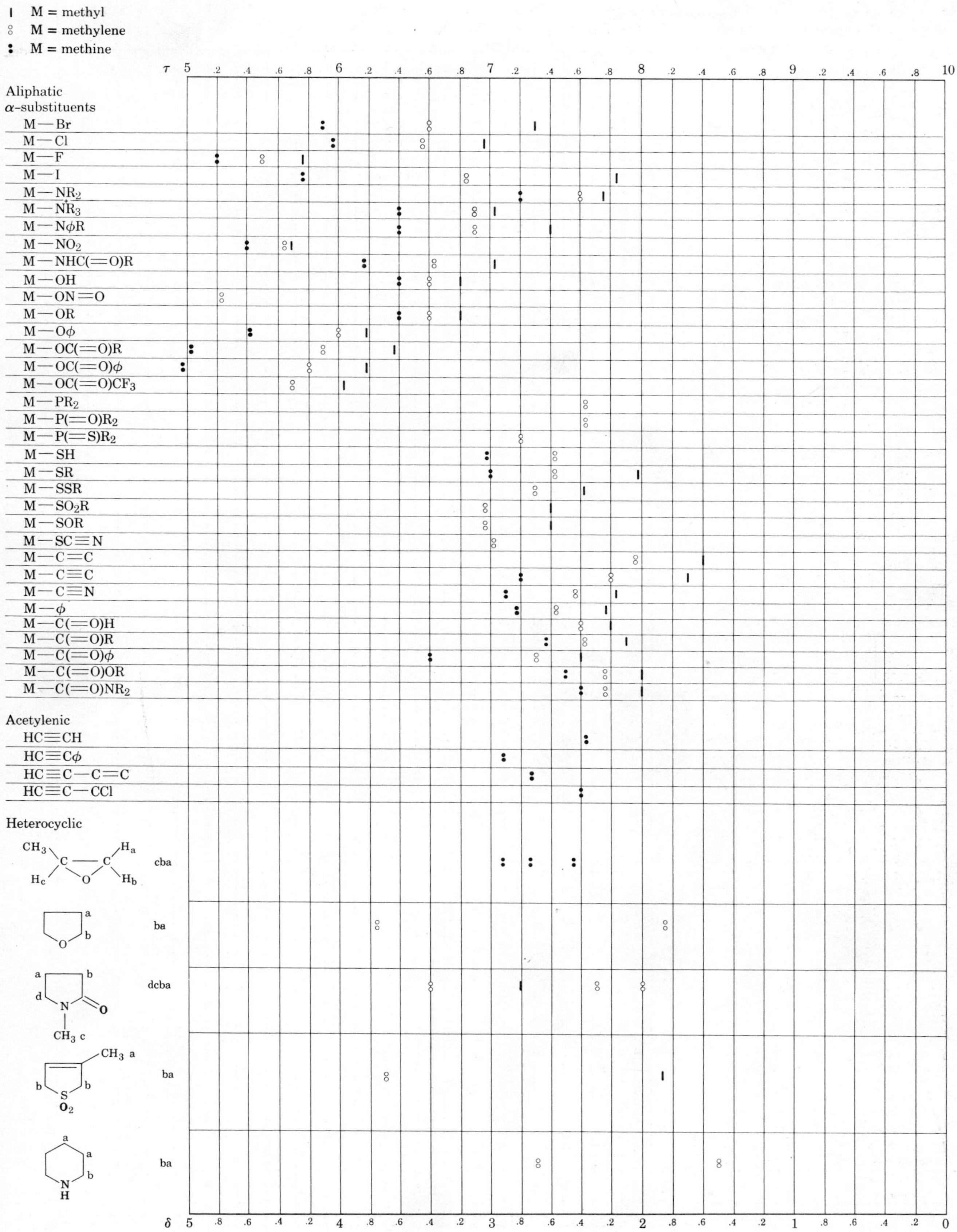

| M = methyl
⁸ M = methylene
: M = methine

τ 5 .2 .4 .6 .8 6 .2 .4 .6 .8 7 .2 .4 .6 .8 8 .2 .4 .6 .8 9 .2 .4 .6 .8 10

Aliphatic
α-substituents

M—Br
M—Cl
M—F
M—I
M—NR_2
M—$\overset{+}{N}R_3$
M—NϕR
M—NO_2
M—NHC(=O)R
M—OH
M—ON=O
M—OR
M—Oϕ
M—OC(=O)R
M—OC(=O)ϕ
M—OC(=O)CF_3
M—PR_2
M—P(=O)R_2
M—P(=S)R_2
M—SH
M—SR
M—SSR
M—SO_2R
M—SOR
M—SC≡N
M—C=C
M—C≡C
M—C≡N
M—ϕ
M—C(=O)H
M—C(=O)R
M—C(=O)ϕ
M—C(=O)OR
M—C(=O)NR_2

Acetylenic

HC≡CH
HC≡Cϕ
HC≡C—C=C
HC≡C—CCl

Heterocyclic

CH_3, H_a, H_c, O, H_b — cba

a, b, O — ba

a, b, d, N, O, CH_3 c — dcba

CH_3 a, b, b, S, O_2 — ba

a, a, b, N, H — ba

δ 5 .8 .6 .4 .2 4 .8 .6 .4 .2 3 .8 .6 .4 .2 2 .8 .6 .4 .2 1 .8 .6 .4 .2 0

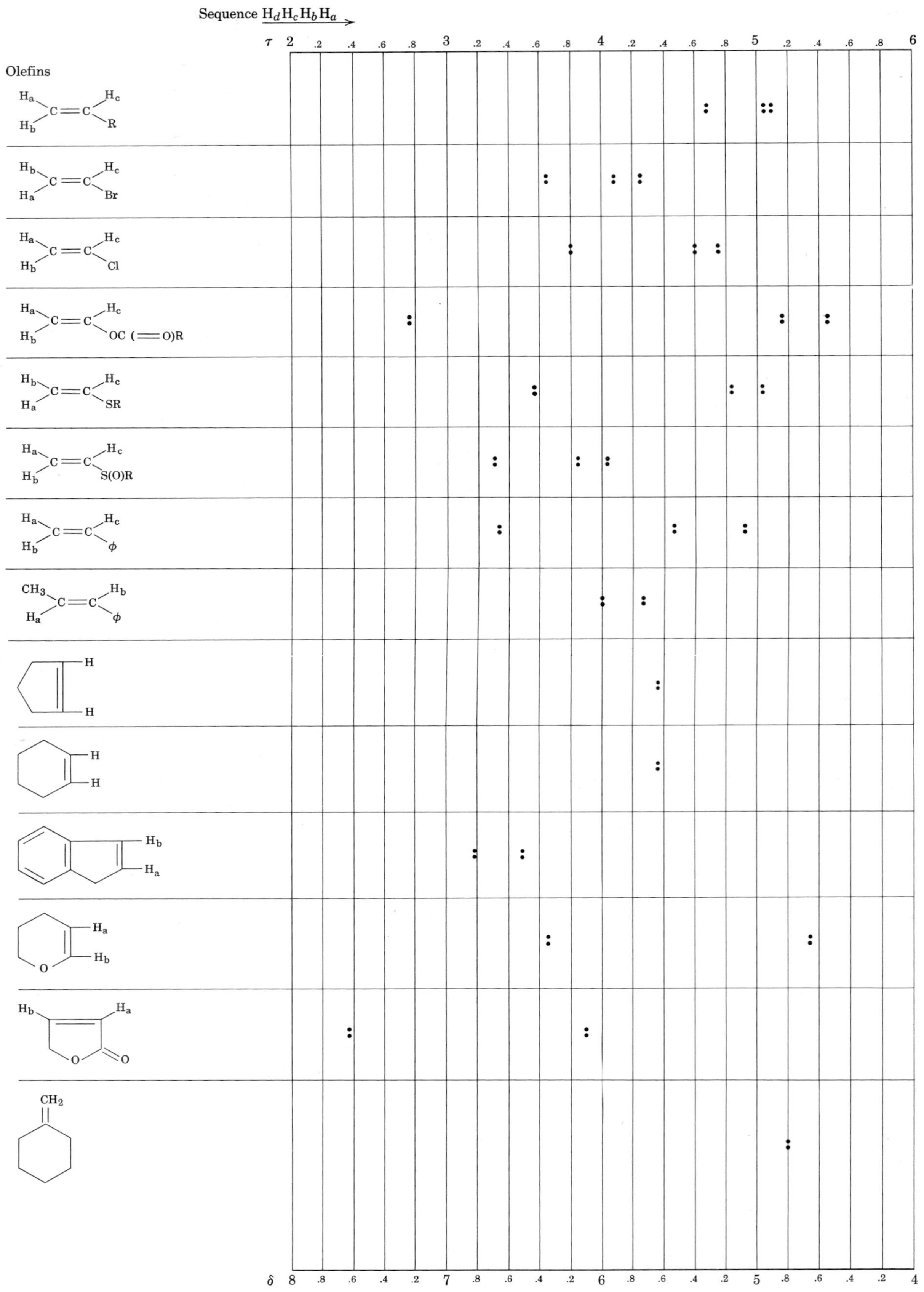

Sequence $H_d H_c H_b H_a \rightarrow$

τ 2 .2 .4 .6 .8 3 .2 .4 .6 .8 4 .2 .4 .6 .8 5 .2 .4 .6 .8 6

Olefins

H_a, H_b C=C H_c, R

H_b, H_a C=C H_c, Br

H_a, H_b C=C H_c, Cl

H_a, H_b C=C H_c, OC (=O)R

H_b, H_a C=C H_c, SR

H_a, H_b C=C H_c, S(O)R

H_a, H_b C=C H_c, ϕ

CH_3, H_a C=C H_b, ϕ

H, H (cyclopentene)

H, H (cyclohexene)

H_b, H_a (indene)

H_a, H_b, O (dihydropyran)

H_b, H_a, O, O (butenolide)

CH_2 (methylenecyclohexane)

δ 8 .8 .6 .4 .2 7 .8 .6 .4 .2 6 .8 .6 .4 .2 5 .8 .6 .4 .2 4

Olefins (Continued)

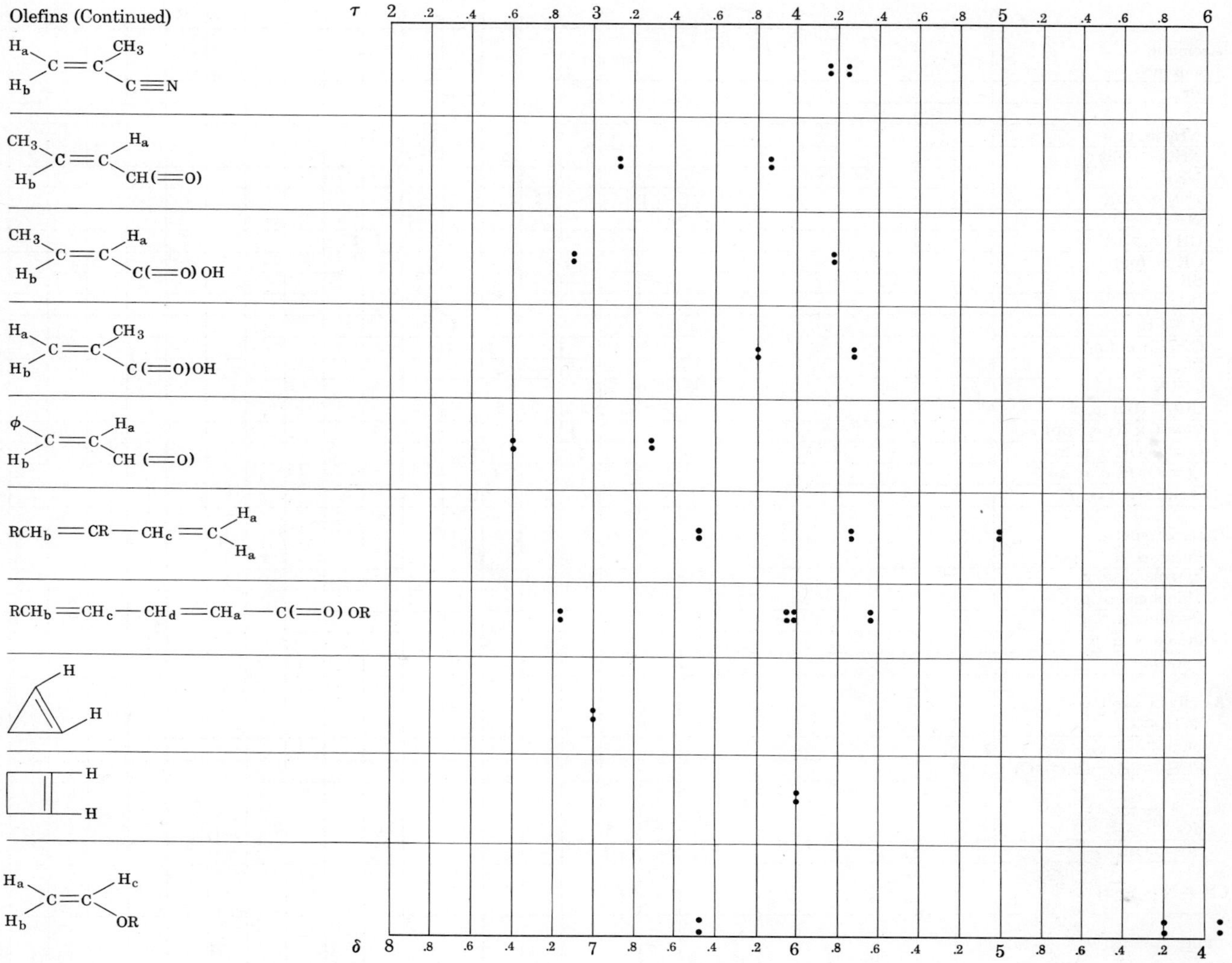

τ 2 .2 .4 .6 .8 3 .2 .4 .6 .8 4 .2 .4 .6 .8 5 .2 .4 .6 .8 6

$H_a(H_b)C{=}C(CH_3)C{\equiv}N$

$CH_3(H_b)C{=}C(H_a)CH({=}O)$

$CH_3(H_b)C{=}C(H_a)C({=}O)OH$

$H_a(H_b)C{=}C(CH_3)C({=}O)OH$

$\phi(H_b)C{=}C(H_a)CH({=}O)$

$RCH_b{=}CR{-}CH_c{=}C(H_a)_2$

$RCH_b{=}CH_c{-}CH_d{=}CH_a{-}C({=}O)OR$

Cyclopropene (H, H)

Cyclobutene (H, H)

$H_a(H_b)C{=}C(H_c)OR$

δ 8 .8 .6 .4 .2 7 .8 .6 .4 .2 6 .8 .6 .4 .2 5 .8 .6 .4 .2 4

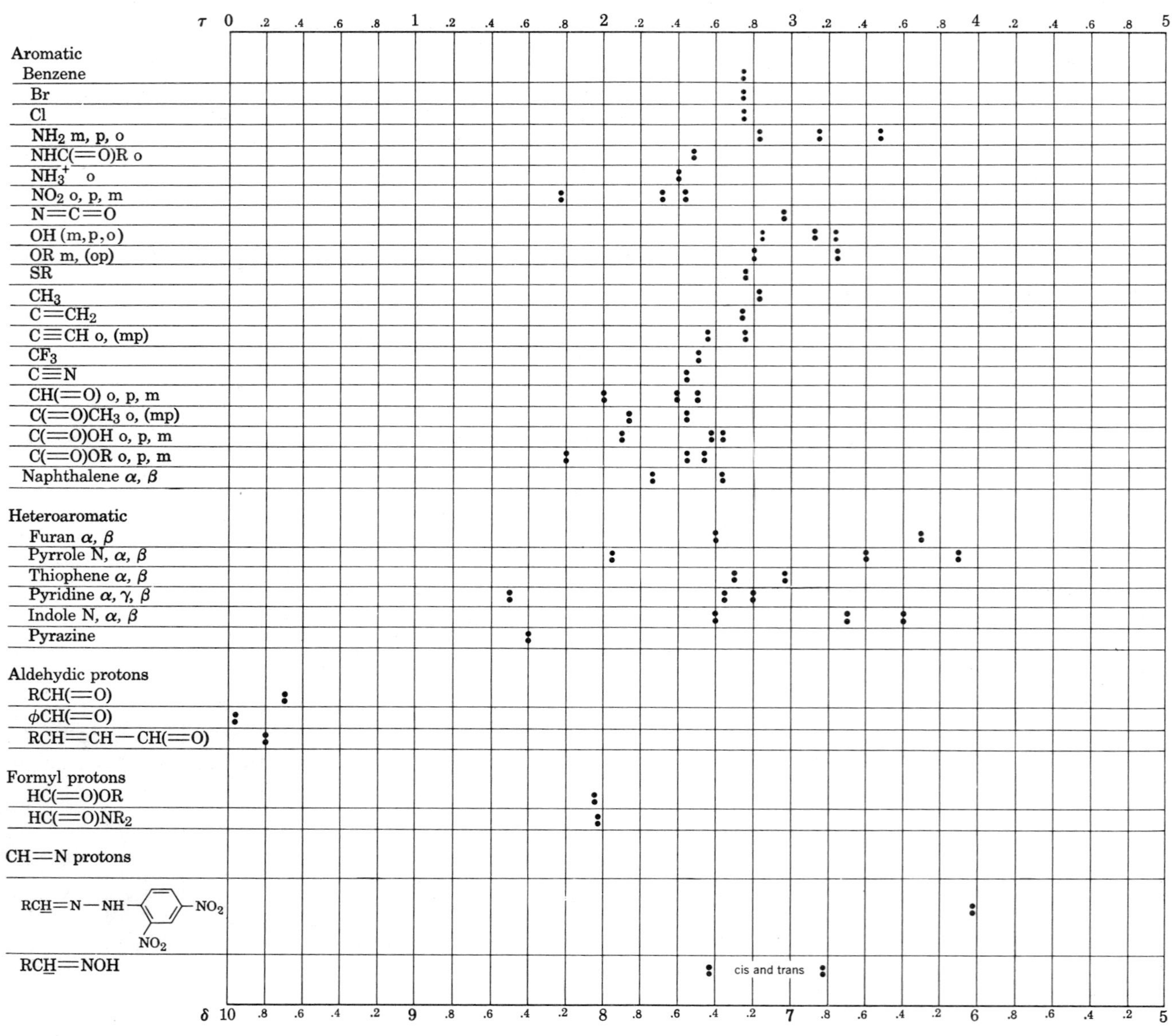
τ 0 .2 .4 .6 .8 1 .2 .4 .6 .8 2 .2 .4 .6 .8 3 .2 .4 .6 .8 4 .2 .4 .6 .8 5
Aromatic
Benzene
Br
Cl
NH2 m, p, o
NHC(=O)R o
NH3+ o
NO2 o, p, m
N=C=O
OH (m,p,o)
OR m, (op)
SR
CH3
C=CH2
C≡CH o, (mp)
CF3
C≡N
CH(=O) o, p, m
C(=O)CH3 o, (mp)
C(=O)OH o, p, m
C(=O)OR o, p, m
Naphthalene α, β
Heteroaromatic
Furan α, β
Pyrrole N, α, β
Thiophene α, β
Pyridine α, γ, β
Indole N, α, β
Pyrazine
Aldehydic protons
RCH(=O)
φCH(=O)
RCH=CH—CH(=O)
Formyl protons
HC(=O)OR
HC(=O)NR2
CH=N protons
RCH=N—NH—NO2
NO2
RCH=NOH
cis and trans
δ 10 .8 .6 .4 .2 9 .8 .6 .4 .2 8 .8 .6 .4 .2 7 .8 .6 .4 .2 6 .8 .6 .4 .2 5

APPENDIX C Shielding Constants and Shift Positions of Aliphatic Methylene Groups Attached to Two Functional Groups.

To obtain a τ value for a disubstituted methylene group, the sum of the appropriate shielding constants for X and Y is subtracted from 9.77 which is the τ value for methane. Thus the value for the methylene protons of ϕ-CH_2—Br is found as follows:

$$\begin{array}{rr} \phi = 1.85 & 9.77 \\ Br = \underline{2.33} & \underline{-4.18} \\ 4.18 & 5.59 \end{array} = \text{calc } \tau \text{ value for —}CH_2\text{—.}$$

Delta values are obtained by adding the sum of the shielding constants to 0.23. Thus the δ value in this example is

$$\begin{array}{r} 0.23 \\ \underline{+4.18} \\ 4.41 \end{array}$$

X or Y	SHIELDING CONSTANTS
—Br	2.33
—Cl	2.53
—I	1.82
—NR_2	1.57
—NHC(=O)R	2.27
—N_3	1.97
—OH	2.56
—OR	2.36
—Oϕ	3.23
—OC(=O)R	3.13
—SR	1.64
—CH_3	0.47
—C=C	1.32
—C≡C	1.44
—ϕ	1.85
—CF_2	1.21
—CF_3	1.14
—C≡N	1.70
—C(=O)R	1.70
—C(=O)OR	1.55
—C(=O)NR_2	1.59

The shielding constants have been used to prepare the chart on pp. 142-143. Several values have been added to the original set of constants.[18]

APPENDIX C τ Values for Methylene Groups Attached to Two Functional Groups X—CH$_2$—Y

FUNCTIONAL GROUP	—Br	—Cl	—I	—NR$_2$	—N$_3$	—NH$\overset{O}{\overset{\Vert}{C}}$R	—$\overset{O}{\overset{\Vert}{C}}\phi$	—OH	—OR	—Oϕ
—Br	5.06 5.11	4.84 4.91	5.62	5.87	5.47	5.17	5.60	4.88	5.08	4.21
—Cl		4.67 4.71	5.01 5.42	5.63	5.27	4.87	5.40	4.68	4.60 4.88	4.01
—I			6.10 6.13	6.38	5.98	5.68	6.11	5.39	5.59	4.84
—NR$_2$				6.90 6.63	6.23	5.93	6.36	5.65	5.85	4.97
—N$_3$					5.85	5.55	5.98	5.24	5.36	4.44
—NH$\overset{O}{\overset{\Vert}{C}}$R						5.27	5.66	4.94	5.06	4.14
—$\overset{O}{\overset{\Vert}{C}}\phi$							6.09	5.37	5.57	4.70
—OH								5.45 4.65	4.85	3.98
—OR									5.45 5.05	4.18
—Oϕ										3.31
—O$\overset{O}{\overset{\Vert}{C}}$R										
—SR										

	—OC(O)R	—SR	—CH$_3$	—C=C	—C≡C	—ϕ	—CF$_2$	—CF$_3$	—C≡N	—C(O)R	—C(O)OR	—C(O)NR$_2$
	4.31	5.80	6.57 6.97	6.07 6.12	6.10 6.00	5.65 5.59	6.24	6.30	5.74	5.74	6.30 5.89	6.08 5.85
	4.11	5.60	6.43 6.77	5.92	5.91 5.80	5.50 5.39	6.03	6.10	5.93 5.54	5.54	5.95 5.69	5.83 5.65
	4.94	6.31	6.80 7.48	6.13 6.63	6.51	6.10	6.74	6.44 6.81	6.35 6.25	6.25	6.40	6.35 6.36
	5.07	6.56	7.37 7.73	6.70 6.88	6.50 6.76	6.52 6.35	6.99	7.06	6.50	6.50	6.83 6.65	6.61
	4.67	6.16	7.33	6.48	6.33	5.96	6.59	6.66	6.10	6.10	6.25	6.21
	4.37	5.86	7.03	6.18	6.03	5.66	6.29	6.36	5.80	5.90 5.80	5.95	5.91
	4.80	6.29	7.46	6.61	6.49	6.08	6.72	6.79	6.23	6.23	6.38	6.34
	4.08	5.57	6.30 6.74	5.87	5.72	5.42	5.99 5.99	6.07	5.51	5.51	5.66	5.62
	4.28	5.77	6.60 6.94	6.05 6.09	5.97	5.30 5.56	6.20	6.27	5.80 5.71	5.71	5.87 5.78	5.82
	3.41	4.90	6.07	5.22	5.10	5.10 4.69	5.33	5.40	4.84	4.84	4.91	4.95
	3.54	5.00	5.75 6.17	5.32	5.29 5.20	4.92 4.79	5.43	5.46	4.90	5.58	5.09	5.05
		6.49	7.47 7.66	6.92 6.81	6.69	6.32 6.28	6.92	6.99	6.43	6.43	6.58	6.54
—CH$_3$			8.83	7.98	7.86	7.45	8.09	8.16	7.60	7.53 7.60	7.75	7.77 7.71
—C=C				7.40 7.13	6.61 7.01	6.70 6.60	7.24	7.31	6.85 6.75	6.75	7.00	6.86
—C≡C					6.89	6.48	7.12	7.19	6.63	6.63	6.78	6.74
—ϕ						6.03 6.07	6.71	6.50 6.78	6.35 6.22	6.45 6.22	6.60 6.37	6.33
—CF$_2$							7.37	7.42	6.88	6.88	7.01	6.97
—CF$_3$								7.49	6.93	6.93	7.08	7.04
—C≡N									6.37	6.37	6.52	6.48
—C(O)R										6.40 6.37	6.63 6.52	6.48
—C(O)OR											6.65 6.67	6.63
—C(O)NR$_2$												6.70 6.59

NOTE: The upper number in each box is an experimental value; the lower number is calculated from the shielding constants. Only τ values are given.

APPENDIX D Protons Subject to Hydrogen-Bonding Effects.

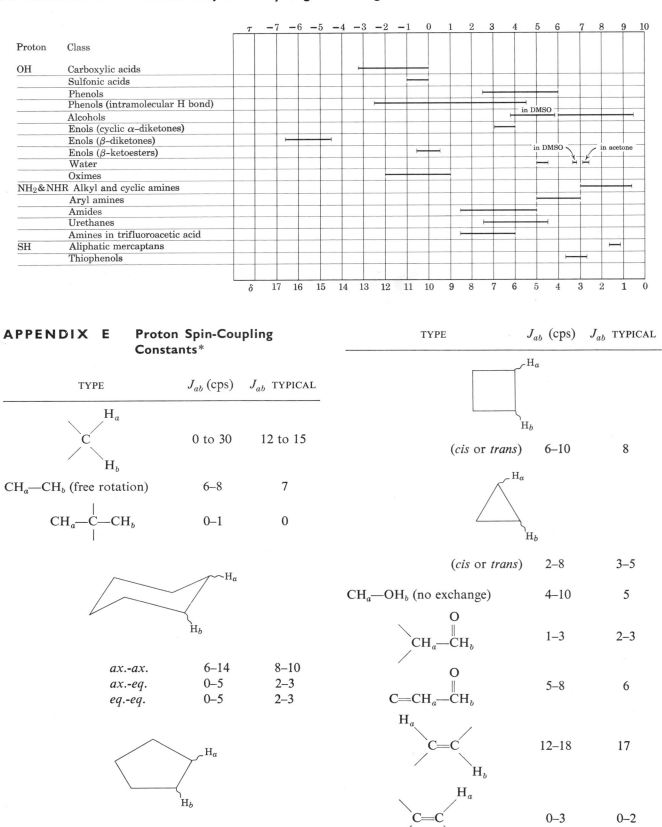

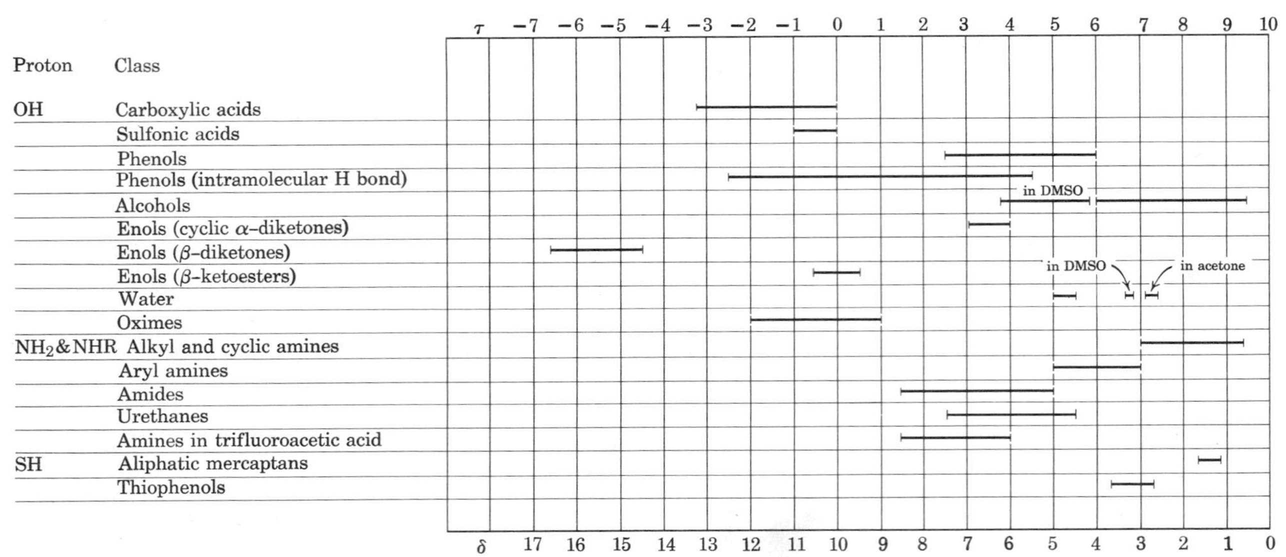

APPENDIX E Proton Spin-Coupling Constants*

TYPE	J_{ab} (cps)	J_{ab} TYPICAL
C (H_a, H_b)	0 to 30	12 to 15
CH_a—CH_b (free rotation)	6–8	7
CH_a—C—CH_b	0–1	0
(H_a, H_b) *ax.-ax.*	6–14	8–10
ax.-eq.	0–5	2–3
eq.-eq.	0–5	2–3
(H_a, H_b) (*cis* or *trans*)	0–7	4–5

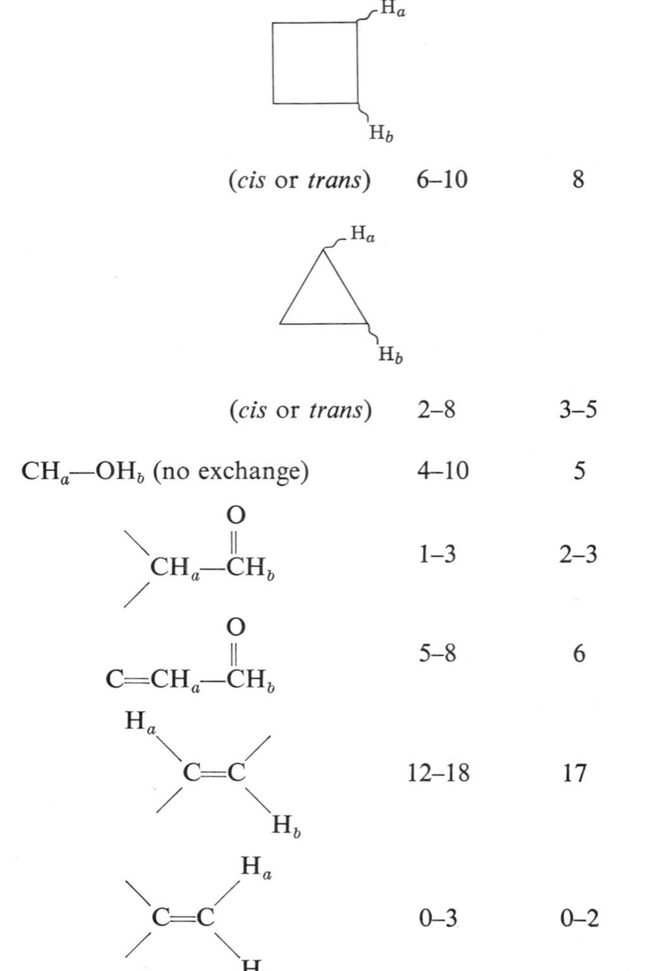

TYPE	J_{ab} (cps)	J_{ab} TYPICAL
(H_a, H_b) (*cis* or *trans*)	6–10	8
(H_a, H_b) (*cis* or *trans*)	2–8	3–5
CH_a—OH_b (no exchange)	4–10	5
CH_a—C(=O)H_b	1–3	2–3
C=CH_a—C(=O)H_b	5–8	6
H_a—C=C—H_b	12–18	17
C=C(H_a)(H_b)	0–3	0–2

TYPE		J_{ab} (cps)	J_{ab} TYPICAL
H_a(C=C)H_b (cis)		6–12	10
CH_a(C=C)CH_b (cis)		0–3	1–2
C=C with CH_a and H_b on the same carbon		4–10	7
C=C with CH_b and H_a trans		0–3	1.5
H_a(C=C)CH_b (cis)		0–3	2
$>C{=}CH_a{-}CH_b{=}C<$		9–13	10
$CH_a{-}C{\equiv}CH_b$		2–3	
$-CH_a{-}C{\equiv}C{-}CH_b-$		2–3	
H_a(C=C)H_b (ring)	5 mem.	3–4	
	6 mem.	6–9	
	7 mem.	10–13	
Benzene, H_a, H_b	J (ortho)	6–10	9
	J (meta)	1–3	3
	J (para)	0–1	~0
Pyridine	J (2–3)	5–6	5
	J (3–4)	7–9	8
	J (2–4)	1–2	1.5
	J (3–5)	1–2	1.5
	J (2–5)	0–1	1
	J (2–6)	0–1	~0
Furan	J (2–3)	1.3–2.0	1.8
	J (3–4)	3.1–3.8	3.6
	J (2–4)	0–1	~0
	J (2–5)	1–2	1.5
Thiophene	J (2–3)	4.9–6.2	5.4
	J (3–4)	3.4–5.0	4.0
	J (2–4)	1.2–1.7	1.5
	J (2–5)	3.2–3.7	3.4
Pyrrole (N–H)	J (1–2)	2–3	
	J (1–3)	2–3	
	J (2–3)	2–3	
	J (3–4)	3–4	
	J (2–4)	1–2	
	J (2–5)	1.5–2.5	
Pyrimidine	J (4–5)	4–6	
	J (2–5)	1–2	
	J (2–4)	0–1	
	J (4–6)	?	
Thiazole	J (4–5)	3–4	
	J (2–5)	1–2	
	J (2–4)	~0	
PROTON-FLUORINE			
H_a–C–F_b		44–81	
$>CH_a{-}CF_b$		3–25	
$>CH_a{-}C{-}CF_b$		0	
H_a(C=C)F_b (cis)		1–8	
H_a(C=C)F_b (trans)		12–40	
Fluorobenzene, H_a		*o* 6–10	
		m 5–6	
		p 2	

* Compiled by Varian Associates.

APPENDIX F Properties of Several Nuclei*

ISOTOPE	NMR FREQUENCY MC FOR A 10 KILOGAUSS FIELD	NATURAL ABUNDANCE %	RELATIVE SENSITIVITY AT CONSTANT FIELD	MAGNETIC MOMENT μ	SPIN NUMBER I	ELECTRICAL QUADRUPOLE MOMENT $e \times 10^{-24}$ cm^2
^{1}H	42.576	99.9844	1.000	2.79268	1/2	...
^{2}H	6.5357	1.56×10^{-2}	9.64×10^{-3}	0.85738	1	2.77×10^{-3}
^{10}B	4.575	18.83	1.99×10^{-2}	1.8005	3	7.4×10^{-2}
^{11}B	13.660	81.17	0.165	2.6880	3/2	3.55×10^{-2}
^{12}C	...	98.9	...	...	0	...
^{13}C	10.705	1.108	1.59×10^{-2}	0.70220	1/2	...
^{14}N	3.076	99.635	1.01×10^{-3}	0.40358	1	7.1×10^{-2}
^{15}N	4.315	0.365	1.04×10^{-3}	−0.28304	1/2	...
^{16}O	...	99.76	...	...	0	...
^{17}O	5.772	3.7×10^{-2}	2.91×10^{-2}	−1.8930	5/2	-4.0×10^{-3}
^{19}F	40.055	100	0.834	2.6273	1/2	...
^{28}Si	...	92.28	...	...	0	...
^{29}Si	8.458	4.70	7.85×10^{-2}	−0.55548	1/2	...
^{30}Si	...	3.02	...	...	0	...
^{31}P	17.236	100	6.64×10^{-2}	1.1305	1/2	...
^{32}S	...	95.06	...	...	0	...
^{33}S	3.266	0.74	2.26×10^{-3}	0.64274	3/2	−0.053
^{34}S	...	4.2	...	...	0	...
^{35}Cl	4.172	75.4	4.71×10^{-3}	0.82091	3/2	-7.9×10^{-2}
^{37}Cl	3.472	24.6	2.72×10^{-3}	0.68330	3/2	-6.21×10^{-2}
^{79}Br	10.667	50.57	7.86×10^{-2}	2.0991	3/2	0.34
^{81}Br	11.499	49.43	9.84×10^{-2}	2.2626	3/2	0.28
^{127}I	8.519	100	9.35×10^{-2}	2.7937	5/2	−0.75

* Varian Associates NMR Table, 4th ed., 1964.

References

1. Bovey, F. A., *Nuclear Magnetic Resonance Spectroscopy*, Academic Press, New York and London, 1969.
2. Bible, R. H., Jr., *Interpretation of NMR Spectra*, Plenum Press, New York, 1965.
3. Bhacca, N. S., and D. H. Williams, *Applications of NMR Spectroscopy in Organic Chemistry*, Holden-Day, San Francisco, 1964.
4. Jackman, L. M., *Applications of Nuclear Magnetic Resonance Spectroscopy in Organic Chemistry*, Pergamon, New York, 1959.
5. Roberts, J. D., *Nuclear Magnetic Resonance Applications to Organic Chemistry*, McGraw-Hill, New York, 1959.
6. Dyer, J. R., *Applications of Absorption Spectroscopy of Organic Compounds*, Chap. 4, Prentice-Hall, Englewood Cliffs, N.J., 1965.
7. Brand, J. C. D., and G. Eglinton, *Applications of Spectroscopy to Organic Chemistry*, Chap. 3, Oldbourne Press, London, 1964.
8. Jackman, L. M., Chap. 5 in *Physical Methods in Organic Chemistry*, J. C. P. Schwarz, Ed., Oliver and Boyd, Edinburgh, 1964.
9. Stothers, J. B., Chap. 4 in *Elucidation of Structures by Physical and Chemical Methods*, K. W. Bentley, Ed., Vol. XI, Part 1, Interscience, New York, 1963.
10. Jardetzky, O., and C. D. Jardetzky, Introduction to Magnetic Resonance Spectroscopy. Methods and Biochemical Applications, in *Methods of Biochemical Analysis*, Vol. IX, D. Glick *et al.*, Eds., Interscience, New York, 1962.
11. Phillips, W. D., "High Resolution ^{1}H and ^{19}F Magnetic Resonance Spectra of Organic Molecules," Chap. 6, in *Determination of Organic Structure by Physical Methods*, Vol. 2, F. C. Nachod and W. D. Phillips, Eds., Academic Press, New York, 1962.

11a. Bose, A. K., "Proton Nuclear Magnetic Resonance Spectroscopy," Chap. 5, in *Interpretive Spectroscopy*, S. K. Freeman, Ed., Rheinhold, New York, 1965.

11b. Bible, R. H., Jr., *Guide to the Empirical Method: A Workbook*, Plenum Press, New York, 1967.

11c. Mathieson, D. W., Ed., *Nuclear Magnetic Resonance for Organic Chemists*, Academic Press, New York, 1967.

12. Pople, J. A., W. G. Schneider, and H. J. Bernstein, *High-Resolution Nuclear Magnetic Resonance*, McGraw-Hill, New York, 1959.

12a. Emsley, J. W., J. Feeney, and L. H. Sutcliffe, *High Resolution Nuclear Magnetical Resonance Spectroscopy*, Vol. I, Pergamon, New York, Vol. 1, 1965; Vol. 2, 1966.

13. Varian Associates, *High Resolution NMR Spectra Catalogue*, Vol. 1, 1962; Vol. 2, 1963.
14. *Nuclear Magnetic Resonance Spectra.* Sadtler Research Laboratories, Philadelphia, Pa.
15. *Nuclear Magnetic Resonance Spectra Data*, American Petroleum Institute, Project 44, Chemical Thermodynamics Properties Center, Agricultural and Mechanical College of Texas, College Station, Texas.
16. Howell, M. G., A. S. Kende, and J. S. Webb, Eds., *Formula Index to NMR Literature Data*, Vols. 1 and 2, Plenum Press, N.Y., Vol. 1, 1964; Vol. 2, 1966.

16a. Hershenson, H. M., *Nuclear Magnetic Resonance and Electron Spin Resonance Spectra. Index for* 1958–1963. Academic Press, New York, 1965.
16b. Preston Technical Abstract Service, Evanston, Ill.
17. Jackman, L. M., F. Sondheimer, Y. Amiel, D. A. Ben-Efraim, Y. Gaoni, R. Wolovsky, and A. A. Bothner-By, *J. Am. Chem. Soc.*, **84,** 4307 (1962).
18. Shoolery, J. N., *Technical Information Bulletin*, **2,** No. 3, Varian Associates, Palo Alto, Calif. B. P. Dailey and J. N. Shoolery, *J. Am. Chem. Soc.*, **77,** 3977 (1955).
19. Bruce, J. M., P. Knowles, *Proc. Chem. Soc.*, **1964,** 294.
20. Moniz, W. B., C. F. Poranski, Jr., and T. N. Hall, *J. Am. Chem. Soc.*, **88**, 190 (1966).
21. McGreer, D. E., and M. M. Mocek, *J. Chem. Ed.*, **40,** 358 (1963).
22. Chapman, O. L., and R. W. King, *J. Am. Chem. Soc.*, **86,** 1256 (1964).
23. Traynham, J. G., and G. A. Knesel, *J. Am. Chem. Soc.*, **87,** 4220 (1965).
24. Anderson, W. R., Jr., and R. M. Silverstein, *Anal. Chem.*, **37,** 1417 (1965).
25. Ref. 2, p. 64, Fig. 3–7.
25a. Wiberg, K. B., and B. J. Nist, *The Interpretation of NMR Spectra*, W. A. Benjamin, New York, 1962.
26. For earlier references, see (a) E. I. Snyder, *J. Am. Chem. Soc.*, **85,** 2624 (1963), and (b) G. M. Whitesides, D. Holtz, and J. D. Roberts, *ibid.*, **86,** 2628 (1964).
27. Silverstein, R. M., J. O. Rodin, D. L. Wood, and L. E. Browne, *Tetrahedron*, **22,** 1929 (1966).
28. Karplus, M., *J. Chem. Phys.*, **30,** 11 (1959).
29. Karplus, M., *J. Am. Chem. Soc.*, **85,** 2870 (1963).
30. Bothner-By, A. A., and C. Naar-Colin, *J. Am. Chem. Soc.*, **83,** 231 (1961).
31. Ref. 3, p. 54.
32. Gutowsky, H. S., M. Karplus, and D. M. Grant, *J. Chem. Phys.*, **31,** 1278 (1959).
33. Reist, E. J., L. V. Fisher, D. E. Gueffroy, and L. Goodman, *J. Org. Chem.*, **31,** 1506 (1966).
34. Freeman, R., and W. A. Anderson, *J. Chem. Phys.*, **37,** 2053 (1962). Varian Technical Information Bulletin, Summer 1965, p. 6.

CHAPTER 5

Ultraviolet Spectrometry

I. INTRODUCTION

Molecular absorption in the ultraviolet and visible region of the spectrum is dependent on the electronic structure of the molecule. Absorption of energy is quantized and results in the elevation of electrons from relatively low-energy orbitals in the ground state to higher-energy orbitals in an excited state. For many electronic structures, the absorption does not occur in the readily accessible portion of the ultraviolet region. In practice, ultraviolet spectrometry is for the most part limited to conjugated systems.

There is, however, an advantage to the selectivity of ultraviolet absorption: characteristic groups may be recognized in molecules of widely varying complexities. A large portion of a relatively complex molecule may be transparent in the ultraviolet so that we may obtain a spectrum similar to that of a much simpler molecule. Thus the spectrum of the male hormone testosterone closely resembles the spectrum of mesityl oxide. The absorption results from the conjugated enone structure of the two compounds.

A detailed mathematical treatment of the origin of ultraviolet or electronic spectra is beyond the scope of this chapter. Rather it is our objective to point out correlations between spectra and structure to be used by the organic chemist. However, enough theory to rationalize these correlations will be presented.

An ultraviolet spectrum is a plot of the wavelength or frequency of absorption versus the absorption intensity (transmittance or absorbance). The data are frequently shown as a graphical plot or tabular presentation of wavelength versus molar absorptivity or log of the molar absorptivity, ϵ_{max} or log ϵ_{max} (see p. 151). The use of molar absorptivity, as the unit of absorption intensity, has the advantage that all intensity values refer to the same number of absorbing species. A tabular presentation is used in Chapters 6 through 8 of this text.

An abundance of reference material relating to the theory and interpretation of ultraviolet spectra is available.[1–11] Two of the most useful references for the organic chemist are the texts by Gillam and Stern[1] and by A. I. Scott.[2] The latter is particularly recommended to the natural-products chemist. The text by Jaffé and Orchin[3] is an excellent source of theory for both the spectroscopist and the organic chemist. Several compilations of ultraviolet spectra and absorption data are available.[12–22] The Sadtler spectra[12] and the volumes of "Electronic Spectral Data"[13–15] are particularly useful to the organic chemist. The Sadtler collection consists of about 16,000 spectra. The Electronic Spectral Data series covers 1946–1955 and 1958–1959; other volumes are now in preparation.

II. THEORY

The ultraviolet portion of the electromagnetic spectrum is shown in Figure 1. Wavelengths in the ultraviolet region are expressed in millimicrons, mμ (1 mμ = 10^{-7} cm) or Angstroms, Å (1 Å = 10^{-8} cm). We are primarily interested in the near ultraviolet (quartz) region extending from 200 to 380 mμ. The atmosphere is transparent in this region, which is readily accessible with quartz optics. Atmospheric absorption starts near 200 mμ and extends into the shorter wavelength region which is accessible through vacuum ultraviolet spectrometry.

The total energy of a molecule is the sum of its binding or electronic energy, its vibrational energy and its rotational energy. The magnitude of these energies decreases in the following order: E_{elec}, E_{vib}, and E_{rot}. Energy absorbed in the ultraviolet region produces changes in the electronic energy of the molecule resulting from transitions of valence electrons in the molecule. These transitions consist of the excitation of an electron from a filled molecular orbital (usually a nonbonding p or bonding π-orbital) to the next higher energy orbital (an antibonding π or σ-orbital). (The antibonding orbital is designated by an asterisk.) Thus, the transition of an electron from a π-bonding orbital to a π-antibonding orbital is indicated $\pi \rightarrow \pi^*$.

The concept of an antibonding orbital can be explained simply by consideration of the ultraviolet absorption of ethylene. The ethylenic double bond, in the ground state, consists of a pair of bonding σ-electrons and a pair of bonding π-electrons. On absorption of ultraviolet radiation near 165 mμ, one of the bonding π-electrons is raised to the next higher energy orbital, an antibonding π-orbital. The orbitals occupied by the π-electron in the ground state and in the excited state are diagrammed in Figure 2.

The shaded volumes indicate regions of maximum electron density. It can be seen that the antibonding π-electron no longer contributes appreciably to the force constant of the C-to-C bond. In fact it negates the bonding power of the remaining unexcited π-electron; the olefinic bond has considerable single-bond character in the excited state.

The relationship between the energy absorbed in an electronic transition and the frequency (ν) or wavelength (λ) of radiation producing the transition is

$$\Delta E = h\nu = \frac{hc}{\lambda}$$

where h is Planck's constant and c is the velocity of

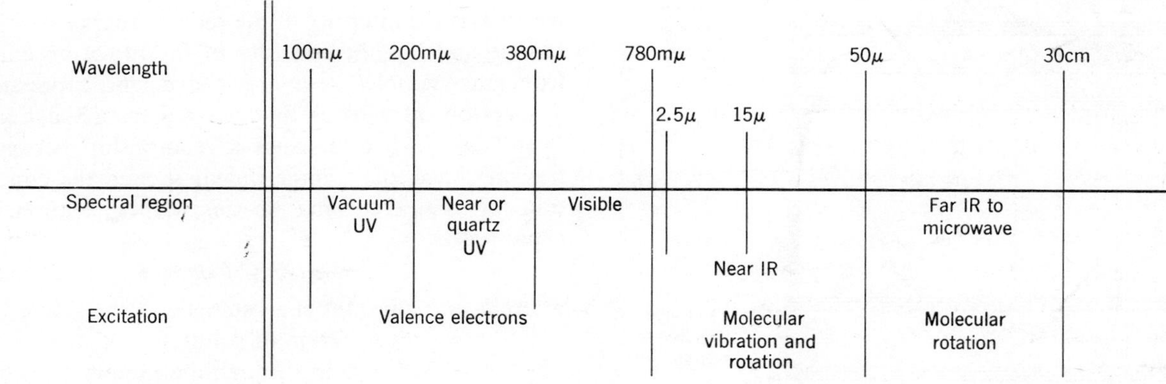

Fig. 1. Electromagnetic Spectrum.

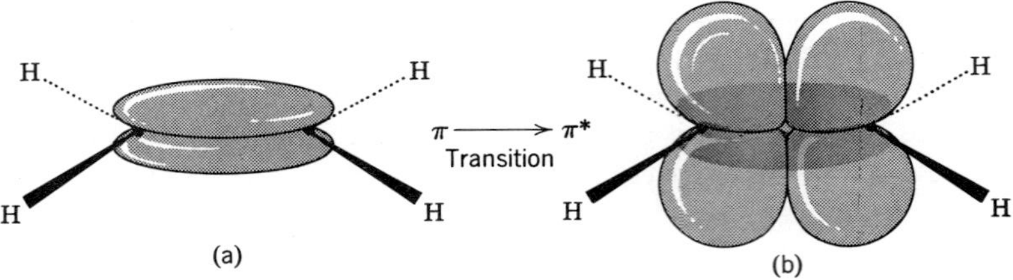

(a) Bonding orbital (π). Both π electrons occupying bonding orbital.

(b) Antibonding orbital (π*). One π electron in bonding orbital, one in antibonding orbital.

A bonding π orbital has a nodal plane in the plane of the molecule. An antibonding π orbital has an additional nodal plane perpendicular to the C to C bond axis.

Fig. 2. π and π* Orbitals.

light. ΔE is the energy absorbed in an electronic transition in a molecule from a low-energy state (ground state) to a high-energy state (excited state). The energy absorbed is dependent on the energy difference between the ground state and the excited state; the smaller the difference in energy, the longer the wavelength of absorption. The excess energy in the excited state may result in disassociation or ionization of the molecule, or it may be reemitted as heat or light. The release of energy as light results in fluorescence or phosphorescence.

Since ultraviolet energy is quantized, the absorption spectrum arising from a single electronic transition should consist of a single discrete line. A discrete line is not obtained since electronic absorption is superimposed upon rotational and vibrational sublevels. The spectra of simple molecules, in the gaseous state, consist of narrow absorption peaks, each representing a transition from a particular combination of vibrational and rotational levels in the electronic ground state to a corresponding combination in the excited state. (This is shown schematically in Figure 3 in which the vibrational levels are designated ν_0, ν_1, ν_2, and so forth.) At ordinary temperatures, most of the molecules in the electronic ground state will be in the zero vibrational level ($G\nu_0$);

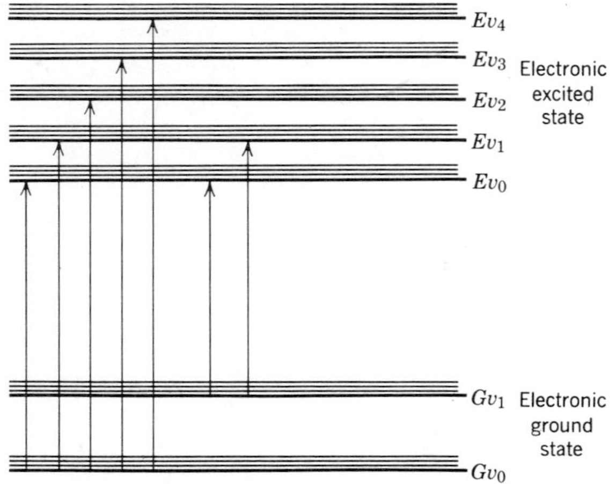

Fig. 3. Energy-level diagram of a diatomic molecule.

consequently, the most probable electronic transitions are from that level. In more complex molecules containing more atoms, the multiplicity of vibrational sublevels and the closeness of their spacing cause the discrete bands to coalesce, and broad absorption bands or "band envelopes" are obtained.

The principal characteristics of an absorption band are its position and intensity. The position of absorption corresponds to the wavelength of radiation whose energy is equal to that required for an electronic transition. The intensity of absorption is largely dependent on two factors: the probability of interaction between the radiation energy and the electronic system to raise the ground level to an excited state, and the polarity of the excited state. The probability of transition is proportional to the square of the transition moment. The transition moment, or dipole moment of transition, is proportional to the change in the electronic charge distribution occurring during excitation. Intense absorption occurs when a transition is accompanied by a large change in the transition moment. Absorption with $\epsilon_{max} > 10^4$ is high intensity absorption; low intensity absorption corresponds to ϵ_{max} values $< 10^3$. Transitions of low probability are forbidden transitions. The intensity of absorption may be expressed as transmittance, defined by

$$\text{Transmittance } (T) = I/I_0$$

where I_0 is the intensity of the radiant energy striking the sample and I is the intensity of the radiation emerging from the sample. A more convenient expression of absorption intensity is that derived from the Lambert-Beer law which establishes a relationship between the transmittance, the sample thickness, and the concentration of the absorbing species. This relationship is expressed as

$$\log_{10} I_0/I = kcb = A$$

where k = a constant characteristic of the solute,
c = concentration of solute,
b = path length through the sample,
A = absorbance (optical density in the older literature).

Table I Summary of Electronic Structure and Transitions

ELECTRONIC STRUCTURE	EXAMPLE	TRANSITION	λ_{max} (mμ)	ϵ_{max}	BAND
σ	Ethane	$\sigma \rightarrow \sigma^*$	135	...	...
n	Water	$n \rightarrow \sigma^*$	167	7,000	...
	Methanol	$n \rightarrow \sigma^*$	183	500	...
	1-Hexanethiol	$n \rightarrow \sigma^*$	224	126	...
	n-Butyl iodide	$n \rightarrow \sigma^*$	257	486	...
π	Ethylene	$\pi \rightarrow \pi^*$	165	10,000	...
	Acetylene	$\pi \rightarrow \pi^*$	173	6,000	...
π and n	Acetone	$\pi \rightarrow \pi^*$	ca. 150	...	...
		$n \rightarrow \sigma^*$	188	1860	...
		$n \rightarrow \pi^*$	279	15	*R*
π–π	1,3-Butadiene	$\pi \rightarrow \pi^*$	217	21,000	*K*
	1,3,5-Hexatriene	$\pi \rightarrow \pi^*$	258	35,000	*K*
π–π and n	Acrolein	$\pi \rightarrow \pi^*$	210	11,500	*K*
		$n \rightarrow \pi^*$	315	14	*R*
Aromatic π	Benzene	Aromatic $\pi \rightarrow \pi^*$	ca. 180	60,000	E_1
		Aromatic $\pi \rightarrow \pi^*$	ca. 200	8,000	E_2
		Aromatic $\pi \rightarrow \pi^*$	255	215	*B*
Aromatic π–π	Styrene	Aromatic $\pi \rightarrow \pi^*$	244	12,000	*K*
		Aromatic $\pi \rightarrow \pi^*$	282	450	*B*
Aromatic π–σ (Hyperconjugated)	Toluene	Aromatic $\pi \rightarrow \pi^*$	208	2,460	E_2
		Aromatic $\pi \rightarrow \pi^*$	262	174	*B*
Aromatic π–π and n	Acetophenone	Aromatic $\pi \rightarrow \pi^*$	240	13,000	*K*
		Aromatic $\pi \rightarrow \pi^*$	278	1,110	*B*
		$n \rightarrow \pi^*$	319	50	*R*
Aromatic π–n (Auxochromic)	Phenol	Aromatic $\pi \rightarrow \pi^*$	210	6,200	E_2
		Aromatic $\pi \rightarrow \pi^*$	270	1,450	*B*

When c is expressed in moles per liter, and the path length (b) through the sample is expressed in centimeters, the preceding expression becomes

$$A = \epsilon cb$$

The term ϵ is known as the molar absorptivity, formerly called the molar extinction coefficient.[23]

The intensity of an absorption band in the ultraviolet spectrum is usually expressed as the molar absorptivity at maximum absorption, ϵ_{max} or log ϵ_{max}. When the constitution of an absorbing material is unknown, the absorptivity may be expressed as

$$E_{1cm}^{1\%} = A/cb$$

where c = concentration in grams per 100 ml,
b = path length through the sample in centimeters.

At this point it is necessary to define certain terms that are frequently used in the discussion of electronic spectra.

CHROMOPHORE. A covalently unsaturated group responsible for electronic absorption (for example, C=C, C=O, and NO_2).

AUXOCHROME. A saturated group which, when attached to a chromophore, alters both the wavelength and the intensity of the absorption maximum (for example, OH, NH_2, and Cl).

BATHOCHROMIC SHIFT. The shift of absorption to a longer wavelength due to substitution or solvent effect (a red shift).

HYPSOCHROMIC SHIFT. The shift of absorption to a shorter wavelength due to substitution or solvent effect (a blue shift).

HYPERCHROMIC EFFECT. An increase in absorption intensity.

HYPOCHROMIC EFFECT. A decrease in absorption intensity.

The absorption characteristics of organic molecules in the ultraviolet region depend on the electronic transitions that can occur and the effect of the atomic environment on the transitions. A summary of electronic structures and transitions that are involved in ultraviolet absorption is presented in Table I.

The relative ease with which the various transitions can occur is summarized in Figure 4. Although no attempt has been made to present energy changes to

Fig. 4. Summary of electronic energy levels.

scale, it is readily seen, for example, that an $n \rightarrow \pi^*$ transition requires less energy than a $\pi \rightarrow \pi^*$ or a $\sigma \rightarrow \sigma^*$ transition.

In discussions of ultraviolet spectra it is customary to refer to absorption bands, characteristic of particular electronic structures, by name or by a letter or numerical designation. Many different designations have been suggested. We shall use the designations of Burawoy[24] and Braude[4] although the original description of the electronic origin of these bands may, in some cases, be archaic. Recognition of these bands in the spectra of organic molecules, and an understanding of their origin and relationship to structure are necessary for the interpretation of ultraviolet spectra.

R-Bands (German *radikalartig*) have their origin in $n \rightarrow \pi^*$ transitions of single chromophoric groups such as the carbonyl or nitro group. The *R*-bands are forbidden bands and are characterized by low molar absorptivities, ϵ_{max} generally less than 100. They are further characterized by the hypsochromic or blue shift observed with an increase in solvent polarity. They frequently remain in the spectrum when modifications in molecular structure introduce additional bands at shorter wavelengths. When additional bands make their appearance, the *R*-band is shifted to a longer wavelength but may be submerged by more intense bands.

K-Bands (German *konjugierte*) appear in the spectra of molecules that have π–π conjugated structures such as butadiene or mesityl oxide. *K*-Bands also appear in the spectra of aromatic molecules possessing chromophoric substitution—styrene, benzaldehyde, or acetophenone. The *K*-bands result from $\pi \rightarrow \pi^*$ transitions and are characterized by high molar absorptivity, $\epsilon_{max} > 10{,}000$.

The *K*-bands of conjugated di- or polyene systems can be distinguished from those of enone systems by observing the effect of changing solvent polarity. The *K*-bands of diene or polyene systems are essentially unresponsive to solvent polarity; the hydrocarbon double bonds are nonpolar. The *K*-bands of enones, however, undergo a bathochromic shift, frequently accompanied by increasing intensity, as the polarity of the solvent is increased. The red shift presumably results from a reduction in the energy level of the excited state accompanying dipole-dipole interaction and hydrogen bonding.

B-Bands (benzenoid bands) are characteristic of the spectra of aromatic or heteroaromatic molecules. Benzene shows a broad absorption band, containing multiple peaks or fine structure, in the near ultraviolet region between 230 and 270 mμ (ϵ of most intense peak ca. 230). The fine structure arises from vibrational sublevels accompanying the electronic transitions. When a chromophoric group is attached to an aromatic ring, the *B*-bands are observed at longer wavelengths than the more intense *K*-bands. For example, styrene has a *K*-band at λ_{max} 244 mμ (ϵ_{max} 12,000), and a *B*-band at λ_{max} 282 mμ (ϵ_{max} 450). When an *R*-band appears in the spectrum of an aromatic compound that contains *K*- and *B*-bands, the *R*-band is shifted to longer wavelengths. The characteristic fine structure of the *B*-bands may be absent in spectra of substituted aromatics. The fine structure is often destroyed by the use of polar solvents.

E-Bands (ethylenic bands), like the *B*-bands, are characteristic of aromatic structures. The origin of the *E*-bands is ascribed to electronic transitions in the benzenoid system of three ethylenic bonds in closed cyclic conjugation.[4] The E_1- and E_2-bands of benzene are observed near 180 mμ and 200 mμ, respectively. Auxochromic substitution brings the E_2 band into the near ultraviolet region, although in many cases it may not appear at wavelengths much over 210 mμ. In auxochromic substitution, the heteroatom with the lone pair of electrons shares these electrons with the π-electron system of the ring, facilitating the $\pi \rightarrow \pi^*$ transition and thus causing a red shift of the *E*-bands. The molar absorptivity of *E*-bands generally varies between 2000 and 14,000.

A bathochromically displaced E_2-band is probably responsible for the intense, fine-structured bands of polynuclear aromatics. With the appearance of the *E*-bands as a result of auxochromic substitution, the *B*-band shifts to longer wavelengths and frequently increases in intensity. Molecules such as benzylidene acetone, in which more complex conjugated chromophoric substitution occurs, produce spectra with both *E*- and *K*-bands; the *B*-bands are obscured by the displaced *K*-bands.

III. INSTRUMENTATION

A modern, recording photoelectric spectrophotometer consists of five sections or areas: (1) radiation source, (2) monochromator, (3) photometer, (4) sample area, and (5) detector area. The optical layout of a typical double-beam instrument is presented in Figure 5.

Radiation Source

The radiation source for the ultraviolet region of the spectrum is a hydrogen discharge tube. The hydrogen discharge tube can be replaced by a tungsten incandescent lamp when absorption in the visible region is to be determined. Mirror *M*1 is rotated manually to focus the light emitted from either source onto the entrance slit (*S*1) of the monochromator.

Monochromator

The light from the source is dispersed into its separate wavelengths by the monochromator. The light that passes through entrance slit *S*1 is collimated into parallel

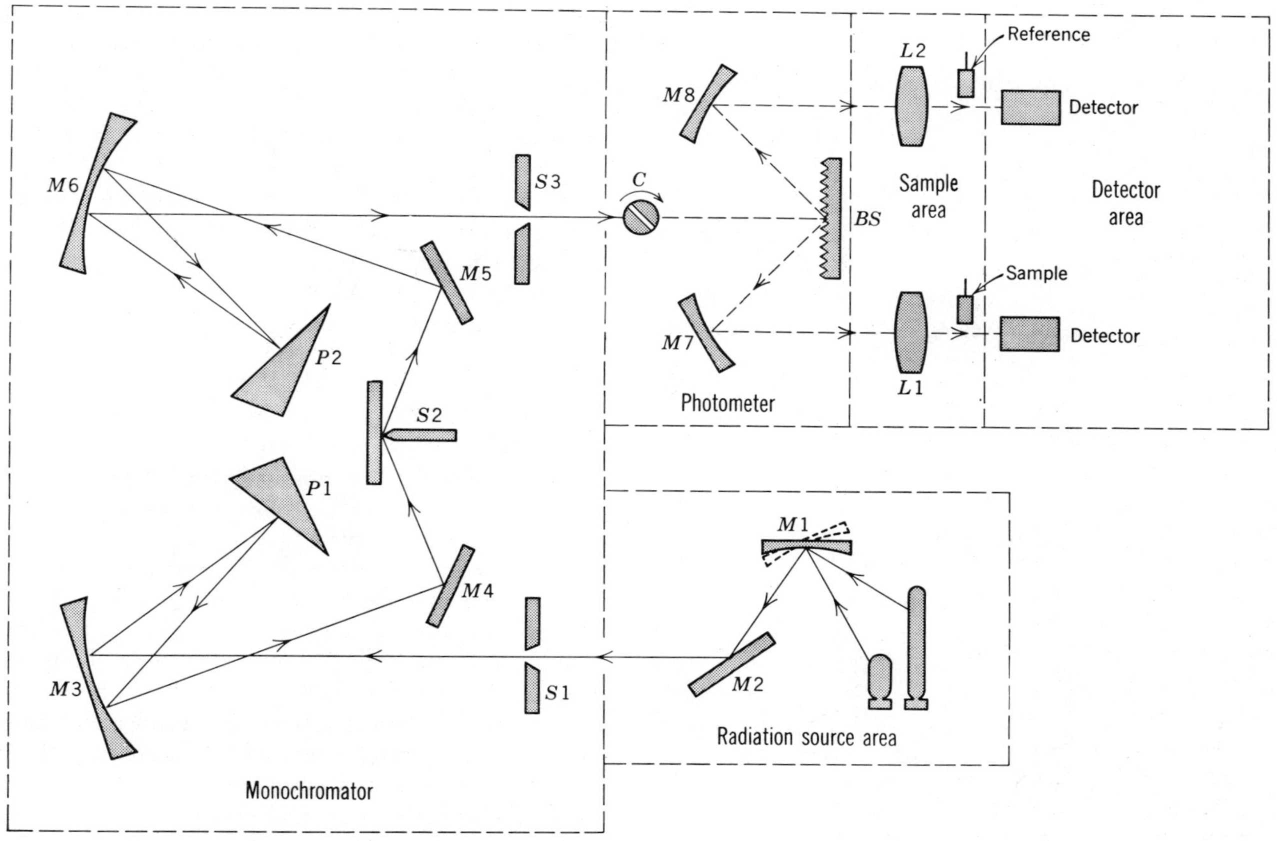

Fig. 5. Optical layout of a double-beam ultraviolet spectrophotometer.

rays by the spherical mirror *M*3 and is reflected to quartz prism *P*1. After the light has passed through prism *P*1, it is reflected back through the prism by a mirrored surface on the back of the prism. Dispersion takes place during both passes through the prism. The light that emerges from *P*1 is reflected to the intermediate slit *S*2 by mirrors *M*3 and *M*4. Since a dispersing prism inherently produces a curved image of a straight slit, entrance slit *S*1 is curved to compensate for the curvature produced in the first stage of the monochromator. Thus the image that strikes the intermediate slit *S*2 is essentially straight. Slit *S*2 consists of a single fixed jaw normal to a mirror. The second jaw of the slit is the image of the fixed jaw in the mirror. The mirror, at slit *S*2, reverses the field of the beam so that comatic aberration introduced by the first stage of the monochromator is removed by the second stage of the monochromator. The light path through the second stage (*M*5, *M*6, and *P*2) is the mirror image of that through the first stage.

The two prisms *P*1 and *P*2 are rotated simultaneously. The wavelength of radiation that appears at exit slit *S*3 is determined by the angular position of the prisms. The rotating mechanism for the prisms is coupled to the recording drum. The double monochromator has two advantages: it doubles dispersion and reduces stray light. Stray light consists of the unwanted wavelengths appearing at slit *S*3. Slit *S*3 is curved to compensate for curvature reintroduced by the second stage of the monochronometer.

Photometer

The monochromatic light that emerges from exit slit *S*3 is pulsed by chopper *C* and split into sample and reference beams by the beam splitter *BS*. The reference and sample beams, reflected from the beam splitter, are reflected by mirrors *M*7 and *M*8 through lenses *L*1 and *L*2 to the sample area. Lenses *L*1 and *L*2 serve to optimize the parallel nature of the rays that pass through the sample area. Optics for the transmission of ultraviolet radiation are made of quartz.

Sample Area

The beams entering the sample area become more concentrated as they pass through the area toward the detectors. Small cells are usually placed in the region nearest the detector area.

The photomultiplier tubes of the detector area are protected from exposure to excessively bright light by automatic shutters that seal the detector area when the sample area is opened.

Detector Area

The radiation beams that pass into the detector area are focused on separate photomultiplier tubes that generate a voltage proportional to the energy that strikes the detectors. The off-balance voltage, resulting from absorption of energy from the sample beam, is balanced by an equivalent voltage tapped from a portion of a slidewire. The recorder pen travels with the contacts on the slidewire. When a linear slidewire is used, the spectra are recorded as wavelength versus transmittance. Since the absorbance (A) equals log $1/T$, the use of a slidewire whose resistance varies logarithmically with length results in a recording linear with respect to absorbance.

IV. SAMPLE HANDLING

Ultraviolet spectra of compounds are usually determined either in the vapor phase or in solution.

A variety of quartz cells is available for the determination of spectra in the gaseous phase. These cells are equipped with gas inlets and outlets and have path lengths from 0.1 mm to 100 mm. Cell jackets are available through which liquids may be circulated for temperature control.

Cells used for the determination of spectra in solution vary in path length from 1 cm to 10 cm. Quartz cells, 1 cm square, are commonly used. These require about 3 ml of solution. Filler plugs are available to reduce the volume and the path length of the 1 cm square cell. Small-volume cells with 1 cm path lengths are also available. Microcells, made of a Teflon capillary and quartz windows, may also be used when only a small amount of solution is available. The use of a beam condenser, to minimize the loss of energy, is advisable when the microcells are used.

In preparing a solution, a sample is accurately weighed and made up to volume in a volumetric flask. Aliquots are then removed and additional dilutions made until the desired concentration has been acquired. Clean cells are of utmost importance. The cells should be rinsed several times with solvent and checked for absorption between successive determinations. It may be necessary to clean the cells with a detergent or hot nitric acid to remove traces of previous samples.

Many solvents are available for use in the ultraviolet region. Three common solvents are cyclohexane, 95% ethanol, and 1,4-dioxane.

A spectrographic grade of cyclohexane is available. Cyclohexane may be freed of aromatic impurities by percolation through activated silica gel, and is transparent down to about 210 mμ. Aromatic compounds, particularly the polynuclear aromatics, are usually soluble and their spectra generally retain their fine-line structure when determined in cyclohexane. The fine structure is often lost in more polar solvents.

Ninety-five per cent ethanol is generally a good choice when a more polar solvent is required. This solvent can generally be used as purchased, but absolute ethanol must be freed of benzene used in its preparation. The last traces of benzene are removed by careful fractional distillation,[25] or by preparative gas chromatography.

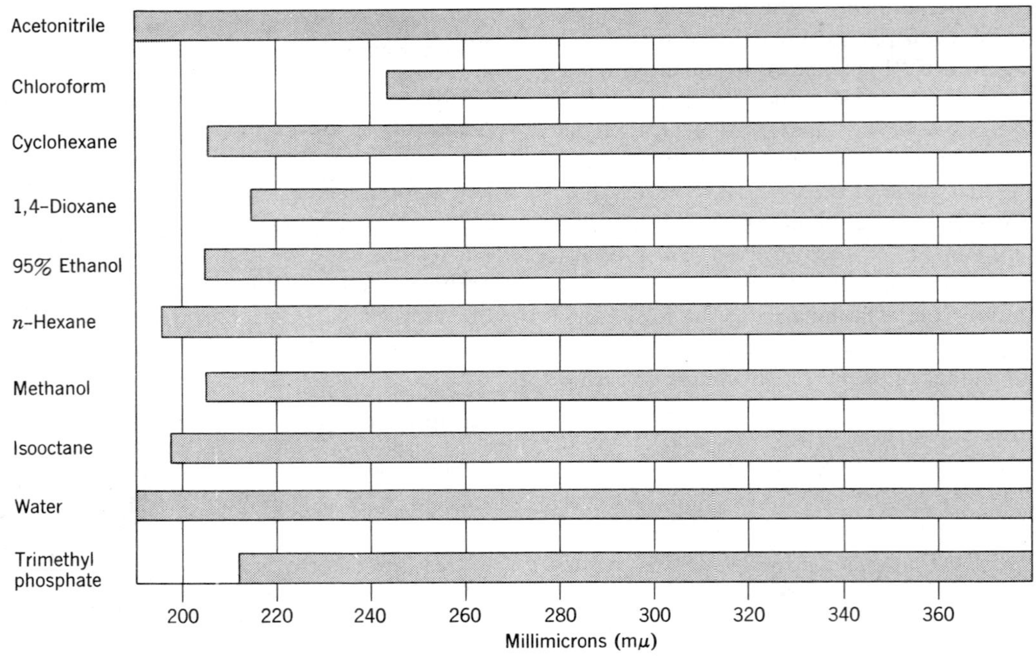

Fig. 6. Useful transparency ranges of solvents in near ultraviolet region.

The lower limit of transparency for ethanol is near 210 mμ.

1,4-Dioxane can be purified by distillation from sodium. Benzene contamination can be removed by the addition of methanol followed by distillation to remove the benzene-methanol azeotrope.[19] 1,4-Dioxane is transparent down to about 220 mμ.

Ultraviolet transparency ranges for a number of solvents are presented in Figure 6. Care should be exercised to choose a solvent that will be inert to the solute. For example, the spectra of aldehydes should not be determined in alcohols. Photochemical reactions may be detected by checking for changes in absorbance with time after exposure to the ultraviolet beam in the instrument.

V. CHARACTERISTIC ABSORPTION OF ORGANIC COMPOUNDS

In our discussion of the theory of electronic or ultraviolet spectra, it was shown that the ability of an organic compound to absorb ultraviolet radiation is dependent on its electronic structure. In the following sections we shall discuss the characteristic absorption of basic electronic structures, and the effects of molecular geometry and substitution on the absorption.

Compounds Containing Only σ-Electrons

Saturated hydrocarbons contain σ-electrons exclusively. Since the energy required to bring about a $\sigma \rightarrow \sigma^*$ transition is of the order of 185 kcal per mole and is available only in the far ultraviolet region, saturated hydrocarbons are transparent in the near ultraviolet region.

Saturated Compounds Containing *n*-Electrons

Saturated compounds containing heteroatoms such as oxygen, nitrogen, sulfur, or the halogens, possess nonbonding electrons (*n*- or *p*-electrons) in addition to σ-electrons. The $n \rightarrow \sigma^*$ transition requires less energy than the $\sigma \rightarrow \sigma^*$ transition, but the majority of compounds in this class still show no absorption in the near ultraviolet. Alcohols and ethers absorb at wavelengths shorter than 185 mμ and therefore are commonly used as solvents for work in the near ultraviolet region. When these compounds are used as solvents, the intense absorption extends into the near ultraviolet, producing end-absorption or cut-off in the 200–220 mμ region.

Sulfides, disulfides, thiols, amines, bromides, and iodides may show weak absorption in the near ultraviolet. Frequently the absorption appears only as a shoulder or an inflection so that its diagnostic value is questionable.

Absorption data for several saturated compounds bearing heteroatoms are presented in Table II.

Table II Absorption Characteristics of Saturated Compounds Containing Heteroatoms ($n \rightarrow \sigma^*$)

COMPOUND	λ_{max}(mμ)	ϵ_{max}	SOLVENT
Methanol	177	200	Hexane
Di-*n*-butyl sulfide	210	1200	Ethanol
	229 (*s*)		
Di-*n*-butyl disulfide	204	2089	Ethanol
	251	398	
1-Hexanethiol	224 (*s*)	126	Cyclohexane
Trimethylamine	199	3950	Hexane
N-Methylpiperidine	213	1600	Ether
Methyl chloride	173	200	Hexane
n-Propyl bromide	208	300	Hexane
Methyl iodide	259	400	Hexane

(*s*) shoulder or inflection

Compounds Containing π-Electrons (Chromophores)

The absorption characteristics of a list of compounds containing single, isolated chromophoric groups are presented in Table III. All the compounds contain π-electrons, and many also contain nonbonding electron pairs. An examination of the absorption data shows that many of these single chromophoric groups absorb strongly in the far ultraviolet region, with no absorption in the near ultraviolet. Those groups containing both π- and *n*-electrons can undergo three transitions: $n \rightarrow \sigma^*$, $\pi \rightarrow \pi^*$, and $n \rightarrow \pi^*$. Absorption of single chromophores in the near ultraviolet region results from the low-energy, forbidden $n \rightarrow \pi^*$ transition.

Ethylenic Chromophore

The isolated ethylenic chromophore is responsible for intense absorption that almost always occurs in the far ultraviolet region. Absorption is due to a $\pi \rightarrow \pi^*$ transition. Ethylene in the vapor phase absorbs at 165 mμ (ϵ_{max} 10,000). A second band near 200 mμ has been attributed to the elevation of two π electrons to π^* orbitals.[3] The intensity of olefinic absorption is essentially independent of solvent because of the nonpolar nature of the olefinic bond.

Alkyl substitution of the parent compound moves the absorption to longer wavelengths. The bathochromic effect is progressive as the number of alkyl groups increases. A double bond exocyclic to two rings absorbs near 204 mμ. The bathochromic shift, accompanying alkyl substitution, results from hyperconjugation, in which the σ-electrons of the alkyl group are mobile enough to interact with the chromophoric group.

Attachment of a heteroatom, containing a nonbonding

Table III Absorption Data for Isolated Chromophores

CHROMOPHORIC GROUP	SYSTEM	EXAMPLE	λ_{max} (mμ)	ϵ_{max}	SOLVENT
Ethylenic	RCH=CHR	Ethylene	165	15,000	Vapor
			193	10,000	
Acetylenic	R—C≡C—R	Acetylene	173	6,000	Vapor
Carbonyl	RR_1C=O	Acetone	188	900	*n*-Hexane
			279	15	
Carbonyl	RHC=O	Acetaldehyde	290	16	Heptane
Carboxyl	RCOOH	Acetic acid	204	60	Water
Amido	$RCONH_2$	Acetamide	<208	...	...
Azomethine	>C=N—	Acetoxime	190	5,000	Water
Nitrile	—C≡N	Acetonitrile	<160	...	...
Azo	—N=N—	Azomethane	347	4.5	...
Nitroso	—N=O	Nitrosobutane	300	100	Ether
			665	20	
Nitrate	$—ONO_2$	Ethyl nitrate	270	12	Dioxane
Nitro	—N(=O)→O	Nitromethane	271	18.6	Alcohol
Nitrite	—ONO	Amyl nitrite	218.5	1,120	Petroleum ether
			346.5†		
Sulfoxide	>S → O	Cyclohexyl methyl sulfoxide	210	1,500	Alcohol
Sulfone	>S(→O)=O	Dimethyl sulfone	<180	...	...

* Most intense peak of fine structure group.

electron pair, to the ethylenic linkage brings about a bathochromic shift. Nitrogen and sulfur atoms are most effective, bringing the absorption well into the near ultraviolet region. Methyl vinyl sulfide, for example, absorbs at 228 mμ (ϵ_{max} 8000).

The absorption characteristics of cyclic monoolefins resemble those of the acyclic compounds, the absorption bearing no apparent relationship to ring size.

When two or more ethylenic linkages appear in a single molecule, isolated from one another by at least one methylene group, the molecule absorbs at the same position as the single ethylenic chromophore. The intensity of absorption is proportional to the number of isolated chromophoric groups in the molecule.

Allenes, in which the ethylenic groups are adjacent, show a strong absorption band in the far ultraviolet region near 170 mμ, with a shoulder on the long wavelength side sometimes extending into the near ultraviolet region.

The single olefinic bond consists of two energy levels (two π orbitals) one bonding one antibonding. In conjugated diene molecules such as 1,3-butadiene, when coplanarity permits, there is an effective overlap of π orbitals resulting in a π–π conjugated system (I).

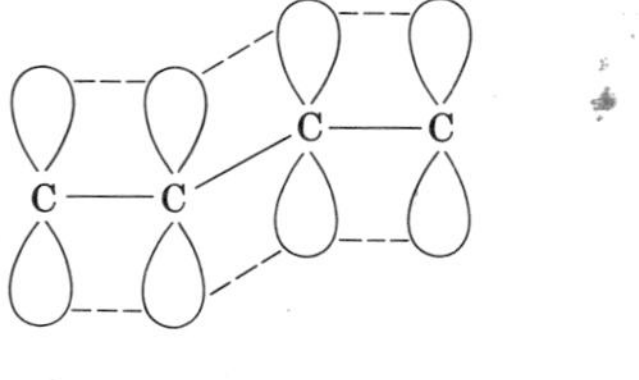

I

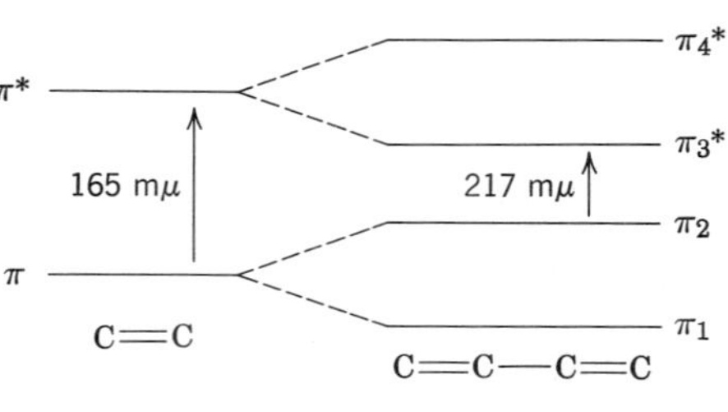

II

This overlap or interaction results in the creation of two new energy levels in butadiene (II).

Acyclic conjugated dienes show intense $\pi \rightarrow \pi^*$ transition bands (*K*-bands) in the 215–230 mμ region. 1,3-Butadiene absorbs at 217 (ϵ_{max} 21,000). Further conjugation, in open-chain trienes and polyenes, results in additional bathochromic shifts accompanied by increases in absorption intensity. The spectra of polyenes are characterized by fine structure, particularly when the spectra are determined in the vapor phase or in nonpolar solvents. Absorption data for several conjugated olefins are presented in Table IV.

Table IV Absorption Data for Conjugated Olefins

COMPOUND	$\pi \rightarrow \pi^*$ TRANSITION (*K*-BAND) λ_{max}(mμ)	ϵ_{max}	SOLVENT
1,3-Butadiene	217	21,000	Hexane
2,3-Dimethyl-1,3-butadiene	226	21,400	Cyclohexane
1,3,5-Hexatriene	253	~50,000	Isooctane
	263	52,500	
	274	~50,000	
1,3-Cyclohexadiene	256	8,000	Hexane
1,3-Cyclopentadiene	239	3,400	Hexane

The bathochromic effect of alkyl substitution in 1,3-butadiene is apparent from the data for 2,3-dimethyl-1,3-butadiene.

In cases where *cis* and *trans* isomers are possible, the *trans* isomer absorbs at the longer wavelength with the greater intensity (see Table V). This difference becomes more pronounced as the length of the conjugated system increases.

Table V $\pi \rightarrow \pi^*$ Transitions (K-Bands) of Conjugated Olefins

COMPOUND	λ_{max}(mμ)	ϵ_{max}	SOLVENT
CH_3—CH=CH—CH=CH_2			
cis-	223	22,600	Ethanol
trans-	223.5	23,000	Ethanol
ϕ—CH=CH—ϕ			
cis-	280	10,500	Ethanol
trans-	295.5	29,000	Ethanol
ϕCH=CH—CH=CH_2			
cis-	268	18,500	Isooctane
trans-	280	27,000	Isooctane

Coplanarity is required for the most effective overlap of the π-orbitals and increased ease of the $\pi \rightarrow \pi^*$ transition. Of the two isomers, the *cis* isomer is more likely to be forced into a nonplanar conformation by steric effects (see discussion of stilbene on p. 165). The greater absorption intensity of the *trans* isomer results from the greater overall length of the transition moment of the excited molecule.

An empirical method for predicting the bathochromic effect of alkyl substitution in 1,3-butadiene has been formulated by Woodward.[26,27] These rules can be summarized as follows:

(1) Each alkyl group, or ring residue, attached to the parent diene (1,3-butadiene), shifts the absorption 5 mμ toward the long wavelength region; and (2) the creation of an exocyclic double bond causes an additional bathochromic shift of 5 mμ, the shift being 10 mμ if the double bond is exocyclic to two rings. For example, $217 + (2 \times 5)$ is the predicted λ_{max} value for 2,3-dimethyl-1,3-butadiene; the observed λ_{max} is 226. These rules can also be applied to polycyclic molecules in which the diene system is heteroannular, that is, having the conjugated diene system shared by two fused rings. A different base value must be used for homoannular systems (see below).

Cholesta-3,5-diene

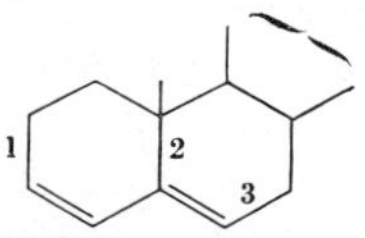

Calc. λ_{max}
217 (base)
15 (3-ring residues, 1, 2, 3)
5 (1-exocyclic C=C)
237

Obs. λ_{max} = 235 (ϵ_{max} 19,000)

Examination of the data in Table IV shows a marked bathochromic shift and a decrease in absorption intensity for the conjugated, monocyclic diene system compared with 1,3-butadiene. Butadiene exists in the preferred *s-trans* (transoid) conformation, whereas the cyclic dienes are forced into an *s-cis* (cisoid) conformation. The reason for the bathochromic shift in the *s-cis* structure, brought about by cyclization, is not clear. The decrease in intensity is more easily explained, since the transition moment of the cyclic or homoannular system is less than that of the acyclic or the heteroannular systems.

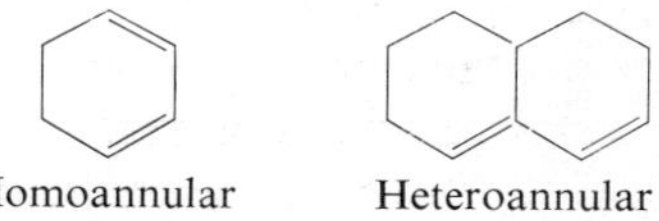

Homoannular   Heteroannular

Rules for predicting the position of absorption of homo- and heteroannular systems are due largely to the work of Fieser.[28] These rules are summarized in Table VI.

The value of these rules in structural studies of natural products will be obvious from two examples.

1. Cholesta-3,5-diene

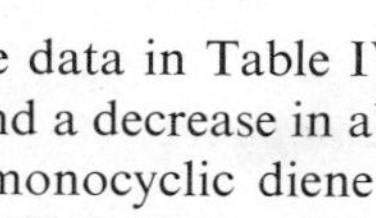

Calc. λ_{max}
214 (base)
15 (3-ring residues, 1, 2, 3)
5 (1-exocyclic C=C)
234

Obs. λ_{max} = 235 (ϵ_{max} 19,000)

Cholesta-2,4-diene

2.

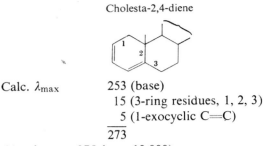

Calc. λ_{max} 253 (base)
15 (3-ring residues, 1, 2, 3)
5 (1-exocyclic C=C)
273

Obs. λ_{max} = 275 (ϵ_{max} 10,000)

Table VI Rules of Diene Absorption

Base value for heteroannular diene	214
Base value for homoannular diene	253
Increments for	
Double bond extending conjugation	30
Alkyl substituent or ring residue	5
Exocyclic double bond	5
Polar groupings: OAc	0
OAlk	6
SAlk	30
Cl, Br	5
$N(Alk)_2$	60
Solvent correction	0
	λ_{calc} = Total

Acetylenic Chromophore

The absorption characteristics of the acetylenic chromophore are more complex than those of the ethylenic chromophore. Acetylene shows a relatively weak band at 173 mμ resulting from a $\pi \rightarrow \pi^*$ transition. Conjugated polyynes show two principal bands in the near ultraviolet which are characterized by fine structure. The short wavelength band is extremely intense and arises from a $\pi \rightarrow \pi^*$ transition.

	λ_{max},	ϵ_{max}	λ_{max},	ϵ_{max}
2,4-hexadiyne	...	...	227	360
2,4,6-octatriyne	207	135,000	268	200
2,4,6,8-decatetrayne	234	281,000	306	180

Carbonyl Chromophore

The carbonyl group contains, in addition to a pair of σ-electrons, a pair of π-electrons and two pairs of nonbonding (*n* or *p*) electrons. Saturated ketones and aldehydes display three absorption bands, two of which are observed in the far ultraviolet region. A $\pi \rightarrow \pi^*$ transition absorbs strongly near 150 mμ; an $n \rightarrow \sigma^*$ transition absorbs near 190 mμ. The third band (*R*-band) appears in the near ultraviolet in the 270–300 mμ region. The *R*-band is weak ($\epsilon_{max} < 30$) and results from the forbidden transition of a loosely held *n*-electron to the π^* orbital, the lowest unoccupied orbital of the carbonyl group. *R*-Bands undergo a blue shift as the polarity of the solvent is increased. Acetone absorbs at 279 mμ in *n*-hexane; in water the λ_{max} is 264.5. The blue shift results from hydrogen bonding which lowers the energy of the *n* orbital. The blue shift can be used as a measure of the strength of the hydrogen bond.

SATURATED KETONES AND ALDEHYDES. Absorption data for several saturated ketones and aldehydes are presented in Table VII.

Table VII Absorption Data for Saturated Aldehydes and Ketones

	$n \rightarrow \pi^*$ TRANSITION (*R*-BAND)		
COMPOUND	λ_{max}(mμ)	ϵ_{max}	SOLVENT
Acetone	279	13	Isooctane
Methyl ethyl ketone	279	16	Isooctane
Diisobutyl ketone	288	24	Isooctane
Hexamethylacetone	295	20	Alcohol
Cyclopentanone	299	20	Hexane
Cyclohexanone	285	14	Hexane
Acetaldehyde	290	17	Isooctane
Propionaldehyde	292	21	Isooctane
Isobutyraldehyde	290	16	Hexane

The bathochromic effect accompanying the introduction of larger and more highly branched alkyl groups in the aliphatic ketones can be seen from the data in Table VII.

Since the $n \rightarrow \pi^*$ absorption of ketones and aldehydes is weak, spectra of derivatives such as the semicarbazones or 2,4-dinitrophenylhyrazones are often used for identification work.

The introduction of an α-halogen atom in an aliphatic ketone has little effect upon the $n \rightarrow \pi^*$ transition. However, α-substitution of halogen atoms in saturated cyclic ketones has a marked effect upon the absorpton characteristics. The λ_{max} of the parent compound is reduced by 5–10 mμ when the substituent is axial and a bathochromic shift of 10–30 mμ occurs when the substituent is equatorial. The bathochromic shift is usually accompanied by a strong hyperchromic effect.

The attachment of groups containing lone electron pairs to carbonyl groups has a marked effect upon the $n \rightarrow \pi^*$ transition. The *R*-band is shifted to shorter wavelengths with little effect upon intensity. The shift in absorption results from a combination of inductive and resonance effects. Substitution may change the energy levels of both the ground state and the excited state, but the important factor is the relative energies of the two levels. Absorption values for the $n \rightarrow \pi^*$ transitions of several simple carbonyl compounds are presented in Table VIII.

α-DIKETONES AND α-KETOALDEHYDES. Acyclic α-diketones, such as biacetyl, exist in the *s-trans* conformation. The spectrum of biacetyl shows the normal weak

Table VIII $n \rightarrow \pi^*$ ***Transitions (R-Bands) of Simple Carbonyl-Containing Compounds***

COMPOUND	$\lambda_{max}(m\mu)$	ϵ_{max}	SOLVENT
Acetaldehyde	293	11.8	Hexane
Acetic acid	204	41	Ethanol
Ethyl acetate	207	69	Pet. ether
Acetamide	220 (*s*)		Water
Acetyl chloride	235	53	Hexane
Acetic anhydride	225	47	Isooctane
Acetone	279	15	Hexane

R-band at 275 mμ and a weak band near 450 mμ resulting from interaction between the carbonyl groups. The position of the long-wavelength band of α-diketones incapable of enolization reflects the effect of coplanarity upon resonance, and hence depends on the dihedral angle ϕ between the carbonyl groups (I, II, III).

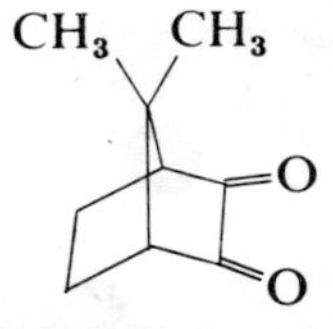

I Camphorquinone
$\phi = 0$–$10°$ λ_{max} 466 mμ

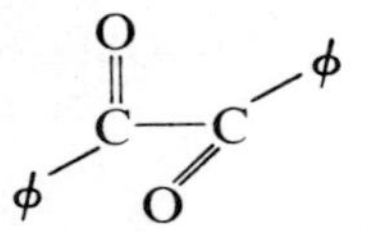

II Benzil
$\phi = 90°$ λ_{max} 370 mμ

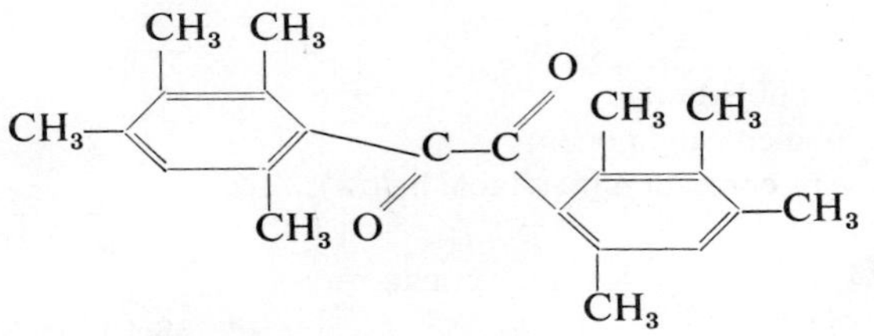

III Isoduril
$\phi = 180°$ λ_{max} 490 mμ

Cyclic α-diketones with α-hydrogen atoms exist in the enolic form, for example, diosphenol. The absorption characteristics of diosphenol appear on p. 161.

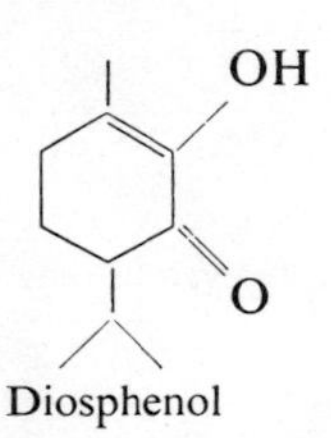

Diosphenol

β-DIKETONES. The ultraviolet spectra of β-diketones depend on the degree of enolization. The enolic form is stabilized when steric considerations permit intramolecular hydrogen bonding. Acetylacetone is a classic example. The enolic species exists to the extent of about 15% in aqueous solution and 91–92% in the vapor phase or in solution in nonpolar solvents. The absorption is dependent on the concentration of the enol tautomer.

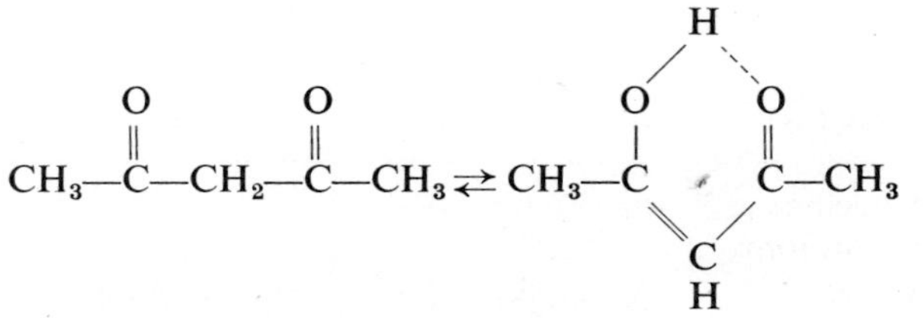

$$CH_3{-}CO{-}CH_2{-}CO{-}CH_3 \rightleftarrows CH_3{-}C(O{-}H)={CH}{-}C(=O){-}CH_3$$

$\lambda_{max}^{H_2O}$ 274, ϵ_{max} 2050

$\lambda_{max}^{Isooctane}$ 272, ϵ_{max} 12,000

Cyclic β-diketones, such as 1,3-cyclohexadione, exist almost exclusively in the enolic form even in polar solvents. The enolic structures show strong absorption in the 230–260 mμ region due to the $\pi \rightarrow \pi^*$ transition in the *s-trans* enone system. 1,3-Cyclohexadione, in ethanol, absorbs at 253 mμ (ϵ_{max} 22,000). The formation of the enolate ion, in alkaline solution, shifts the strong absorption band into the 270 to 300 mμ region.

α,β-UNSATURATED KETONES AND ALDEHYDES. Compounds containing a carbonyl group in conjugation with an ethylenic group are called *enones*. Spectra of enones are characterized by an intense absorption band (*K*-band) in the 215–250 mμ region (ϵ_{max} usually 10,000–20,000), and a weak $n \rightarrow \pi^*$ band (*R*-band) at 310–330 mμ. The weak *R*-band is frequently poorly defined. Absorption data for several conjugated ketones and aldehydes are presented in Table IX.

Table IX Absorption Data for Conjugated Ketones and Aldehydes

	K-BAND		*R*-BAND		
COMPOUND	λ_{max} (mμ)	log ϵ_{max}	λ_{max} (mμ)	log ϵ_{max}	SOLVENT
Methyl vinyl ketone	212.5	3.85	320	1.43	Ethanol
Methyl isopropenyl ketone	218	3.90	315	1.4	Ethanol
Acrolein	210	4.06	315	1.41	Water
Crotonaldehyde	220	4.17	322	1.45	Ethanol
Crotonaldehyde	214	4.20	329	1.39	Isooctane
			341	1.38	
			352 (*s*)	1.25	

(*s*) shoulder.

Since carbonyl compounds are polar, the positions of the *K*- and *R*-bands of enones are both dependent on the solvent. The hypsochromic effect on the *R*-band with increasing solvent polarity has already been discussed (p. 158). The *K*-bands of enones undergo a bathochromic shift with increasing solvent polarity. The solvent effect on the spectrum of mesityl oxide

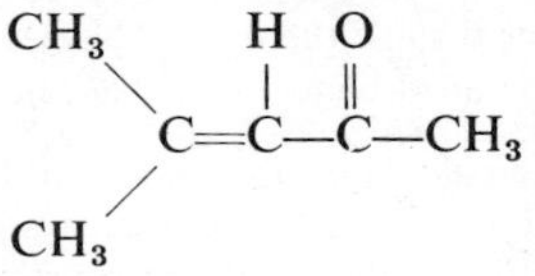

$$(CH_3)_2C{=}CH{-}CO{-}CH_3$$

is summarized in Table X.

Table X Effect of Solvent Polarity on the Spectrum of Mesityl Oxide

SOLVENT	TRANSITION $\pi \rightarrow \pi^*(\lambda_{max}\ m\mu)$	$n \rightarrow \pi^*(\lambda_{max}\ m\mu)$
Isooctane	230.6	321
Chloroform	237.6	314
Water	242.6	Submerged under *K*-band

The intensity of the *K*-band may be reduced to less than 10^4 in cases where steric hindrance prevents coplanarity. This frequently occurs in cyclic systems such as IV.[28a]

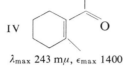

IV

λ_{max} 243 $m\mu$, ϵ_{max} 1400

Woodward has derived empirical generalizations for the effect of substitution on the position of the *K*-band in the spectra of α,β-unsaturated ketones.[26,27] The positions of the *K*-bands that result from substitution in the basic formula

$$R{-}\overset{\overset{\displaystyle O}{\|}}{C}{-}\overset{\alpha}{C}{=}C\begin{matrix}\beta \\ \beta\end{matrix}$$

are summarized as follows:

SUBSTITUTION		PROBABLE λ_{max} ($m\mu$)
Unsubstituted		215
α or β	No exocyclic C=C	225
$\alpha\beta$ or $\beta\beta$	No exocyclic C=C	235
$\alpha\beta$ or $\beta\beta$	One exocyclic C=C	240
$\alpha\beta\beta$	No exocyclic C=C	247
$\alpha\beta\beta$	One exocyclic C=C	252

The spectra of α,β-unsaturated aldehydes are similar to those of the α,β-unsaturated ketones. The *R*-bands occur in the 350–370 $m\mu$ region and exhibit some fine structure when the spectra are determined in nonpolar solvents.

Similar rules apply to the cyclopentenone system[28]

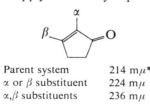

Parent system	214 $m\mu$*
α or β substituent	224 $m\mu$
α,β substituents	236 $m\mu$

* This value can be calculated from data in Table XI.
202 (Base value to form 5-membered cyclic enone)
12 (β-substituent, bond to form ring)
214

More extensive rules of enone absorption have been summarized by Fieser.[29] These rules appear as Table XI.

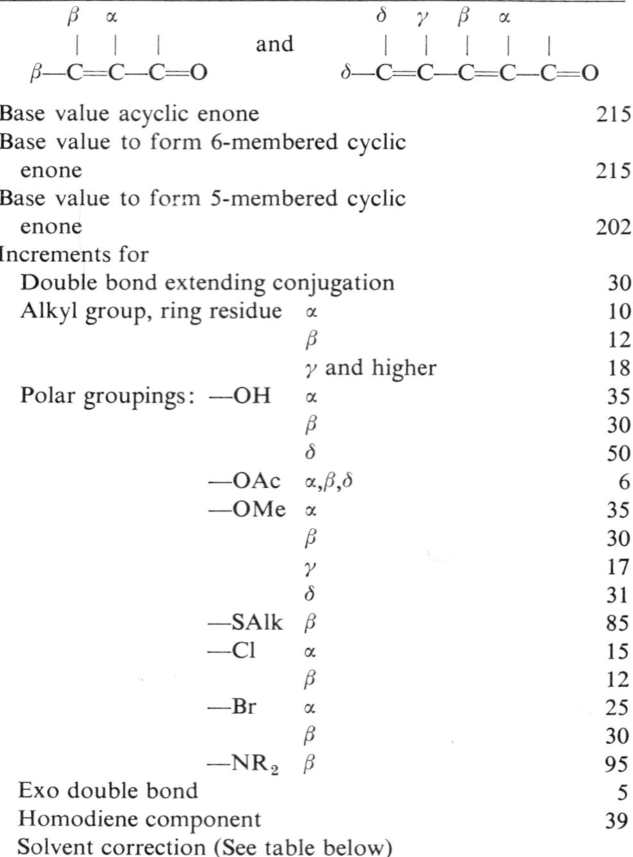

Table XI Rules of Enone Absorption

$\beta{-}\overset{\beta}{C}{=}\overset{\alpha}{C}{-}C{=}O$ and $\delta{-}\overset{\delta}{C}{=}\overset{\gamma}{C}{-}\overset{\beta}{C}{=}\overset{\alpha}{C}{-}C{=}O$

Base value acyclic enone		215
Base value to form 6-membered cyclic enone		215
Base value to form 5-membered cyclic enone		202
Increments for		
Double bond extending conjugation		30
Alkyl group, ring residue	α	10
	β	12
	γ and higher	18
Polar groupings: —OH	α	35
	β	30
	δ	50
—OAc	α,β,δ	6
—OMe	α	35
	β	30
	γ	17
	δ	31
—SAlk	β	85
—Cl	α	15
	β	12
—Br	α	25
	β	30
—NR_2	β	95
Exo double bond		5
Homodiene component		39
Solvent correction (See table below)		
		λ_{calc} = Total

SOLVENT CORRECTIONS

SOLVENT	CORRECTION $m\mu$
Ethanol	0
Methanol	0
Dioxane	+5
Chloroform	+1
Ether	+7
Water	−8
Hexane	+11
Cyclohexane	+11

A few examples will serve to illustrate the usefulness of these correlations.

1. 1-Acetylcyclohexene

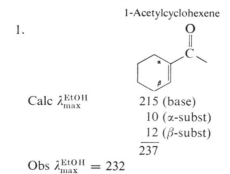

Calc λ_{max}^{EtOH} 215 (base)
10 (α-subst)
12 (β-subst)
237

Obs λ_{max}^{EtOH} = 232

Cholesta-1,4-diene-3-one

2.

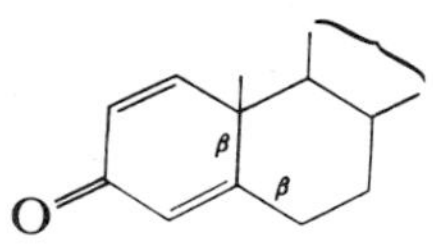

Calc λ_{max}^{EtOH} 215 (base)
24 (2 β-subst)
5 (1-exo C=C)
244

Obs λ_{max}^{EtOH} = 245

Cross conjugation has little effect on the λ_{max} of cholesta-1,4-diene-3-one. The calculations used were for an enone (β,β-disubstituted) with no correction required for the double bond in the 1,2 position.

Enol of 1,2-cyclopentadione

3.

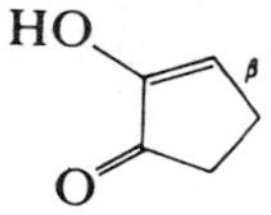

Calc λ_{max}^{EtOH} 202 (base)
12 (β-subst)
35 (α-OH)
249

Obs λ_{max}^{EtOH} = 247

Diosphenol

4.

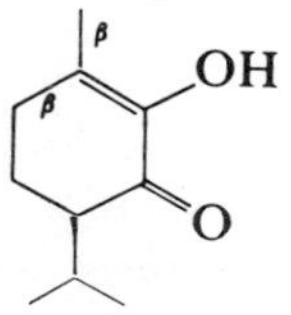

Calc λ_{max}^{EtOH} 215 (base)
24 (2β-subst)
35 (α-OH)
274

Obs λ_{max}^{EtOH} = 270

The spectrum of *p*-benzoquinone

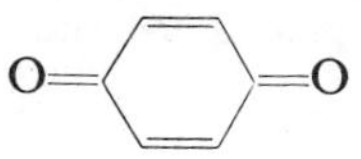

is that of a typical α,β-unsaturated ketone, the strong *K*-band appearing at 245 mμ with a weak *R*-band near 435 mμ.

There are cases where the C=O and the C=C are nonconjugated in the classical sense but where interaction does occur to produce an absorption band. In structures where this occurs, the C=O and C=C groups must be oriented so that there can be effective overlap of the π orbitals. For example, the structure CH_2= ◇ =O shows a moderately strong band near 214 mμ with a normal weak *R*-band at 284 mμ. Similar effects are observed when there can be effective overlap of the π orbital of the C=O group and the *p* (or *n*-) orbitals of a heteroatom. For example,

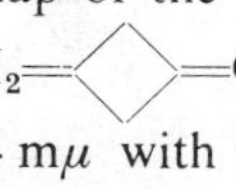

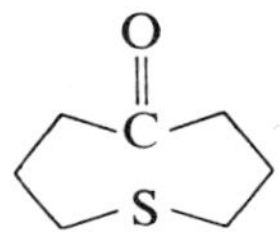

λ 238 mμ, ϵ_{max} 2535

The interaction in these apparently nonconjugated systems is known as transannular conjugation.[30]

α,β-Unsaturated aldehydes present spectra similar to the α,β-unsaturated ketones. Calculations are based upon a base value of 207 mμ for acrolein.

CARBOXYLIC ACIDS. Saturated carboxylic acids show a weak absorption band near 200 mμ resulting from the forbidden $n \rightarrow \pi^*$ transition. The position of the band undergoes a small bathochromic shift with an increase in chain length. This band is of little diagnostic value.

α,β-Unsaturated acids display a strong *K*-band characteristic of the conjugated system. In the first member of the series, acrylic acid, the absorption occurs near 200 mμ, ϵ_{max} 10,000. Alkyl substitution in this basic structure results in a bathochromic shift of the *K*-band in much the same manner as observed for α,β-unsaturated ketones. The extension of conjugation produces further bathochromic shifts accompanied by an increase in the band intensity and the appearance of fine structure (Table XII). The attachment of an electronegative group on the α-carbon also produces a bathochromic shift.

Table XII Absorption Maxima of Unsaturated Carboxylic Acids and Esters[2,31]

	λ_{max}^{EtOH} ($\pm$5 mμ)
α or β-monosubstituted	208
α,β- or β,β-disubstituted	217
α,β,β-trisubstituted	225
Each C=C extending conjugation	+30
Each γ or δ alkyl subsitituent	+18
Each exo C=C	+5

The absorption characteristics of several α,β-unsaturated acids are summarized in Table XIII.

ESTERS AND LACTONES. Esters and sodium salts of carboxylic acids show absorption at wavelengths and intensities comparable to the parent acid. Conjugated, unsaturated lactones display spectra similar to unsaturated esters. The spectra of simple unsaturated lactones show end absorption in the 200–240 mμ region. Extended conjugation produces a bathochromic shift of the *K*-band.

AMIDES AND LACTAMS. α,β-Unsaturated amides and lactams show absorption in the near ultraviolet at λ_{max} 200–220, $\epsilon_{max} < 10,000$. α,β-Unsaturated lactams show a second band near 250 mμ ($\epsilon_{max} \sim 1000$).

Table XIII Absorption of α,β-Unsaturated Acids

COMPOUND	λ_{max}^{EtOH}	ϵ_{max}
CH_2=CH—COOH	200	10,000
CH_3CH=CH—COOH (*trans*)	205	14,000
CH_3CH=CH—COOH (*cis*)	205.5	13,500
CH_2=C(CH_3)—COOH	210	. . .
(S)=C(H)—COOH	220	14,000
(S)=C(CN)—COOH	235	12,500
CH_3—$(CH=CH)_2$—COOH	254	25,000
CH_3—$(CH=CH)_3$—COOH	294	37,000
CH_3—$(CH=CH)_4$—COOH	332	49,000

Azomethines and Oximes

These structures show no absorption in the near ultraviolet unless the >C=N— group is involved in conjugation. In the spectra of conjugated azomethines and oximes the *K*-band appears in the 220–230 mμ region, $\epsilon_{max} > 10,000$. Acidification of the azomethines, producing a positive charge on the nitrogen, shifts the absorption to the 270–290 mμ region.

Nitriles and Azo Compounds

α,β-Unsaturated nitriles absorb just inside the near ultraviolet region, near 213 mμ, $\epsilon_{max} \sim 10,000$.

The azo group is analogous to the ethylenic linkage with two σ bonds being replaced by two lone pairs of electrons (—N̈=N̈—). The $\pi \rightarrow \pi^*$ transition occurs in the far ultraviolet. The $n \rightarrow \pi^*$ band in aliphatic azo compounds appears near 350 mμ with the expected low intensity, $\epsilon_{max} < 30$. *trans*-Azobenzene absorbs at 320 mμ (ϵ_{max} 21,000). Comparable absorption for *trans*-stilbene occurs at 295 mμ (ϵ_{max} 28,000).

Compounds With N to O Bonds

Four groups contain multiple nitrogen to oxygen linkages: nitro, nitroso, nitrates, and nitrites. All of these structures show weak absorption in the near ultraviolet region resulting from an $n \rightarrow \pi^*$ transition.

The absorption of several typical compounds containing nitrogen to oxygen linkages are presented in Table XIV.

Table XIV Absorption of Compounds Containing Nitrogen-Oxygen Linkages

COMPOUND	$n \rightarrow \pi^*$ TRANSITION (*R*-BAND) λ_{max}	ϵ_{max}	SOLVENT
Nitromethane	275	15	Heptane
2-Methyl-2-nitropropane	280.5	23	Heptane
1-Nitro-1-propene	229	9400	Ethanol
	235	9800	
Nitrosobutane	300	100	Ether
	665	20	
Octyl nitrate	270*	15	Pentane
Cyclohexyl nitrate	270*	22	. . .
n-Butyl nitrite	218	1050	Ethanol
	313–384†	17–45	

* This is typically a point of inflection in the spectra of nitrates.
† This region is one of fine structure with bands roughly 10 mμ apart. The band with maximum absorption occurs at 357 mμ.

The effect of conjugation upon the absorption characteristics of the nitro group is apparent from the data for 1-nitro-1-propene. The strong *K*-band ($\pi \rightarrow \pi^*$ transition) submerges the weak *R*-band.

Multiple Bonded Sulfur Groups

Aliphatic sulfones are transparent in the near ultraviolet region. The sulfur atom in sulfones has no lone-pair electrons, and the lone pairs of electrons associated with the oxygen atoms, appear to be tightly bound. In an α,β-unsaturated sulfone, such as ethyl vinyl sulfone, a band appears in the 210 mμ region resulting from resonance between the S to O linkage and the ethylenic linkage.

Saturated sulfoxides absorb near 220 mμ with intensities of the order of 1500. This absorption involves an $n \rightarrow \pi^*$ transition in the S → O group and thus undergoes a hypsochromic shift as solvent polarity is increased. Aromatic sulfoxides show an intense *K*-band in addition to the displaced *B*-band.

In compounds containing the —S(=O)—X grouping, the position of the $n \rightarrow \pi^*$ band depends on the electronegativity of X; the greater the electronegativity, the shorter will be the wavelength of absorption.

Simple thioketones of the dialkyl- or alkylaryl types are unstable and generally exist as trimers. Thiobenzophenone is monomeric as are compounds in which the thione group is attached to an electron-donating group such as $—NR_2$. The $n \rightarrow \pi^*$ transition of the C=S group in thioketones occurs at a longer wavelength than the analogous C=O transition because the energy of the nonbonding electron pair of the sulfur atom lies at a higher level than the corresponding electrons of the oxygen atom. Compounds containing the C=S group also display intense bands in the 250–320 mμ region which presumably arise from $\pi \rightarrow \pi^*$ and $n \rightarrow \sigma^*$ transitions in the C=S group.

The $n \rightarrow \pi^*$ bands of several thiocarbonyl compounds are summarized in Table XV.

Table XV** $n \rightarrow \pi^*$ **Transitions in Thiocarbonyl Compounds

COMPOUND	$n \rightarrow \pi^*$ TRANSITION (R-BAND)	
	λ_{max} (mμ)	log ϵ_{max}
Thiobenzophenone	599	2.81
Thioacetamide	358	1.25
Thiourea	291 (*s*)	1.85

(*s*) shoulder.

Benzene Chromophore

Benzene displays three absorption bands: 184 mμ (ϵ_{max} 60,000), 204 mμ (ϵ_{max} 7900), and 256 mμ (ϵ_{max} 200). These bands originate from $\pi \rightarrow \pi^*$ transitions. The intense band near 180 mμ results from an allowable transition, whereas the weaker bands near 200 and 260 mμ result from forbidden transitions in the highly symmetrical benzene molecule. Different notations have been used to designate the absorption bands of benzene; these are summarized in Table XVI. We shall use the designation of *E* and *B* bands employed by Braude.

Table XVI** **Benzene Bands

184 mμ	204 mμ	256 mμ	REF.
180	200	260	8
E^1	E_2	B	4
—	K	B	24
$A_{1g} \rightarrow E_{1u}$	$A_{1g} \rightarrow B_{1u}$	$A_{1g} \rightarrow B_{2u}$	6
Second Primary	First Primary	Secondary	32, 33

The *B*-band of benzene and many of its homologs is characterized by considerable fine structure. This is particularly true of spectra determined in the vapor phase or in nonpolar solvents. The fine structure originates from sub-levels of vibrational absorption upon which the electronic absorption is superimposed (Figure 7, p. 166). In polar solvents, interactions between solute and solvent tend to reduce the fine structure.

Substitution of alkyl groups on the benzene ring produces a bathochromic shift of the *B*-band, but the effect of alkyl substitution upon the *E*-bands is not clearly defined. The absorption characteristics of the *B*-bands of several alkylbenzenes are presented in Table XVII.

Table XVII** **Absorption Data for Alkylbenzenes (B-Bands)

COMPOUND	λ_{max} (mμ)*	ϵ_{max}
Benzene	256	200
Toluene	261	300
m-Xylene	262.5	300
1,3,5-Trimethylbenzene	266	305
Hexamethylbenzene	272	300

* λ_{max} of most intense peak in band with fine structure.

The bathochromic shift is attributed to hyperconjugation in which the σ-electron of an alkyl C—H bond participate in resonance with the ring. The methyl group is more effective in hyperconjugation than other alkyl groups.

H^+
H—C=(ring)$^-$
H

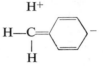

The addition of a second alkyl group into the molecule is most effective in producing a red shift if it is in the *para* position. The *para* isomer absorbs at the longest wavelength with the largest ϵ_{max}. The *ortho* isomer generally absorbs at the shortest wavelength with reduced ϵ_{max}. This effect is attributed to steric interactions between the *ortho* substituents which effectively reduces hyperconjugation.

Substitution on the benzene ring of auxochromic groups (OH, NH_2, etc.) shifts the *E*- and *B*-bands to longer wavelengths, frequently with intensification of the *B*-band and loss of its fine structure, because of *n*-π conjugation (Table XVIII.)

Conversion of a phenol to the corresponding anion results in a bathochromic shift of the E_2- and *B*-bands and an increase in ϵ_{max} because an additional pair of nonbonding electrons in the anion is available for interaction with the π-electron system of the ring. When aniline is converted to the anilinium cation, the pair of nonbonding electrons of aniline is no longer available for interaction with the π-electrons of the ring, and a spectrum almost identical to that of benzene results.

Confirmation of a suspected phenolic structure may be obtained by comparison of the ultraviolet spectra obtained for the compound in neutral and in alkaline solution (pH 13). Similar confirmatory information for a suspected aniline derivative may be obtained by a comparison of spectra determined in neutral and acid solution (pH 1).

Interaction between the nonbonding electron pair(s) of a heteroatom attached to the ring and the π-electrons of the ring is most effective when the *p* orbital of the nonbonding electrons is parallel to the π orbitals of the

Table XVIII Effect of Auxochromic Substitution on the Spectrum of Benzene

	E_2-BAND		B-BAND		
COMPOUND	λ_{max} (mμ)	ϵ_{max}	λ_{max} (mμ)	ϵ_{max}	SOLVENT
Benzene	204	7,900	256	200	Hexane
Chlorobenzene	210	7,600	265	240	Ethanol
Thiophenol	236	10,000	269	700	Hexane
Anisole	217	6,400	269	1,480	2% Methanol
Phenol	210.5	6,200	270	1,450	Water
Phenolate anion	235	9,400	287	2,600	Aq. alkali
o-Catechol	214	6,300	276	2,300	Water (pH 3)
o-Catecholate anion	236.5	6,800	292	3,500	Water (pH 11)
Aniline	230	8,600	280	1,430	Water
Anilinium cation	203	7,500	254	160	Aq. acid
Diphenyl ether	255	11,000	272	2,000	Cyclohexane
			278	1,800	

ring. Thus, bulky substitution in the ortho position of molecules such as N,N-dimethylaniline causes a hypsochromic shift in the E_2-band, accompanied by a marked reduction in ϵ_{max}.

N,N-Dimethylaniline	λ_{max} 251	ϵ_{max} 15,500
2-Methyl-N,N-dimethylaniline	λ_{max} 248	ϵ_{max} 6360

Direct attachment of an unsaturated group (chromophore) to the benzene ring produces a strong bathochromic shift of the B-band, and the appearance of a K-band ($\epsilon_{max} > 10{,}000$) in the 200 to 250 m$\mu$ region. (Table XIX). The overlap of absorption positions of the K-band, and the displaced E-bands of auxochromically substituted benzenes, may lead to confusion in the interpretation of ultraviolet spectra. Generally E-bands are less intense. The B-bands are sometimes buried under the K-bands.

The data in Table XIX show that in certain structures, such as acetophenone and benzaldehyde, displaced B- and R-bands can still be recognized.

When auxochromic groups appear on the same ring as the chromophore, both groups influence the absorption. The influence is most pronounced when an electron donating group and electron attracting group are para to one another (complementary substitution) (Table XX).

The red shift and increase in intensity of the K-band are related to contributions of the following polar resonance forms:

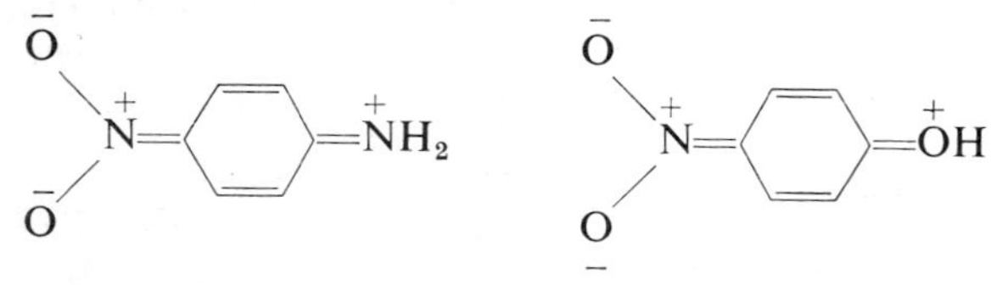

O^-, O^- $\overset{+}{N}$=(ring)=$\overset{+}{N}H_2$ O^-, O^- $\overset{+}{N}$=(ring)=$\overset{+}{O}H$

Biphenyl is the parent molecule of a series of compounds in which two aromatic rings are in conjugation. Resonance energy is at a maximum when the rings are coplanar and essentially zero when the rings are at 90° to one another.

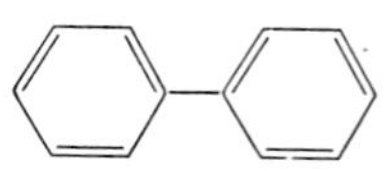

K-Band λ_{max} 252 ϵ_{max} 19,000
Biphenyl

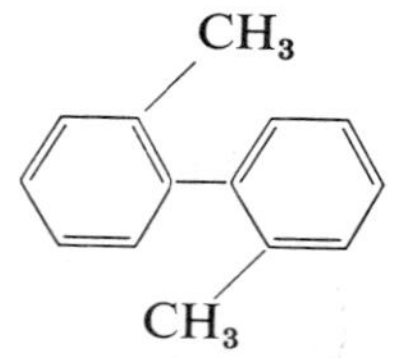

CH_3, CH_3
B-Band λ_{max} 270 ϵ_{max} 800
2,2′-Dimethylbiphenyl

The effect of forcing the rings out of coplanarity is readily seen from a comparison of the absorption characteristics of biphenyl and its 2,2′-dimethyl homolog whose absorption characteristics are similar to those of *o*-xylene.

Introduction of a methylene group between two chromophores is generally considered capable of destroying conjugation. In some diphenylmethanes, however, there is an effective overlap of π orbitals of the two rings resulting in homoconjugation. The absorption of 4-nitro-4′-methoxydiphenylmethane is not merely the sum of the absorption of *p*-nitrotoluene and *p*-methoxytoluene.

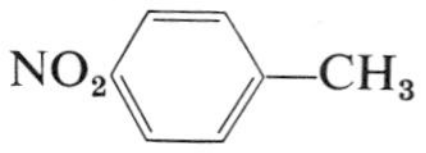

NO_2–(ring)–CH_3

λ_{max}	ϵ_{max}
274	9,490

CH_3–(ring)–OCH_3

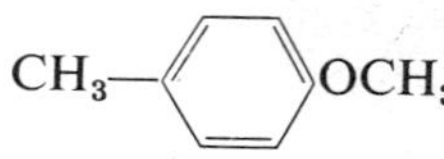

λ_{max}	ϵ_{max}
277	2,190
285.5	1,786

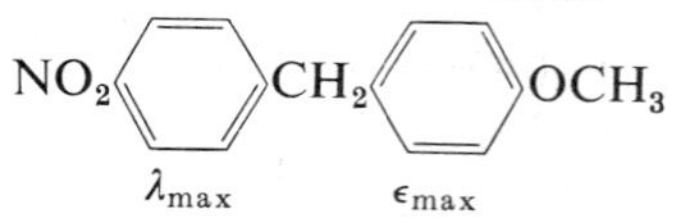

NO_2–(ring)–CH_2–(ring)–OCH_3

λ_{max}	ϵ_{max}
280	24,400
287	16,800

The first homolog in the diphenyl polyene series (ϕ-(C=C)$_n$-ϕ) is stilbene. Stilbene offers an interesting

Table XIX Absorption Characteristics of Chromophoric Substituted Benzenes

COMPOUND	*K*-BAND λ_{max} (mμ)	ϵ_{max}	*B*-BAND λ_{max} (mμ)	ϵ_{max}	*R*-BAND λ_{max} (mμ)	ϵ_{max}	SOLVENT
Benzene	...	...	255	215	...	...	Alcohol
Styrene	244	12,000	282	450	...	...	Alcohol
Phenylacetylene	236	12,500	278	650	...	...	Hexane
Benzaldehyde	244	15,000	280	1,500	328	20	Alcohol
Acetophenone	240	13,000	278	1,100	319	50	Alcohol
Nitrobenzene	252	10,000	280	1,000	330	125	Hexane
Benzoic acid	230	10,000	270	800	...	...	Water
Phenyl cyanide	224	13,000	271	1,000	...	...	Water
Diphenyl sulfoxide	232	14,000	262	2,400	...	...	Alcohol
Phenyl methyl sulfone	217	6,700	264	977			...
Benzophenone	252	20,000			325	180	Alcohol
Biphenyl	246	20,000	submerged		...	...	Alcohol
Stilbene(*cis*)	283	12,300*	submerged		...	...	Alcohol
Stilbene(*trans*)	295†	25,000*	submerged		...	...	Alcohol

* Intense bands also occur in the 200–230 mμ region.
† Most intense band of fine structure.

example of steric effects in electronic spectra.

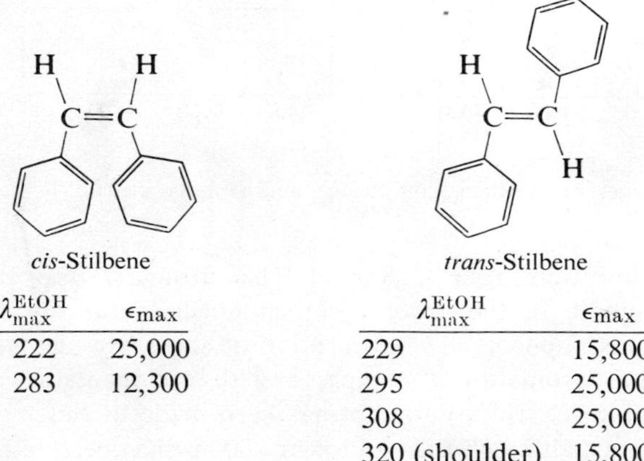

cis-Stilbene

λ_{max}^{EtOH}	ϵ_{max}
222	25,000
283	12,300

trans-Stilbene

λ_{max}^{EtOH}	ϵ_{max}
229	15,800
295	25,000
308	25,000
320 (shoulder)	15,800

The destruction of coplanarity by steric interference, in the *cis*-structure, is reflected by the lowered intensity of the 283-mμ band compared with the corresponding band (295 mμ) in the *trans* isomer. The *B*-band appears to be swamped by this intense absorption.

The absorption bands of the parent stilbene molecule move to longer wavelengths and increase in intensity as n, in ϕ-(CH=CH)$_n$-ϕ, increases. When n equals 7, the molecule absorbs in the 400–465 region with ϵ_{max} 135,000.

Two common series of aromatic compounds are the linear series such as anthracene and the angular series such as phenanthrene. Although the polynuclear aromatics might well be treated as individual chromophores, a correlation between the bands of benzene and the acenes, such as naphthalene, can be made.[3] These correlations appear in Table XXI.

Table XX Absorption Characteristics of Disubstituted Benzenes

COMPOUND	*K*-BAND λ_{max}	ϵ_{max}	*B*-BAND λ_{max}	ϵ_{max}
o-NO_2 Phenol	279	6,600	351	3,200
m-NO_2 Phenol	274	6,000	333	1,960
p-NO_2 Phenol	318	10,000	submerged	
o-NO_2 Aniline	283	5,400	412	4,500
m-NO_2 Aniline	280	4,800	358	1,450
p-NO_2 Aniline	381	13,500	submerged	

As the number of condensed rings increases in the acene series the absorption moves to progressively longer wavelengths until it occurs in the visible region

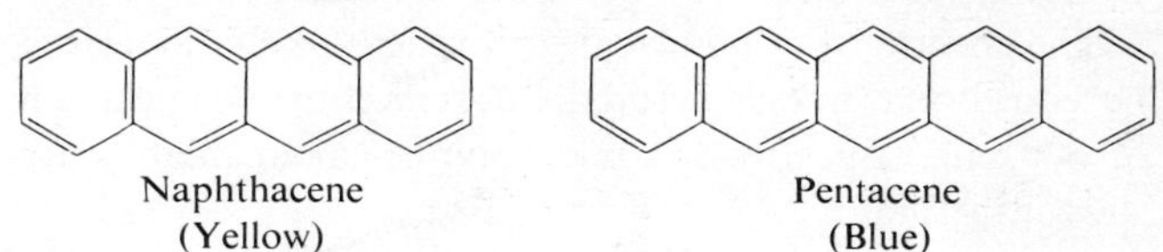

Naphthacene (Yellow) Pentacene (Blue)

Table XXI Correlation of Aromatic Absorption

COMPOUND	E_1-BAND λ_{max} (ϵ_{max})	E_2-BAND λ_{max} (ϵ_{max})	*B*-BAND λ_{max} (ϵ_{max})	λ_{max} (ϵ_{max})
Benzene	184 (60,000)	204 (7900)	256 (200)	
Naphthalene	221 (133,000)	286 (9300)	312 (289)	
Anthracene	256 (180,000)	375 (9000)	Submerged	221 (14,500)

The angular polycyclic compounds, the phenenes, also show a bathochromic shift of the three band system with

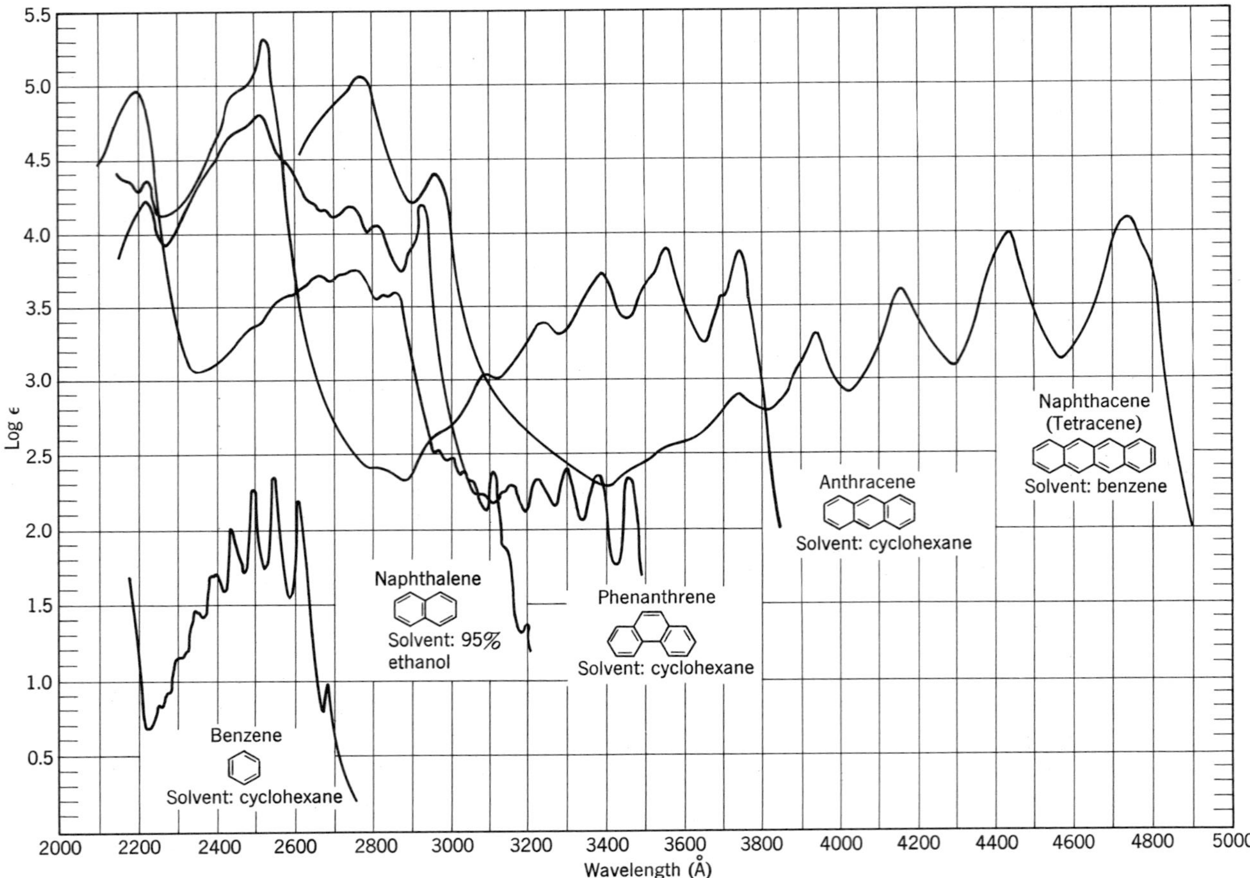

Fig. 7. Electronic absorption spectra of benzene, naphthalene, phenanthrene, anthracene, and naphthacene.

an increase in the number of rings. However, the increase in λ_{max}, per ring added, is less than for the acenes. The three band system is still distinct for phenanthrene but in the spectrum of anthracene the E_2-band has already swamped the *B*-band.

The spectra of polynuclear aromatics are characterized by vibrational fine-structure as observed in the spectrum of benzene. Spectra of some polynuclear aromatics are shown in Figure 7.

Heteroaromatic Compounds

Saturated five- and six-membered heterocyclic compounds are transparent at wavelengths longer than 200 mμ. Only the unsaturated heterocyclic compounds (heteroaromatics) show absorption in the near ultraviolet region.

FIVE MEMBERED RINGS. There is no agreement in the theoretical interpretation of the spectra of five-membered-ring heteroaromatic compounds. The absorption of these compounds has been compared to that of cyclopentadiene, the *cis*-diene analog, which shows strong diene absorption near 200 mμ and moderately intense absorption near 238 mμ. The aromatic properties increase in the order cyclopentadiene, furan, pyrrole, and thiophene. The absorption of some five-membered heteroaromatics is compared with cyclopentadiene in Table XXII. No attempt has been made to classify the bands, although the band near 200 mμ has been likened to the E_2-band of benzene, and the long wavelength band frequently has fine structure analogous to the *B*-band of benzene.

Auxochromic or chromophoric substitution of the five-membered unsaturated heterocyclics causes a bathochromic shift and an increase in the intensity of the bands of the parent molecule (Table XXIII).

SIX MEMBERED RINGS. The spectrum of pyridine is similar to that of benzene. The *B*-band of pyridine, however, is somewhat more intense and has less distinct fine structure than that of benzene (Figure 8). This transition is allowed for pyridine, but forbidden for the symmetrical benzene molecule. The weak *R*-band expected for an $n \rightarrow \pi^*$ transition in pyridine has been observed in vapor phase spectra. This band is generally swamped by the more intense *B*-band when the spectrum is determined in solution.

An increase in solvent polarity has little or no effect

***Table XXII* Absorption Data for Some Five-Membered Heteroaromatics**

COMPOUND	BAND I λ_{max}	BAND I ϵ_{max}	BAND II λ_{max}	BAND II ϵ_{max}	SOLVENT
Cyclo-pentadiene	200	10,000	238.5	3,400	Hexane
Furan	200	10,000	252	1*	Cyclohexane
Pyrrole†	211	15,000	240	300*	Hexane
Thiophene	231	7,100	269.5	1.5*	Hexane
Pyrazole	214	3,160	...	...	Ethanol

* These weak bands may be due to impurities rather than a forbidden transition ($n \rightarrow \pi^*$) of a heteroaromatic molecule.[34]

† See Table XXIII for different assignment of bands in the spectrum of pyrrole.

on the position or intensity of the *B*-band of benzene, but produces a marked hyperchromic effect on the *B*-band of pyridine and its homologs. The hyperchromic effect undoubtedly results from hydrogen bonding

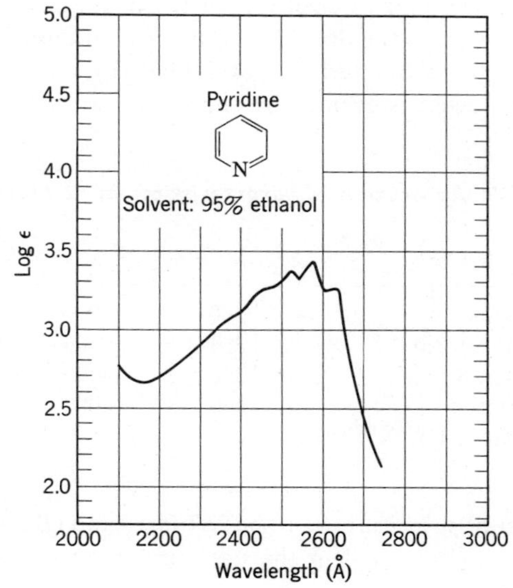

Fig. 8. Ultraviolet spectrum of pyridine.

***Table XXIII* Absorption Characteristics of Five-Membered Heteroaromatics[3]**

PARENT	SUBSTITUENT	BAND I λ_{max} (mμ)	BAND I ϵ_{max}	BAND II λ_{max} (mμ)	BAND II ϵ_{max}
Furan		200	10,000	252	1
Furan	2-CHO	227	2,200	272	13,000
Furan	2-C(=O)—CH_3	225	2,300	270	12,900
Furan	2-COOH	214	3,800	243	10,700
Furan	2-NO_2	225	3,400	315	8,100
Furan	2-Br, 5-NO_2	...	...	315	9,600
Pyrrole		183	...	211	15,000
Pyrrole	2-CHO	252	5,000	290	16,600
Pyrrole	2-C(=O)—CH_3	250	4,400	287	16,000
Pyrrole	2-COOH	228	4,500	258	12,600
Pyrrole	2-C(=O)O—Et 3-Me 4Et 5-CHO	231	14,200	303	21,100
Pyrrole	1-C(=O)—CH_3	234	10,800	288	760
Thiophene		231	7,100	...	...
Thiophene	2-CHO	265	10,500	279	6,500
Thiophene	2-C(=O)—CH_3	252	10,500	273	7,200
Thiophene	2-COOH	249	11,500	269	8,200
Thiophene	2-NO_2	268–272	6,300	294–298	6,000
Thiophene	2-Br	236	9,100	...	...

through the lone pair of electrons of the nitrogen atom. The extreme case is the absorption of a pyridinium salt. The absorption characteristics of 2-methylpyridine (α-picoline), in several solvents, are shown in Table XXIV.

Table XXIV Absorption Characteristics of 2-Methylpyridine

SOLVENT	λ_{max} (mμ)	ϵ_{max}
Hexane	260	2000
Chloroform	263	4500
Ethanol	260	4000
Water	260	4000
Ethanol-HCl(4:1)	262	5200

The effect of substitution on the 257 mμ band (*B*-band) of pyridine is illustrated in the data presented in Table XXV.

Table XXV Absorption Characteristics of Pyridine Derivatives

DERIVATIVE	$\lambda_{max}^{(pH>7)}$	ϵ_{max}
Pyridine	257	2,750
	270	450
2-CH_3	262	3,560
3-CH_3	263	3,110
4-CH_3	255	2,100
2-F	257	3,350
2-Cl	263	3,650
2-Br	265	3,750
2-I	272	400
2-OH	230	10,000
	295	6,300
4-OH	239	14,100
3-OH	260	2,200

The absorption of the 2-OH and 4-OH pyridines is attributed to the pyridone structures. Tautomerism in hydroxy- and aminopyridines is discussed thoroughly in Reference 2.

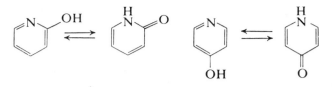

The spectra of heteroaromatics appear to be related to their isocyclic analogs (Table XXVI).

The spectra of the diazines are similar to those of pyridine (Figure 9). In addition to the enhanced *B*-band, still retaining some fine structure, the enhanced $n \rightarrow \pi^*$ bands are quite prominent.

The absorption of the diazines, for example the pyrazines, respond to solvent polarity in a manner

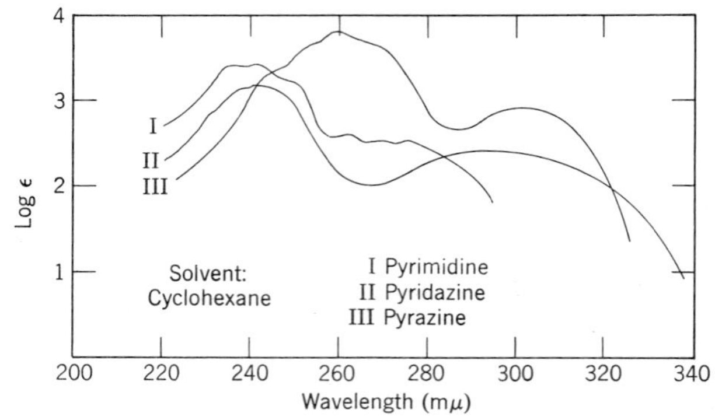

Fig. 9.

similar to the pyridines. The *B*-band undergoes a hyperchromic shift with an increase in solvent polarity with little or no effect upon λ_{max}. The *R*-band, of course, disappears in acid solution since the nonbonding electrons of the free base are now involved in salt formation.

Table XXVI Absorption Characteristics of Some Heteroaromatics Containing Nitrogen and Their Isocyclic Analogs

COMPOUND	E_1-BAND*		E_2-BAND*		*B*-BAND*		SOLVENT
	λ_{max} (mμ)	ϵ_{max}	λ_{max} (mμ)	ϵ_{max}	λ_{max} (mμ)	ϵ_{max}	
Benzene	184	60,000	204	7,900	256	200	...
Naphthalene	221	100,000	286	9,300	312	280	...
Quinoline	228	40,000	270	3,162	315	2,500	Cyclohexane
iso-Quinoline	218	63,000	265	4,170	313	1,800	Cyclohexane
Anthracene	256	180,000	375	9,000	...	...	...
Acridine	250	200,000	358	10,000	...	...	Ethanol

* All of the bands frequently contain fine structure.

References

1. Gillam, A. E., and E. S. Stern, *An Introduction to Electronic Absorption Spectroscopy in Organic Chemistry*, 2nd ed., Edward Arnold, London, 1957.
2. Scott, A. I., *Interpretation of the Ultraviolet Spectra of Natural Products*, Pergamon Press (The Macmillan Co.), New York, 1964.
3. Jaffé, H. H., and Milton Orchin, *Theory and Application of Ultraviolet Spectroscopy*, John Wiley, New York, 1962.
4. Braude, E. A., "Ultra-Violet Light Absorption and the Structure of Organic Compounds," *Ann. Repts. on Progress Chem.*, Chemical Society of London, Vol. XLII (1945), pp. 105–30.
5. Braude, E. A., "Ultraviolet and Visible Light Absorption," Chap. 4, pp. 131–94, in *Determination of Organic Structures by Physical Methods*, Academic Press, New York, 1955.
6. Duncan, A. B. F., and F. A. Matsen, "Electronic Spectra in the Visible and Ultraviolet," Vol. IX, pp. 581–706, in *Technique of Organic Chemistry*, A. Weissberger, Ed., Interscience, New York, 1956.
7. Bauman, R. P., *Absorption Spectroscopy*, John Wiley, New York, 1962.
8. Rao, C. N. R., *Ultra-Violet and Visible Spectroscopy, Chemical Applications*, Butterworths, London, 1961.
9. Brand, J. C. D., and G. Eglinton, *Applications of Spectroscopy to Organic Chemistry*, Oldbourne, London, 1965.
10. Phillips, J. P., *Spectra Structure Correlation*, Academic Press, New York, 1964.
11. Forbes, W. F., Chap. I in *Interpretive Spectroscopy*, S. K. Freeman, Ed., Reinhold Publishing Corp., New York, N.Y. 1965.
12. *Ultraviolet Reference Spectra*, Sadtler Research Laboratories, 3314–20 Spring Garden St., Philadelphia, Pa. Each spectrum presented on $8\frac{1}{2}'' \times 11''$ page.
13. *Electronic Spectral Data*, Vol. I, M. J. Kamlet, Ed., Interscience, New York, 1960. Covers literature 1946–1952.
14. *Organic Electronic Spectral Data*, Vol. II, H. G. Ungnade, Ed., Interscience, New York, 1960. Covers literature 1953–1955.
15. *Organic Electronic Spectral Data*, Vol. IV, J. P. Phillips and F. C. Nachod, Ed., Interscience, New York, 1963. Covers literature 1958–1959.
16. Hershenson, H. M., *Ultraviolet Absorption Spectra*, Index for 1954–1957, Academic Press, New York, 1959.
17. Lang, L., *Absorption Spectra in the Ultraviolet and Visible Region*, Academic Press, New York, 1961–1965, 5 volumes.
18. *Ultraviolet Spectral Data*, Manufacturing Chemists Association Research Project, Carnegie Institute of Technology, Pittsburgh, Pa.
19. Friedel, R. A., and Milton Orchin, *Ultraviolet Spectra of Aromatic Compounds*, John Wiley, New York, 1951. Revised ed., 1958.
20. *Catalog of Ultraviolet Absorption Spectrograms*, American Petroleum Institute Project 44, Carnegie Institute of Technology, Pittsburgh, Pa.
21. ASTM Index to Ultraviolet and Visible Spectra. ASTM Technical Publication No. 357, American Society for Testing Materials, 1916 Race St., Philadelphia, Pa. (1963).
22. UV-Atlas of Organic Compounds, Photoelectric Spectrometry Group, London, and Institut für Spektrochemie und Angewandte Spektroskopie, Dortmund, Butterworths, London.
23. "Spectrometry Nomenclature," *Anal. Chem.*, **37**, 1814 (1965).
24. Burawoy, A., *Ber.*, **63**, 3155 (1930); *J. Chem. Soc.*, 1177 (1939).
25. Riddick, J. A., and E. E. Toops, Jr., "Organic Solvents," Vol. VII, p. 339, in *Technique of Organic Chemistry*, A. Weissberger, Ed., Interscience, New York, 1955.
26. Woodward, R. B., *J. Am. Chem. Soc.*, **63**, 1123 (1941).
27. Woodward, R. B., *ibid.*, **64**, 72, 76 (1942).
28. Frank, R. L., R. Armstrong, J. Kwiatek, and H. A. Price, *J. Am. Chem. Soc.*, **70**, 1379 (1948).

28a. Turner, R. B., and D. M. Voitle, *J. Am. Chem. Soc.*, **73**, 1403 (1951).

29. Fieser, L. M., and Fieser, M., *Natural Products Related to Phenanthrene*, Reinhold, New York, 1949, p. 184 ff.
30. Ferguson, N. F., and J. C. Nnadi, *J. Chem. Ed.*, **42**, 529 (1965).
31. Nielson, A. T., *J. Org. Chem.*, **22**, 1539 (1957).
32. Doub, L., and J. M. Vandenbelt, *J. Am. Chem. Soc.*, **69**, 2714 (1947).
33. Doub, L., and J. M. Vandenbelt, *J. Am. Chem. Soc.*, **71**, 2414 (1949).
34. Katritzky, A. R., Ed., Vol. II, *Physical Methods in Heterocyclic Chemistry*, Academic Press, New York and London, 1963.

CHAPTER 6

Sets of Spectra Translated into Compounds

In practice, identification of an organic compound begins with a history, and large areas are quickly excluded from further consideration. Since, with a few exceptions, we dispense with a history, the limits will be set as follows: The compounds are quite pure; they may contain carbon, hydrogen, oxygen, nitrogen, sulfur, and the halogens in any combination; since the table of isotope contributions runs only to a molecular weight of 250, the examples will be limited to this range. Within these restrictions, we can still cover a vast expanse of organic chemistry.

Additional information, usually a history, would probably be necessary to identify a compound that contained boron, silicon, or phosphorus in addition to the above elements. But it is hardly likely that a chemist would encounter such compounds without prior knowledge that these elements are present.

The interpreter and correlator of data has always lived on the edge of uncertainty. How pure is his compound, how reliable his data, how relevant his reference material? There are few unequivocal data, either spectrometric or chemical; thus there is no substitute for experience and a broad knowledge of chemistry. Nor is there a prescribed procedure. In general, we attempt as a first step to establish a molecular formula from the parent peak and the isotope contributions. In a number of cases, the parent peak is so small that the isotope contributions cannot be accurately measured. We settle for the molecular weight. In some cases, the parent peak may be missing. We then try to establish the molecular weight from other evidence. In many cases this can be done from the fragmentation pattern and from the other spectra at hand. In other cases, we may resort to preparation of appropriate derivatives, to other methods of obtaining molecular weights, or to other methods of determining elemental composition. Recent improvements in combustion analysis permit C, H, and N determinations on less than a milligram of sample.

We use the obvious features of one spectrum to bring out the more subtle aspects of another. The power of this methodology lies in the complementary features of the four spectra. Confirmation is obtained by comparison with the spectra of an authentic sample. Let us work through the twenty samples comprising this chapter.

We may not always come up with an unequivocal structure; nor do we in any system of organic analysis. However, we should at least be able to narrow down the possibilities to several structures (often isomers) and to indicate the steps required to complete the identification.

Mass spectra were obtained on the Consolidated Electrodynamics Corporation Model 21-103C. The lower limit of the fragmentation patterns is mass 20. Peaks of less than 3% relative intensity are not reported except for the parent and isotope peaks. Infrared spectra were run on the Perkin-Elmer Corporation Model 221 and 137. NMR spectra were run on the Varian Associates Model A-60, HR-60, and HA-100; samples were dissolved in carbon tetrachloride or deuterated chloroform, and 1% tetramethylsilane in the solution was used as a reference. Ultraviolet spectra were obtained from the literature, or were run on Applied Physics Corporation's Cary Model 14M at pH 7, pH 1, and pH 13. Only the pH 7 spectrum is recorded unless a change occurred at pH 1 or pH 13.

Infrared Spectrum

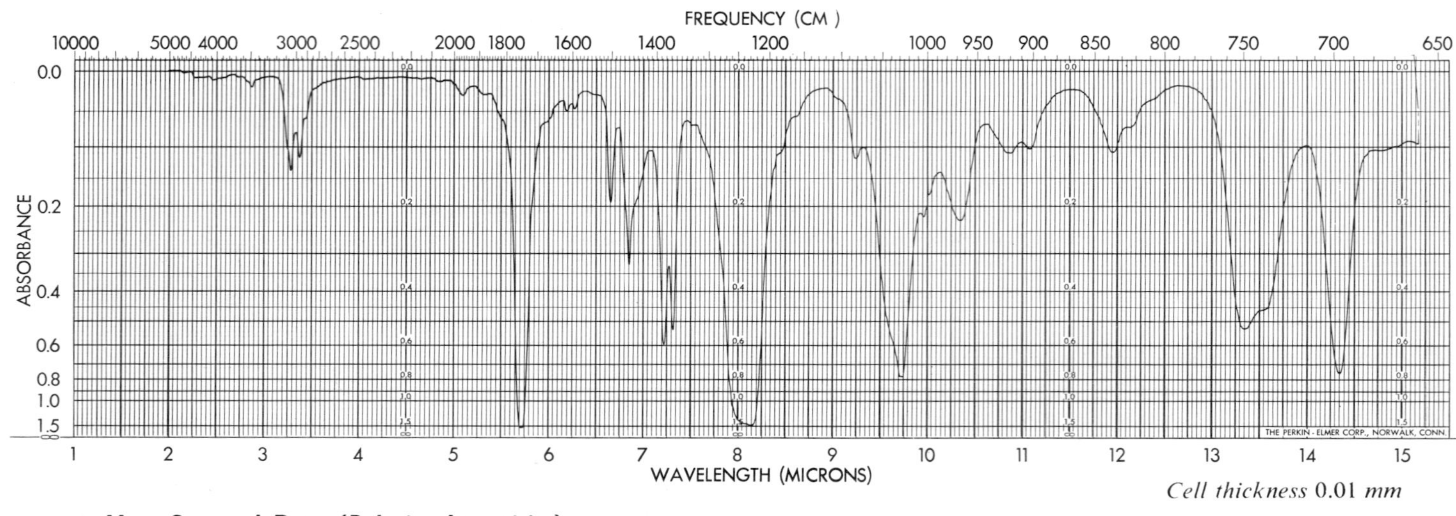

Cell thickness 0.01 *mm*

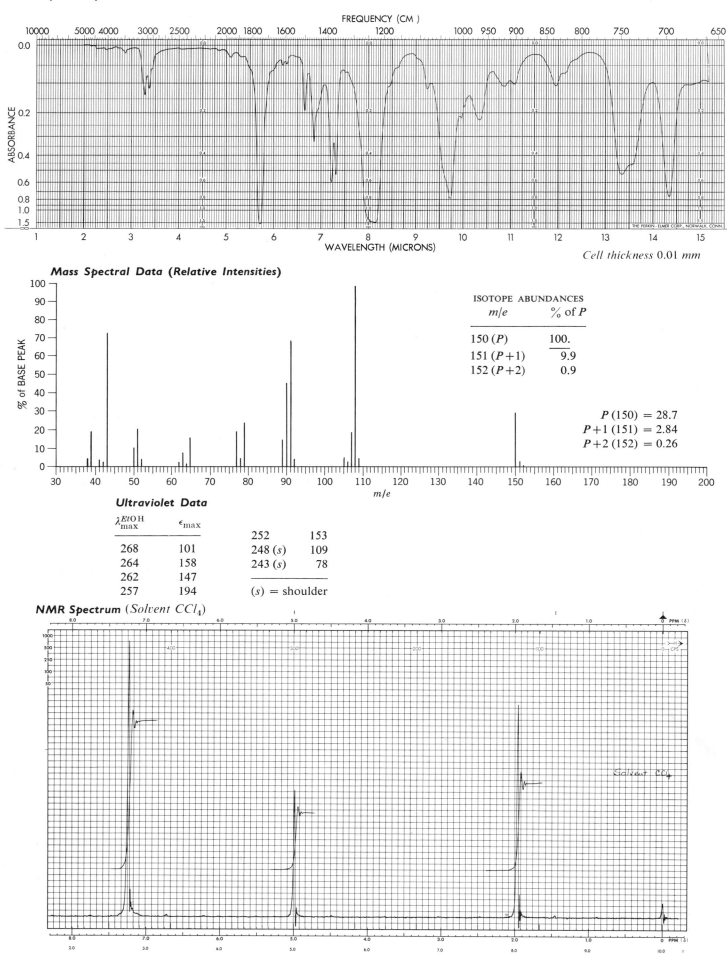

Mass Spectral Data (Relative Intensities)

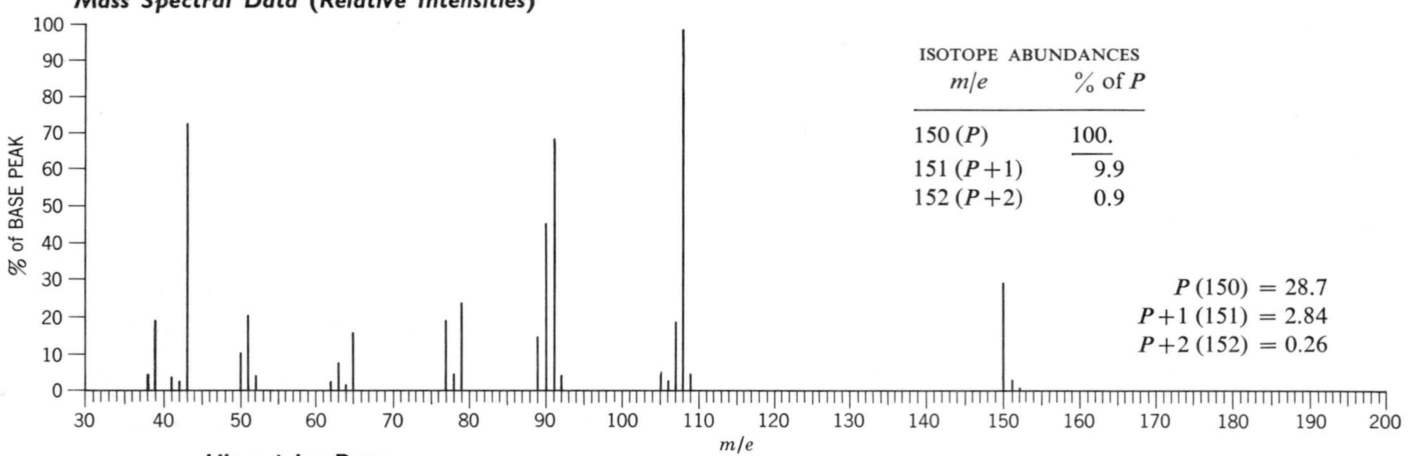

ISOTOPE ABUNDANCES

m/e	% of P
150 (P)	100.
151 (P+1)	9.9
152 (P+2)	0.9

P (150) = 28.7
P+1 (151) = 2.84
P+2 (152) = 0.26

Ultraviolet Data

λ_{max}^{EtOH}	ϵ_{max}
268	101
264	158
262	147
257	194
252	153
248 (s)	109
243 (s)	78

(s) = shoulder

NMR Spectrum (*Solvent* CCl_4)

Solvent CCl_4

COMPOUND NUMBER 1

The first step in translating these four spectra into a molecular structure is to establish a molecular formula. The parent peak is 150; this is the molecular weight. The parent peak is an even number. We are, therefore, permitted either no nitrogen atoms, or an even number of them. The $P+2$ peak obviously does not allow for the presence of sulfur or halogen atoms.

We now look in Appendix A of Chapter 2 under molecular weight 150, and find 29 formulas of molecular weight 150 containing only CHN and O. Our $P+1$ peak is 9.9% of the parent peak. We list the formulas whose calculated isotopic contribution to the $P+1$ peak falls—to be arbitrary—between 9.0 and 11.0; we also list their $P+2$ values:

FORMULA	$P+1$	$P+2$
$C_7H_{10}N_4$	9.25	0.38
$C_8H_8NO_2$	9.23	0.78
$C_8H_{10}N_2O$	9.61	0.61
$C_8H_{12}N_3$	9.98	0.45
$C_9H_{10}O_2$	9.96	0.84
$C_9H_{12}NO$	10.34	0.68
$C_9H_{14}N_2$	10.71	0.52

Three of these formulas can be eliminated because they contain an odd number of nitrogen atoms. The $P+2$ peak is 0.9% of the parent; this best fits $C_9H_{10}O_2$, which we shall tentatively designate as our molecular formula. We make a mental note that both the intensity of the parent peak, and the C-to-H ratio of the formula indicate aromaticity.

The infrared spectrum shows a C═O band at about 1745 cm^{-1} (5.73 μ). This, together with the presence of two O atoms in the formula, suggests an ester. We look for confirmation in the C—O—C stretching region and note the large broad band at about 1225 cm^{-1} (8.15 μ) characteristic of an acetate. Two large bands at about 749 cm^{-1} (13.35 μ) and 697 cm^{-1} (14.35 μ) suggest a singly substituted benzene ring.

The presence of a benzene ring and an acetate group is established. Furthermore, we note from the position of the carbonyl band that the C═O moiety is not conjugated with the ring. This is confirmed by the wavelengths and intensities of the ultraviolet absorption peaks which also eliminate a ketone from consideration. Subtraction of a singly substituted benzene ring and an acetate group from the molecular formula gives the following:

molecular formula	$C_9H_{10}O_2$
$C_6H_5 + CH_3\overset{\overset{\displaystyle O}{\|}}{C}—O$	$C_8H_8O_2$
remaining	CH_2

It takes no great imagination to insert the CH_2 between the ring and the acetate group, and write

$$C_6H_5—CH_2O\overset{\overset{\displaystyle O}{\|}}{C}CH_3$$

The NMR spectrum provides almost conclusive confirmation for the above structure. We see three sharp unsplit peaks in the following positions and with the following integrated intensities

τ	δ	INTENSITY
2.78	7.22	5
5.00	5.00	2
8.04	1.96	3

The five protons at δ 7.22, τ 2.78, of course, are the five benzene-ring protons. The singlet of two protons at δ 5.00, τ 5.00 represents the methylene group substituted by a phenyl and an ester group. And, of course, the singlet of three protons at δ 1.96, τ 8.04 represents the methyl group.

We can obtain additional confirmation by returning to the mass spectrum and considering the fragmentation pattern (see Appendix B, Chapter 2) in view of the information at hand. The base peak at 108 is a rearrangement peak representing cleavage of an acetyl group (43) and rearrangement of a single hydrogen atom (Chapter 2, p. 23). The large peak at mass 91 is the benzyl (or tropylium) ion formed by cleavage beta to the ring. And the large peak at mass 43, of course, represents the acetyl fragment. The peaks at 77, 78, and 79 are additional evidence for the benzene ring.

We can state with a high degree of confidence that the compound represented by these spectra is:

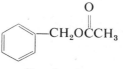

$$C_6H_5—CH_2O\overset{\overset{\displaystyle O}{\|}}{C}CH_3$$

Benzyl acetate

There are, of course, a number of other sequences to the identity of this compound. Having established the molecular fomula, we could note at once the characteristic benzene ring peak at δ 7.22, τ 2.78, in the NMR spectrum. We could confirm this by the typical "benzenoid" fine structure absorption in the ultraviolet spectrum. The base peak in the mass spectrum is a common rearrangement peak, and the mass 91 peak immediately calls to mind the benzyl (or tropylium) structure. The large mass 43 peak strongly suggests the CH_3CO group in view of the C=O peak in the infrared. Subtraction of a benzyl and an acetyl group from the formula leaves a mass of 16; consideration of the infrared spectrum leaves very little question as to how to handle this oxygen atom.

The student will find it instructive to write the possible isomeric structures and to eliminate them on spectrometric grounds.

Infrared Spectrum — Compound 6-2

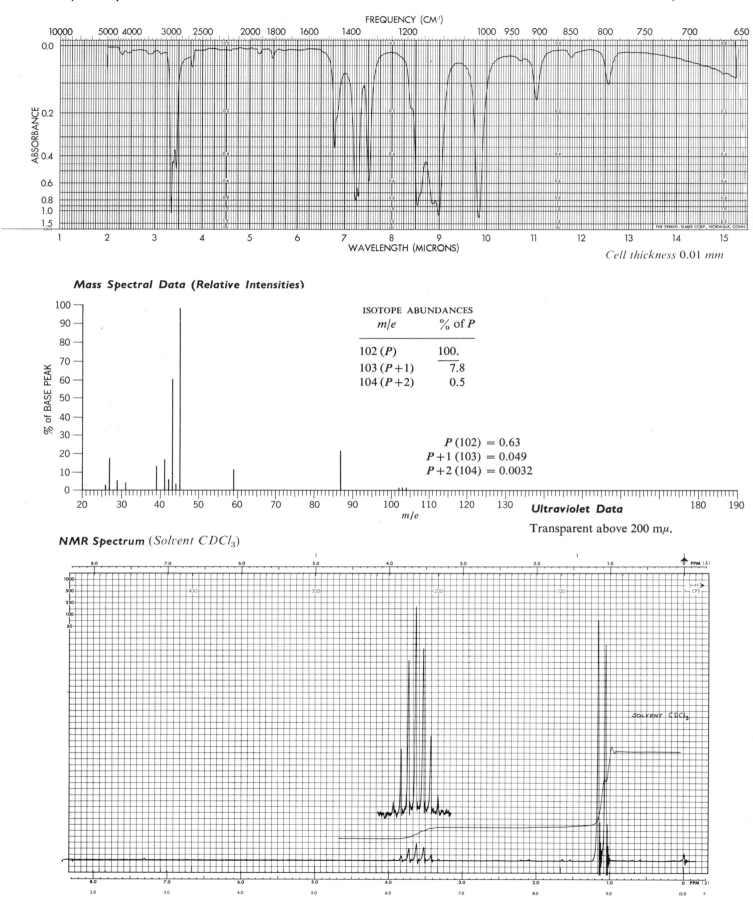

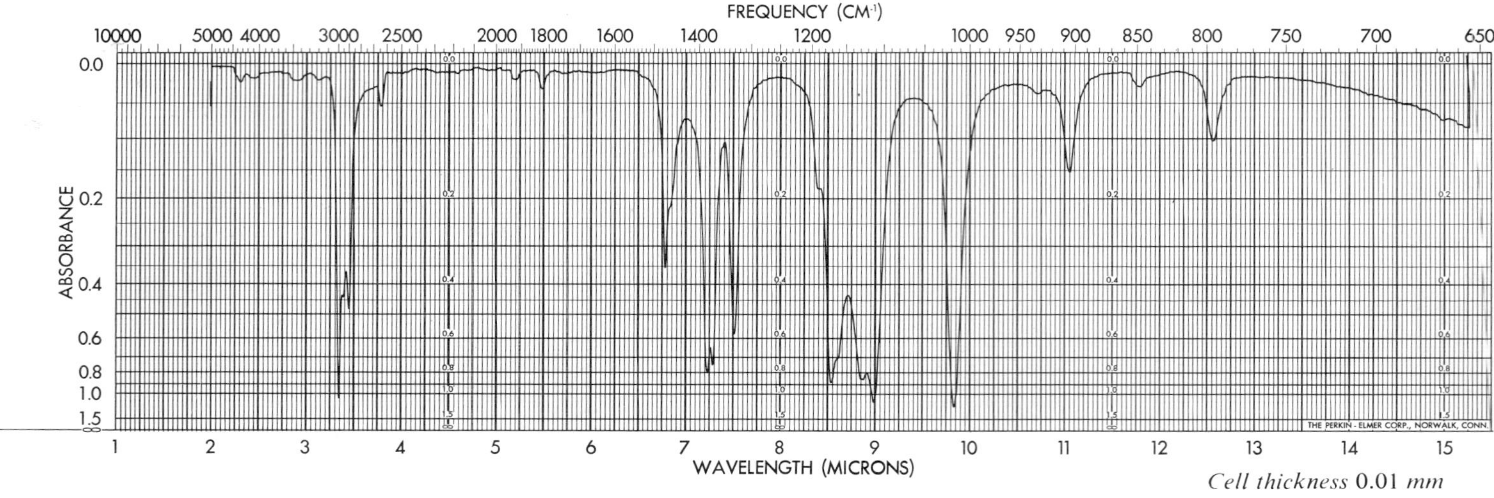

Cell thickness 0.01 *mm*

Mass Spectral Data (Relative Intensities)

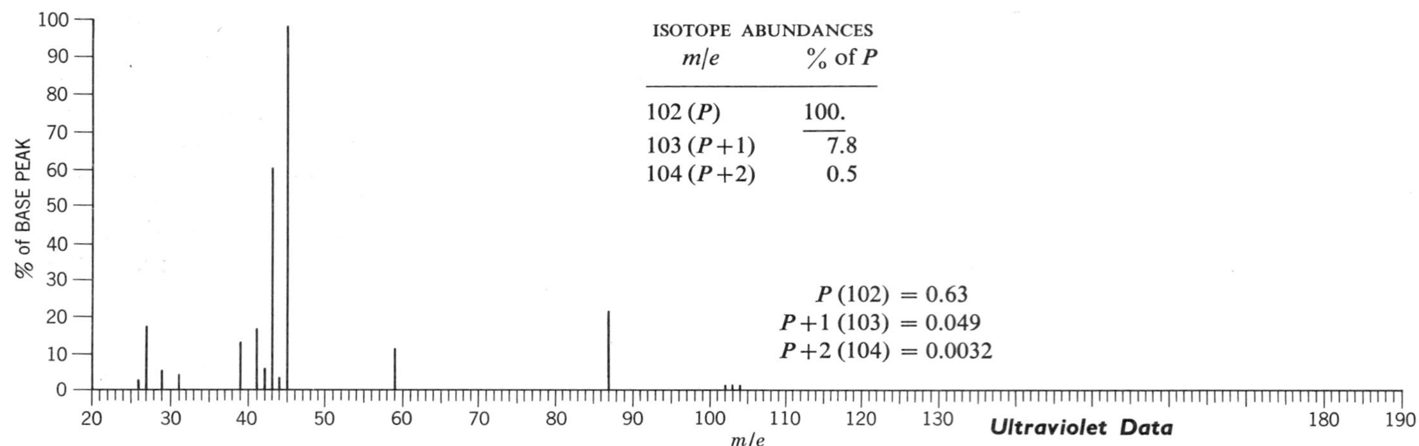

ISOTOPE ABUNDANCES

m/e	% of *P*
102 (*P*)	100.
103 (*P*+1)	7.8
104 (*P*+2)	0.5

$P\,(102) = 0.63$
$P+1\,(103) = 0.049$
$P+2\,(104) = 0.0032$

Ultraviolet Data

Transparent above 200 mμ.

NMR Spectrum (*Solvent CDCl$_3$*)

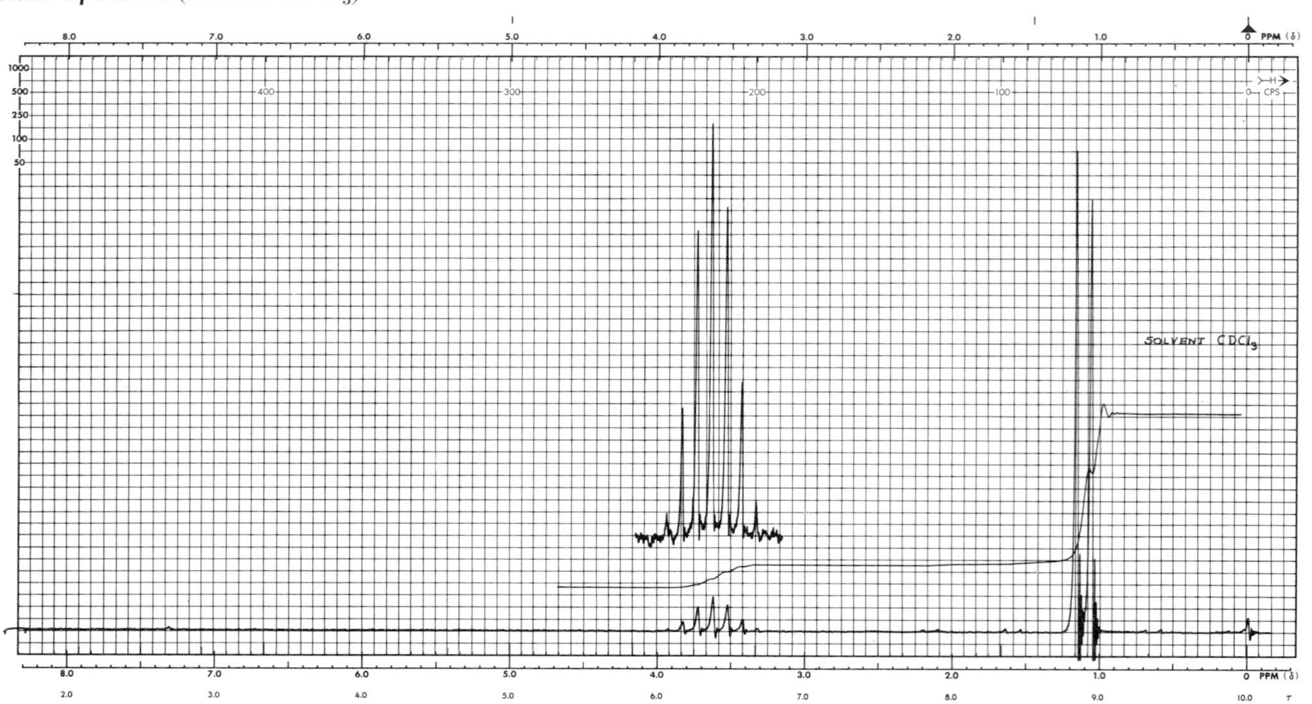

COMPOUND NUMBER 2

In accordance with our usual procedure, we write the possible molecular formulas (together with the $P+1$ and $P+2$ peaks) under the molecular weight, in this case, 102:

FORMULA	$P+1$	$P+2$
$C_5H_{14}N_2$	6.39	0.17
$C_6H_2N_2$	7.28	0.23
$C_6H_{14}O$	6.75	0.39
C_7H_2O	7.64	0.45
C_8H_6	8.74	0.34

The best fit to our $P+1$ (7.8) and $P+2$ (0.5) values is C_7H_2O. But this is a trivial formula as is $C_6H_2N_2$. The next best fit is $C_6H_{14}O$. We shall proceed on this basis. Sulfur or halogen is not permitted.

The compound is aliphatic on the basis of the C-to-H ratio, the general appearance of the IR spectrum (though the C—H stretch is at rather a high frequence), the lack of absorption in the ultraviolet spectrum, and the absence of peaks at low field in the NMR spectrum.

There is no carbonyl or hydroxyl absorption in the infrared spectrum. Since the formula requires an oxygen atom, we consider some type of ether, and look for C—O absorption which we find (split) at about 1130 to 1110 cm^{-1} (8.7 to 9.0 μ).

The NMR spectrum is quite definitive. The doublet and the symmetrical heptet in the integrated ratio of 6:1 spell out an isopropyl group. Obviously the molecule is symmetrical about the oxygen atom. We write:

$$\begin{array}{ccc} CH_3 & & CH_3 \\ & \diagdown \quad \diagup & \\ & CH—O—CH & \\ & \diagup \quad \diagdown & \\ CH_3 & & CH_3 \end{array}$$

Diisopropyl ether

The infrared doublet at 1380 cm^{-1} (7.23 μ) and 1370 cm^{-1} (7.28 μ) confirms the isopropyl group. The rather high-frequency C—H stretching peak is explained by the presence of the oxygen atom. The strong band at 1170 cm^{-1} (8.55 μ) is a C—C stretch intensified by branching.

The base peak (45) in the mass spectrum results from double cleavage with rearrangement of a hydrogen atom. This is prominent in α-substituted ethers. Removal of a methyl group accounts for the mass 87 peak. C—O cleavage with retention of the charge on the alkyl portion results in the large mass 43 peak. (See Chapter 2, p. 19.)

Infrared Spectrum

Compound 6-3

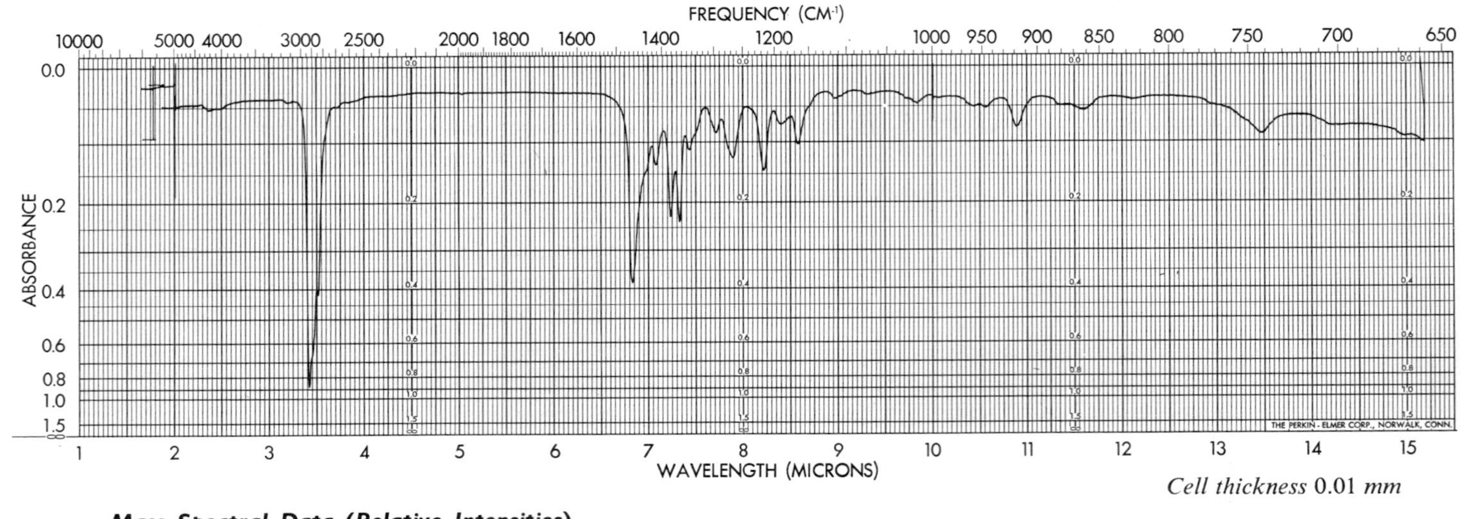

Cell thickness 0.01 *mm*

Mass Spectral Data (Relative Intensities)

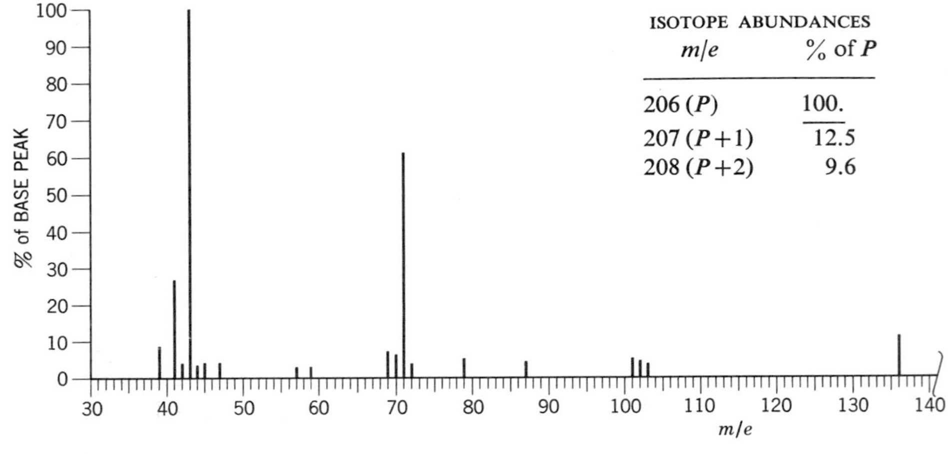

ISOTOPE ABUNDANCES

m/e	% of P
206 (P)	100.
207 ($P+1$)	12.5
208 ($P+2$)	9.6

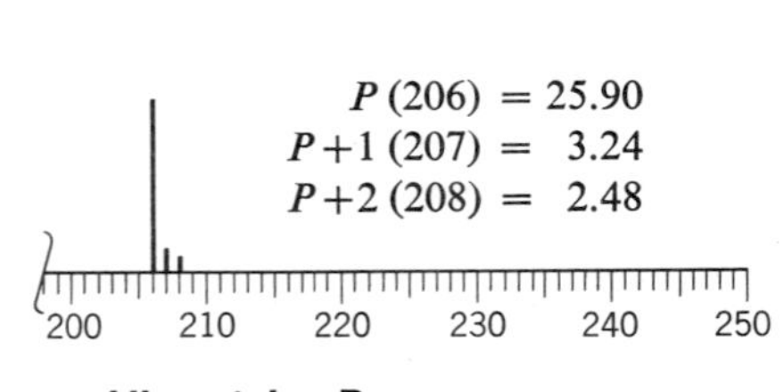

Ultraviolet Data

λ_{max}^{EtOH}	$\log \epsilon_{max}$
248	2.55

NMR Spectrum (*Solvent* $CDCl_3$)

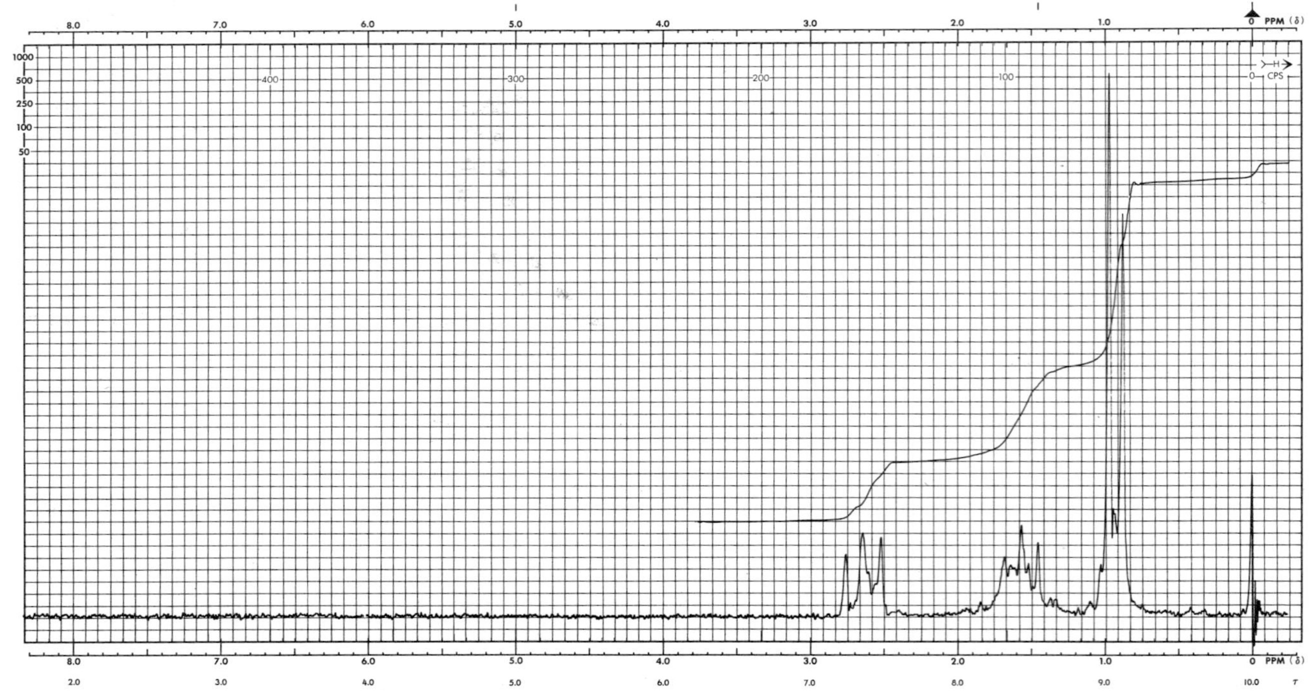

COMPOUND NUMBER 3

Following our usual practice, we strike immediately for the parent peak (206) and start to list possibilities under that molecular weight. But consideration of the $P+2$ peak brings us up short. Obviously, we are no longer dealing with compounds containing only C, H, O, and N. The $P+2$ peak is too small for a chlorine or a bromine atom (see Table II, Chapter 2) and too large for a sulfur atom. But it will accommodate two sulfur atoms very nicely.

We subtract the mass of two sulfur atoms from 206 and get 142, which is the weight of the rest of the molecule. We now compile the list of possibilities from the table under 142, using the $P+1$ peak (and, of course, the fact that 142 is an even number) to narrow the possible molecular formulas. The $P+1$ peak becomes 12.5 minus 2 × 0.78 which gives 10.9; this removes the contribution of the two ^{33}S atoms.

FORMULA	$P+1$
$C_{10}H_6O$	10.94
$C_{10}H_{22}$	11.16
$C_{11}H_{10}$	12.05

The infrared and the NMR spectra convey a strong impression that we are dealing with an aliphatic compound. The ultraviolet spectrum is not especially informative. The infrared gives no evidence for the presence of an oxygen atom; in fact, it is rather featureless save for the strong aliphatic C—H stretching bands at 2915 to 2841 cm^{-1} (3.43 to 3.52 μ), the CH_2 and CH_3 bending vibration at 1464 cm^{-1} (6.83 μ), and the twin peaks at 1381 and 1364 cm^{-1} (7.24 and 7.33 μ), which we may often associate with chain branching.

Although $C_{11}H_{10}$ is a possible formula, we can find no support for unsaturated character. We find no evidence for the presence of oxygen, so we write $C_{10}H_{22}S_2$.

The base peak, mass 43, in the mass spectrum allows us to write $CH_3CH_2CH_2$ or CH_3CHCH_3. We choose the latter for several reasons. A base peak is more likely to result from cleavage at a branch. The large doublet in the NMR spectrum is familiar as the methyl protons of an isopropyl group. We also associated a pair of peaks in the infrared spectrum with chain branching.

We note a slightly distorted triplet in the NMR spectrum centered on δ 2.65, τ 7.35. This represents two protons (possibly CH_2) if we assign six protons to the large methyl doublet. A sulfur atom adjacent to the methylene group would account for its downfield shift.

The integrator shows that the multiplet centered at about δ 1.55, τ 8.45 contains three protons. It cannot be a methyl group because that would have produced a quartet rather than a triplet at the downfield position. It must then be another methylene and contain the CH group whose proton is responsible for producing the large doublet upfield. The extraneous peaks in and around the triplet at δ 1.55, τ 8.45 must then belong to the CH proton. We now have enough information to write

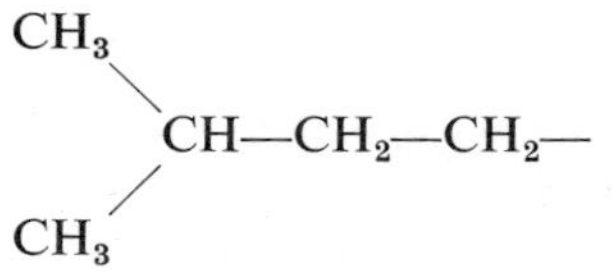

$$\begin{array}{l} CH_3 \\ \quad \diagdown \\ \quad\; CH—CH_2—CH_2— \\ \quad \diagup \\ CH_3 \end{array}$$

Since this is exactly one-half of the required weight of the alkyl portion, we may exercise a modicum of chemical sense and write the full structure

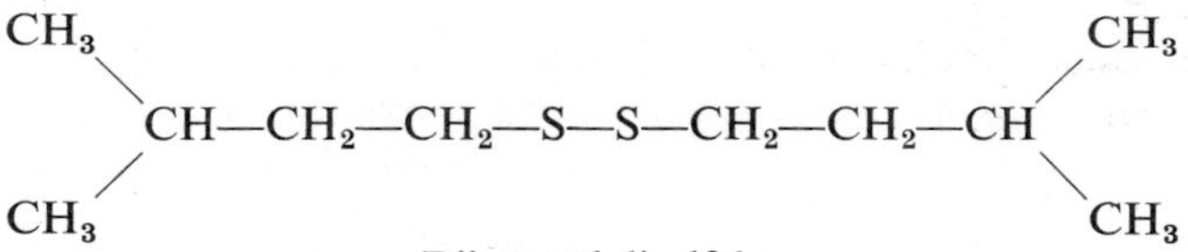

$$\begin{array}{lcr} CH_3 & & CH_3 \\ \quad\diagdown & & \diagup\quad \\ & CH—CH_2—CH_2—S—S—CH_2—CH_2—CH & \\ \quad\diagup & & \diagdown\quad \\ CH_3 & & CH_3 \end{array}$$

Diisoamyl disulfide

The fragmentation pattern, although complex, bears this structure out. The large peak at 71 represents cleavage next to the sulfur with retention of the charge on the alkyl fragment. The peak at 136 results from the same cleavage with shift of a hydrogen atom to the sulfur-containing fragment which retains the charge.

We have not rigorously proved that the two sulfur atoms are contiguous, although the ultraviolet spectrum supports the disulfide structure. But it would be difficult to write another structure to fit the spectra. We could carry out reductive cleavage and obtain conclusive spectral data on the resulting mercaptan.

Note the typical distortions in the NMR spectrum due to virtual coupling.

Infrared Spectrum

Compound 6-4

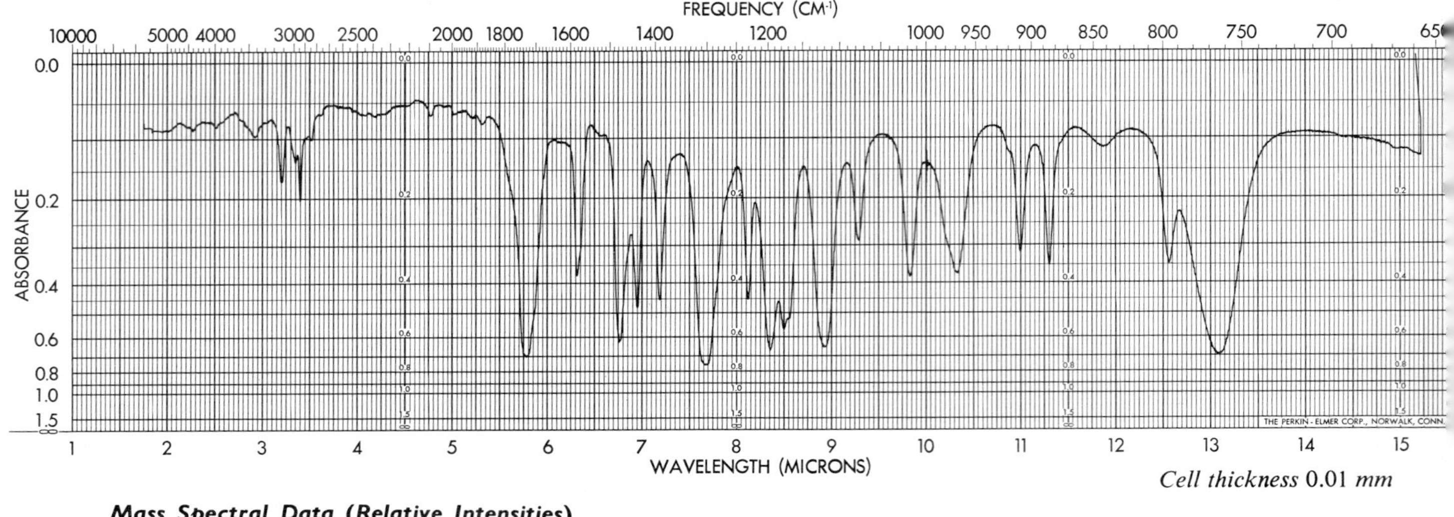

Cell thickness 0.01 *mm*

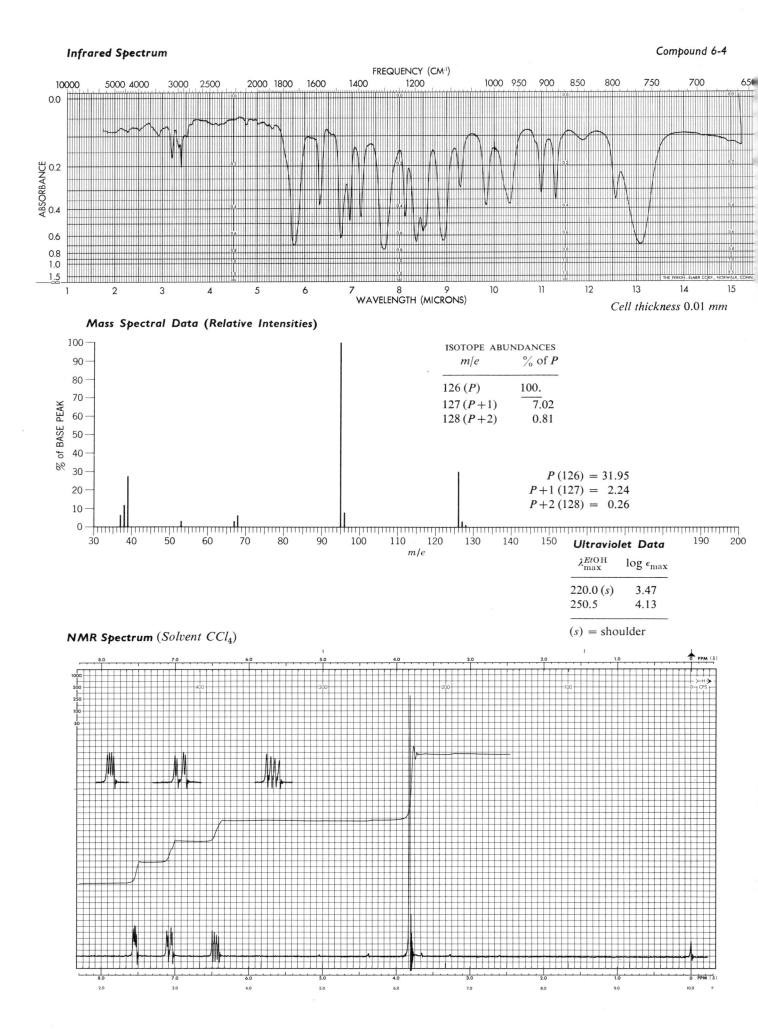

Mass Spectral Data (Relative Intensities)

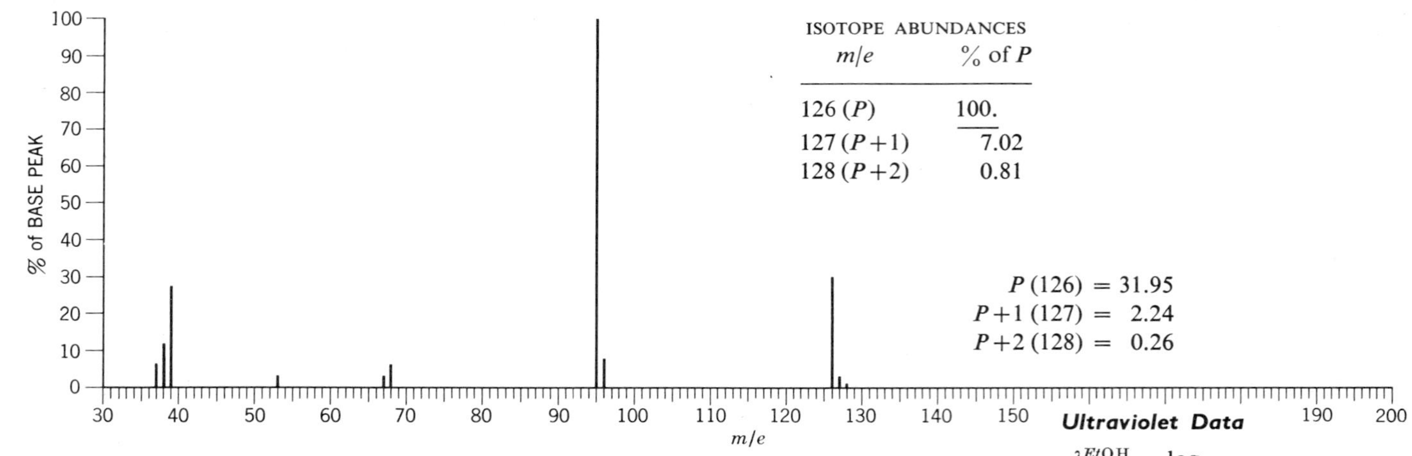

ISOTOPE ABUNDANCES

m/e	% of *P*
126 (*P*)	100.
127 (*P*+1)	7.02
128 (*P*+2)	0.81

P (126) = 31.95
$P+1$ (127) = 2.24
$P+2$ (128) = 0.26

Ultraviolet Data

λ_{max}^{EtOH}	$\log \epsilon_{max}$
220.0 (*s*)	3.47
250.5	4.13

(*s*) = shoulder

NMR Spectrum (*Solvent* CCl_4)

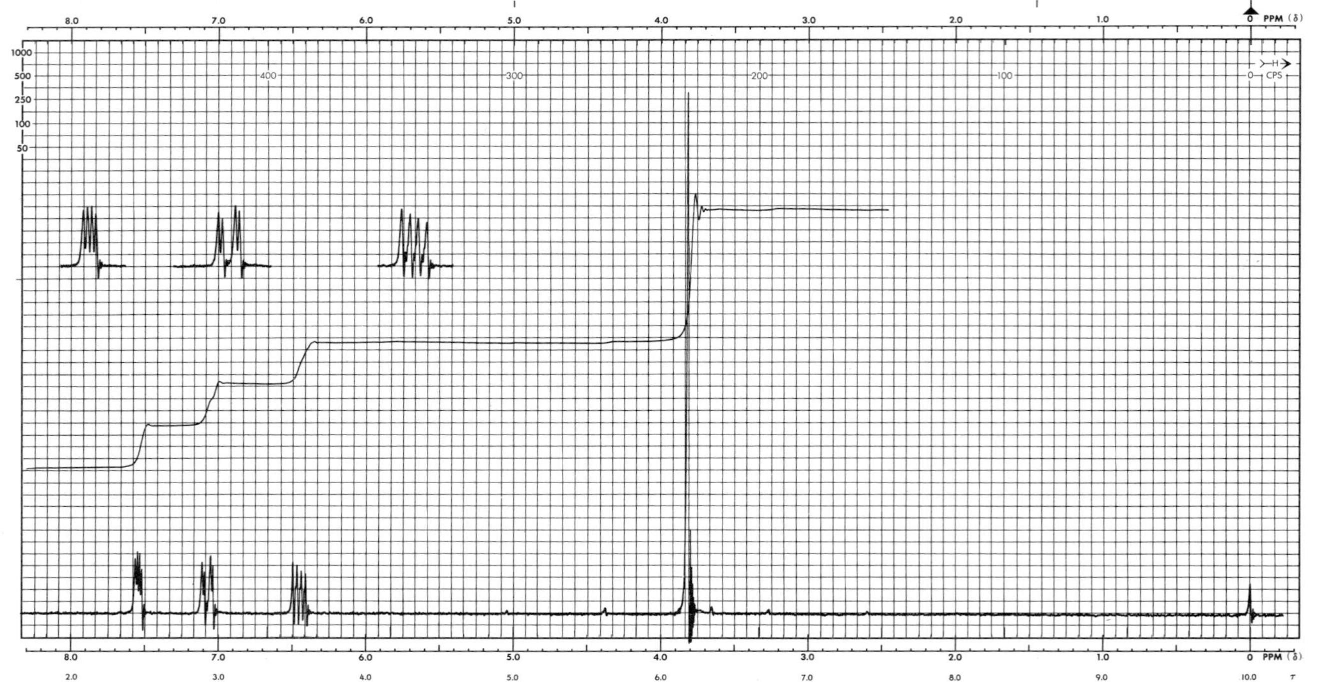

COMPOUND NUMBER 4

The following molecular formulas fit our data for the parent peak and the $P+1$ peak:

FORMULA	$P+1$	$P+2$
$C_5H_6N_2O_2$	6.34	0.57
$C_5H_{10}N_4$	7.09	0.22
$C_6H_6O_3$	6.70	0.79
$C_6H_{10}N_2O$	7.45	0.44

The formula that best fits our $P+2$ peak is $C_6H_6O_3$. We should bear in mind, however, that the $P+2$ peak may be higher than the calculated figure, and we accept $C_6H_6O_3$ only as a tentative formula.

The formula and the general appearance of the infrared spectrum suggest aromaticity. We note strong peaks beyond 800 cm^{-1} (12.5 μ), two strong peaks at 1587 cm^{-1} (6.30 μ) and 1479 cm^{-1} (6.76 μ), and a medium peak at 3106 cm^{-1} (3.22 μ). The intense band in the ultraviolet spectrum at 250 mμ is suggestive of a chromophore conjugated with an aromatic ring. The striking pattern at the low-field end of the NMR spectrum demands an aromatic ring of some sort.

A conspicuous feature of the infrared spectrum is the C=O peak at 1730 cm^{-1} (5.78 μ). Bearing in mind that we are probably dealing with a conjugated chromophore, we can make a choice between a ketone and an ester. We lean toward an ester because the conjugated ketone C=O bands are usually at lower frequency. We also look in vain for the long wavelength *R*-band of conjugated ketones in the ultraviolet spectrum. (We should recall, however, that heteroaromatic ketones do not show a detectable *R*-band.) There are a number of strong bands between 1420 and 1110 cm^{-1} (7.05 and 9.0 μ) some of which may be associated with an ester C—O absorption. And, of course, the empirical formula permits an ester group plus another oxygen.

Now we can profitably consider the base peak, mass 95, in the mass spectrum. The base peak arises from a loss of mass 31, and this loss is practically diagnostic for a methyl ester. We can write

Ar—C(=O) ⋮ —OCH$_3$
95

The mass 95 component then must be C_4H_3O—C=O, and we write the structural formula

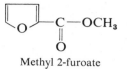

(furan ring)—C(=O)—OCH$_3$

Methyl 2-furoate

The NMR spectrum is nicely in accord with this structure. We see three separate ring-protons at low field, and the three protons of the methyl group as a sharp singlet at δ 3.81, τ 6.19. From low to high field the three low-field peaks (multiplets) represent the five-proton, the three-proton, and the four-proton, respectively. Each is shifted downfield, by the carboxylate substituent, from its position in an unsubstituted furan ring, the three-proton being most strongly affected.

These multiplets afford a tidy demonstration of spin-spin coupling. The system is *AMX* with three coupling constants. The five-proton is coupled with the four-proton (J_{54} = 2 cps) and with the three-proton (J_{53} = 1 cps). The five-proton, therefore, shows two pairs of peaks.

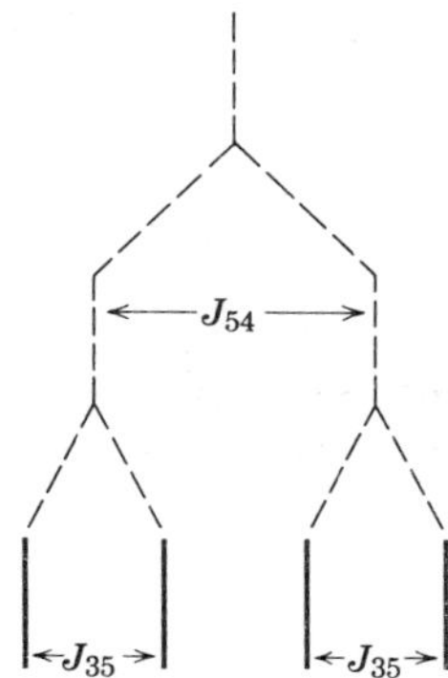

The three-proton is coupled with the four-proton (J_{34} = 3.5 cps) and with the five-proton (J_{35} = 1 cps). The three-proton, thus, shows two pairs.

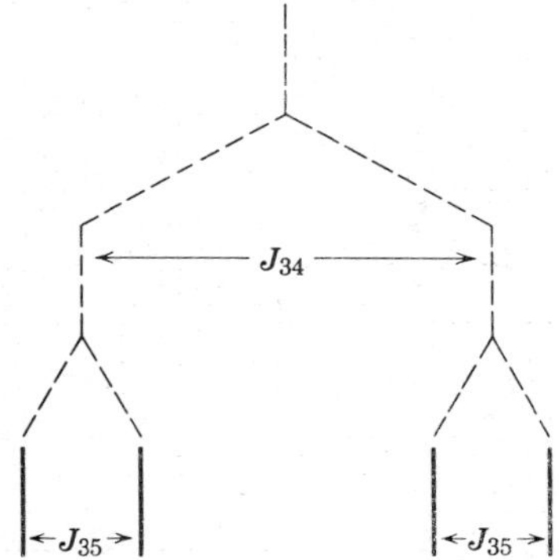

The four-proton is coupled with the three-proton (J_{43} = 3.5 cps) and with the five-proton (J_{45} = 2 cps).

Again we see two pairs.

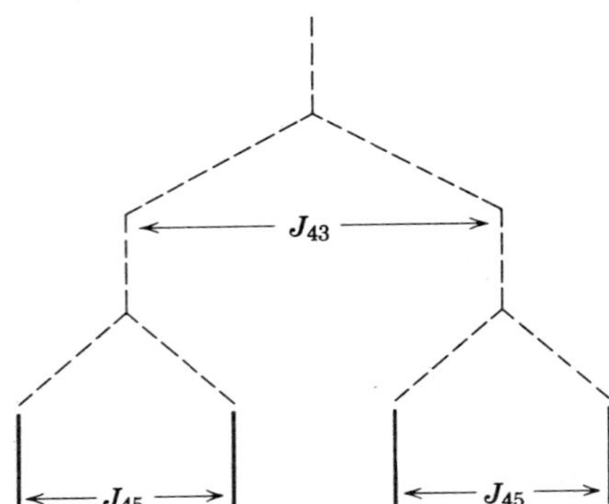

The couplings can be summed up as follows:

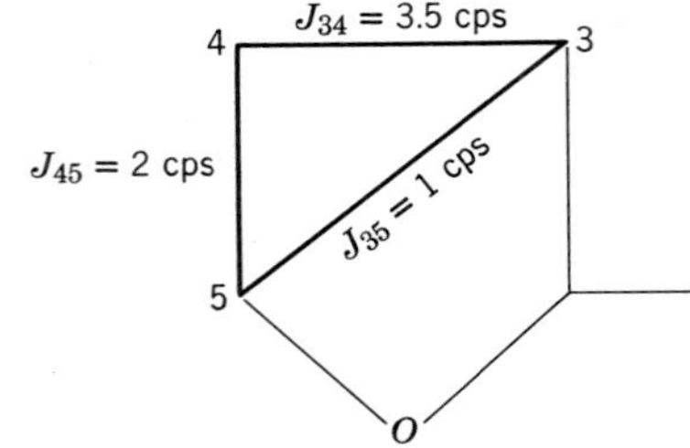

Note that methyl 3-furoate would give an entirely different NMR pattern.

Infrared Spectrum *Compound 6-5*

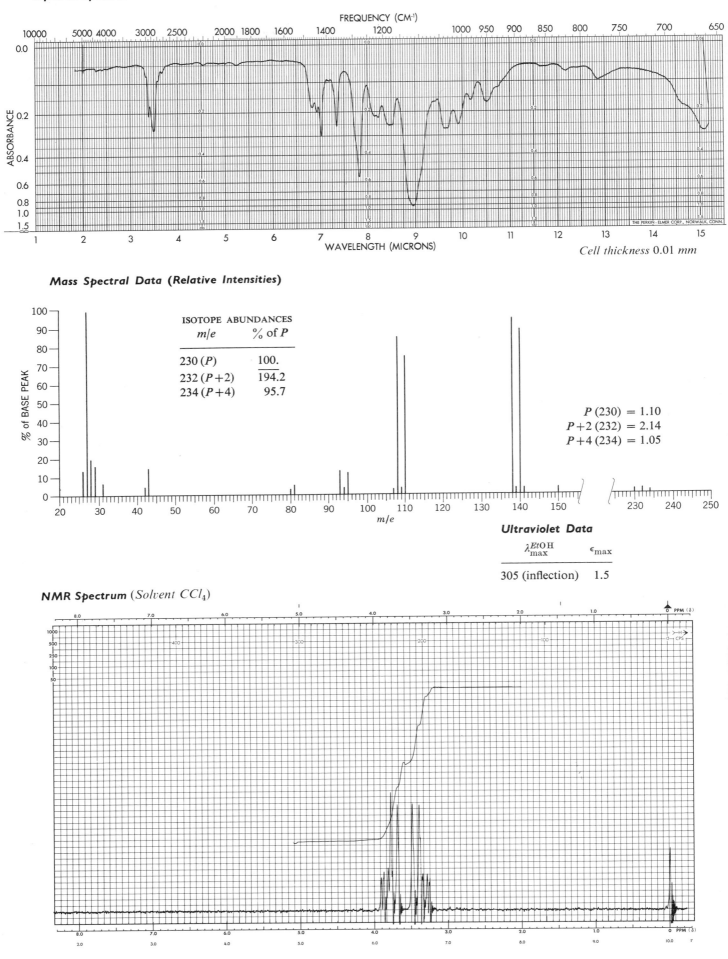

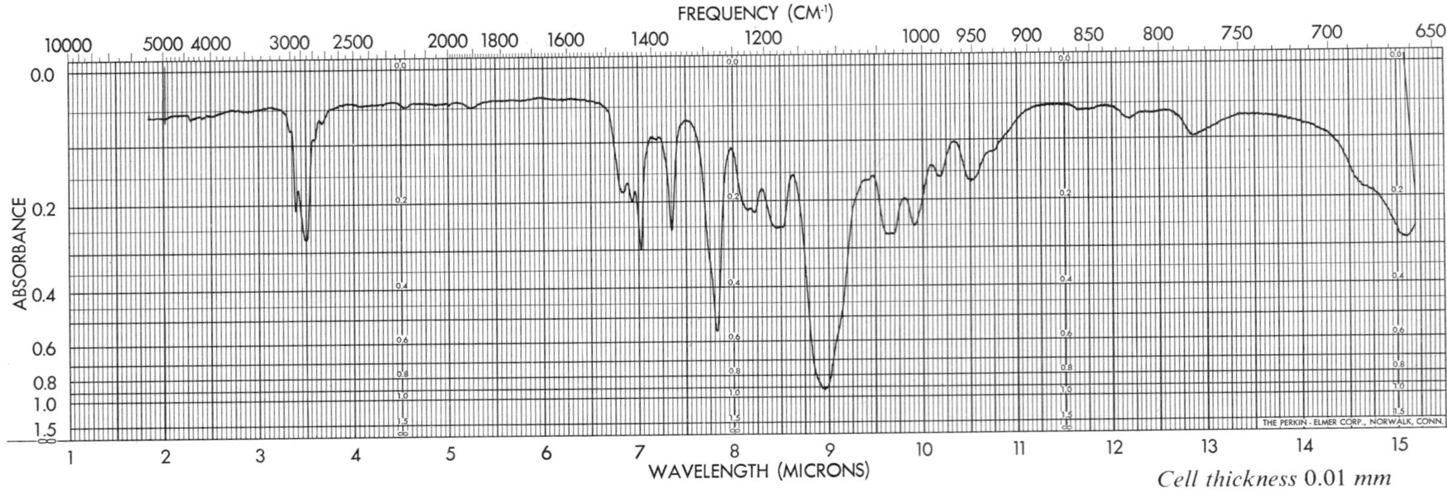

Cell thickness 0.01 *mm*

Mass Spectral Data (Relative Intensities)

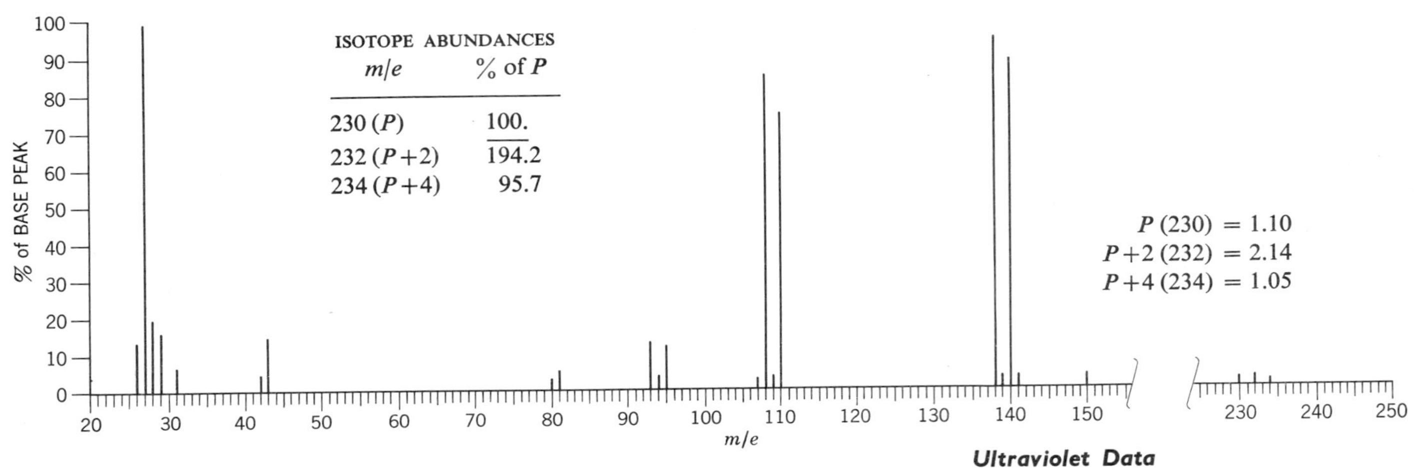

ISOTOPE ABUNDANCES

m/e	% of *P*
230 (*P*)	100.
232 (*P*+2)	194.2
234 (*P*+4)	95.7

P (230) = 1.10
P+2 (232) = 2.14
P+4 (234) = 1.05

Ultraviolet Data

λ_{max}^{EtOH}	ϵ_{max}
305 (inflection)	1.5

NMR Spectrum (*Solvent* CCl_4)

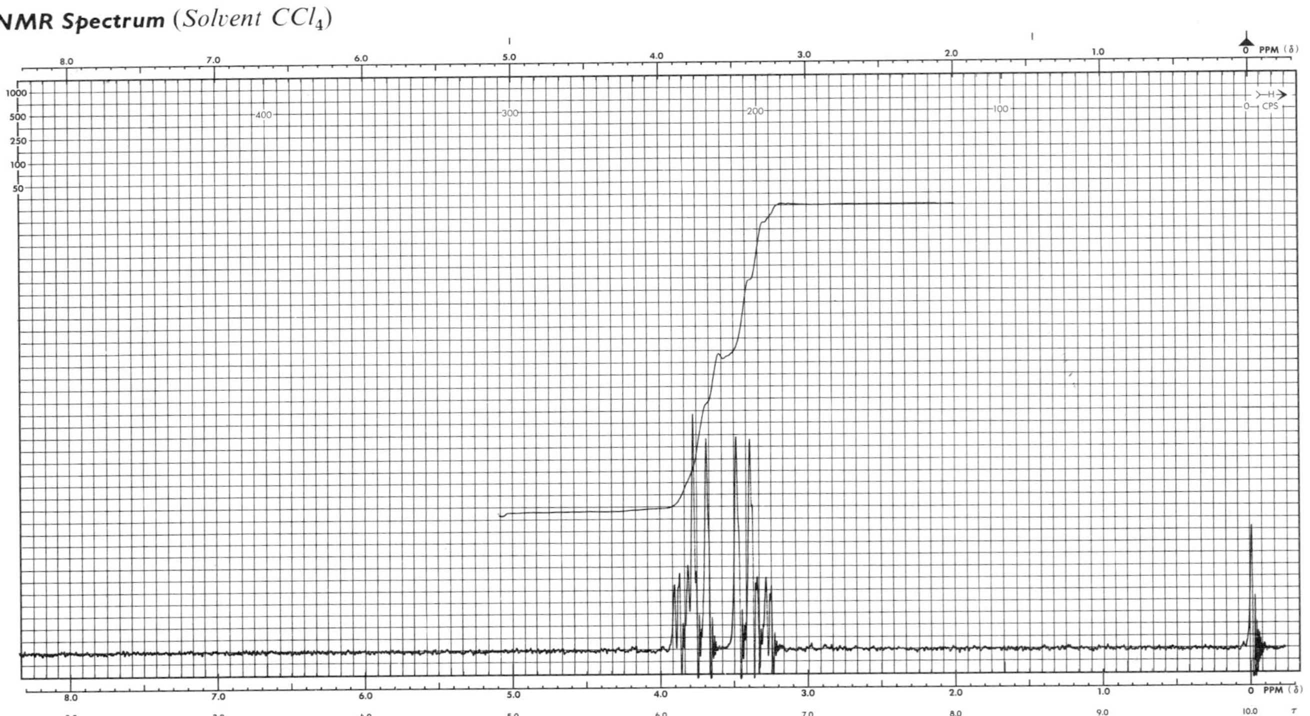

COMPOUND NUMBER 5

The characteristic $P+2$ and $P+4$ pattern indicates the presence of two bromine atoms. Subtracting 2×79 from the molecular weight leaves a mass of 72 for the rest of the molecule.

The strongest peak in the infrared spectrum at 1117 cm^{-1} (8.95 μ) strongly suggests an aliphatic ether. Since no nitrogen- or other oxygen-containing group appears to be present, we can assume, tentatively, that the remaining fragment is C_4H_8O. The weak inflection in the ultraviolet spectrum may simply result from the accumulation of atoms with nonbonding electrons.

The striking symmetry of the NMR spectrum suggests a symmetrical molecule. If we dispose our fragments, Br_2, —O—, and C_4H_8, in a symmetrical pattern, there are two possibilities

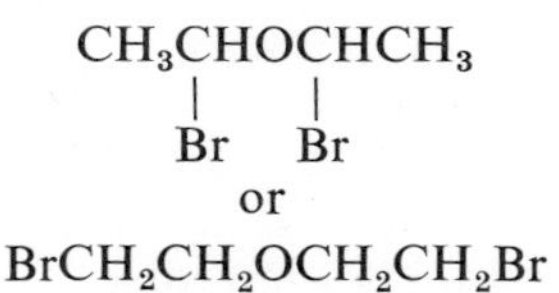

The first compound would give an A_3X NMR spectrum consisting of a one-proton quartet quite far downfield ($\delta \sim 5.0$, τ 5.0) and a doublet rather upfield ($\delta \sim 2.0$, τ 8.0). The second compound would give an A_2B_2 pattern in accord with that observed.

The fragmentation pattern, though complex, affords ample confirmation. Characteristic bromine-containing pairs are discernible at m/e 138 and 140 (loss of CH_2Br with H transfer), 108 and 110 (loss of OCH_2CH_2Br with H transfer), and 93 and 95 (CH_2Br^+).

The compound is

$$BrCH_2CH_2OCH_2CH_2Br$$

$\beta\beta'$-dibromodiethyl ether

The CH_2 adjacent to O is deshielded by O by about 2.15 units (the normal CH_2 absorption is δ 1.25, τ 8.75, and the position for CH_2O is δ 3.40, τ 6.60). This methylene group is also deshielded by the Br atom by about 0.48 units. Its calculated position, then, is about δ 3.88, τ 6.12, in fair agreement with the downfield absorption. Similarly, the position of the methylene adjacent to Br can be calculated to be about δ 3.40, τ 6.60, again in fair agreement with the upfield absorption. The strong peak in the infrared spectrum at 1279 cm^{-1} (7.82 μ) is attributed to a CH_2Br wag.

Infrared Spectrum

Compound 6-6

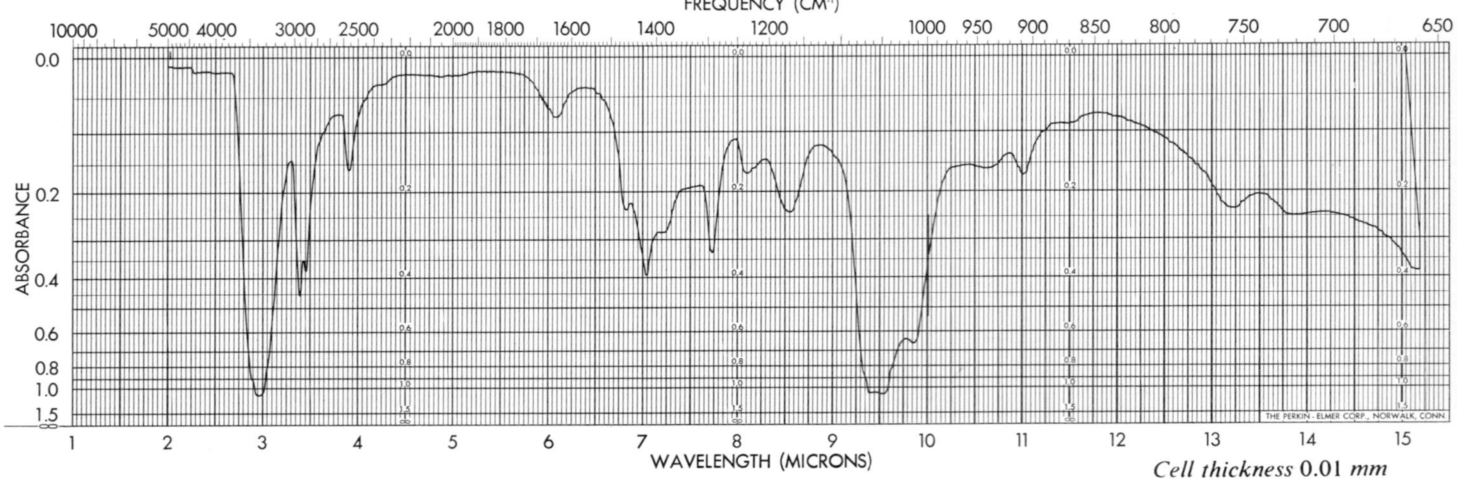

Cell thickness 0.01 *mm*

Mass Spectral Data (Relative Intensities)

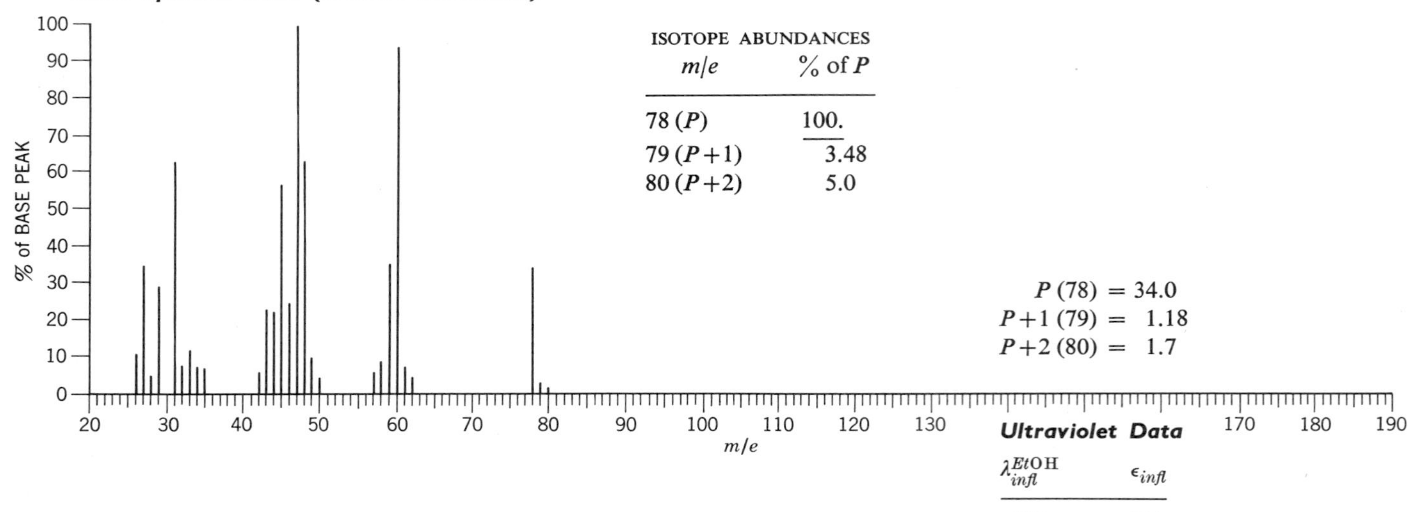

ISOTOPE ABUNDANCES

m/e	% of P
78 (P)	100.
79 ($P+1$)	3.48
80 ($P+2$)	5.0

P (78) = 34.0
$P+1$ (79) = 1.18
$P+2$ (80) = 1.7

Ultraviolet Data

λ_{infl}^{EtOH}	ϵ_{infl}
232	136

infl = inflection

NMR Spectrum (*Solvent* $CDCl_3$)

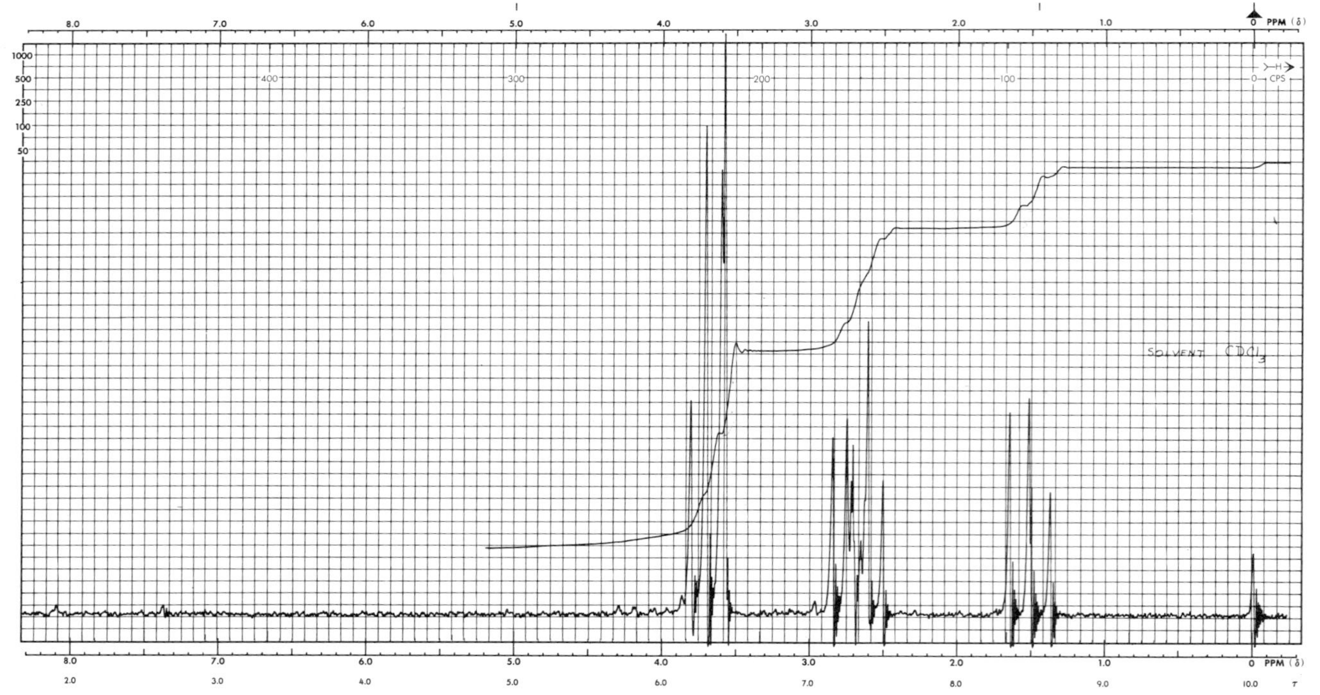

COMPOUND NUMBER 6

We immediately note the large $P+2$ peak which suggests that one sulfur atom is present. We then list the possible formulas under mass 46 (78−32). We should list all except the trivial formulas and those containing an odd number of N atoms; we also subtract 0.78 from the $P+1$ peak, which leaves 2.70. But this turns out to leave us with only a single choice, C_2H_6O. The molecular formula, therefore, is C_2H_6OS.

The infrared spectrum shows a strong, rather broad band at 3367 cm^{-1} (2.97 μ). Our impression is that we are dealing with an alcohol, and the very broad band at about 1050 cm^{-1} (9.5 μ) suggests a primary alcohol. Our attention is then caught by a rather weak band at 2558 cm^{-1} (3.91 μ), which practically spells out a mercaptan group. In this case, the infrared spectrometer is at some disadvantage with respect to the nose. Had this been a thin film spectrum, we might have missed the S—H stretching band.

We now have the fragments: CH_2OH and SH. This only leaves a CH_2 group to fit in, and we write

$HOCH_2CH_2SH$

2-Mercaptoethanol

Some of the major fragmentation peaks can be assigned as follows:

HO—CH_2—CH_2—SH (cleavage after HO: 60)

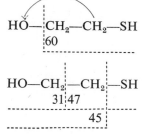

HO—CH_2—CH_2—SH (31 | 47; 45)

The NMR spectrum provides exhaustive confirmation for the structure written. It also shows a number of interesting features. The starting point is the distribution of protons as shown by the integration curve. If we assume that the triplet at the high-field position contains one proton, then the next cluster of peaks contains two protons, and the low-field peaks account for three protons. At first glance, this does not seem reasonable. But we must bear several things in mind. First, the positions of the OH peak and the SH peak depend on concentration. Since the OH-group forms stronger hydrogen bonds than the SH-group, it is likely to be further down-field at a given concentration. Second, the OH proton will undergo rapid exchange under normal condition and will usually appear as a single peak; the SH proton, under the same conditions will not exchange rapidly (at least in a nonaqueous solvent), and the peak will be split by the adjacent methylene group.

We see then that the upfield triplet (with slight second-order splitting of the middle peak) represents the SH proton coupled with (split by) the adjacent methylene group; the coupling constant is 8 cps. The adjacent methylene group is split into a doublet by the SH proton (coupling constant, of course, is 8 cps), and again into a triplet by the other methylene group with a coupling constant of 6 cps. This is a somewhat distorted A_2M_2X system with two coupling constants. An idealized diagram is as follows:

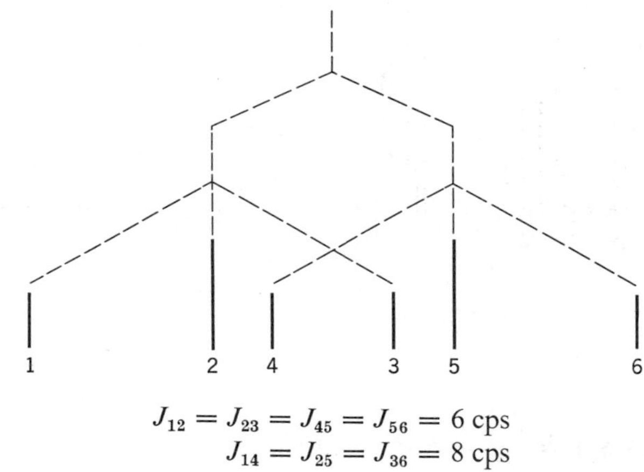

$$J_{12} = J_{23} = J_{45} = J_{56} = 6 \text{ cps}$$
$$J_{14} = J_{25} = J_{36} = 8 \text{ cps}$$

The low-field peaks must then consist of a triplet with a coupling constant of 6 cps, and it must also contain the OH-proton. We do indeed see a triplet with the upfield peak distorted by the peak of the OH proton with which it almost coincides. The hydroxyl proton peak can be shifted by change of concentration, solvent, or temperature. Both the OH and SH peaks can be removed by shaking with deuterium oxide; this, of course, would collapse the CH_2S multiplet to a triplet.

Compound 6-7

Infrared Spectrum

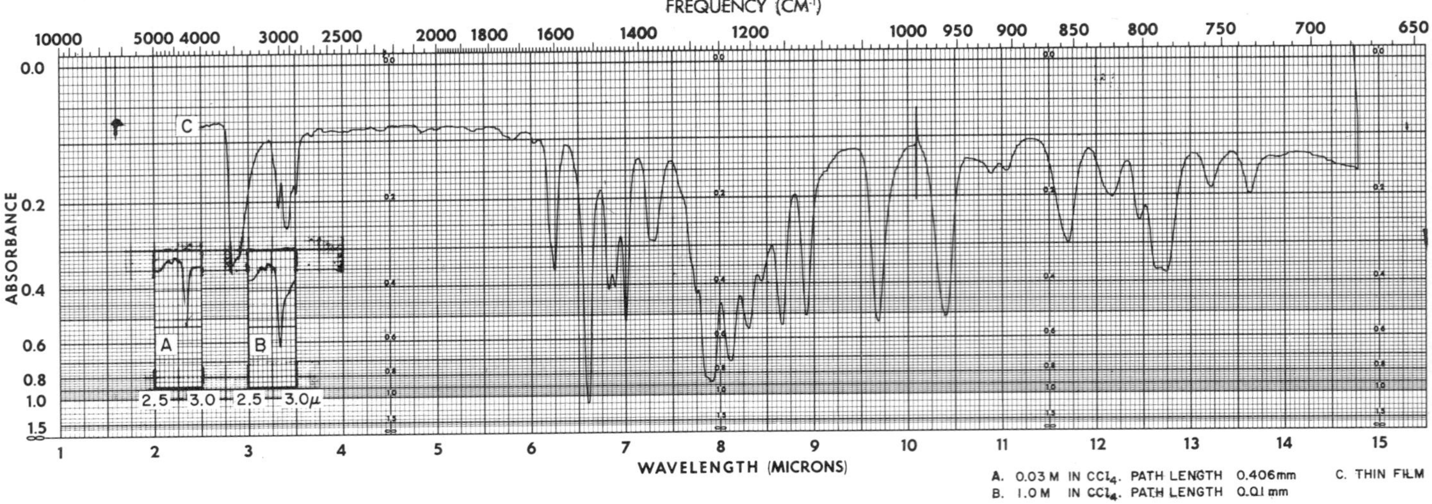

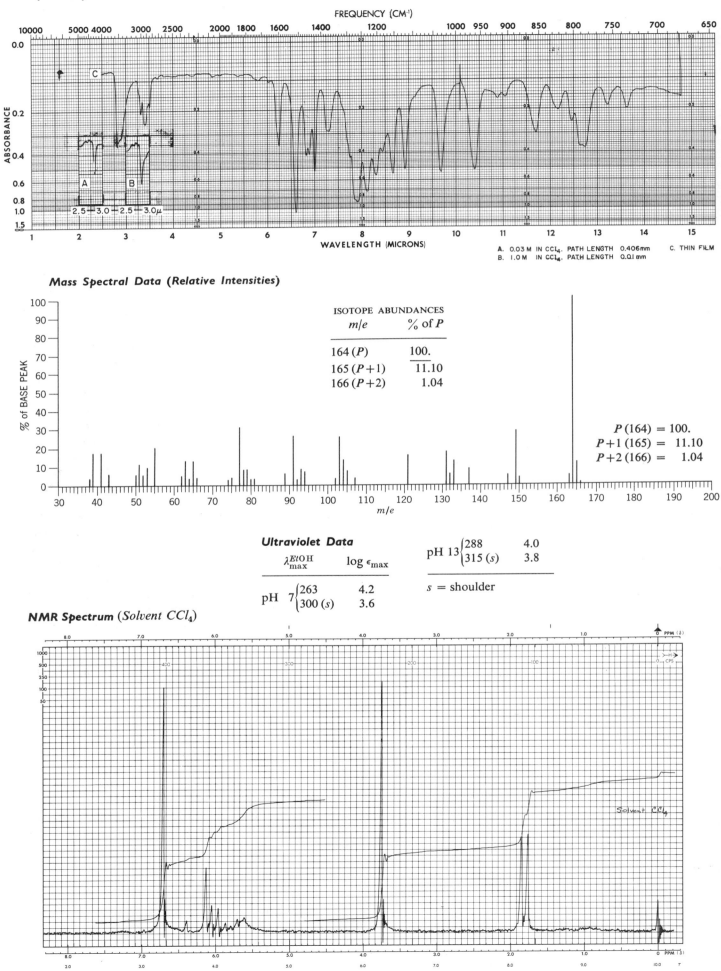

Mass Spectral Data (Relative Intensities)

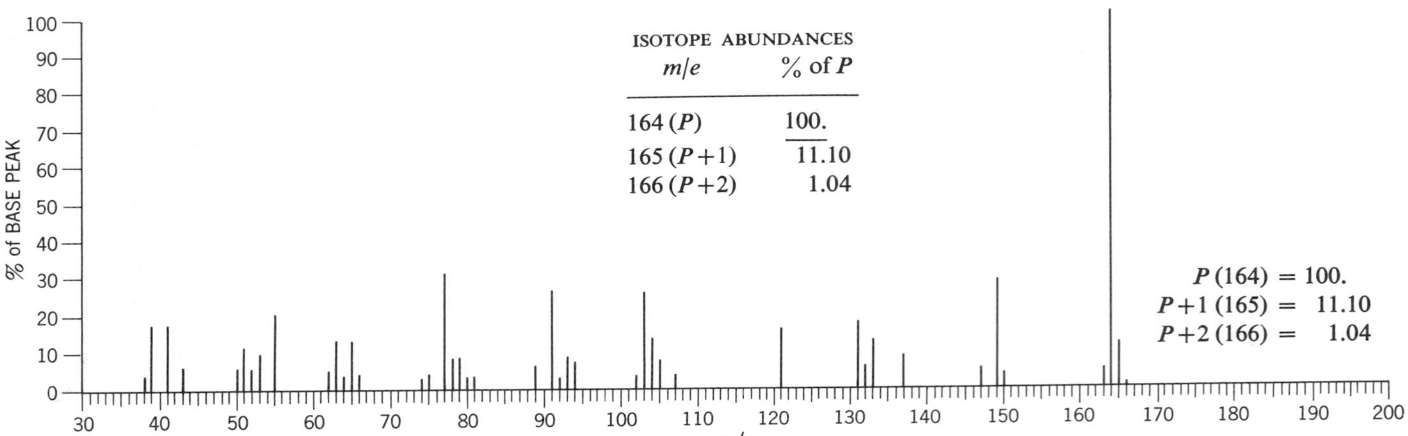

ISOTOPE ABUNDANCES

m/e	% of P
164 (P)	100.
165 ($P+1$)	11.10
166 ($P+2$)	1.04

P (164) = 100.
$P+1$ (165) = 11.10
$P+2$ (166) = 1.04

Ultraviolet Data

	λ_{max}^{EtOH}	log ϵ_{max}
pH 7	263	4.2
	300 (s)	3.6
pH 13	288	4.0
	315 (s)	3.8

s = shoulder

NMR Spectrum (*Solvent CCl_4*)

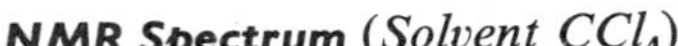

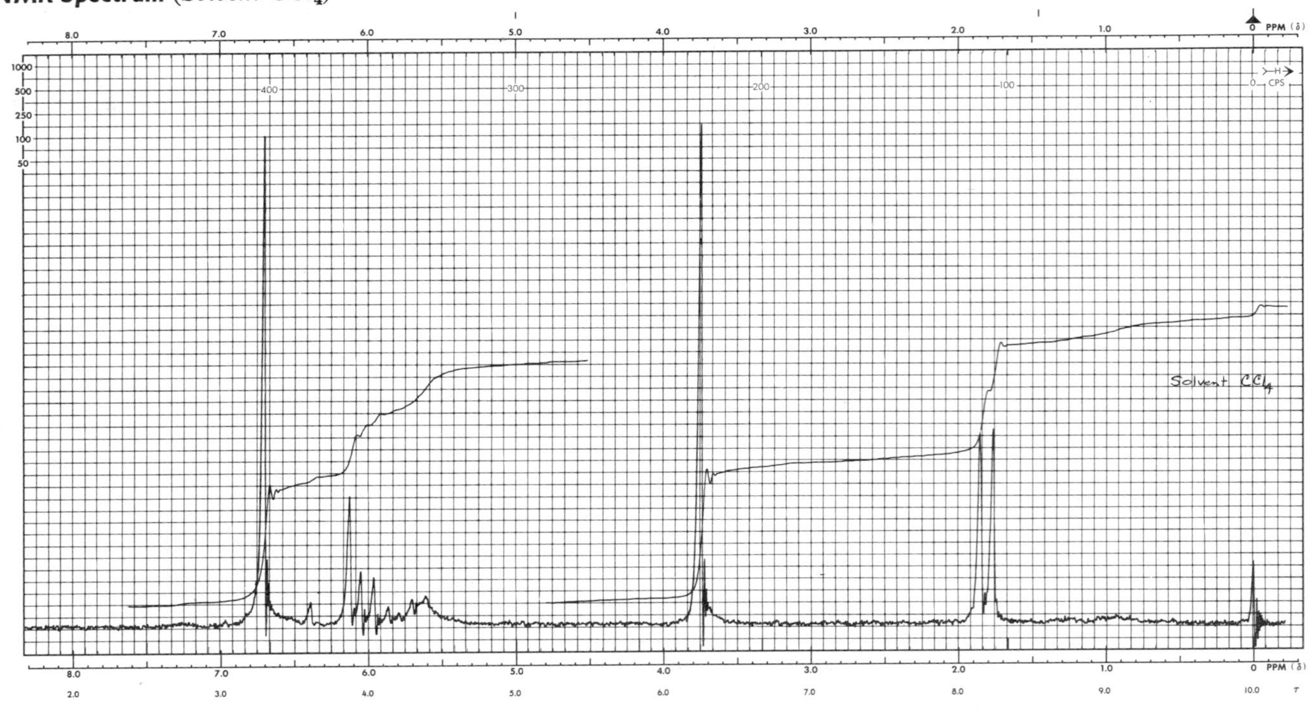

COMPOUND NUMBER 7

The following molecular formulas fit the data for the parent peak and the $P+1$ peak. We have eliminated trivial formulas and those containing an odd number of nitrogen atoms.

FORMULA	$P+1$	$P+2$
$C_8H_8N_2O_2$	9.61	0.81
$C_8H_{12}N_4$	10.36	0.49
$C_9H_8O_3$	9.97	1.05
$C_9H_{12}N_2O$	10.72	0.72
$C_{10}H_{12}O_2$	11.08	0.96
$C_{10}H_{16}N_2$	11.83	0.64

On the basis of the $P+2$ peak, we can tentatively eliminate $C_8H_{12}N_4$ and $C_{10}H_{16}N_2$. The presence of an aromatic ring is indicated by the NMR peak at δ 6.70, τ 3.30 (distinctly upfield from the position of an unsubstituted benzene ring) and the general appearance of the infrared spectrum. We note a small peak at 3030 cm^{-1} (3.30 μ), strong peaks between 1600 and 1430 cm^{-1} (6.2 and 7.0 μ), and several moderately strong peaks in the low-frequency (long wavelength) region. As additional confirmation of aromaticity, we note that the parent peak in the mass spectrum is also the base peak.

A conspicuous feature of the infrared spectrum is the rather strong absorption at 3510 cm^{-1} (2.85 μ). This is either an OH or an NH stretching band. We look to the region between 1230 and 1010 cm^{-1} (8.13 and 9.90 μ) for confirmation of OH absorption, but we are frustrated by the large number of bands in this region.

The ultraviolet spectrum gives us a good deal of information. The shift in wavelength at pH 13 is diagnostic for a phenol. Furthermore, the intense *K*-band at 263 mμ is indicative of a chromophore conjugated with the ring. In the absence of a carbonyl band in the infrared spectrum, we would suspect a C═C group. We quickly confirm this possibility by the olefinic proton absorption in the NMR spectrum at about δ 6.0, τ 4.0. A strong peak in the infrared spectrum at 965 cm^{-1} (10.36 μ) is evidence for *trans* olefinic hydrogens. The peak at 1605 cm^{-1} (6.25 μ) can partially be ascribed to the conjugated C═C stretching vibration.

At this point we have the following information:

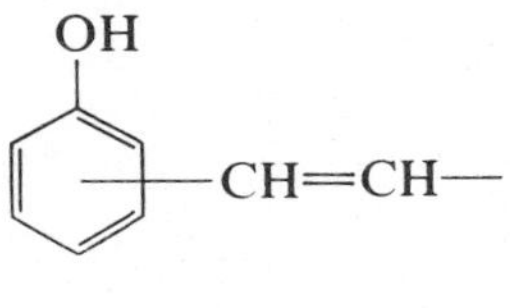

OH
(benzene ring)—CH═CH—

We now turn our attention to the doublet centered at δ 1.81, τ 8.19. The shift position is right for an allylic methyl group, and its existence as a doublet can be justified. We write

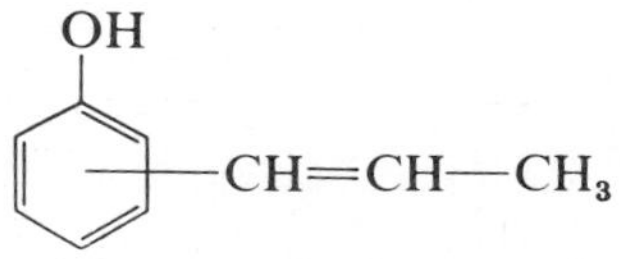

OH
(benzene ring)—CH═CH—CH$_3$

We consider the singlet in the NMR spectrum at δ 3.75, τ 6.25. The integrator indicates that this peak also contains three protons; this methyl group could be on a ring, an oxygen, a nitrogen, or a quarternary carbon. Its shift position is best satisfied by putting it on an oxygen and putting the oxygen on the ring. We have the following:

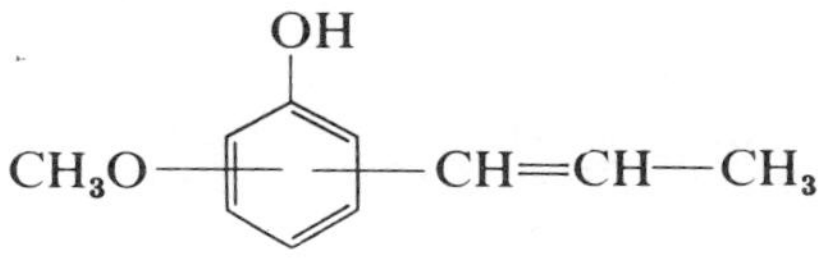

OH
CH$_3$O—(benzene ring)—CH═CH—CH$_3$

This adds up to 164 and to the formula $C_{10}H_{12}O_2$. The benzene peak at δ 6.70, τ 3.30 contains three protons; the complex olefinic multiplet also accounts for three protons. Obviously, the phenolic proton is hidden under the olefinic multiplet; it could either be moved by change of temperature, solvent, or concentration, or eliminated by shaking with D_2O. It is probably the broadened peak at $\sim\delta$ 5.60, τ 4.40. The olefinic proton near the ring is shown by the badly distorted doublet ($J \sim 16$) whose center of gravity is δ ~6.2, τ 3.8.

Assignment of the positions of the substituents is not easy. We cannot rely upon the C—H out-of-plane deformations in the long-wavelength region of the infrared spectrum because of the polar nature of the substituents. The NMR, which is usually very helpful for distinguishing among isomers, is of little use because the ring protons are all at the same shift value. We might note that the phenolic OH band in the infrared spectrum is at an unusually high frequency (short wavelength) for a neat sample, and is not shifted on dilution; this suggests intramolecular hydrogen bonding to the ether oxygen. The fragmentation spectrum is complex.

However, an organic chemist would recognize isoeugenol as a likely choice, and he would indeed find that the compound is

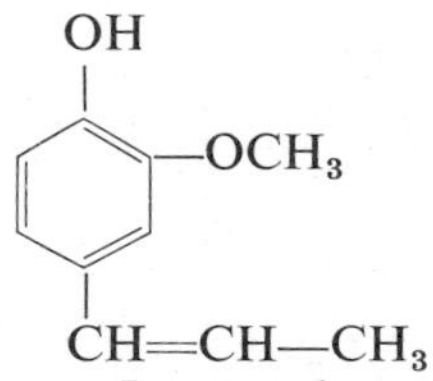

OH
(benzene ring)—OCH$_3$
CH═CH—CH$_3$

Isoeugenol

If isoeugenol did not come to mind, the organic chemist has enough information to decide on a degradation procedure. He might well ozonize the double bond and proceed to identify vanillin.

Infrared Spectrum *Compound 6-8*

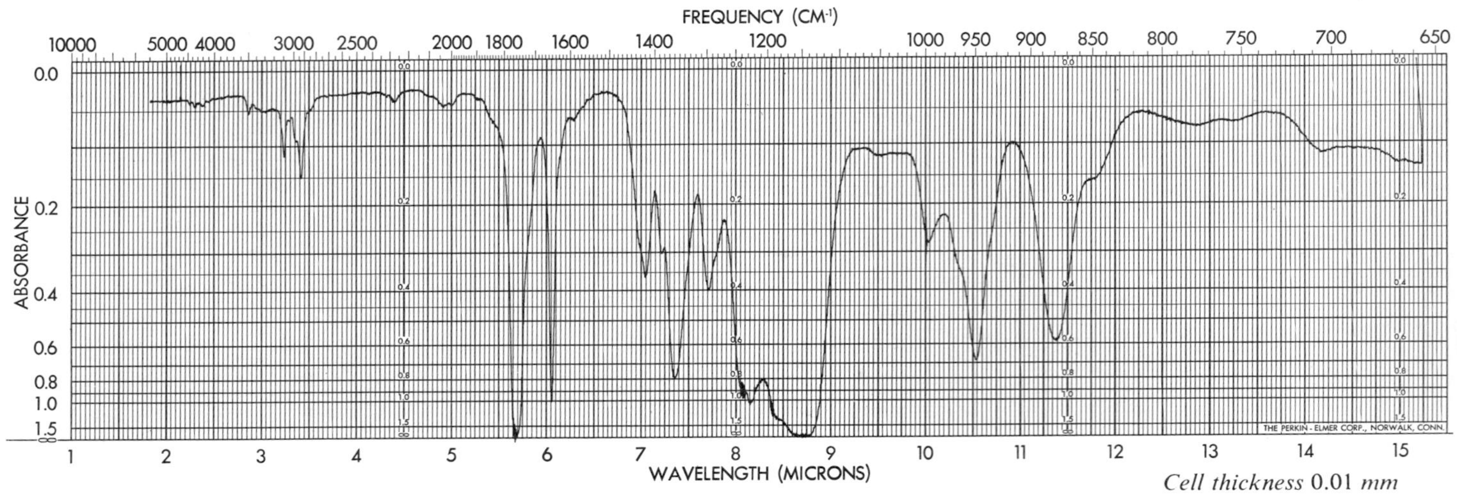

Cell thickness 0.01 *mm*

Mass Spectral Data (Relative Intensities)

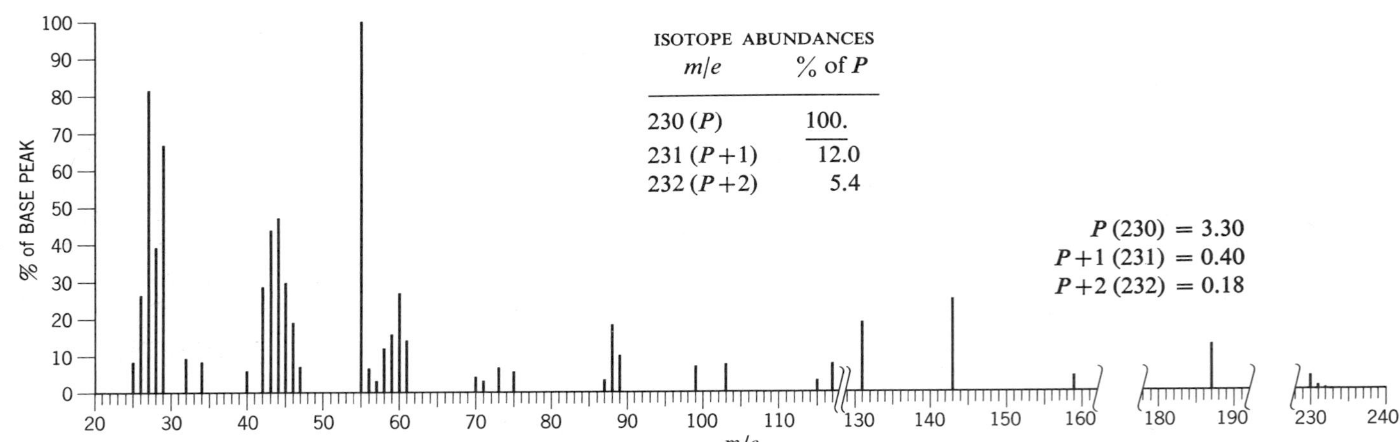

ISOTOPE ABUNDANCES

m/e	% of *P*
230 (*P*)	100.
231 (*P*+1)	12.0
232 (*P*+2)	5.4

P (230) = 3.30
P+1 (231) = 0.40
P+2 (232) = 0.18

Ultraviolet Data

Featureless above 210 mμ.

NMR Spectrum (*Solvent* CCl_4)

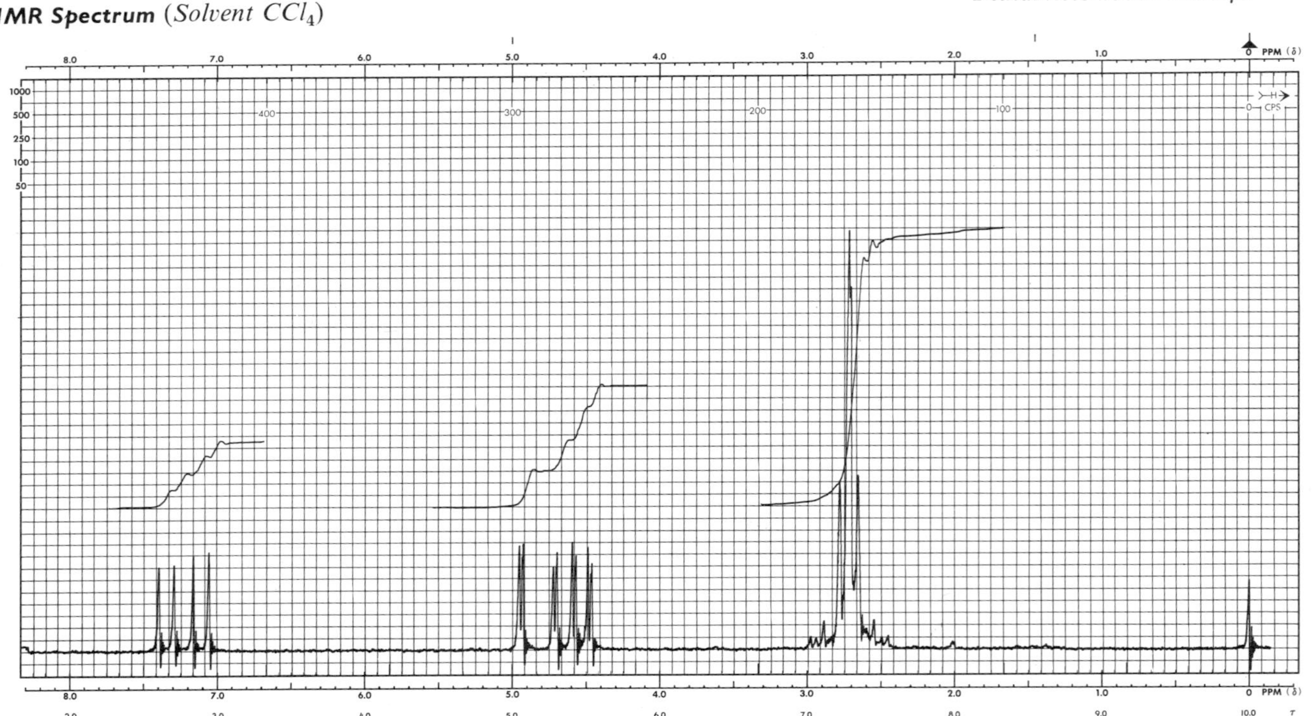

COMPOUND NUMBER 8

The $P+2$ peak indicates that the molecule contains a single sulfur atom. We therefore select the following possible formulas for the rest of the molecule under mass 198 after correcting $P+1$ for the presence of the ^{33}S isotope, and eliminating trivial formulas and those containing an odd number of N atoms.

$C_8H_{14}N_2O_2$
$C_9H_{14}N_2O$
$C_9H_{18}N_4O$
$C_{10}H_{14}O_4$
$C_{10}H_{18}N_2O_2$
$C_{11}H_{18}O_3$

The infrared spectrum affords a wealth of obvious information. The band at 1760 cm^{-1} (5.68 μ) together with the strong broad absorption centered at $\sim$1150 cm^{-1} ($\sim$8.70 μ) suggests an ester group, although we note that the C═O band is at rather short wavelength for esters. An olefinic bond is certainly indicated by the sharp absorptions at 3090 cm^{-1} (3.24 μ) and at 1650 cm^{-1} (6.06 μ). In this context, and noting the unusual intensity of the latter peak, we are justified in considering the strong bands at 949 cm^{-1} (10.54 μ) and 878 cm^{-1} (11.39 μ) to be displaced vinyl bands. There is no evidence for aromaticity, nitrogen- or other oxygen-containing groups, or a sulfhydryl group. We are probably dealing with a sulfide.

The NMR pattern is nicely in accord with our assumptions. We should expect an *ABX* or an *ABC* pattern from a vinyl group. The pattern is strikingly *ABX* because of strong deshielding of one of the vinyl protons.

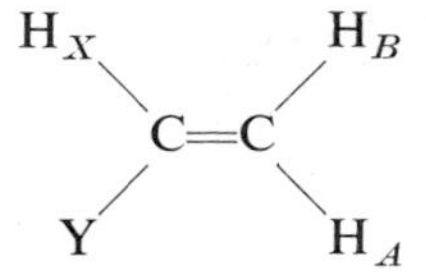

$$\begin{array}{ccc} H_X & & H_B \\ & C{=}C & \\ Y & & H_A \end{array}$$

The *X* proton at δ 7.21, τ 2.79 consists of two pairs (J_{AX} = 14 cps, J_{BX} = 7 cps). The *A* protons at δ 4.81, τ 5.19 consists of two pairs (J_{AX} = 14 cps, J_{AB} = 2 cps), as does the *B* proton at δ 4.52, τ 5.48 (J_{BX} = 7 cps, J_{AB} = 2 cps).

At this stage, the following fragments are evident: —S—, $\overset{\text{O}}{\overset{\|}{\text{—CO—}}}$ and CH═CH$_2$. If the vinyl group is attached to the oxygen atom of the ester group, we can justify the deshielded vinyl proton and, incidently, the somewhat shielded positions of the terminal protons resulting from the canonical contribution:

$$\overset{\text{O}}{\overset{\|}{\text{—C}}}\text{—}\overset{+}{\text{O}}{=}\text{CH—}\overset{-}{\text{C}}\text{H}_2$$

The C═O band in the infrared spectrum fits a vinyl ester.

The proton ratio, from low to high field, in the NMR spectrum is 1:2:4. The four-proton multiplet centered at about δ $\sim$2.7 τ 7.3 can be recognized as a very close A_2B_2 pattern resulting from two adjacent, similarly shielded methylene groups, —CH$_2$CH$_2$— (see Chapter 4, Figure 22d).

The sum of these fragments is equal to one-half the weight of the sulfur-free part of the molecule. This observation and the symmetrical appearance of the NMR spectrum lead us to assemble the fragments as a symmetrical sulfide, which is in accord with one of the possible molecular formulas $C_{10}H_{14}O_4$(S).

$$CH_2{=}CHO\underset{\underset{O}{\|}}{C}CH_2CH_2SCH_2CH_2\underset{\underset{O}{\|}}{C}OCH{=}CH_2$$

Divinyl β,β'-thiodipropionate

The fragmentation pattern is complex, but confirmational information can be gleaned. The peak at *m/e* 187 represents loss of OCH═CH$_2$, that at *m/e* 131 represents cleavage at one C—S bond with charge retention on the sulfur. The base peak at *m/e* 55 probably results from successive cleavage of a C—S and C—O bond with transfer of H to give the CH$_2$═CHC═O moiety. The large peak at *m/e* 27 is the CH$_2$═CH fragment. Absence of a *P* minus H$_2$S fragment is additional evidence in favor of a sulfide over a mercaptan.

By utilizing the α and β shift positions, given in the Appendix, we can calculate the position for the CH$_2$C═O absorption to be δ 2.70, τ 7.30, and that for the CH$_2$S absorption, δ 2.75, τ 7.25. Agreement with the observed positions is good.

Infrared Spectrum *Compound 6-9*

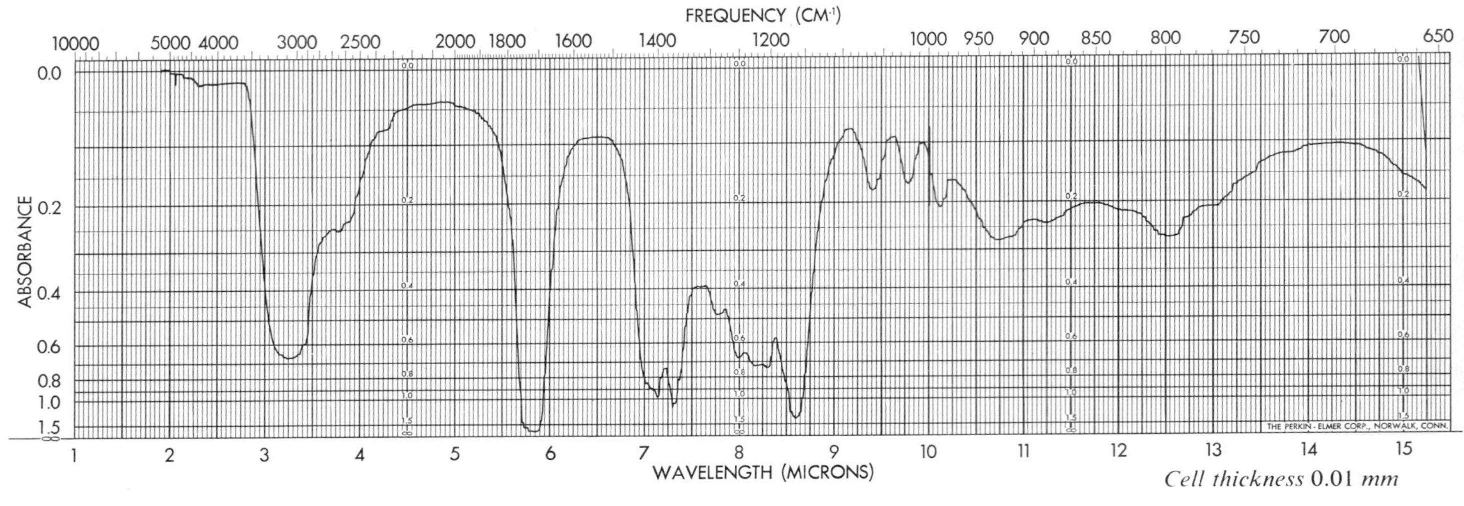

Cell thickness 0.01 *mm*

Mass Spectral Data (Relative Intensities)

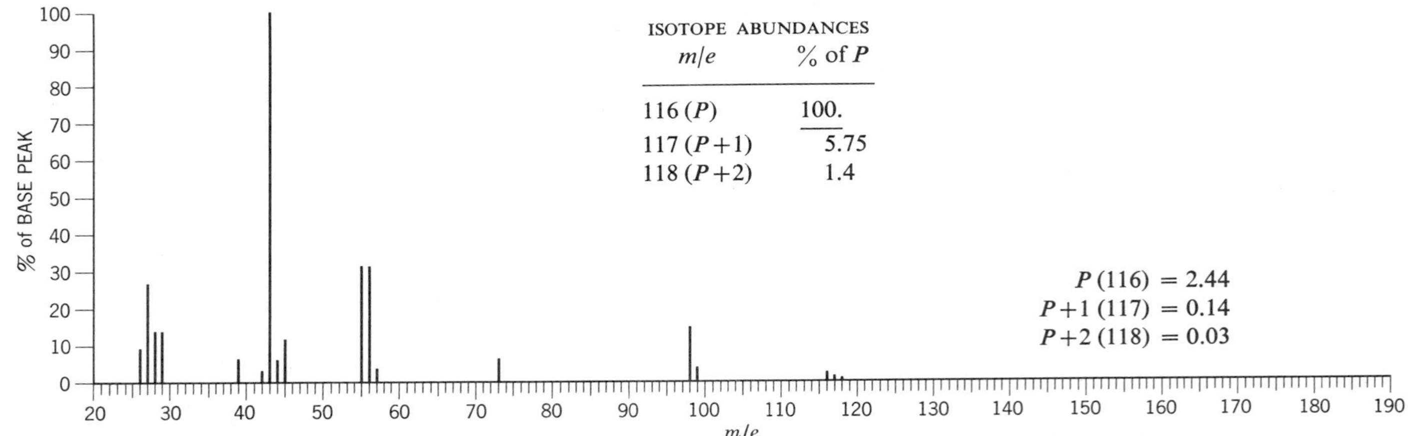

ISOTOPE ABUNDANCES

m/e	% of *P*
116 (*P*)	100.
117 (*P*+1)	5.75
118 (*P*+2)	1.4

P (116) = 2.44
P+1 (117) = 0.14
P+2 (118) = 0.03

Ultraviolet Data

λ_{max}^{EtOH}	$\log \epsilon_{max}$
262	1.5

NMR Spectrum (*Solvent* CCl_4)

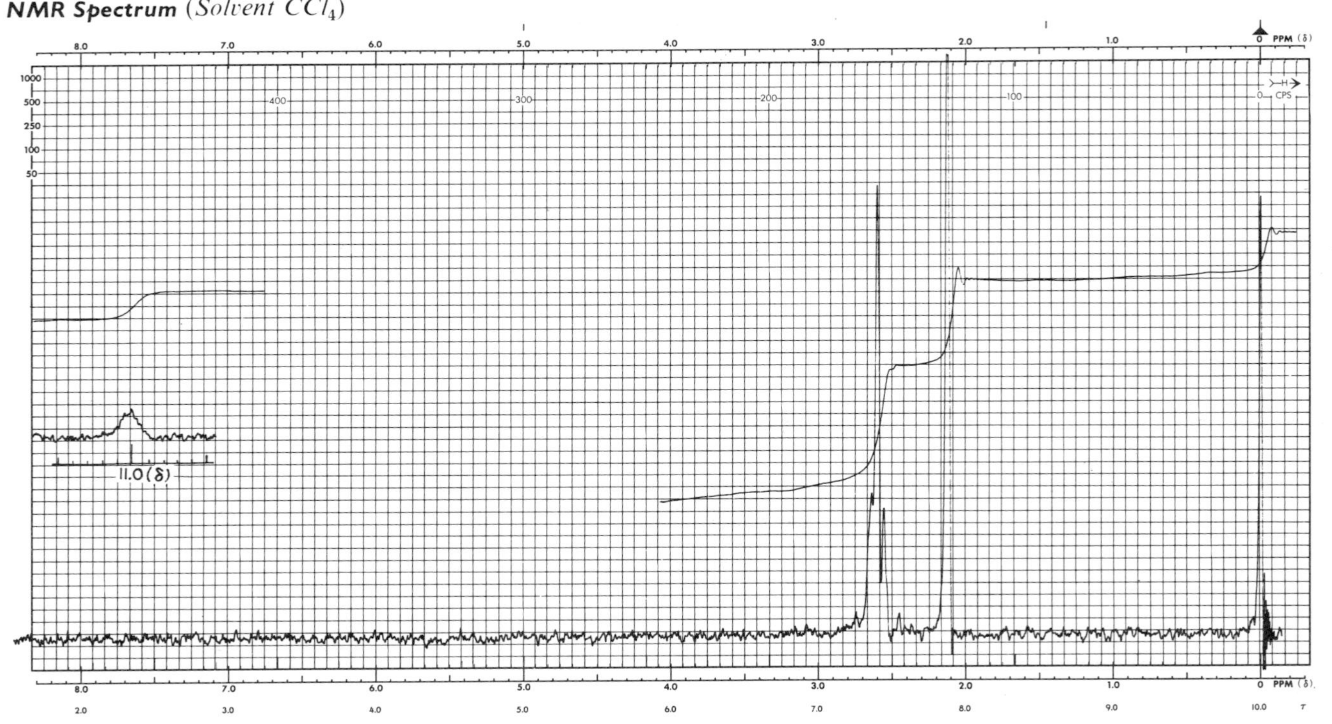

COMPOUND NUMBER 9

We list the molecular formulas under mass 116 that give a reasonable fit for the $P+1$ value of 5.75%.

FORMULA	$P+1$	$P+2$
$C_3H_8N_4O$	4.94	0.30
$C_4H_4O_4$	4.54	0.88
$C_4H_8N_2O_2$	5.29	0.52
$C_4H_{12}N_4$	6.04	0.16
$C_5H_8O_3$	5.65	0.73
$C_5H_{12}N_2O$	6.40	0.37
$C_6H_{12}O_2$	6.75	0.59

The formulas that best fit our $P+1$ value and our $P+2$ value (1.4%) are $C_4H_4O_4$, $C_4H_8N_2O_2$, $C_5H_8O_3$, and $C_6H_{12}O_2$.

The infrared spectrum points to an aliphatic carboxylic acid. We note the very broad, bonded OH-stretching absorption extending between about 3330 and 2300 cm^{-1} (3.0 and 4.3 μ) with its characteristic pattern on its low frequency (long wavelength) side. The strong C=O band at 1715 cm^{-1} (5.83 μ) satisfies the requirement for an aliphatic carboxylic acid. We find ready confirmation by noting the carboxylic acid proton at δ 11.0, $\tau -1.0$ in the NMR spectrum

But the ultraviolet spectrum interposes a caveat. The low-intensity absorption at 262 mμ suggests an aliphatic unconjugated ketone. There is only one C=O band in the infrared spectrum, but it is rather broad; it must accommodate both the ketone and the acid C=O band. The fragmentation pattern does not resemble that of an ordinary aliphatic carboxylic acid; for one thing, there is no pronounced peak at mass 60. Since we are dealing with a ketone group in the molecule, we assume that the base peak of 43 in the mass spectrum arises from $CH_3C{=}O$. We now have the fragments $CH_3C{=}O$ and COOH which add up to mass 88. These leave us with an unknown mass of 28 for which we can write either C=O or $CH_2{-}CH_2$ or N_2.

The NMR spectrum allows us to make an unequivocal choice. The large singlet at δ 2.12, τ 7.88 must be the CH_3 group on the ketone carbonyl. If this peak contains three protons, then the absorption at δ 2.60, τ 7.40 contains four protons. These must result from adjacent methylene groups which have almost the same chemical shift. We now write the structure

$$CH_3\underset{\displaystyle \overset{\|}{O}}{C}CH_2CH_2COOH$$

Levulinic acid

Infrared Spectrum

Compound 6-10

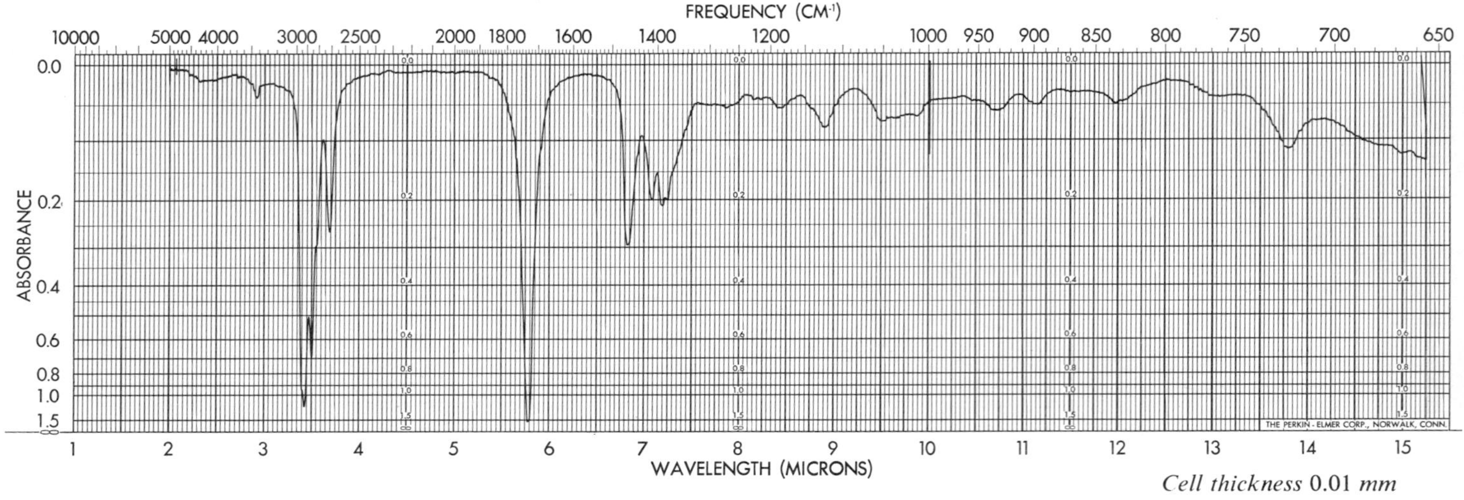

Cell thickness 0.01 *mm*

Mass Spectral Data (Relative Intensities)

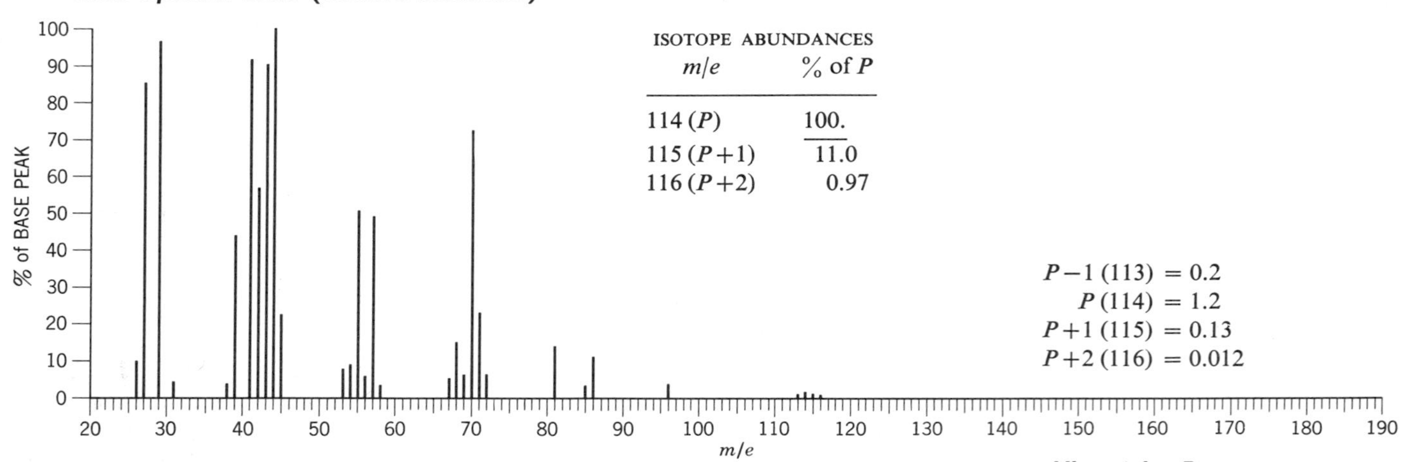

ISOTOPE ABUNDANCES

m/e	% of *P*
114 (*P*)	100.
115 (*P*+1)	11.0
116 (*P*+2)	0.97

$P-1\ (113) = 0.2$
$P\ (114) = 1.2$
$P+1\ (115) = 0.13$
$P+2\ (116) = 0.012$

Ultraviolet Data

$\lambda_{max}^{Cyclohexane}$	ϵ_{max}
292	23.2

NMR Spectrum (*Solvent* $CDCl_3$)

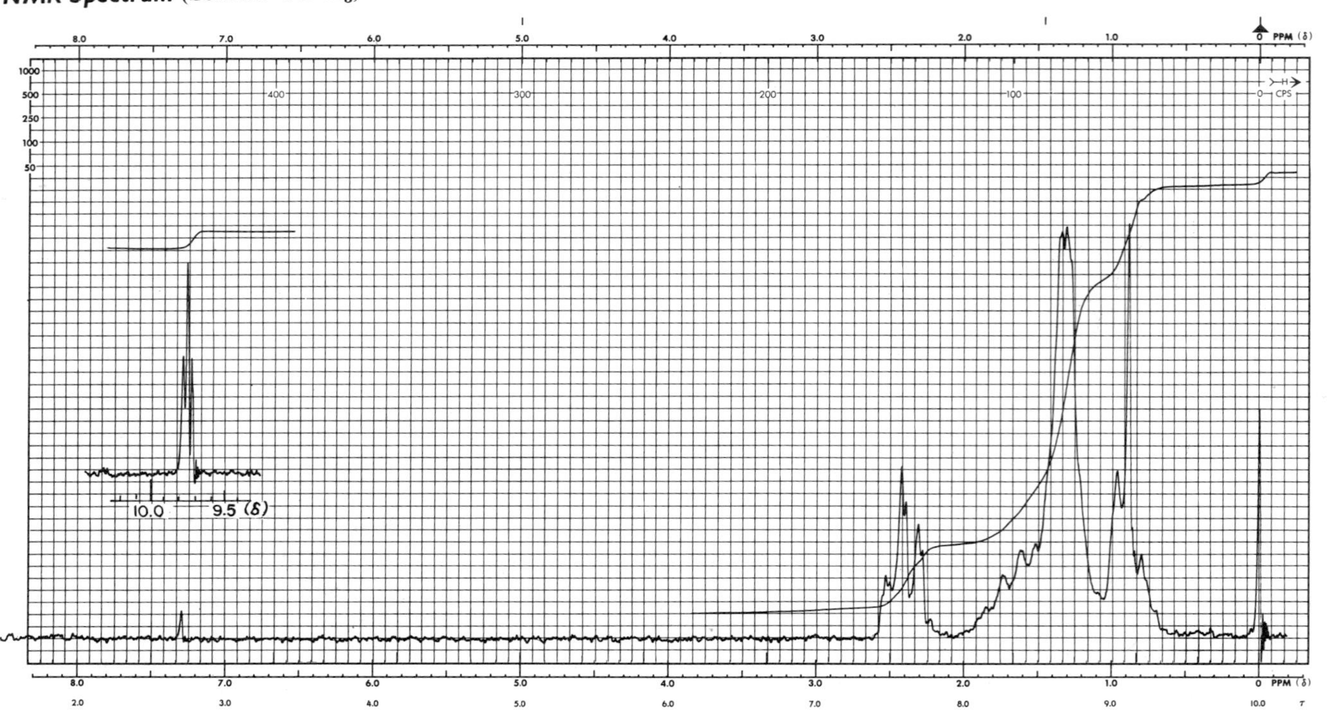

COMPOUND NUMBER 10

In accordance with our usual procedure, we look at the molecular formulas under the parent mass (114) and try to select formulas that match our $P+1$ and $P+2$ peaks. But in this case, we find that our $P+1$ peak is too high to match any of the formulas listed. The high value of the $P+1$ peak can mean impurities. A more likely explanation is that this spectrum was obtained at a rather high inlet pressure in order to see the weak parent peak; we see a contribution to the $P+1$ peak from a bimolecular addition of hydrogen to the parent ion. This is a common occurrence with molecules containing a hetero atom, which, as we shall see, is present. No sulfur or halogen is present.

The C=O band in the infrared spectrum at 1730 cm^{-1} (5.78 μ), together with the CH stretching band at 2703 cm^{-1} (3.70 μ), spells out an aldehyde group. This is readily confirmed by the characteristic ultraviolet spectrum, by the triplet in the NMR spectrum at δ 9.75, τ 0.25, and by the typical aldehyde base peak at mass 44. Furthermore, we know that we are dealing with an aliphatic primary aldehyde by the triplet structure of the aldehydic proton in the NMR (split by CH_2), by the weak parent peak and the mass 44 base peak in the mass spectrum, and by the lack of aromatic structure in either the NMR or the infrared spectra.

The absorption at δ 2.42, τ 7.58 in the NMR must represent the CH_2 next to the aldehyde group. It is split into a triplet by an adjacent CH_2 and again into a doublet by the aldehydic proton (small coupling constant). We now have

$$—CH_2CH_2CHO$$

mass 57

and we need a moiety of mass 57 to account for a molecular weight of 114. We could write

$$C_4H_9$$
$$C_3H_5O$$
$$C_2H_5N_2$$

The NMR integrator permits an unequivocal choice. If we assign one proton to the aldehydic absorption, and two protons to the adjacent methylene, there are eleven protons under the high-field absorption of which two belong to the β-methylene group. That leaves nine protons for the missing moiety which is obviously C_4H_9. Furthermore, we can make out a distorted triplet centered on δ 0.89, τ 9.11 which represents a CH_3 group. The ratio of the area of this triplet to the area of the absorption of the methylene groups between δ 2.0, τ 8.0, and δ 1.1, τ 8.9 is 3:8. Therefore, the chain is not branched. The compound is

$$CH_3CH_2CH_2CH_2CH_2CH_2CHO$$

Heptaldehyde

The peaks in the mass spectrum at mass 96 ($P-H_2O$), mass 86 ($P-CO$), and at mass 70 ($P-CH_2CHOH$) confirm the choice of mass 114 as the parent peak despite its low intensity. The aliphatic chain is apparent in the sequence m/e 29, 43, 57, and 71.

Infrared Spectrum

Compound 6-11

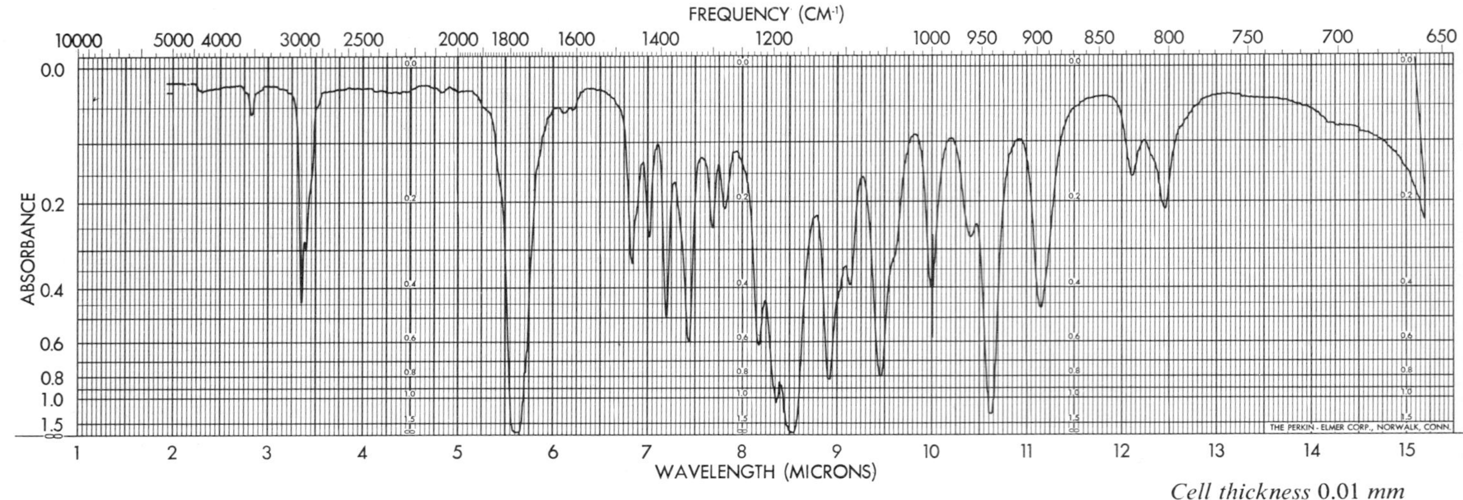

Cell thickness 0.01 *mm*

Mass Spectral Data (Relative Intensities)

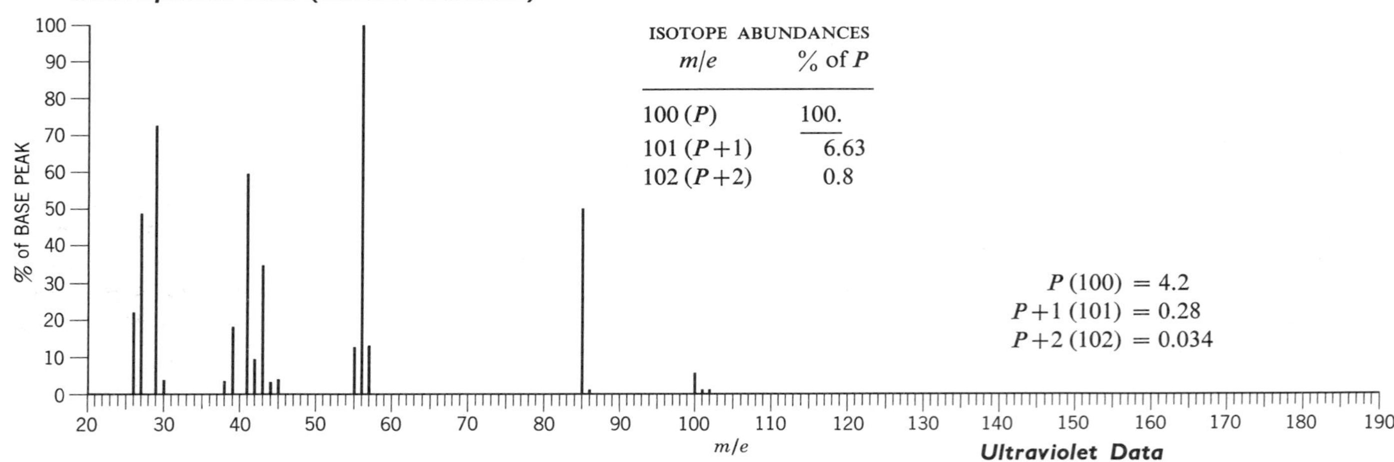

ISOTOPE ABUNDANCES

m/e	% of P
100 (P)	100.
101 (P+1)	6.63
102 (P+2)	0.8

$P(100) = 4.2$
$P+1\ (101) = 0.28$
$P+2\ (102) = 0.034$

Ultraviolet Data

Transparent above 200 mμ.

NMR Spectrum (*Solvent CCl$_4$*)

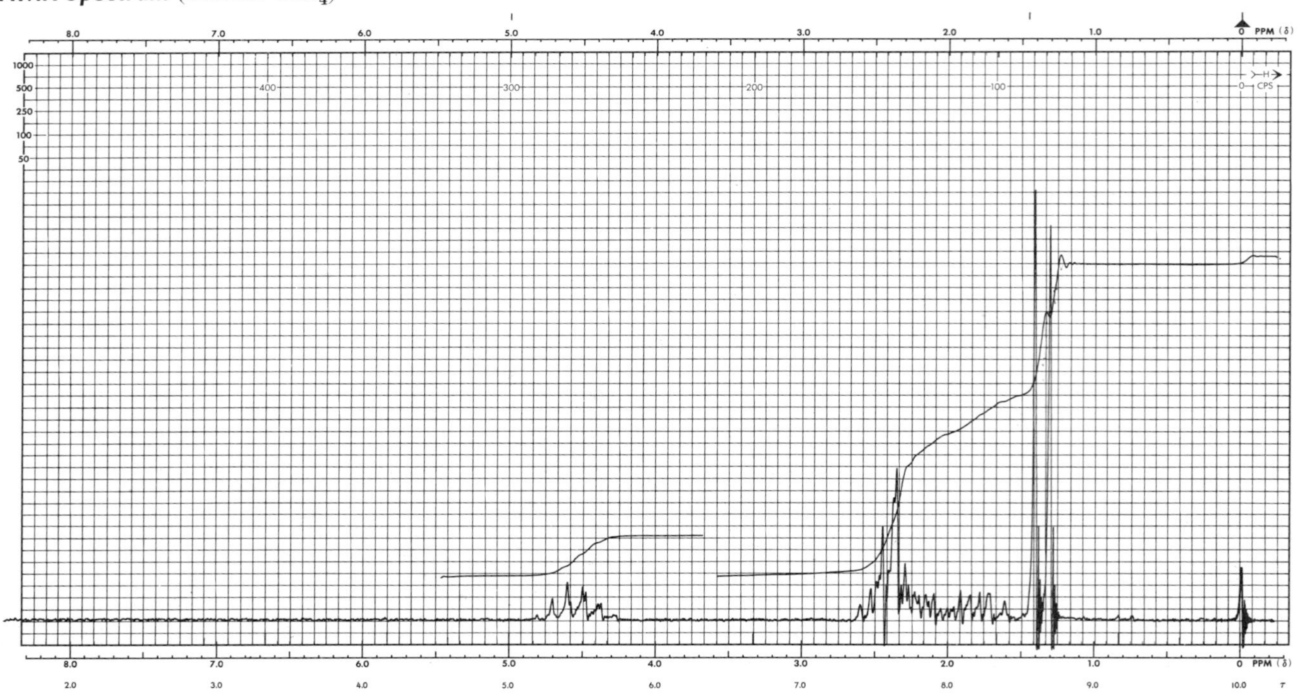

COMPOUND NUMBER 11

The likely molecular formulas under mass 100 on the basis of our $P+1$ peak (6.63%) are

FORMULA	$P+1$	$P+2$
$C_4H_8N_2O$	5.25	0.31
$C_5H_8O_2$	5.61	0.53
$C_5H_{12}N_2$	6.36	0.17
$C_6H_{12}O$	6.72	0.39

Our $P+2$ peak (0.8%) would tend to favor $C_5H_8O_2$, but $C_6H_{12}O$ is a possibility because of its close agreement with the $P+1$ peak.

The strong C=O band at 1780 cm^{-1} (5.62 μ) in the infrared, together with the strong broad absorption band at 1170^{-1} (8.55 μ), suggests an ester, but the C=O band is at a rather high frequency (short wavelength) for an ordinary ester. Halogen substituents would account for this, but, obviously, chlorine or bromine are absent. Even more obviously, iodine is not present, but fluorine must still be kept in mind.

There is moderate absorption in the infrared spectrum in the low-frequency (long wavelength) end of the spectrum, but none between 1667 and 1471 cm^{-1} (6.0 and 6.8 μ); nor is there anything to suggest aromatic CH stretching vibration. On balance, we do not seem to be dealing with an aromatic compound. This impression is reinforced by the ultraviolet and the NMR spectra.

Since two oxygen atoms are probably present, we adopt $C_5H_8O_2$ as the molecular formula, (forgetting about fluorine for the moment). The formula suggests unsaturation, but none of the spectra bear out this possibility. We therefore consider a ring and, recalling the position of the C=O band in the infrared spectrum, we are led to a five-membered ring lactone. The peak at m/e 85 ($P-15$) and the base peak at m/e 56 (elimination of $CH_3CH{=}O$) spell out

CH_3—HC—H_2C—CH_2—C(=O)—O— (ring)

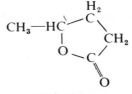

γ-Valerolactone

The upfield, 3-proton doublet in the NMR spectrum represents the $C\underline{H}_3$—CH absorption. The strongly deshielded position of the CH absorption (a slightly distorted sextet at δ 4.55, τ 5.45), places the CH on the oxygen atom. The integrator shows four protons between about δ 2.6, τ 7.4, and δ 1.5, τ 8.5.

Infrared Spectrum

Compound 6-12

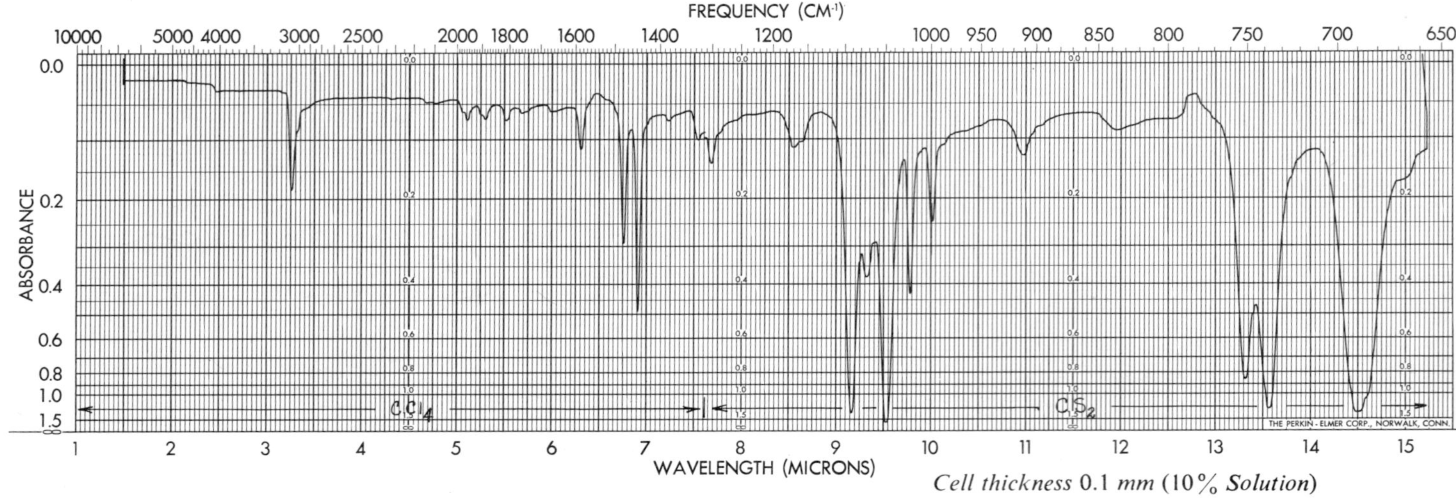

Cell thickness 0.1 *mm* (10% *Solution*)

Mass Spectral Data (Relative Intensities)

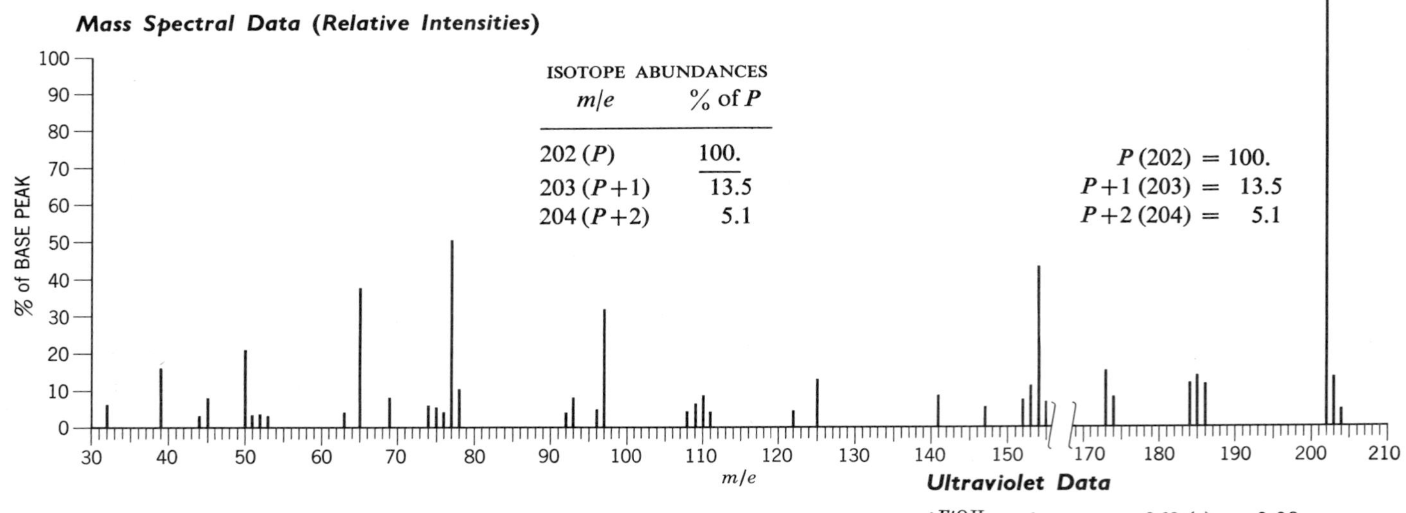

ISOTOPE ABUNDANCES

m/e	% of *P*
202 (*P*)	100.
203 (*P*+1)	13.5
204 (*P*+2)	5.1

Ultraviolet Data

λ_{max}^{EtOH}	log ϵ_{max}
232	4.15
262 (*s*)	3.38

(*s*) = shoulder

NMR Spectrum (*Solvent* CCl_4)

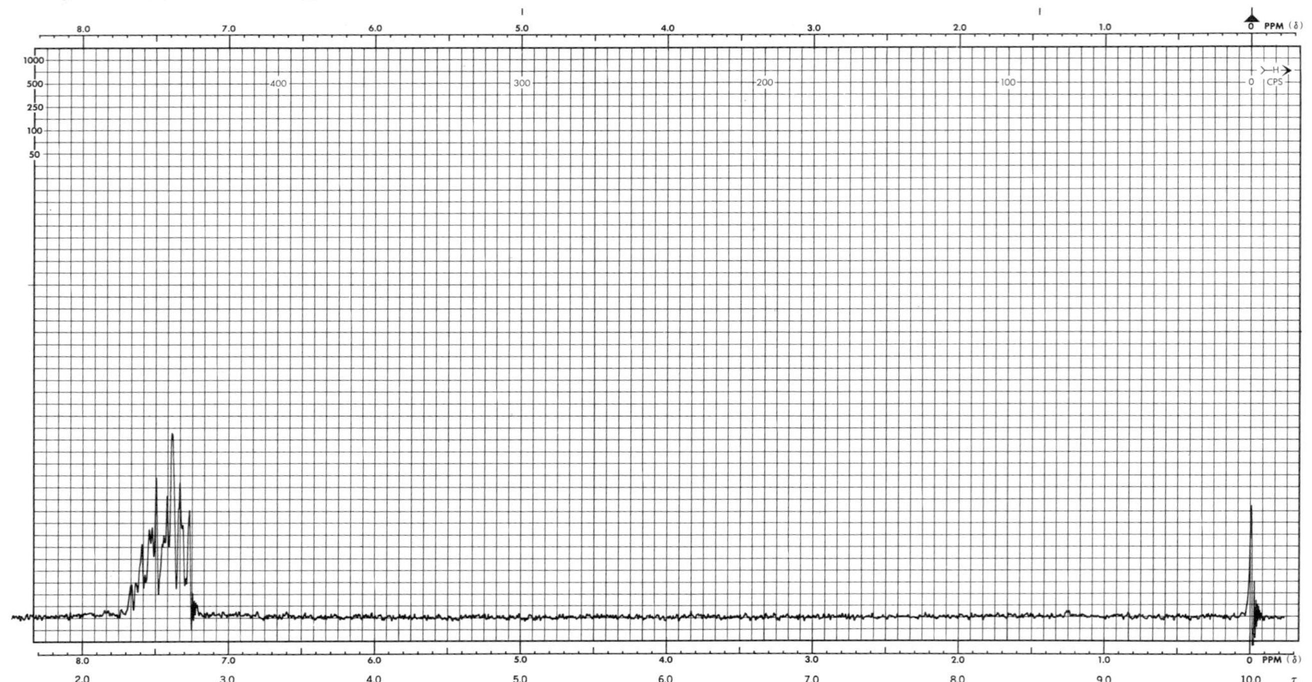

COMPOUND NUMBER 12

The $P+2$ peak indicates the presence of one sulfur atom. We select the following possible formulas for the rest of the molecules under mass 170 after correcting the $P+1$ peak for the ^{33}S isotope:

$C_{10}H_6N_2O$
$C_{10}H_{22}N_2$
$C_{11}H_6O_2$
$C_{11}H_{10}N_2$
$C_{11}H_{22}O$
$C_{12}H_{10}O$
$C_{12}H_{26}$

The intensity of the parent peak and general appearance of the IR spectrum strongly suggest aromaticity as does the UV spectrum, which also points to a chromophore conjugated with the aromatic system. The NMR spectum is equally definitive; in fact, all the protons are aromatic. For want of evidence to the contrary, we can tentatively assume that no nitrogen atoms are present, and we are left with only two likely molecular formulas.

$C_{11}H_6O_2S$
and
$C_{12}H_{10}OS$

The long wavelength bands in the IR are accepted, with the usual reservations, as evidence for a singly substituted benzene ring (one of the bands is split). A conspicuous peak at *m/e* 77 (and a smaller one at *m/e* 78) can be adduced as additional evidence for a benzene ring. Given this evidence and the similarity of the shift positions of all the protons, we are justified in choosing $C_{12}H_{10}OS$ as the molecular formula and assuming that two benzene rings are present. If, in fact, the rings are singly substituted, we are forced to write

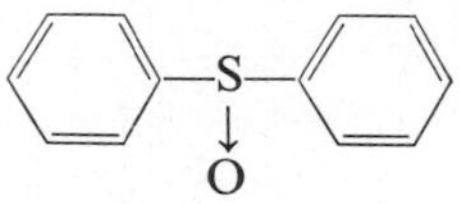

Diphenyl sulfoxide

This might also have been deduced from the strong $S \rightarrow O$ band in the infrared system at 1048 cm^{-1} (9.54 μ). The strong *K*-band in the UV spectrum is in accord with this structure as are the main fragmentation peaks. Expulsion of SO and formation of a C—C bond explain the prominent peak at *m/e* 154.

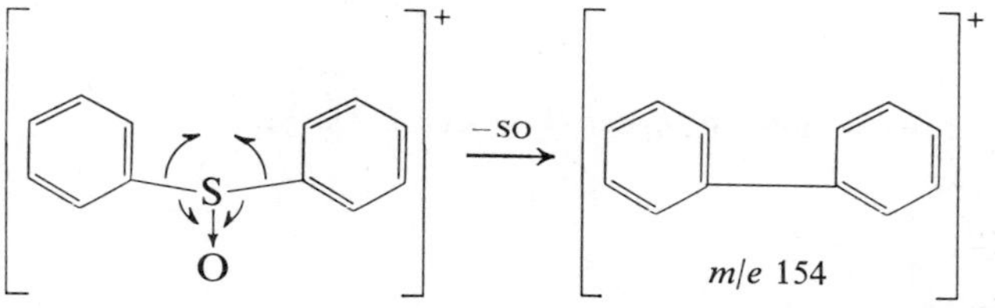

−SO

m/e 154

The peak at *m/e* 125 results from cleavage of one S—C bond to give

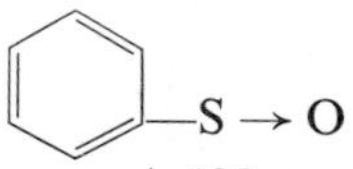

—S → O

m/e 125

The peak at *m/e* 97 is more difficult to rationalize. Presumably, a complex rearrangement yields the ion

S^+

m/e 97

The strong IR band at 1090 cm^{-1} (9.18 μ) has been described as a phenyl-S stretch, presumably with some contribution from the canonical form

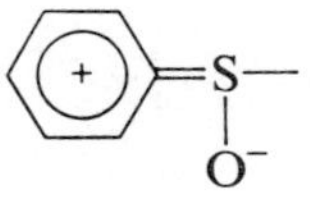

Infrared Spectrum

Compound 6-13

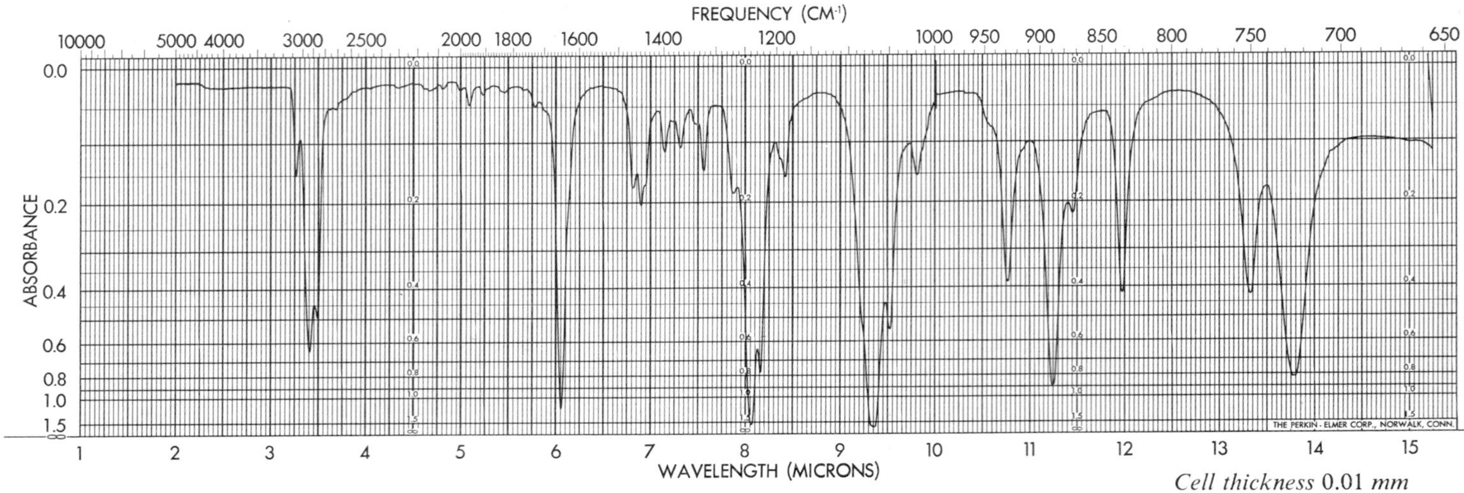

Cell thickness 0.01 *mm*

Mass Spectral Data (Relative Intensities)

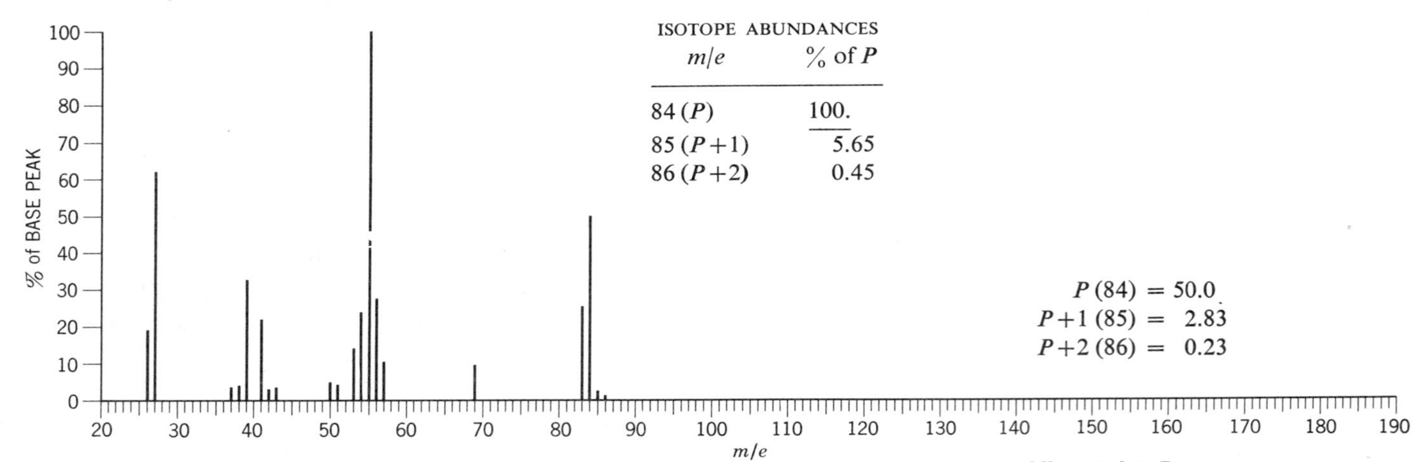

ISOTOPE ABUNDANCES

m/e	% of *P*
84 (*P*)	100.
85 (*P*+1)	5.65
86 (*P*+2)	0.45

P (84) = 50.0
$P+1$ (85) = 2.83
$P+2$ (86) = 0.23

Ultraviolet Data

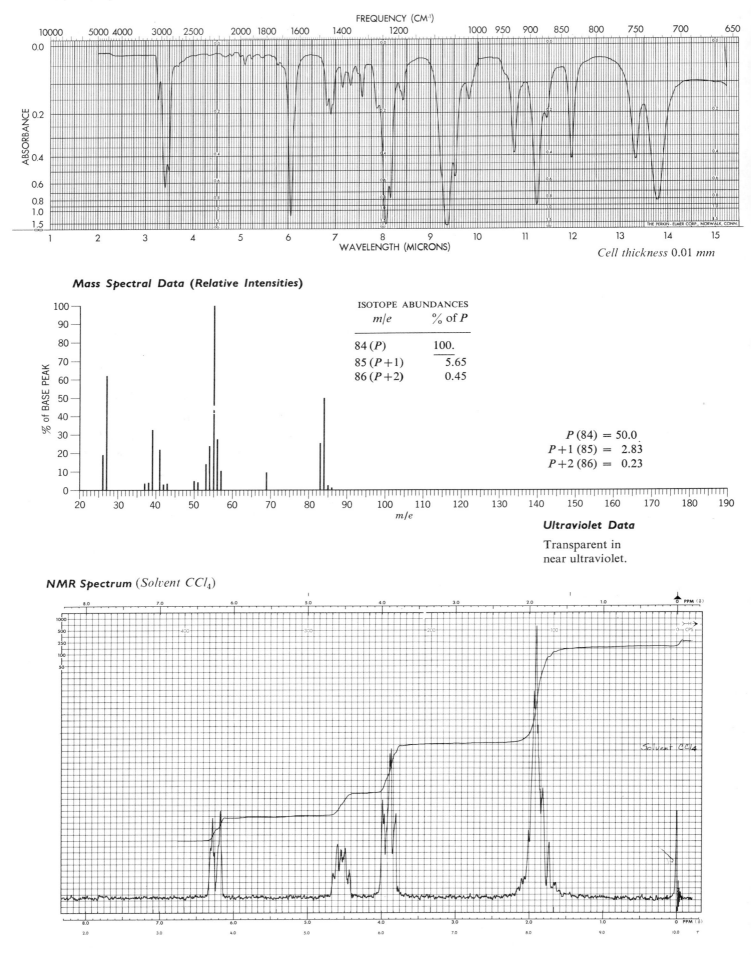

Transparent in near ultraviolet.

NMR Spectrum (*Solvent* CCl_4)

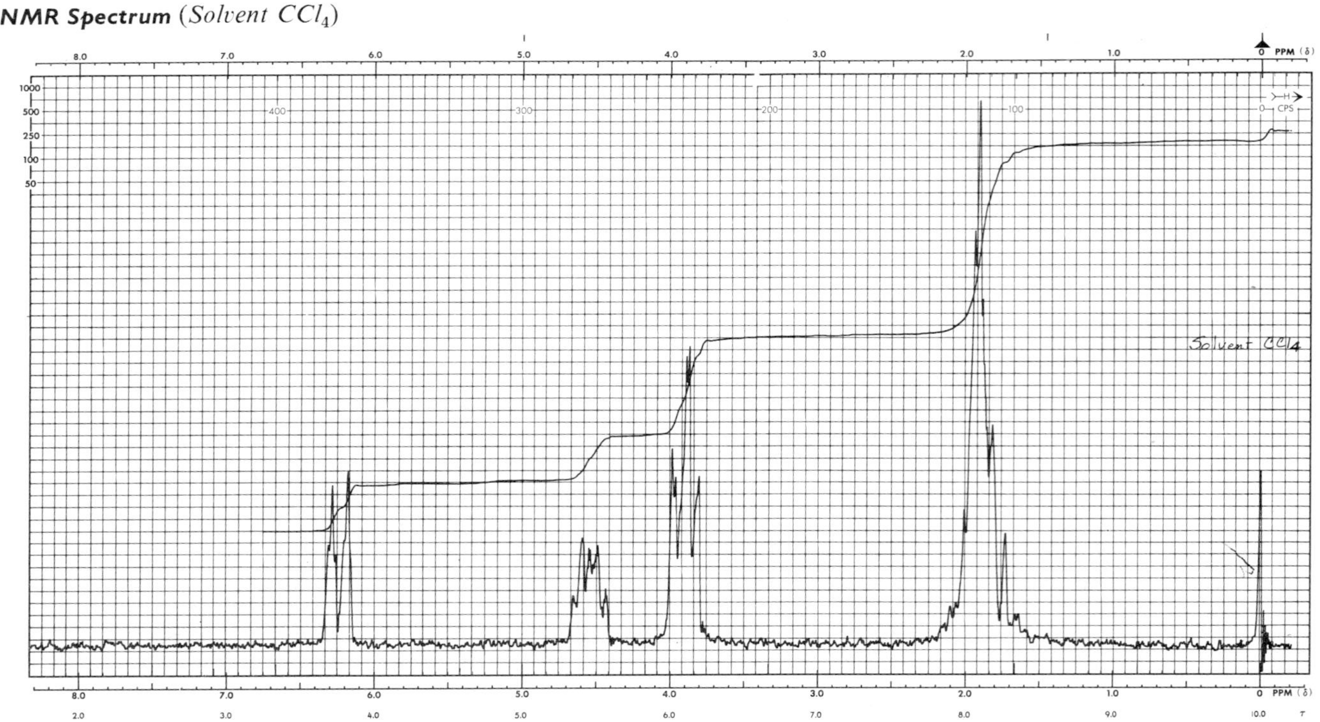

COMPOUND NUMBER 13

The possible molecular formulas for a molecular weight of 84 are

FORMULAS	$P+1$	$P+2$
$C_4H_4O_2$	4.47	0.48
$C_4H_8N_2$	5.21	0.11
C_5H_8O	5.57	0.33
C_6H_{12}	6.67	0.19

The best match for the $P+1$ peak (5.65%) and for the $P+2$ peak (0.45%) is C_5H_8O. This means two "unsaturated sites."

The general impression given by the infrared spectrum is that we are dealing with an aromatic carbonyl compound. But discrepancies rapidly become apparent. For one thing, the ultraviolet spectrum effectively rules out aromatic or heteroaromatic ring systems; there is no evidence for a ketone or aldehyde group. A closer look at the infrared spectrum reveals a disturbing ratio of the intensities of the aliphatic CH stretching absorption at 2933 cm^{-1} (3.41 μ) and the "carbonyl" band at 1650 cm^{-1} (6.06 μ). The molecular formulas do not permit a heavily alkylated ring system.

The NMR spectrum shows a doublet (with additional splitting) at δ 6.21, τ 3.79. This is at the high-field end for aromatic and heteroaromatic protons, and at the low-field end for olefinic protons. If we assume that we are dealing with an olefin, the spectra all make more sense. The "carbonyl" band in the infrared now becomes an intensified C=C stretching band. The small peak at 3058 cm^{-1} (3.27 μ) is obviously the olefinic CH stretching band, and the long wavelength absorption must be a strong *cis* CH=CH out-of-plane bending band.

If we assign one olefinic proton to the downfield absorption in the NMR spectrum, we can then tentatively assign another olefinic proton to the multiplet at δ 4.55, τ 5.45. We can detect the same spacing ($J = 7$ cps) in both sets of peaks; this coupling constant is of the proper magnitude for *cis* olefinic protons.

In order to explain the extreme downfield position of one olefinic CH, we will place the oxygen atom, allowed by the empirical formula, adjacent to this CH. We can now write —O—CH=CH—. The intense bands at 1241 cm^{-1} (8.06 μ) and 1070 cm^{-1} (9.35 μ) in the infrared spectrum will support an unsaturated ether structure.

We now subtract the unsaturated ether moiety from the molecular formula

$$\begin{array}{c} C_5H_8O \\ C_2H_2O \\ \hline C_3H_6 \end{array}$$

Further consideration of the NMR spectrum allows us to make a rational distribution of the C and H atoms. The six protons are distributed under two peaks in the ratio of 2:4. The smaller peak, an apparent triplet with additional splitting, is moved strongly downfield; we are justified in putting a methylene on the oxygen atom

$$—H_2C—O—CH=CH—.$$

The upfield absorption is caused by CH_2—CH_2 whose shift positions are similar. We can now close the gap with —CH_2—CH_2— and write

```
        CH2
       /   \
     HC     CH2
     ||     |
     HC     CH2
       \   /
         O
```

Dihydropyran

Note the very small allylic coupling evident in the downfield absorption in the NMR spectrum. At better resolution, each peak would be a triplet. Virtual coupling distorts the triplet at δ 3.89, τ 6.11.

Infrared Spectrum

Compound 6-14

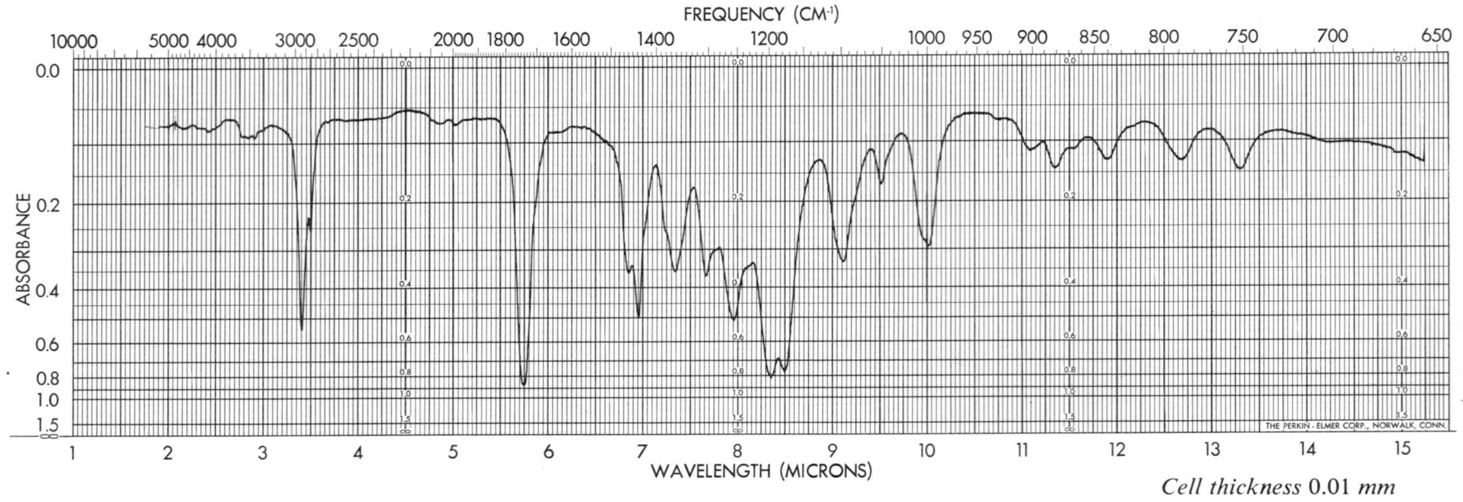

Cell thickness 0.01 *mm*

Mass Spectral Data (Relative Intensities)

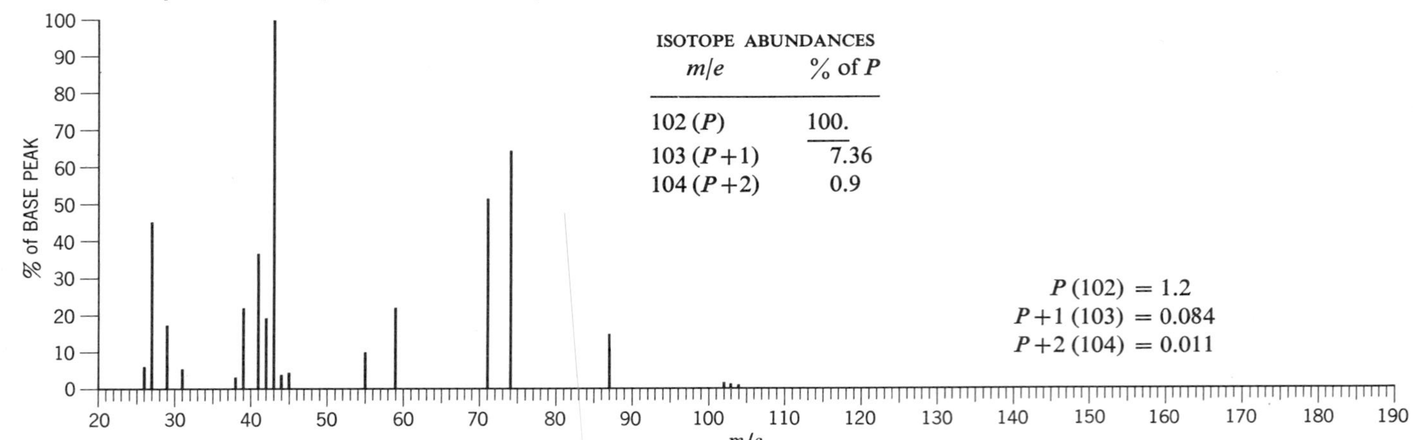

ISOTOPE ABUNDANCES

m/e	% of *P*
102 (*P*)	100.
103 (*P*+1)	7.36
104 (*P*+2)	0.9

P (102) = 1.2
P+1 (103) = 0.084
P+2 (104) = 0.011

Ultraviolet Data

Transparent above 210 mμ.

NMR Spectrum (*Solvent* CCl_4)

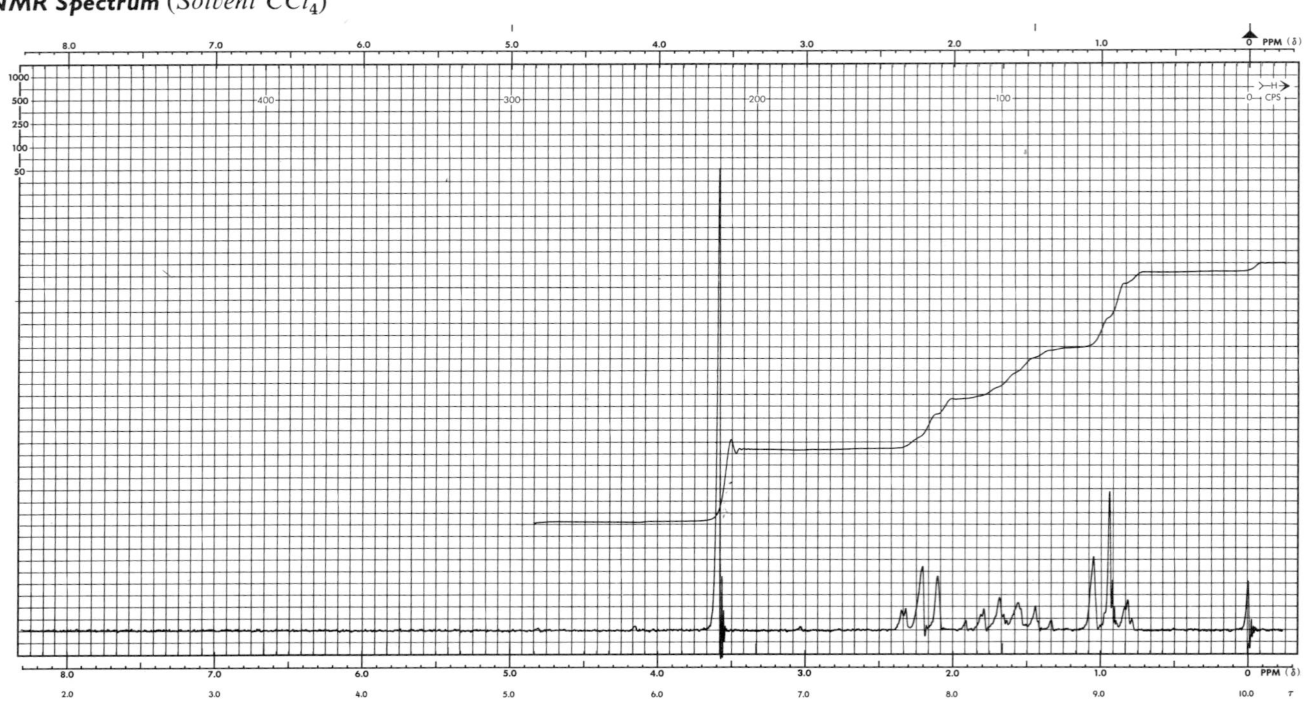

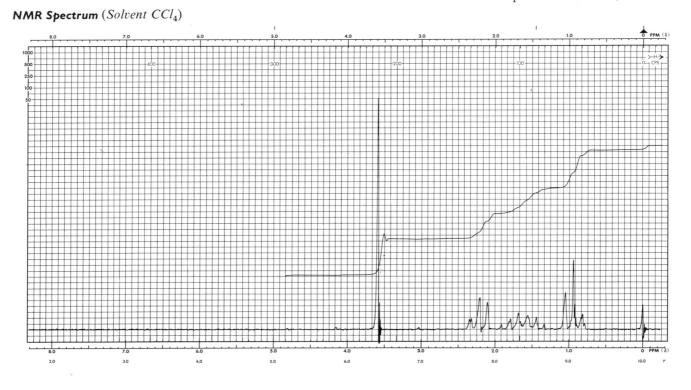

COMPOUND NUMBER 14

The following are likely molecular formulas.

$$C_5H_{14}N_2$$

$$C_6H_{14}O$$

However, the IR spectrum strongly indicates an ester group. Furthermore, an intense peak at P minus 31 in the mass spectrum and a singlet in the NMR spectrum at δ 3.60, τ 6.40 suggest a methyl ester. Apparently the $P+1$ peak is unreliable; in fact, it is too large because the mass spectrum was run at high inlet pressure in order to see the weak parent peak.

All spectra show lack of aromaticity. If we subtract the mass of $\overset{\overset{\displaystyle O}{\|}}{C}OCH_3$ from the molecular weight, we have mass 43 for the rest of the molecule which must be either a propyl or an isopropyl fragment. The triplet, sextet, triplet (all slightly distorted) in a 3:2:2 ratio in NMR spectrum certainly spell out a propyl fragment. The compound is

$$CH_3CH_2CH_2\overset{\overset{\displaystyle O}{\|}}{C}OCH_3$$

Methyl *n*-butyrate

The fragmentation spectrum offers further confirmation. The peak at m/e 74 is the typical methyl ester rearrangement ion, $\left[\begin{array}{c} CH_2{=}\underset{\displaystyle OH}{\underset{|}{C}}{-}OCH_3 \end{array}\right]^+$; that at m/e 59 is $\left[\begin{array}{c} CH_3O\underset{\displaystyle O}{\underset{\|}{C}} \end{array}\right]^+$, and that at m/e 43 is $[CH_3CH_2CH_2]^+$.

Infrared Spectrum

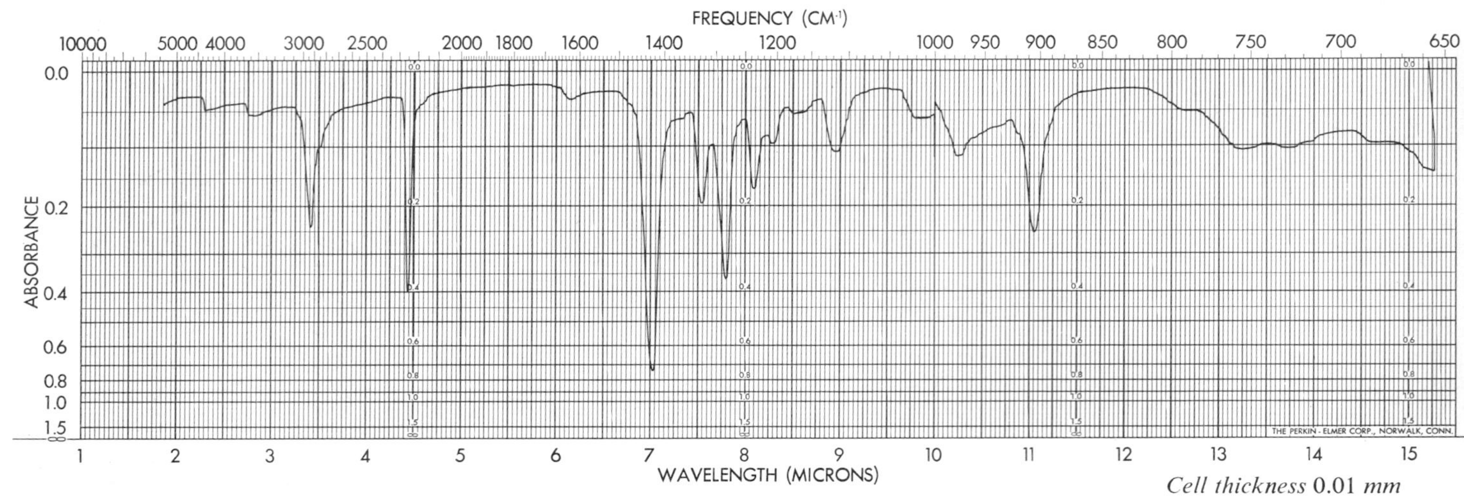

Cell thickness 0.01 *mm*

Mass Spectral Data (Relative Intensities)

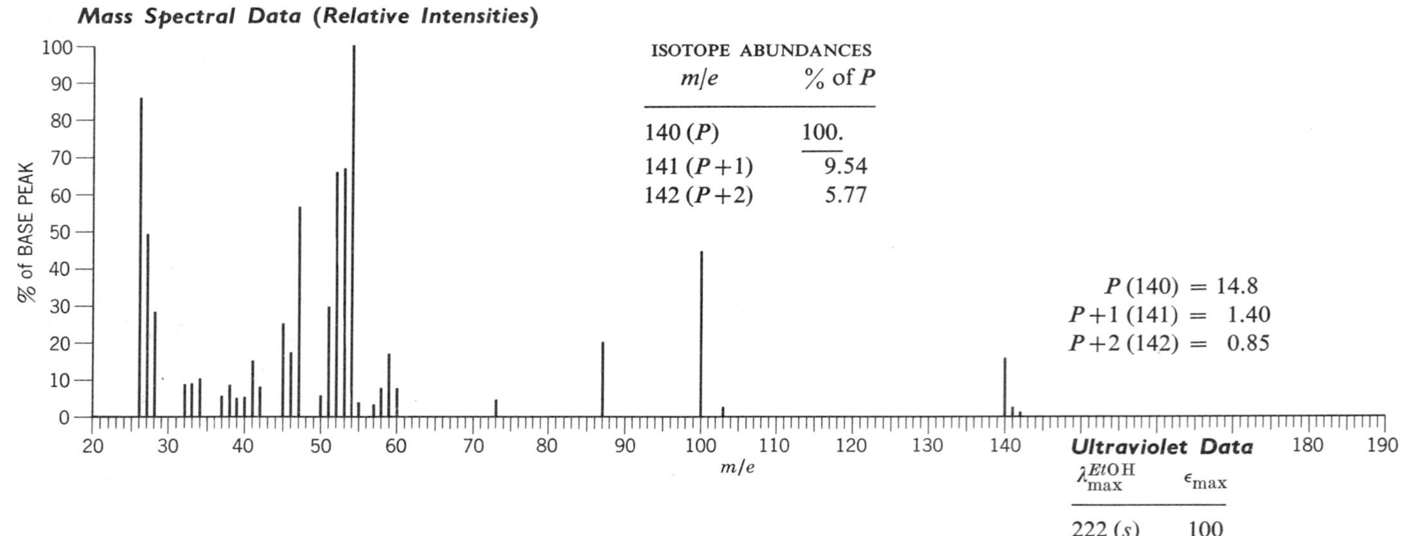

ISOTOPE ABUNDANCES

m/e	% of *P*
140 (*P*)	100.
141 (*P*+1)	9.54
142 (*P*+2)	5.77

P (140) = 14.8
P+1 (141) = 1.40
P+2 (142) = 0.85

Ultraviolet Data

λ_{max}^{EtOH}	ϵ_{max}
222 (*s*)	100

(*s*) = shoulder

NMR Spectrum (*Solvent* $CDCl_3$)

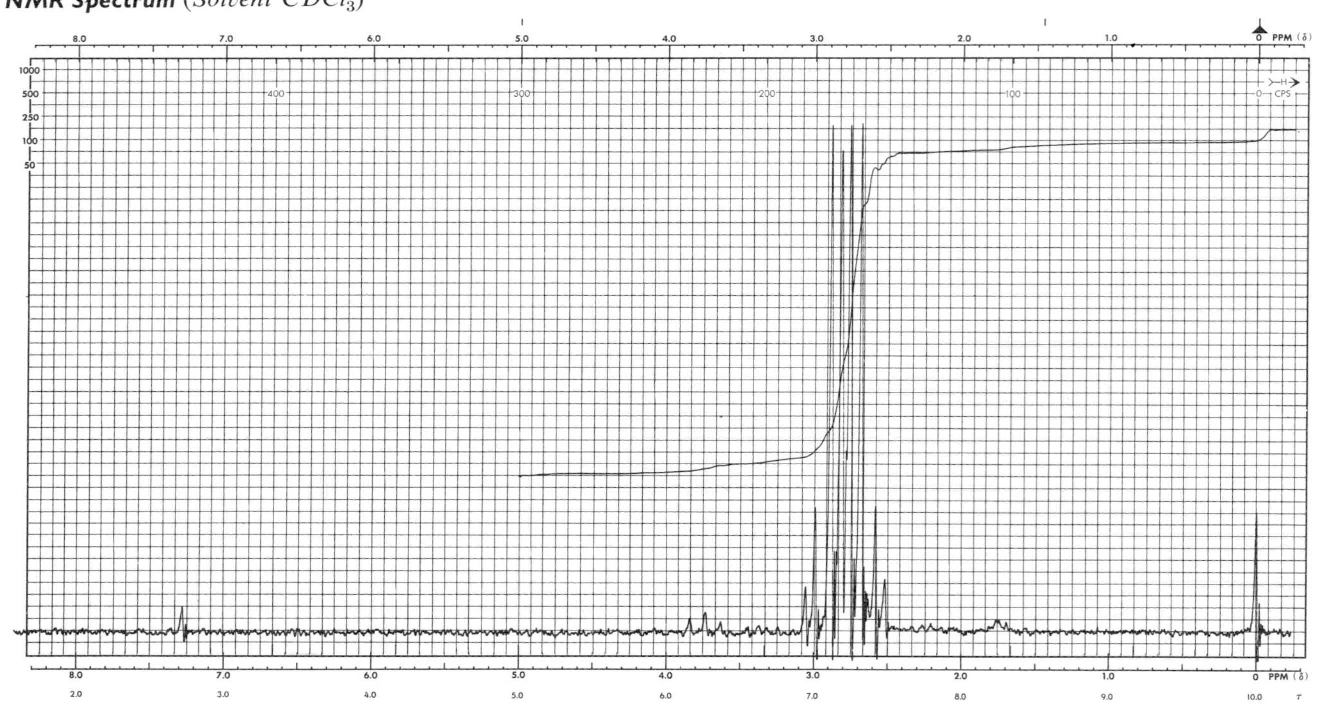

COMPOUND NUMBER 15

The molecular weight is 140, and the compound obviously contains one atom of sulfur. We look under mass 108, allowing for a 0.78 contribution to the $P+1$ peak. We write the partial formulas starting arbitrarily with $P+1 = 6.27$ and eliminating formulas containing an odd number of nitrogen atoms:

FORMULA	$P+1$
$C_5H_4N_2O$	6.27
$C_6H_4O_2$	6.63
$C_6H_8N_2$	7.38
C_7H_8O	7.73
C_8H_{12}	8.84

The infrared spectrum conveys an aliphatic impression; nor is there any indication of unsaturation or aromaticity in the ultraviolet or NMR spectrum. The sharp band at 2247 cm^{-1} (4.45 μ) in the infrared stands out conspicuously. There are only a few possibilities: An isocyanate or a nitrile are the most probable candidates.

Thus far, we can account for a sulfur atom, presumably as a sulfide, and for a nitrogen atom. In order to account for the even mass, we need another nitrogen atom which could be another isocyanate or nitrile group or possibly a tertiary amine. The correct empirical formula must be either $C_5H_4N_2O$ or $C_6H_8N_2$. Neither empirical formula will accommodate two isocyanate groups.

Let us consider the fragmentation pattern. The base peak is mass 54 which is just half of the nonsulfur-containing moiety. We seem to be dealing with a symmetrical molecule, and a glance at the NMR spectrum confirms this. We think in terms of a symmetrical dinitrile. Confirmational details now become apparent. The next largest peak in the fragmentation pattern is mass 26, obviously a C≡N group. The mass 41 peak (CH_2—C≡N + H), which we look for in aliphatic nitriles, is prominent. The mass 100 peak is large, and this may result from loss of a CH_2C≡N fragment. There appear to be a number of rearrangement peaks; this is reasonable in a molecule containing three heteroatoms.

The base peak of mass 54 must represent

$$CH_2—CH_2—C{\equiv}N$$

and the complete molecule must be

$$N{\equiv}C—CH_2—CH_2—S—CH_2—CH_2—C{\equiv}N$$

β,β'-Thiodipropionitrile

The NMR spectrum is an example of an A_2B_2 coupling with a small $\Delta\nu/J$ ratio. The large peak in the IR spectrum at 1420 cm^{-1} (7.04 μ) represents the methylene scissoring band shifted by the functional groups.

Infrared Spectrum

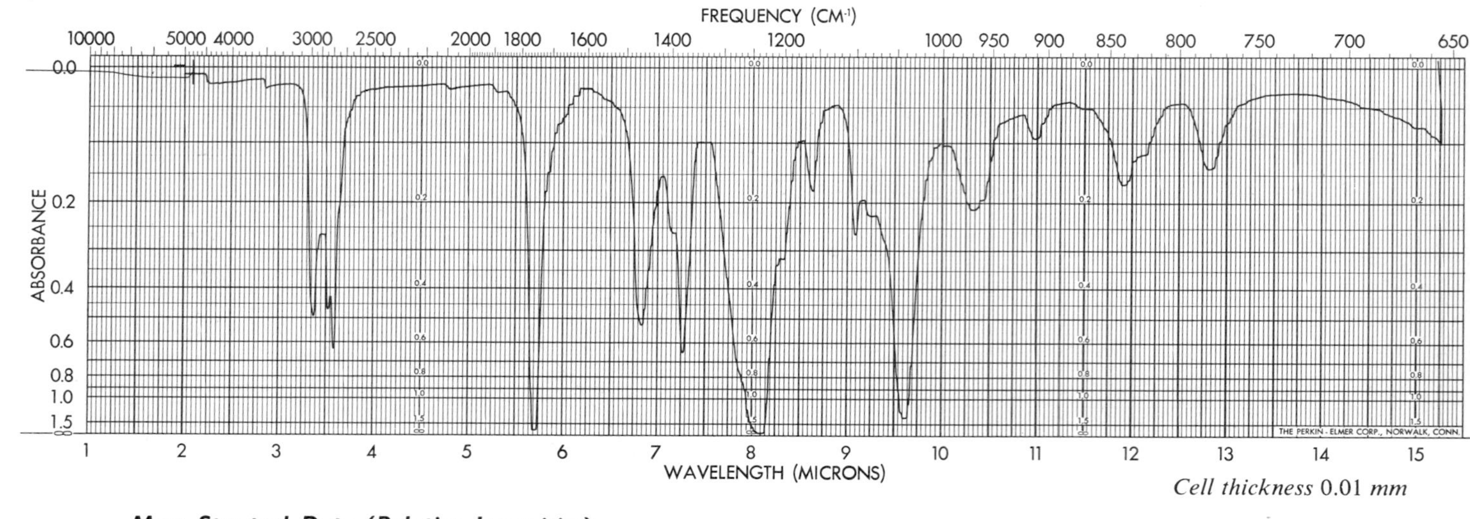

Cell thickness 0.01 *mm*

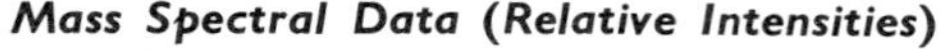

Mass Spectral Data (Relative Intensities)

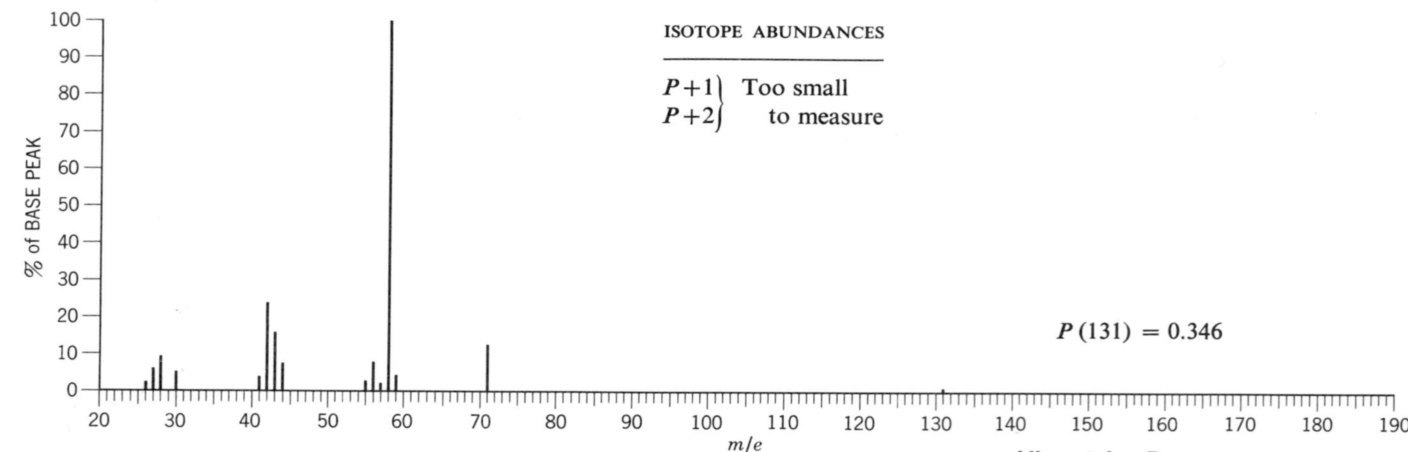

ISOTOPE ABUNDANCES

$P+1$, $P+2$: Too small to measure

$P(131) = 0.346$

Ultraviolet Data

Transparent above 210 mμ.

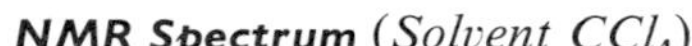

NMR Spectrum (*Solvent* CCl_4)

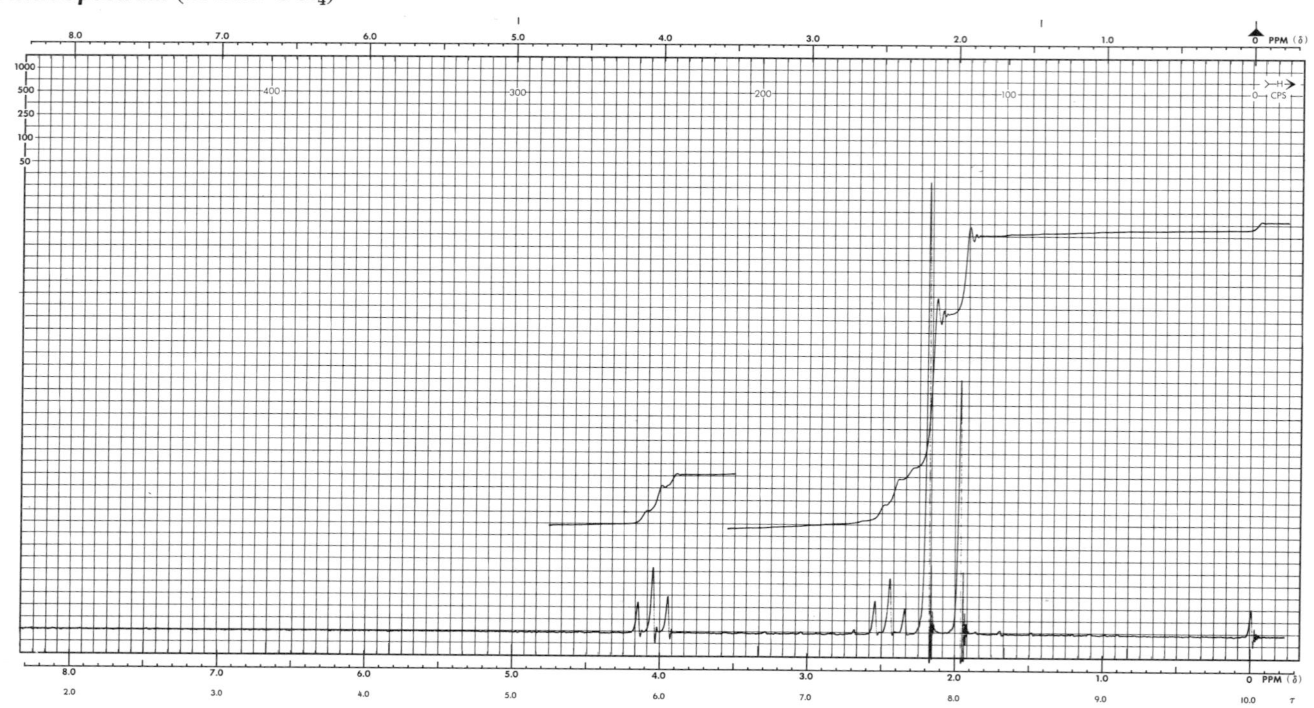

COMPOUND NUMBER 16

The parent ion peak (mass 131) of this compound was very small. The $P+1$ and $P+2$ peaks were too small for accurate measurement of intensity, and we cannot arrive at a molecular formula.

The molecular weight calls for an odd number of nitrogen atoms; let us begin with a single nitrogen atom. In the absence of evidence for primary or secondary amines, nitriles, amides, nitro compounds, or heteroaromatic compounds, we shall assume we may be dealing with a tertiary amine. There is no evidence for unsaturation or aromaticity in any of the spectra.

The infrared spectrum shows a strong carbonyl band at 1748 cm^{-1} (5.72 μ) and a typical broad strong C—O band at about 1235 cm^{-1} (8.10 μ). This combination is evidence for the presence of an acetate group. As supporting evidence there is a prominent mass 43 ($CH_3C{=}O$) in the mass spectrum, and a singlet at δ 1.95, τ 8.05 in the NMR spectrum, which we may attribute to the CH_3 of the acetate group.

The NMR spectrum shows two triplets of equal areas with the same spacings. We are justified in writing —CH_2—CH_2— and in placing the more deshielded methylene group on the oxygen of the acetate group; thus,

$$-CH_2-CH_2-O-\overset{\overset{\large O}{\|}}{C}-CH_3$$

We have postulated the presence of a tertiary amine group. The molecular weight allows for C_2H_6N. The singlet at δ 2.20, τ 7.80 in the NMR, with double the area of the acetate CH_3 group, permits us to write

$$(CH_3)_2N-$$

We can now write the complete structure

$$(CH_3)_2N-CH_2-CH_2-O-\overset{\overset{\large O}{\|}}{C}-CH_3$$

2-Dimethylaminoethyl acetate

There are other possible lines of observation and reasoning we could have followed. The base peak, mass 58, is a characteristic amine fragmentation peak which results from cleavage of the C—C bond next to the nitrogen atom. This, together with consideration of the other spectra, would have lead us directly to the fragment

$$(CH_3)_2N-CH_2-$$

The bands in the IR spectra at 2850 cm^{-1} (3.51 μ) and 2790 cm^{-1} (3.58 μ) are the C—H stretchings of the methyl groups on nitrogen. The band at 1040 cm^{-1} (9.62 μ) is characteristic of acetates of primary alcohols.

Infrared Spectrum *Compound 6-17*

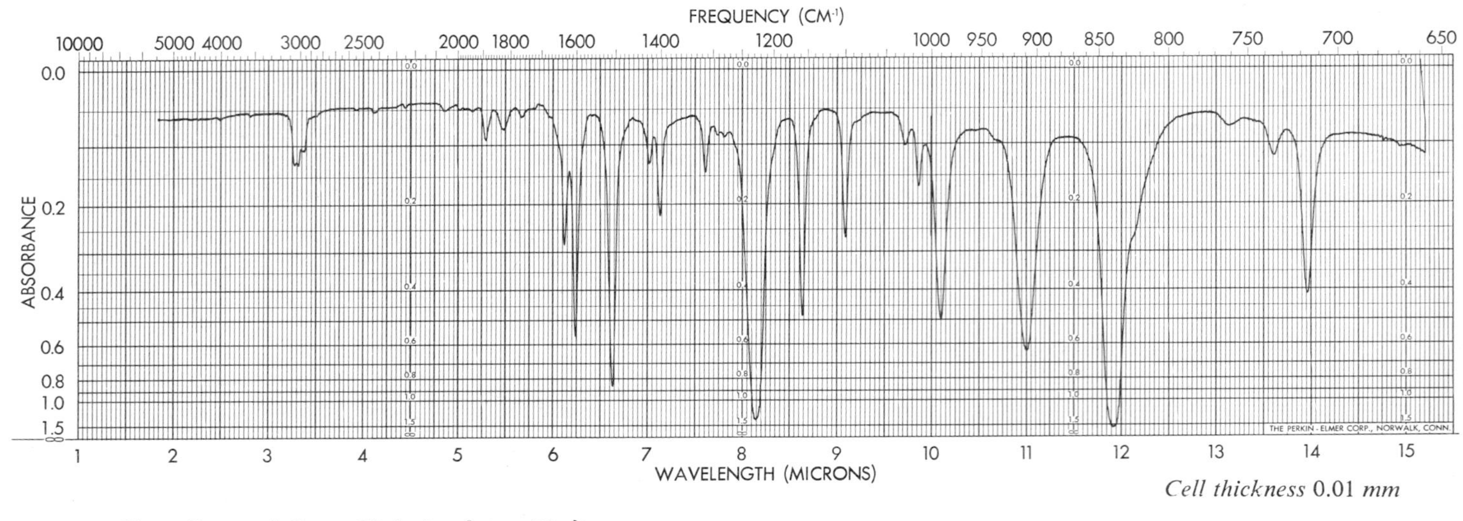

Cell thickness 0.01 *mm*

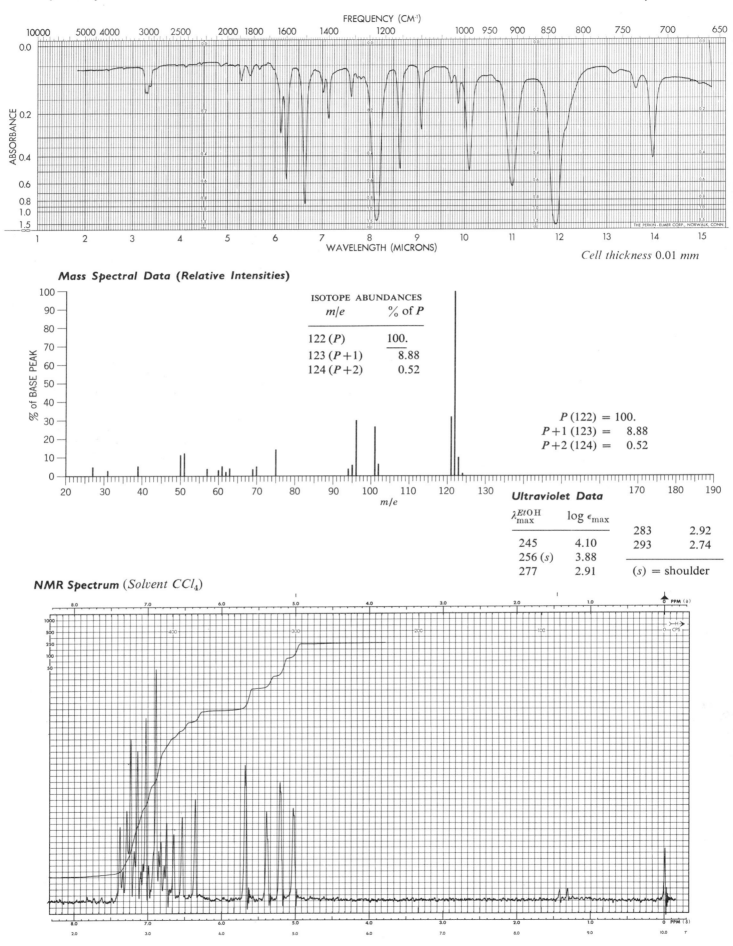

Mass Spectral Data (Relative Intensities)

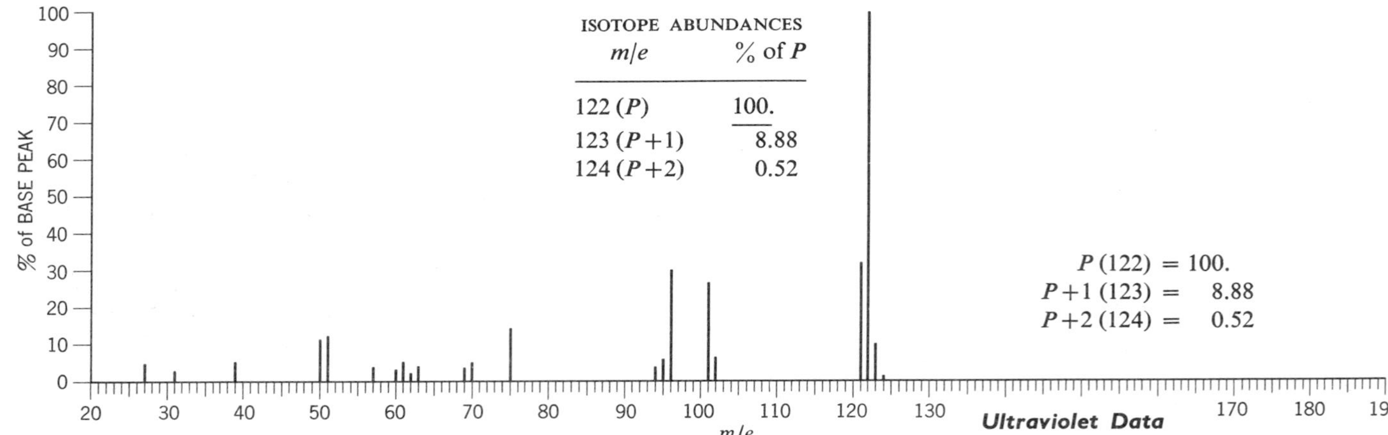

ISOTOPE ABUNDANCES

m/e	% of *P*
122 (*P*)	100.
123 (*P*+1)	8.88
124 (*P*+2)	0.52

P (122) = 100.
P+1 (123) = 8.88
P+2 (124) = 0.52

Ultraviolet Data

λ_{max}^{EtOH}	log ϵ_{max}
245	4.10
256 (*s*)	3.88
277	2.91
283	2.92
293	2.74

(*s*) = shoulder

NMR Spectrum (*Solvent* CCl_4)

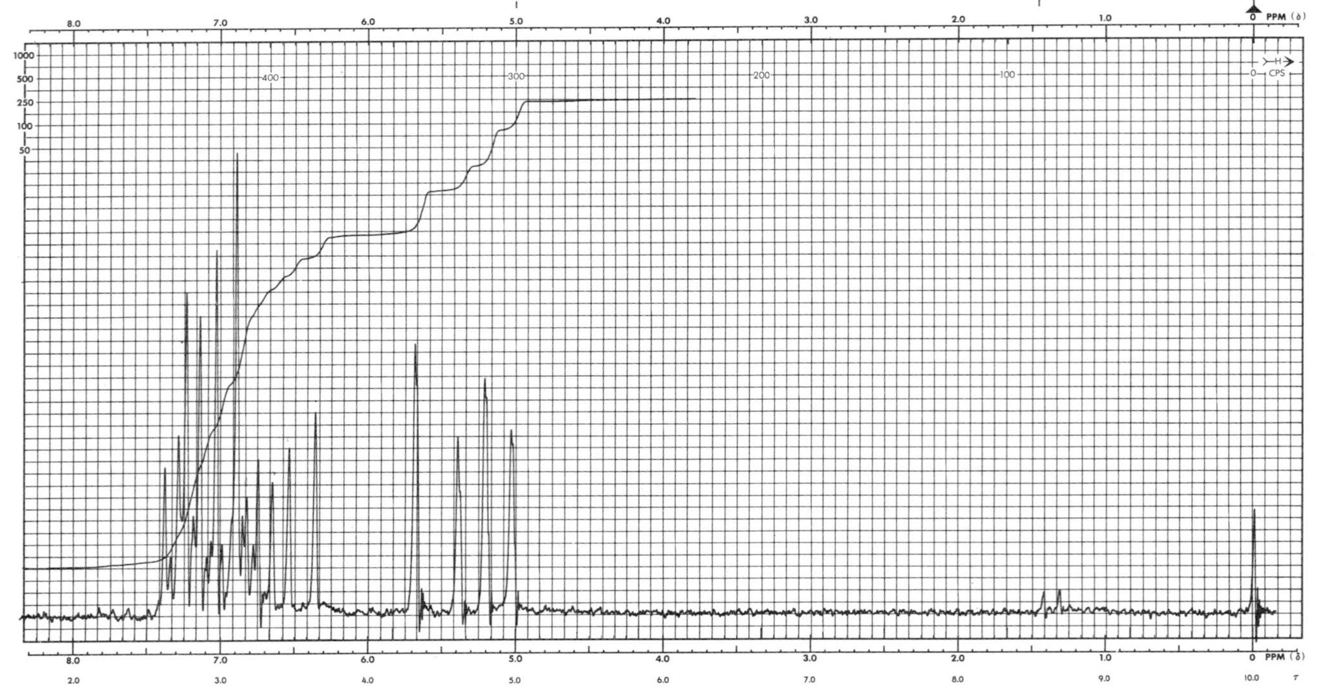

COMPOUND NUMBER 17

Possible molecular formulas are:

$C_7H_6O_2$
$C_7H_{10}N_2$
$C_8H_{10}O$
C_9H_{14}

The intensity of the parent peak, the IR, UV, and NMR spectra suggest aromaticity; in fact, the latter spectrum shows no saturated aliphatic protons.

The strongest band in the IR spectrum (838 cm^{-1}, 11.9 μ) suggests a *p*-disubstituted benzene. The next most intense band (1226 cm^{-1}, 8.15 μ) may be the aromatic C—O stretch of an aromatic ether. The prominent bands at 990 cm^{-1} (10.1 μ) and 909 cm^{-1} (11.0 μ) together with the sharp band at 1633 cm^{-1} (6.12 μ) are good evidence for a vinyl group. The intense *K*-band in the UV spectrum at 245 mμ argues for conjugation of the vinyl group with the benzene ring. A vinyl *ABX* pattern can be recognized in the olefinic region of the NMR spectrum.

Given these fragments

—C₆H₄—O—   CH=CH$_2$

and a molecular weight of 122, we cannot write a *p*-vinyl aromatic ether. In fact, none of the listed molecular formulas seem to fit, and we are in trouble.

The evidence for a vinyl group seems sound. The *X* proton of the *ABX* pattern in the NMR is rather far downfield; this strengthens the argument for placing the vinyl group on the ring. However, there is something odd about the aromatic pattern in the NMR spectrum; it lacks the typical symmetry and apparent simplicity of the $A_2'B_2'$ pattern for a *p*-disubstituted ring. Thus far, we seem to be justified in writing

(C₆H₄)—CH=CH$_2$

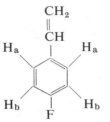

All difficulties vanish when we subtract the mass of this moiety from the molecular weight; the difference is mass 19 which can be accounted for by a fluorine atom. An aromatic C—F stretch explains the band in the IR spectrum at 1226 cm^{-1} (8.15 μ). If we place the fluorine atom para to the vinyl group to justify the IR band at 838 cm^{-1} (11.9 μ), we can rationalize the aromatic splitting.

CH$_2$=CH— ring with H$_a$, H$_a$ (ortho to vinyl), H$_b$, H$_b$ (ortho to F), F

p-Fluorostyrene

Actually, the pattern is *AA'BB'X* and is very complex. However, we can reconcile the severe distortions and extra peaks, and, with a pair of dividers, approximate a first-order analysis by considering H$_a$, H$_b$ and F to give an *AMX* pattern. H$_a$ (δ ~7.25, τ 2.75) is split by H$_b$ (J_{ab} ~ 8 cps) and by F (J_{aF} ~ 6 cps) to give the two pairs of peaks at the downfield edge of the spectrum. H$_b$ is split by H$_a$ (J_{ab} ~ 8 cps) and by F (J_{bF} ~ 8 cps); we can pick out the triplet centered at δ 6.90, τ 3.10, one peak of which overlaps one peak of the *X* proton of the vinyl groups.

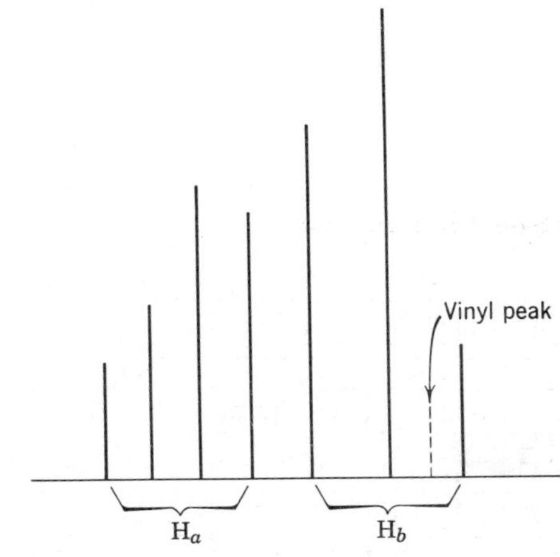

The fragmentation pattern is not much help.

Infrared Spectrum

Compound 6-18

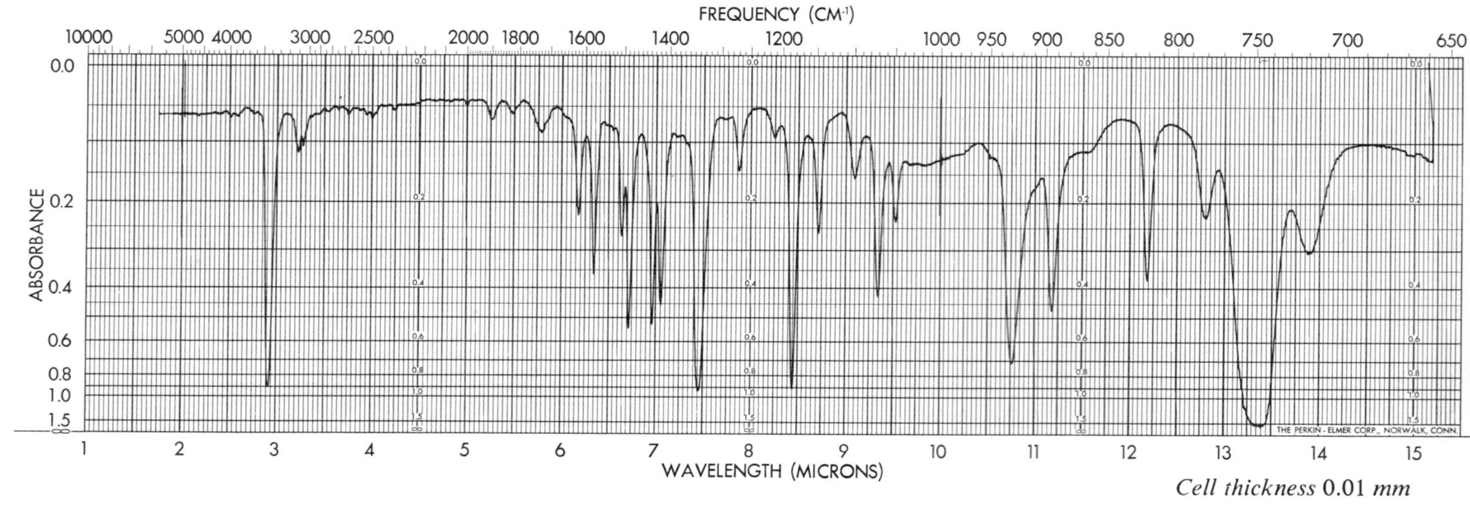

Cell thickness 0.01 *mm*

Mass Spectral Data (Relative Intensities)

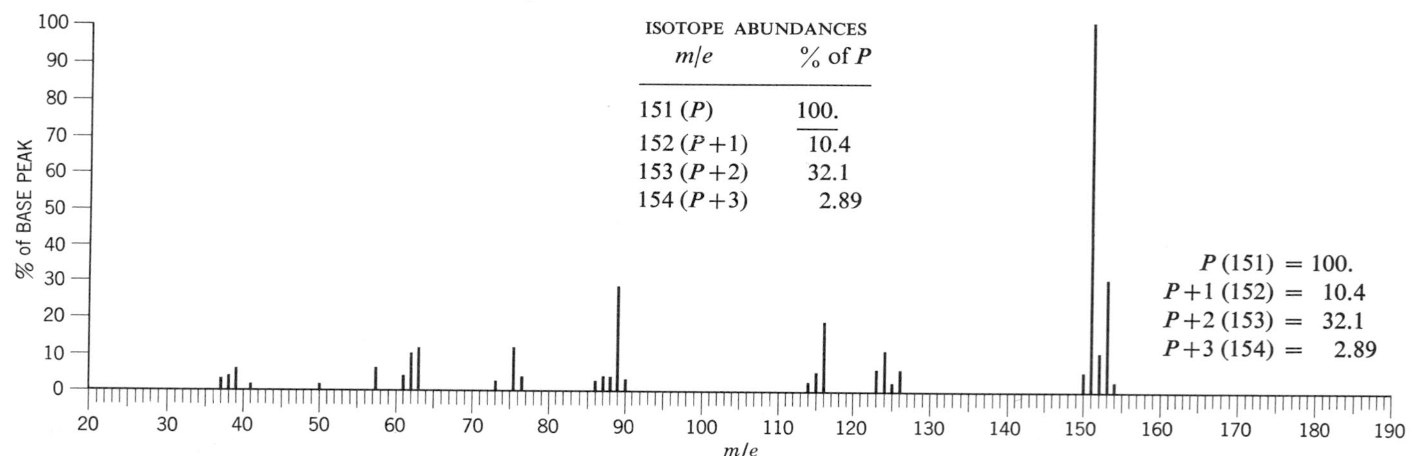

ISOTOPE ABUNDANCES

m/e	% of *P*
151 (*P*)	100.
152 (*P*+1)	10.4
153 (*P*+2)	32.1
154 (*P*+3)	2.89

P (151) = 100.
P+1 (152) = 10.4
P+2 (153) = 32.1
P+3 (154) = 2.89

Ultraviolet Data

λ_{max}^{EtOH}	log ϵ_{max}
218	4.61
272	3.88
278	3.89
288	3.77

NMR Spectrum (*Solvent* CCl_4)

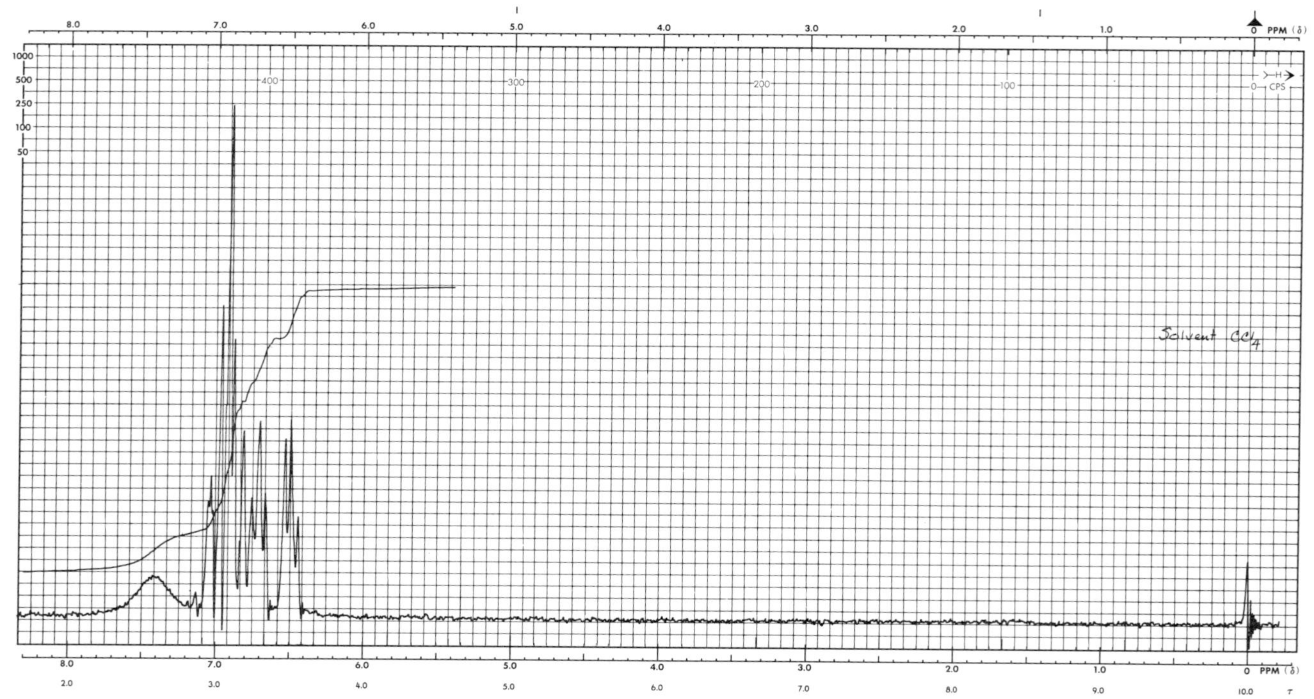

COMPOUND NUMBER 18

The $P+2$ peak (32.1%) allows for the presence of a single chlorine atom. We subtract mass 35 from the parent mass and obtain mass 116 for the rest of the molecule. The best fit to our $P+1$ peak is afforded by the following partial formulas:

FORMULA	$P+1$
$C_7H_4N_2$	8.39
$C_7H_{16}O$	7.86
C_8H_4O	8.75
C_8H_6N	9.12
C_9H_8	9.85

Since the parent mass is an odd number, the molecule contains an odd number of nitrogen atoms. Since the parent peak is also the base peak, the compound is probably aromatic. The only one of our formulas that fits is C_8H_6N.

Supporting evidence for a high degree of aromaticity is found in all of the spectra. The CH stretching region of the infrared, in fact, shows only aromatic C—H absorption. There are five strong bands between 1667 and 1429 cm^{-1} (6.0 and 7.0 μ) and four strong bands between 1000 and 715 cm^{-1} (10.0 and 14.0 μ). The strong sharp band at 3413 cm^{-1} (2.93 μ) is an invitation to place a hydrogen atom on the nitrogen atom we know to be present.

We are obviously not dealing with an aliphatic amine. Nor does an aromatic amine or a pyridine type molecule fit the picture; in the former case, we would have noted a hypsochromic shift in the ultraviolet absorption at pH 1, and in the latter case, enhanced absorption. No change in the ultraviolet spectrum is reported.

The NMR spectrum shows a broad, flat absorption centered at δ 7.40, τ 2.60. This is a typical NH absorption. Its downfield position, together with the failure mentioned above to respond to change in pH is strongly suggestive of a pyrrole or an indole NH.

With this information, we would write a chloroindole structure with the Cl atom on the benzene ring. The protons on the pyrrole ring are visible as triplets centering at δ 6.71, τ 3.29 for the 2-H, and at δ 6.50, τ 3.50 for the 3-H. Apparently the protons are not only coupled to each other, but each is also coupled to the proton on nitrogen. It is not possible from the available data to assign the position of Cl substitution because a Cl atom has very little effect on the position of ring protons. Reference spectra are needed to tell us that the compound is

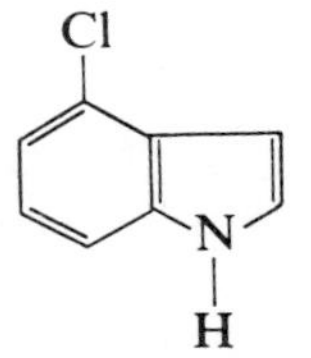

Cl

N

H

4-Chloroindole

The half-mass peaks at m/e 57½, 75½, and 76½ are doubly charged particles of mass 115, 151, and 153, respectively.

Infrared Spectrum

Compound 6-19

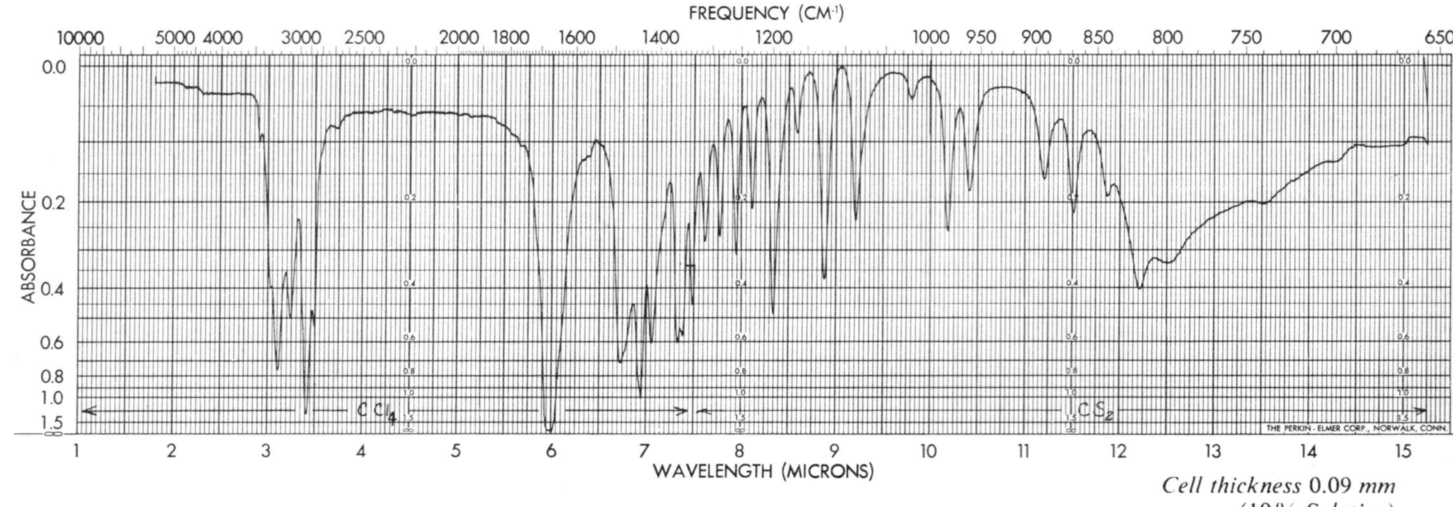

Cell thickness 0.09 *mm*
(10% *Solution*)

Mass Spectral Data (Relative Intensities)

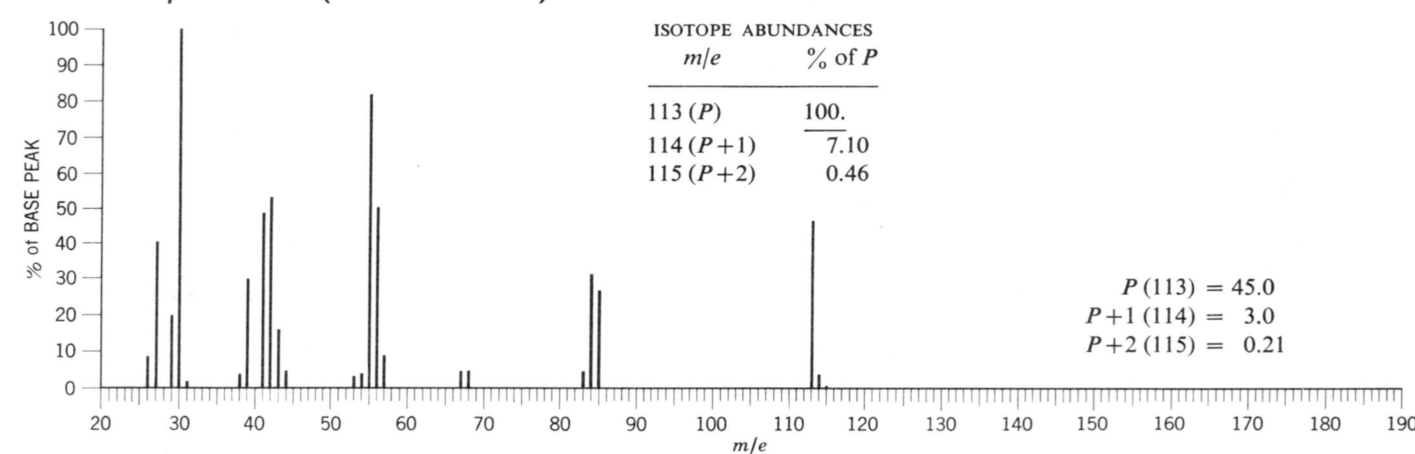

ISOTOPE ABUNDANCES

m/e	% of *P*
113 (*P*)	100.
114 (*P*+1)	7.10
115 (*P*+2)	0.46

Ultraviolet Data

*Et*OH–Featureless above 210 mμ.

NMR Spectrum (*Solvent* CCl_4)

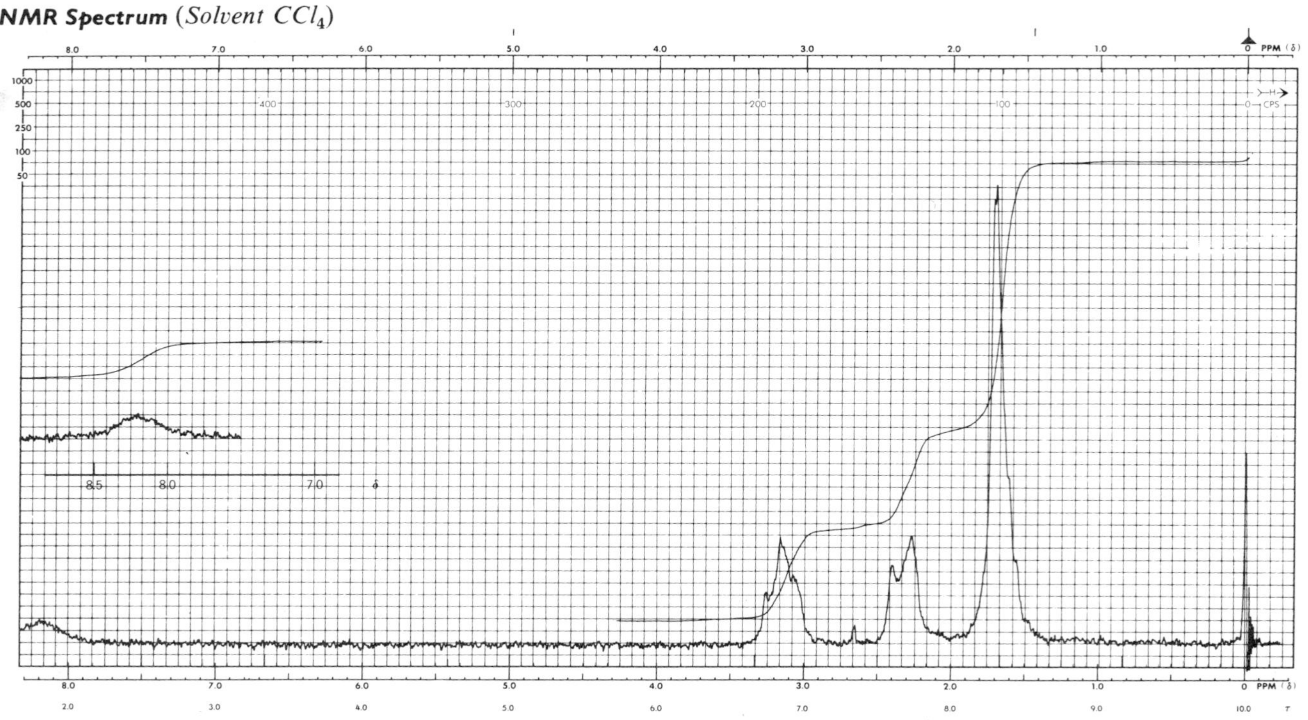

COMPOUND NUMBER 19

Under mass 113, we select the following molecular formulas which contain an odd number of nitrogen atoms:

FORMULA	$P+1$	$P+2$
$C_5H_7NO_2$	5.98	0.55
$C_5H_{11}N_3$	6.72	0.19
$C_6H_{11}NO$	7.08	0.42
$C_7H_{15}N$	8.19	0.29

The best fit is $C_6H_{11}NO$; there are two "unsaturated sites." The strong carbonyl band at 1669 cm^{-1} (5.99 μ), in the infrared spectrum, together with the series of bands in the region between 3448 and 3077 cm^{-1} (2.90 and 3.25 μ) suggests an amide group, but the absence of an amide II band makes a lactam seem more likely. The ultraviolet and the NMR spectra rule out aromatic structure and olefinic protons, although very broad absorption in the long wavelength region of the infrared spectrum may have raised the question of aromaticity. This long wavelength absorption is probably the out-of-plane NH bending vibration.

The molecular weight permits us to write a six-carbon lactam structure. All that remains is to determine the size of the ring and positions of substituents. We can ascribe the broad flat absorption centered at about δ 8.2, τ 1.8 in the NMR spectrum to a hydrogen on a lactam nitrogen. We have the following fragment:

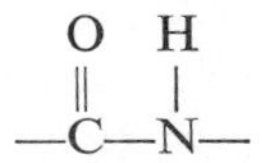

$$-\overset{\overset{\displaystyle O}{\|}}{C}-\overset{\overset{\displaystyle H}{|}}{N}-$$

The broad apparent triplet at δ 3.2, τ 6.8 in the NMR spectrum must represent a CH_2 group on the N atom, and a somewhat less deshielded CH_2 group on the C=O group would account for the absorption at about δ 2.3, τ 7.7. The integrator tells us that there are six protons under the peak centered at δ 1.70, τ 8.30.

The compound can now be formulated as

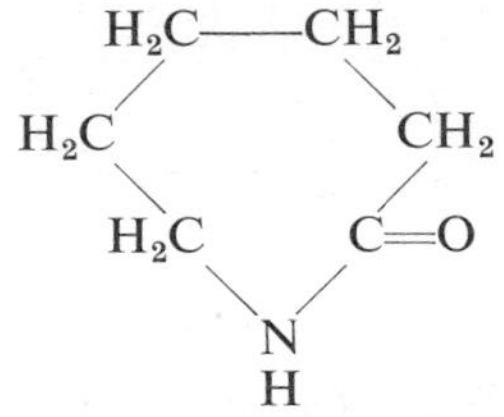

H₂C——CH₂ / H₂C CH₂ / H₂C C=O / N / H

ϵ-Caprolactam

The absorption at δ 3.2, τ 6.8 is broadened by coupling to the NH as well as by virtual coupling. The absorption at δ 2.3, τ 7.7 is broadened and distorted by virtual coupling and a small $\Delta\nu/J$ ratio. The base peak at m/e 30 may result as follows:

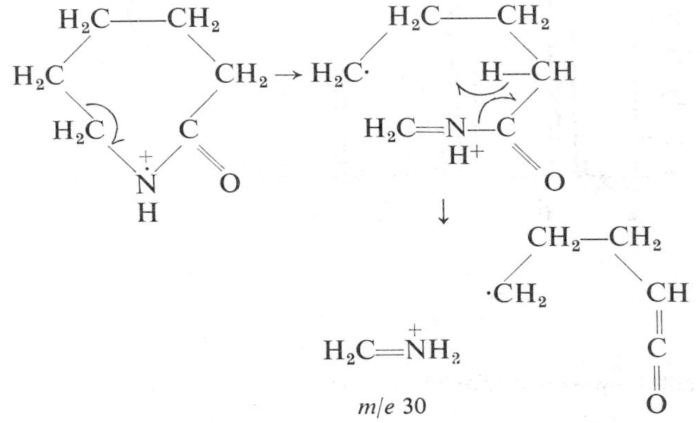

$H_2C\overset{+}{=}NH_2$

m/e 30

Infrared Spectrum

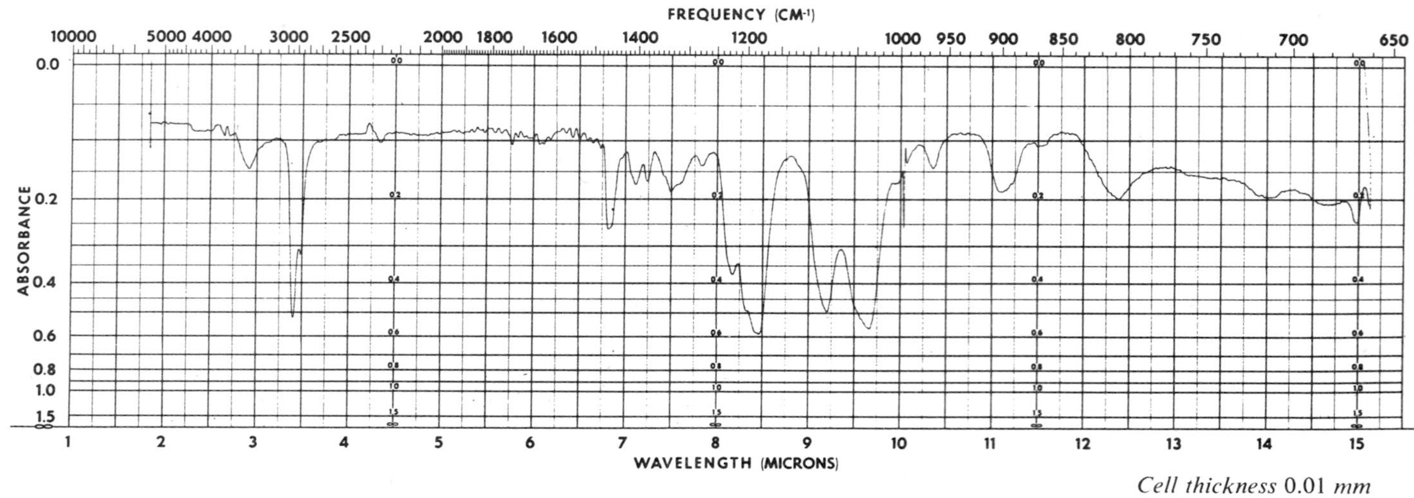

Cell thickness 0.01 *mm*

Mass Spectral Data (Relative Intensities)

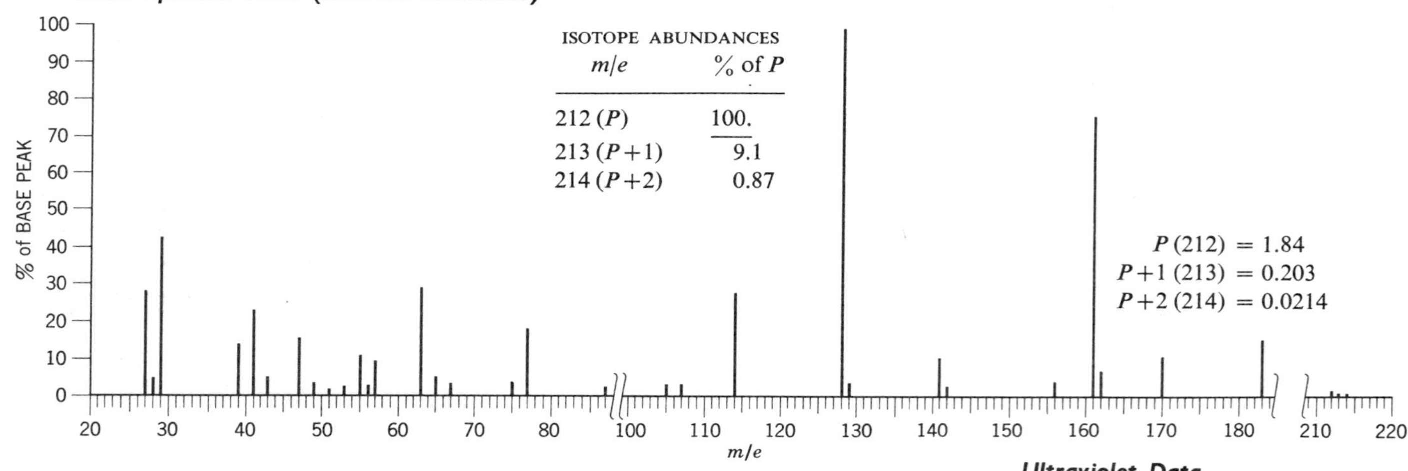

ISOTOPE ABUNDANCES

m/e	% of P
212 (P)	100.
213 ($P+1$)	9.1
214 ($P+2$)	0.87

$P(212) = 1.84$
$P+1\ (213) = 0.203$
$P+2\ (214) = 0.0214$

Ultraviolet Data

Featureless beyond 210 mμ.

NMR Spectrum (*Solvent* CCl_4)

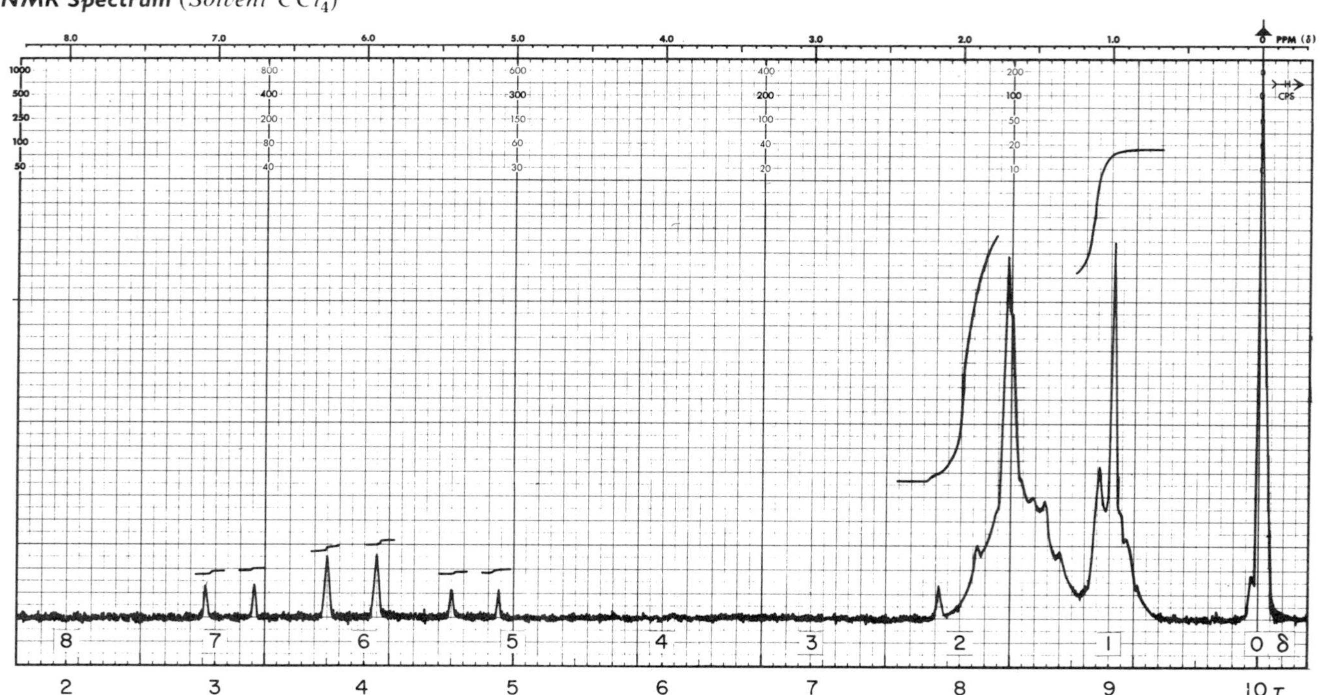

COMPOUND NUMBER 20

This example is presented to show some of the limitations of the methodology.

It is not likely that the four spectra presented would furnish sufficient evidence to identify this compound. However, given its history, we make the identification quite readily.

The compound was isolated as an unexpected, but rational, by-product from the following synthesis (S. A. Fuqua, W. G. Duncan, and R. M. Silverstein, *J. Org. Chem.*, **30**, 2543 (1965)):

$$C_6H_5-\underset{\underset{O}{\|}}{C}-C_6H_5 + Bu_3P + CF_2ClCOONa \xrightarrow[DMF]{160^\circ}$$

$$Bu_3P\rightarrow O + C_6H_5-\underset{\underset{CF_2}{\|}}{C}-C_6H_5$$

The reaction should proceed by formation of a Wittig reagent from the phosphine and the CF_2 carbene formed by pyrolysis of sodium chlorodifluoroacetate. The Wittig reagent should react with the ketone.

$$Bu_3P{=}CF_2 + C_6H_5-\underset{\underset{O}{\|}}{C}-C_6H_5 \rightarrow$$

$$C_6H_5-\underset{\underset{CF_2}{\|}}{C}-C_6H_5 + Bu_3P\rightarrow O$$

The molecular weight of the by-product is 212. It is obvious from the spectra that the material is not a benzophenone derivative. Rather, aliphatic absorption predominates in the spectra. The compound may contain phosphorus or fluorine or both. Obviously no chlorine is present. The strong absorption at 1182 cm^{-1} (8.46 μ) may be aliphatic P→O absorption, and that at 1087 cm^{-1} (9.20 μ) and 1033 cm^{-1} (9.68 μ) may result from C—F stretching. The puzzling thing is that if we have the P→O group present, we cannot possibly have three butyl groups; the compound is not the usual product $Bu_3P\rightarrow O$.

Suppose we assume displacement of one of the butyl group; this leaves mass 51 short of the molecular weight. It does not take long to propose CHF_2 as a possible fragment, and to confirm it with the striking NMR pattern. If the upfield protons represent the 18 protons of the butyl groups, the entire downfield pattern represents a single proton, centered at δ 6.07, τ 3.93. The proton is split into a triplet by the geminal F atoms (J_{HF} 49.4 cps), and each peak is again split into a doublet by the P atom (J_{HP} 19.4 cps). The compound is therefore.

$$Bu-\overset{\overset{O}{\uparrow}}{\underset{\underset{CHF_2}{|}}{P}}-Bu$$

Dibutyldifluoromethylphosphine oxide

Some of the major fragmentation peaks can be accounted for: *m/e* 183 (parent minus CH_3CH_2), *m/e* 161 (P minus CHF_2), *m/e* 47 (P→O). The base peak, *m/e* 128 must result from complex rearrangements. The $P+1$ and $P+2$ peaks are in agreement with the calculated values for the proposed structure.

The rationale for this unexpected product depends on rearrangement of the initial Wittig reagent.

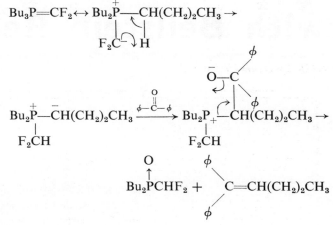

$$Bu_3P{=}CF_2 \leftrightarrow Bu_2\overset{+}{P}(\overset{-}{C}F_2)-CH(CH_2)_2CH_3 \;(\text{H}) \rightarrow$$

$$Bu_2\overset{+}{P}(F_2CH)-\overset{-}{C}H(CH_2)_2CH_3 \xrightarrow{\phi-\overset{O}{\overset{\|}{C}}-\phi} Bu_2\overset{+}{P}(F_2CH)-CH(CH_2)_2CH_3\,(-\overset{-}{O}-C\phi_2) \rightarrow$$

$$Bu_2\overset{\overset{O}{\uparrow}}{P}CHF_2 + \phi_2C{=}CH(CH_2)_2CH_3$$

CHAPTER 7

Sets of Spectra with Beilstein References

This chapter consists of ten sets of spectra. Each compound represented by a set of spectra is identified by a reference to Beilstein. We again remind the reader that the compounds contain only C, H, O, N, S, and the halogens.

Infrared Spectrum

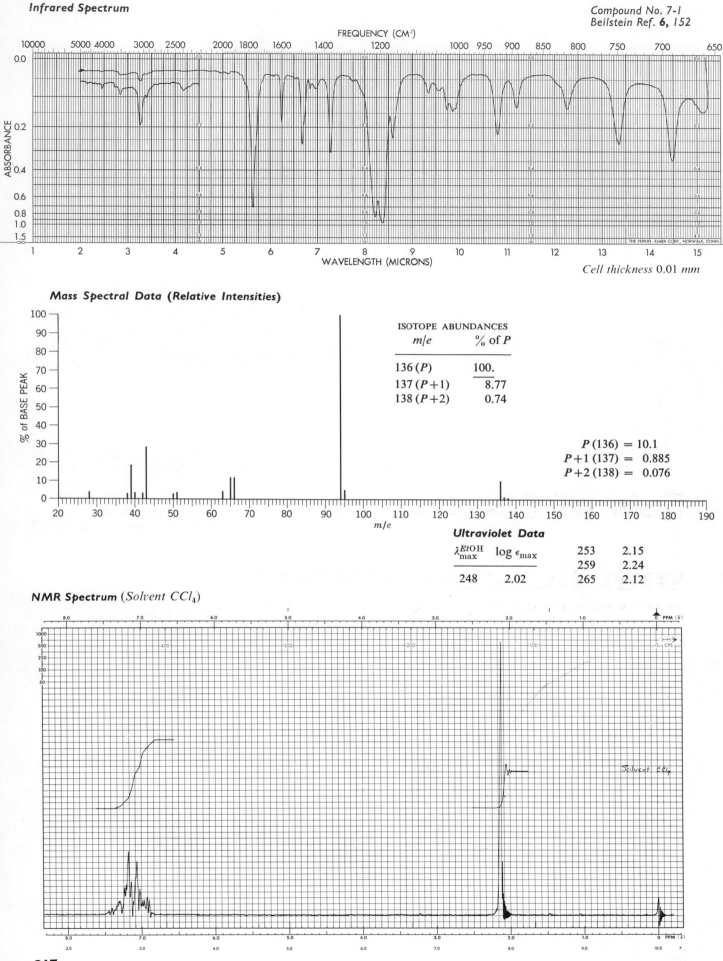

Compound No. 7-1
*Beilstein Ref. **6**, 152*

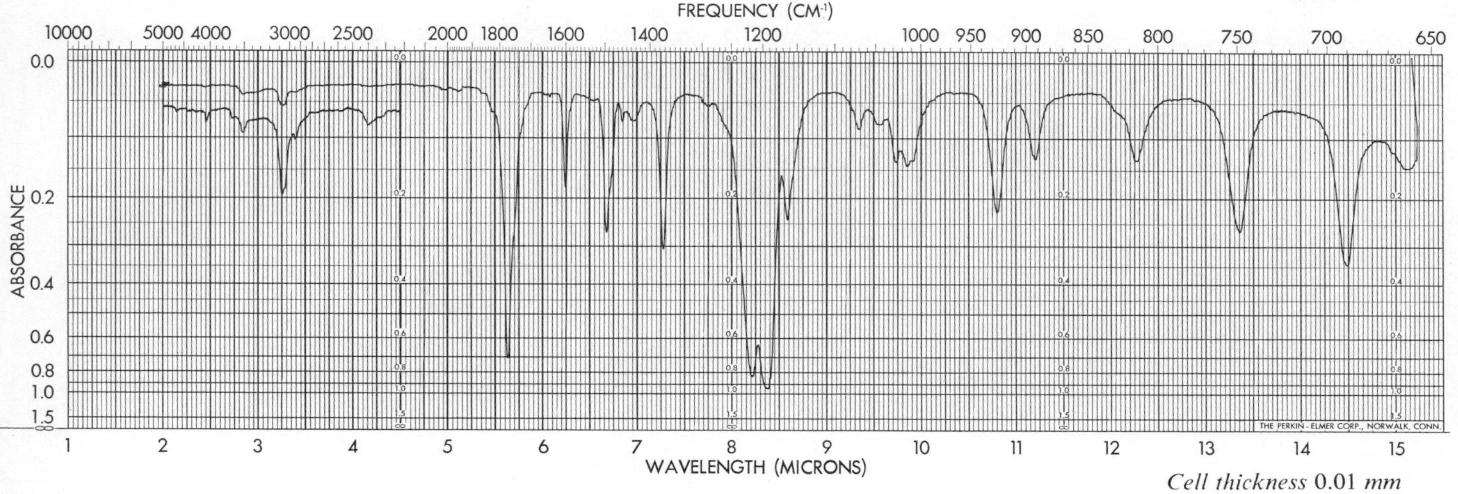

Cell thickness 0.01 *mm*

Mass Spectral Data (Relative Intensities)

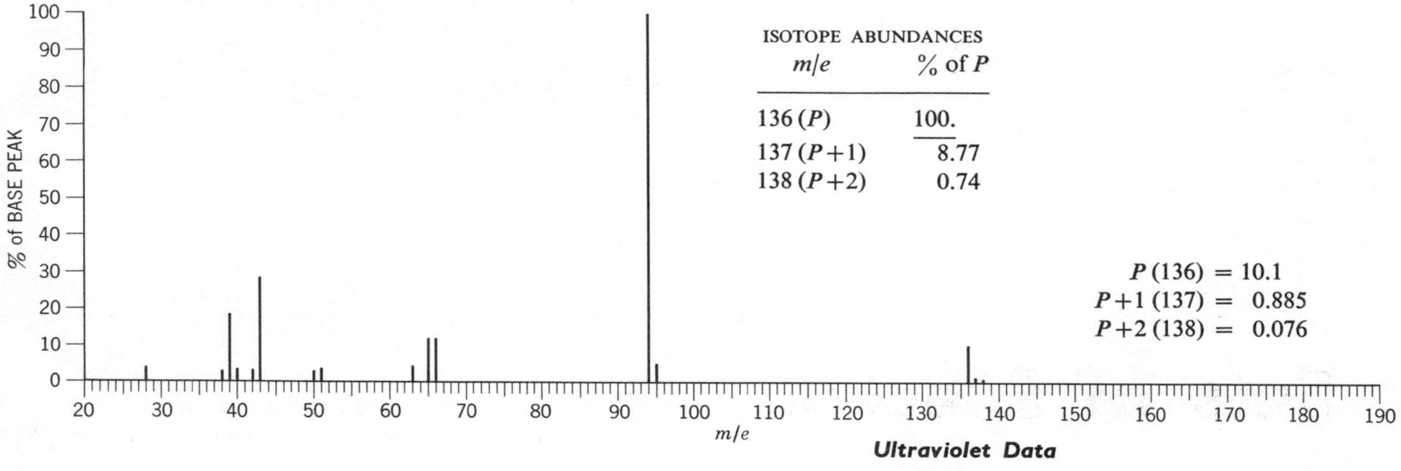

ISOTOPE ABUNDANCES

m/e	% of *P*
136 (*P*)	100.
137 (*P*+1)	8.77
138 (*P*+2)	0.74

P (136) = 10.1
P+1 (137) = 0.885
P+2 (138) = 0.076

Ultraviolet Data

λ_{max}^{EtOH}	log ϵ_{max}
248	2.02
253	2.15
259	2.24
265	2.12

NMR Spectrum (*Solvent* CCl_4)

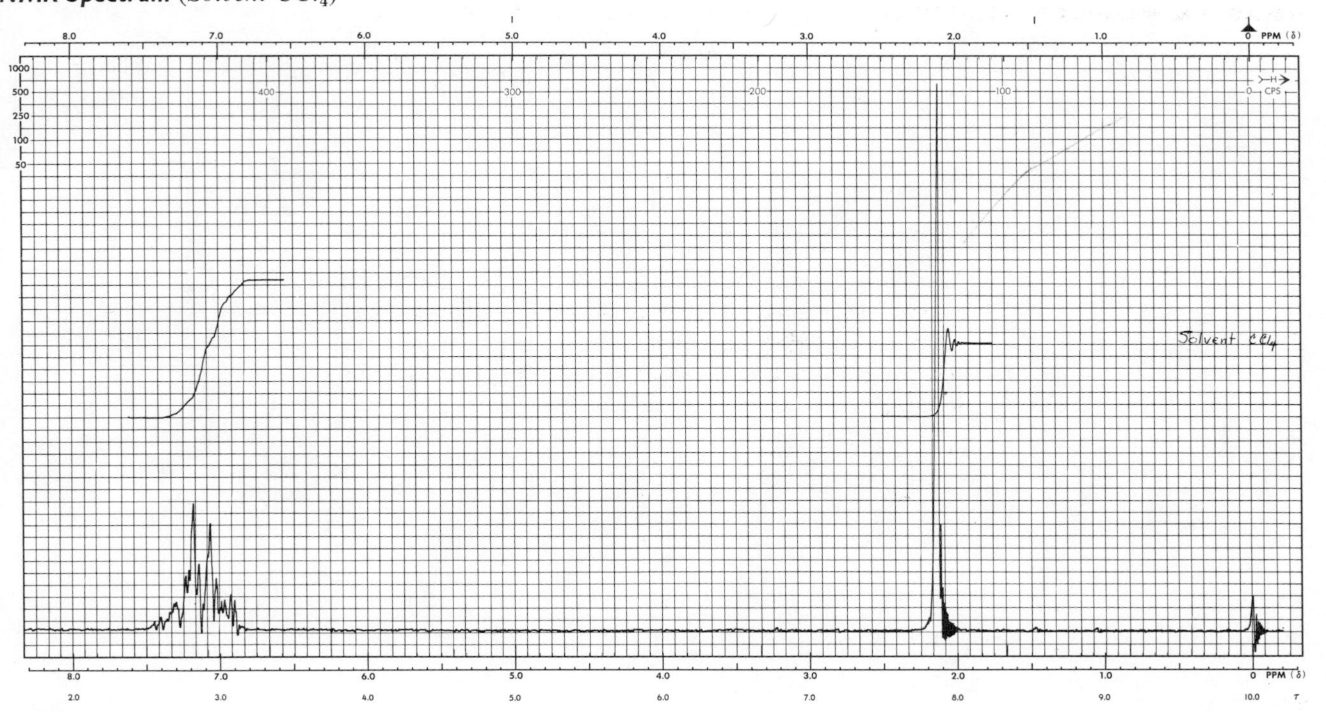

Infrared Spectrum

Compound No. 7-2
Beilstein Ref. I, 405

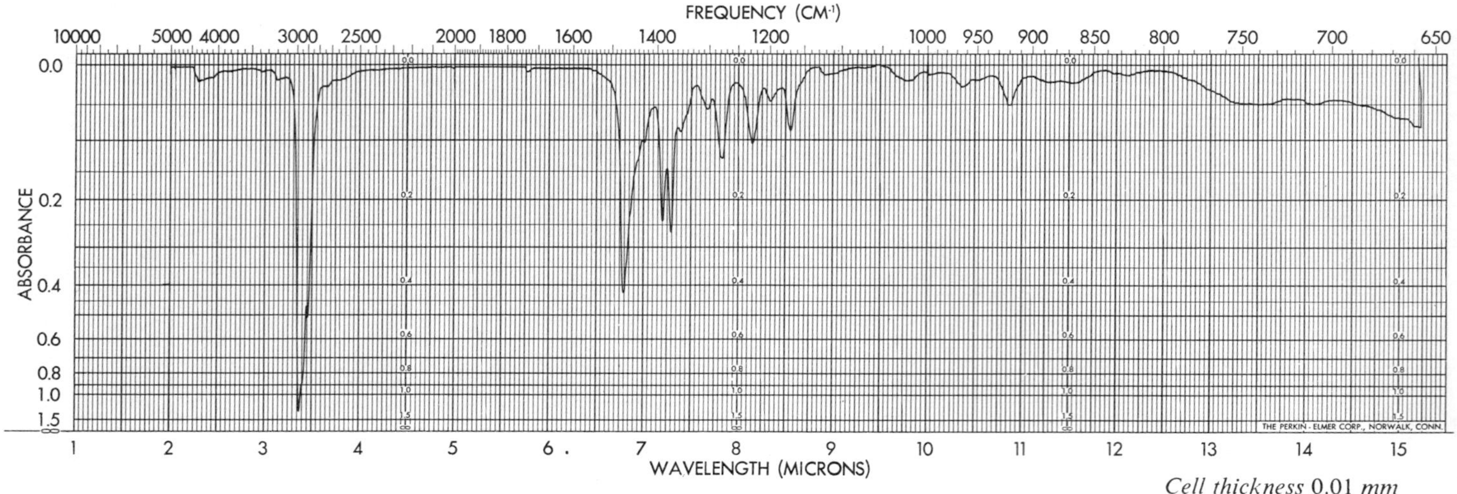

Cell thickness 0.01 *mm*

Mass Spectral Data (Relative Intensities)

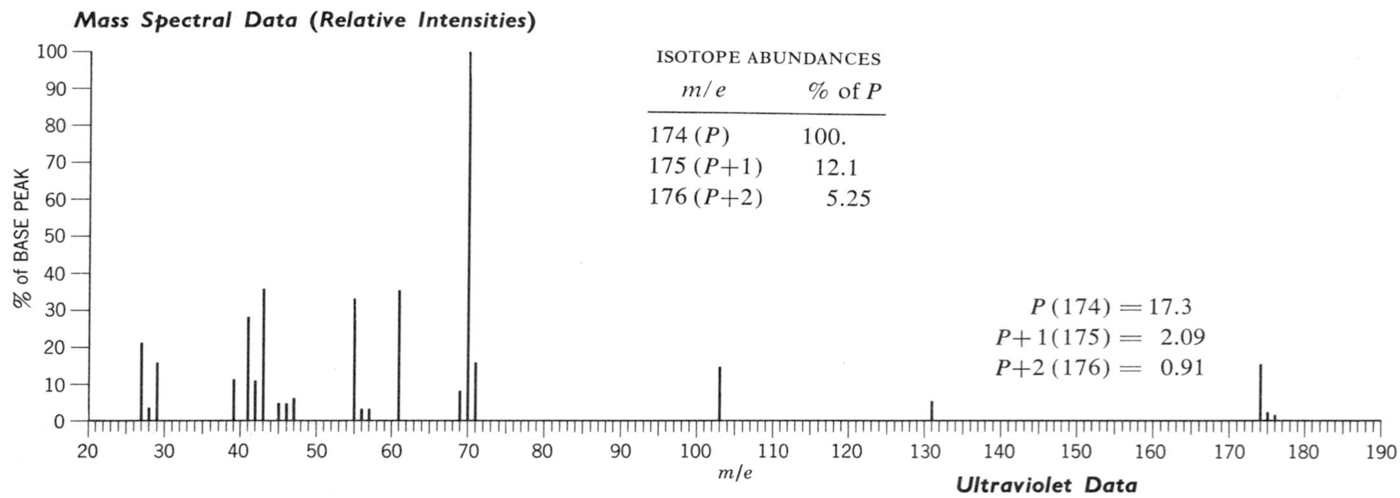

ISOTOPE ABUNDANCES

m/e	% of *P*
174 (*P*)	100.
175 (*P*+1)	12.1
176 (*P*+2)	5.25

P (174) = 17.3
P+1 (175) = 2.09
P+2 (176) = 0.91

Ultraviolet Data

Featureless beyond 210 mμ.

NMR Spectrum (Solvent $CDCl_3$)

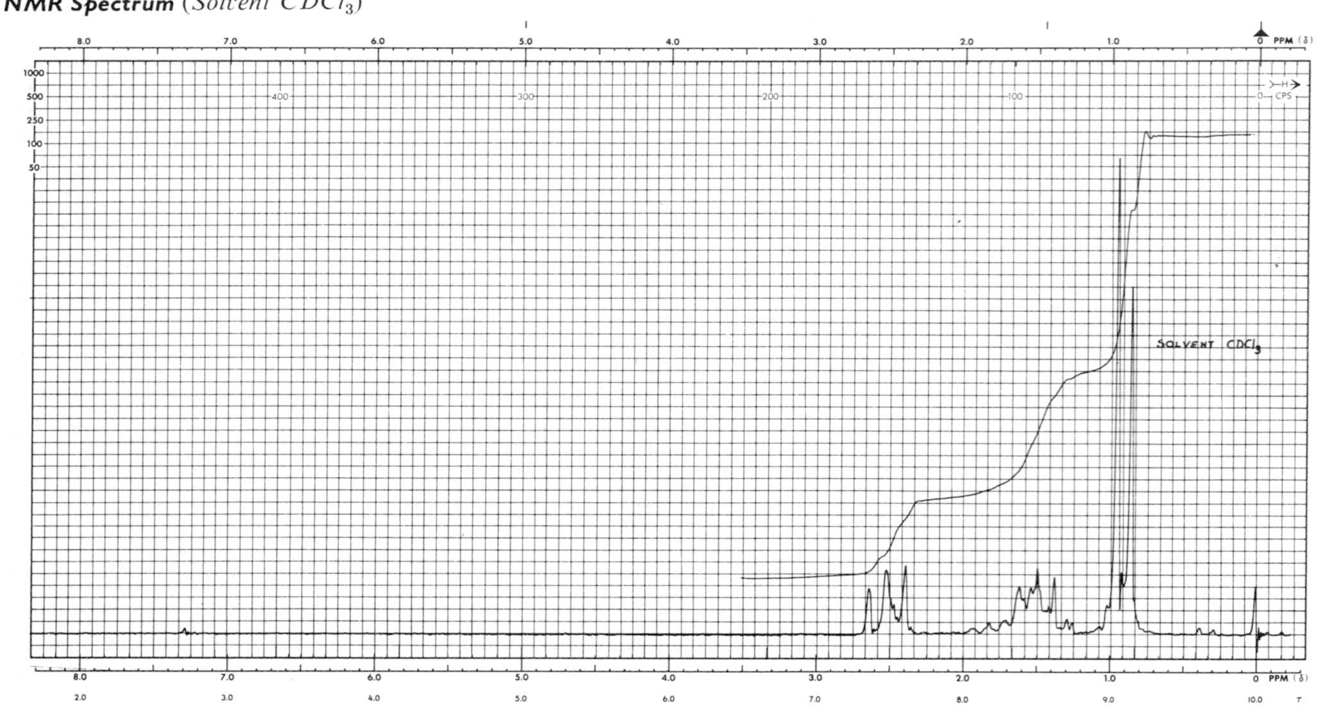

Infrared Spectrum

Compound No. 7-3
Beilstein Ref. **2,** *136*

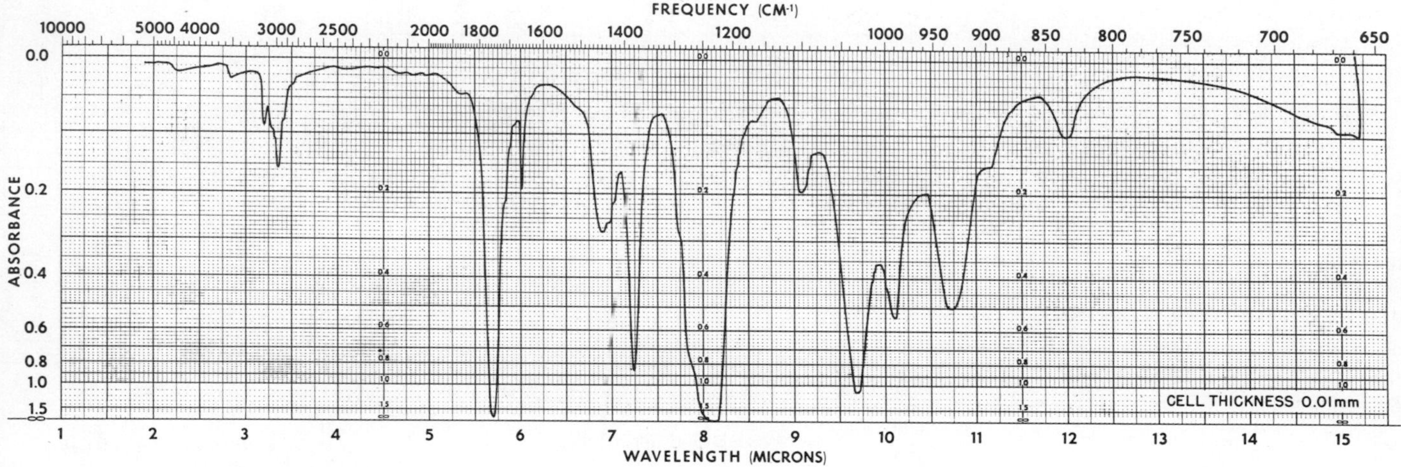

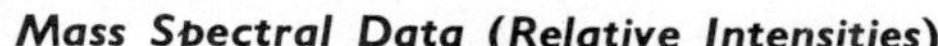

Mass Spectral Data (Relative Intensities)

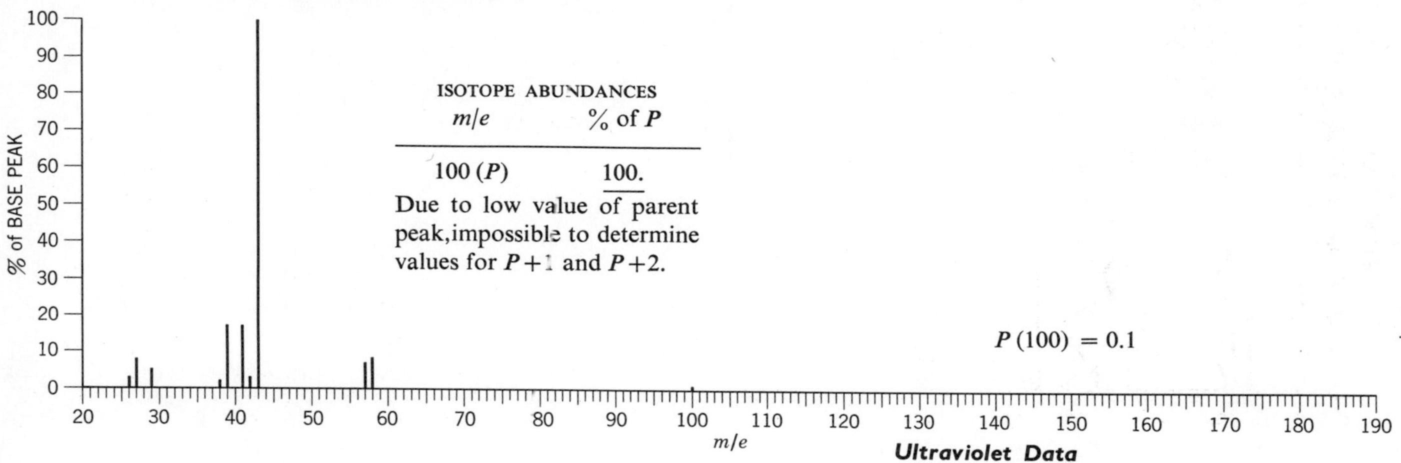

ISOTOPE ABUNDANCES

m/e	% of *P*
100 (*P*)	100.

Due to low value of parent peak, impossible to determine values for $P+1$ and $P+2$.

$P(100) = 0.1$

Ultraviolet Data

Transparent above 210 mμ.

NMR Spectrum (*Solvent* CCl_4)

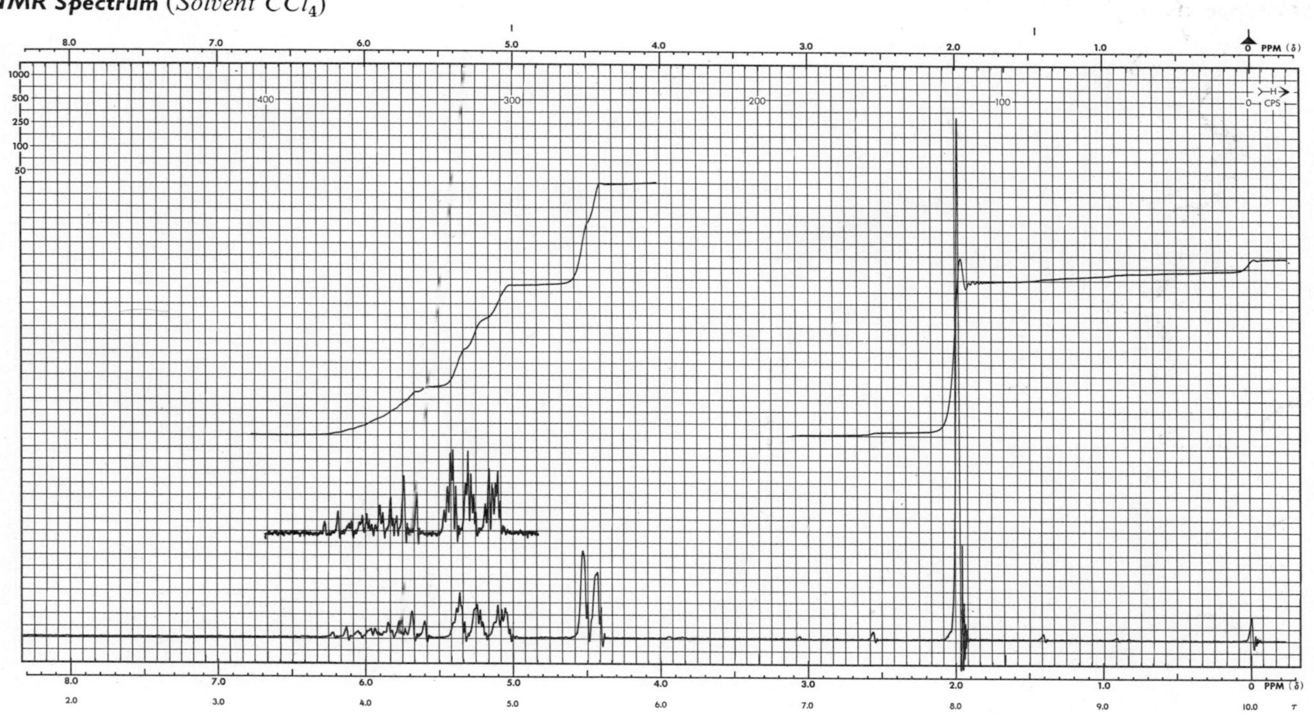

Infrared Spectrum

Compound No. 7-4
Beilstein Ref. **7**, 271

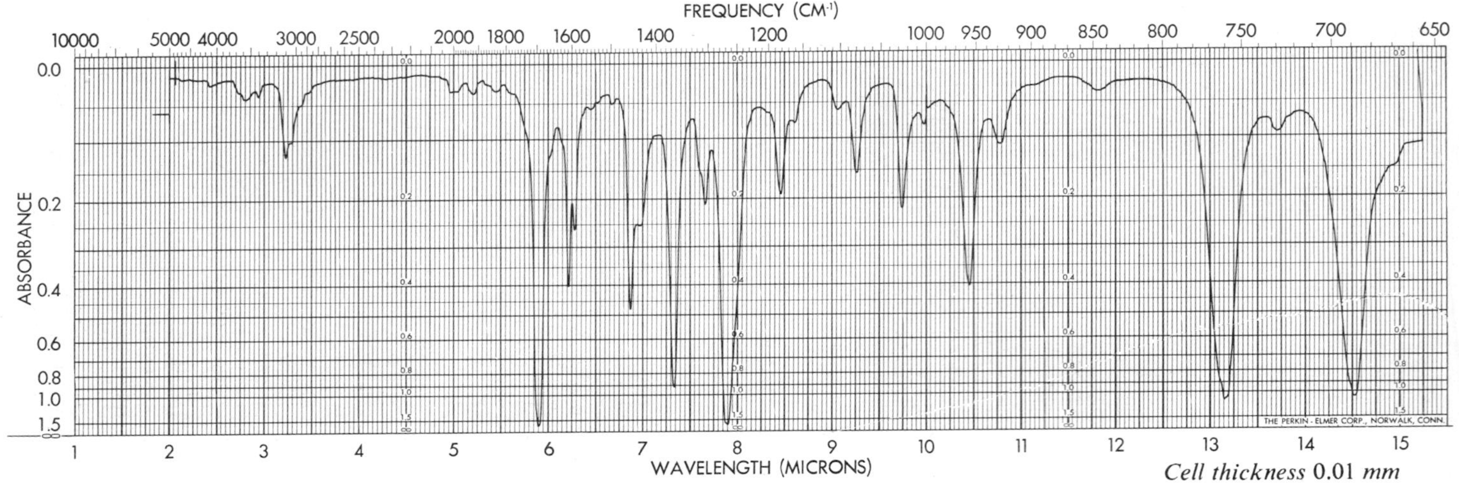

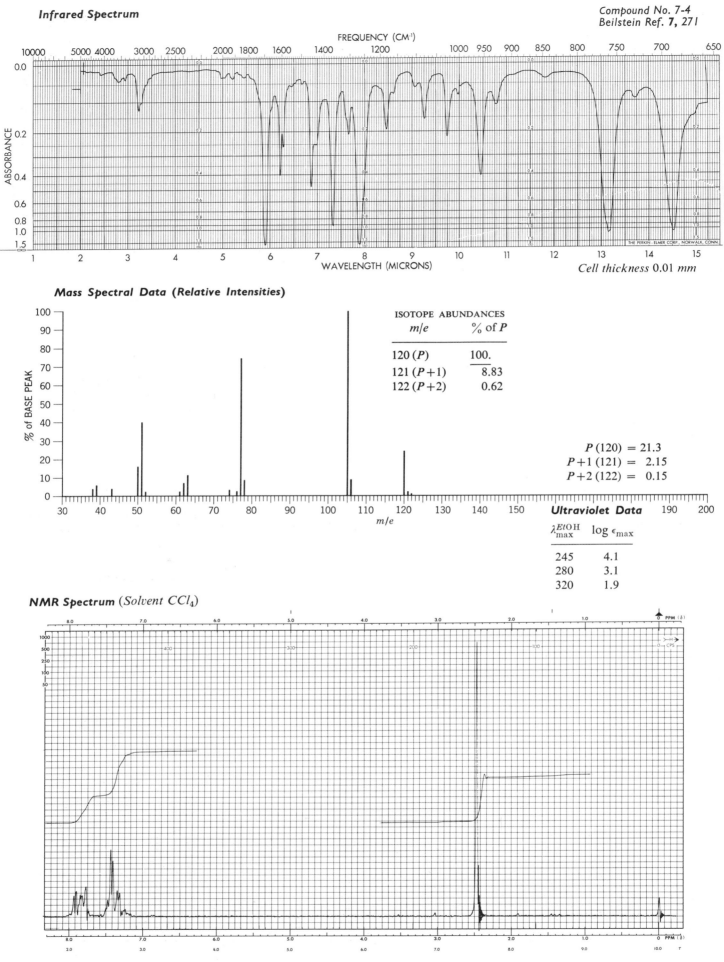

Mass Spectral Data (Relative Intensities)

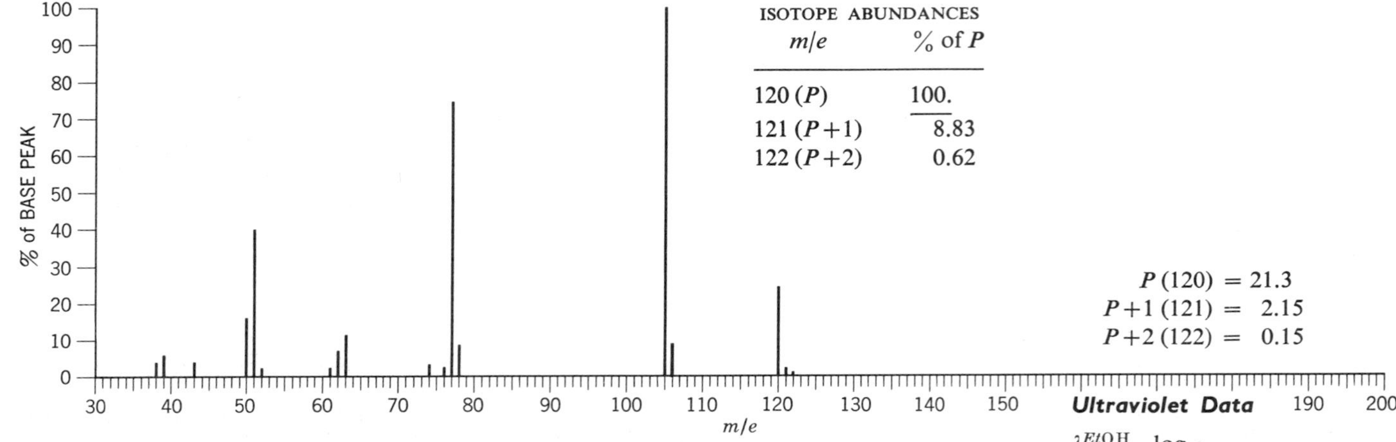

ISOTOPE ABUNDANCES

m/e	% of *P*
120 (*P*)	100.
121 (*P*+1)	8.83
122 (*P*+2)	0.62

P (120) = 21.3
P+1 (121) = 2.15
P+2 (122) = 0.15

Ultraviolet Data

λ_{max}^{EtOH}	$\log \epsilon_{max}$
245	4.1
280	3.1
320	1.9

NMR Spectrum (*Solvent* CCl_4)

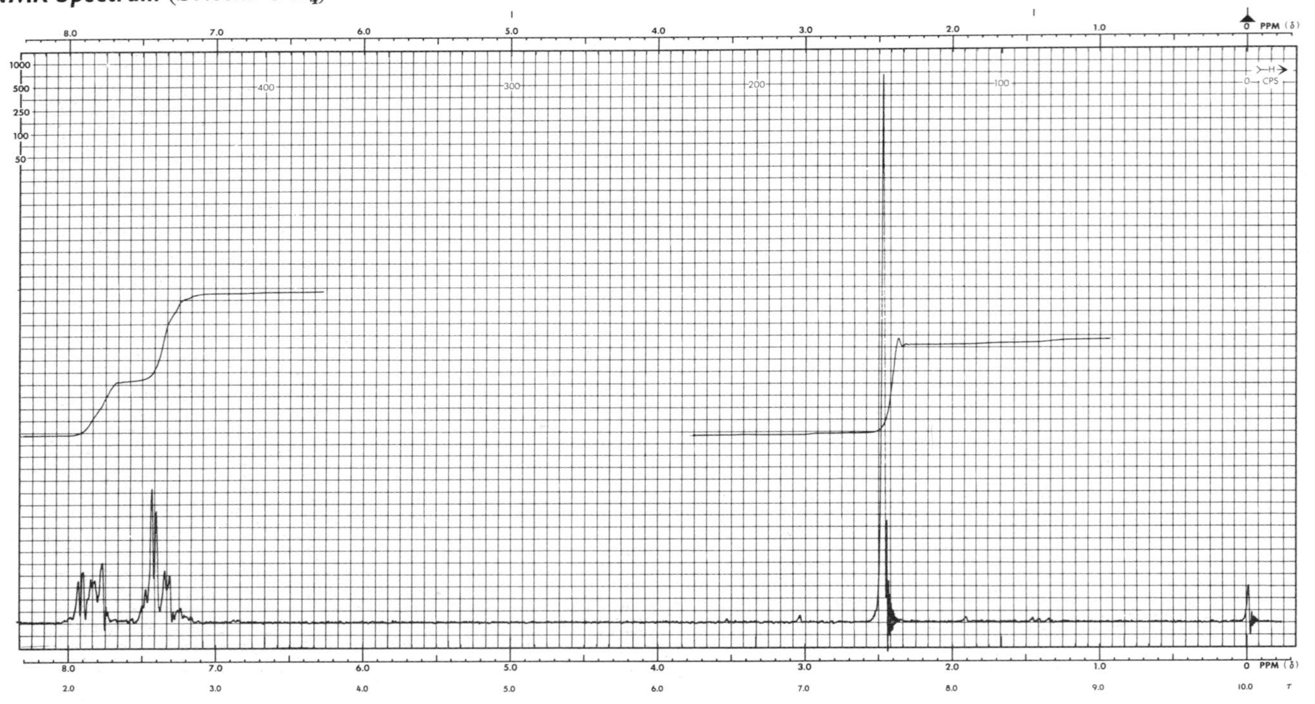

Compound No. 7-5
*Beilstein Ref. **2,** 321*

Infrared Spectrum

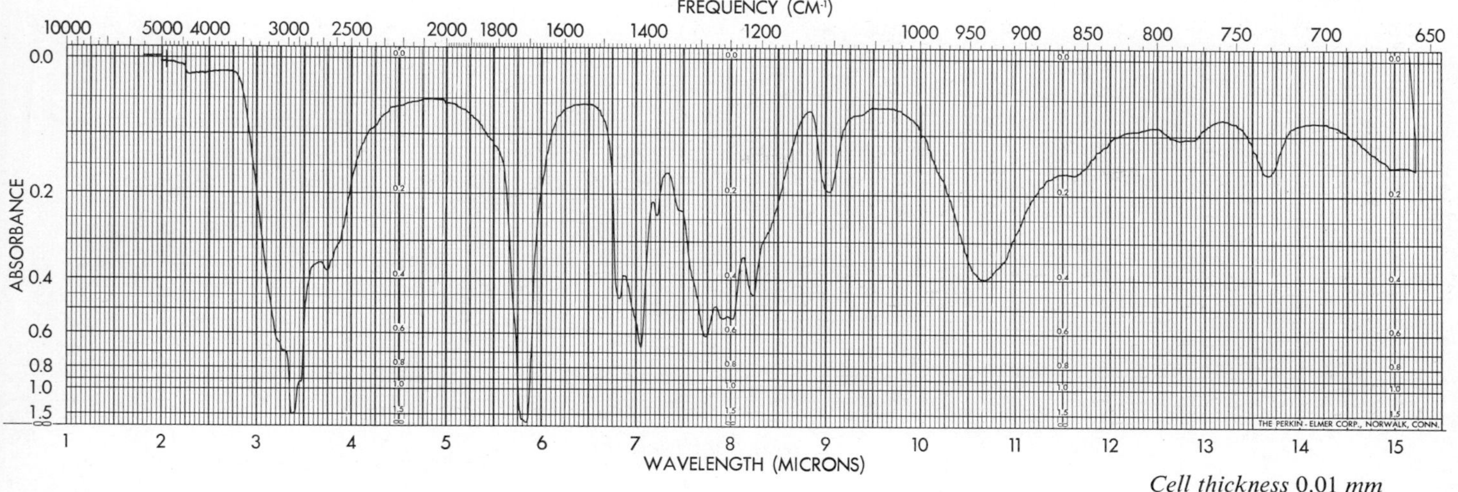

Cell thickness 0.01 *mm*

Mass Spectral Data (Relative Intensities)

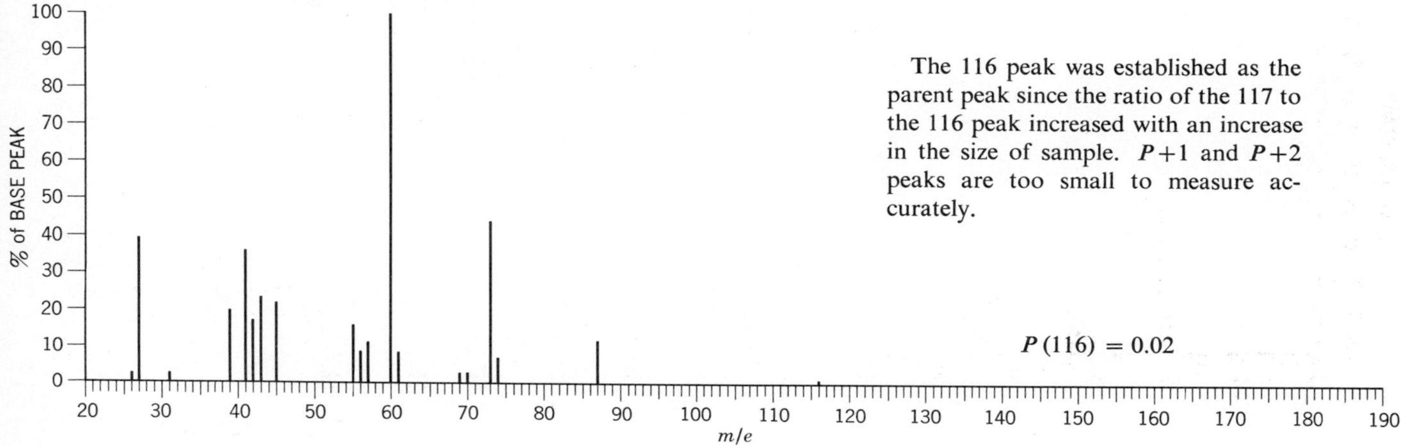

The 116 peak was established as the parent peak since the ratio of the 117 to the 116 peak increased with an increase in the size of sample. $P+1$ and $P+2$ peaks are too small to measure accurately.

$P(116) = 0.02$

Ultraviolet Data

Featureless beyond 210 mμ.

NMR Spectrum (*Solvent* CCl_4)

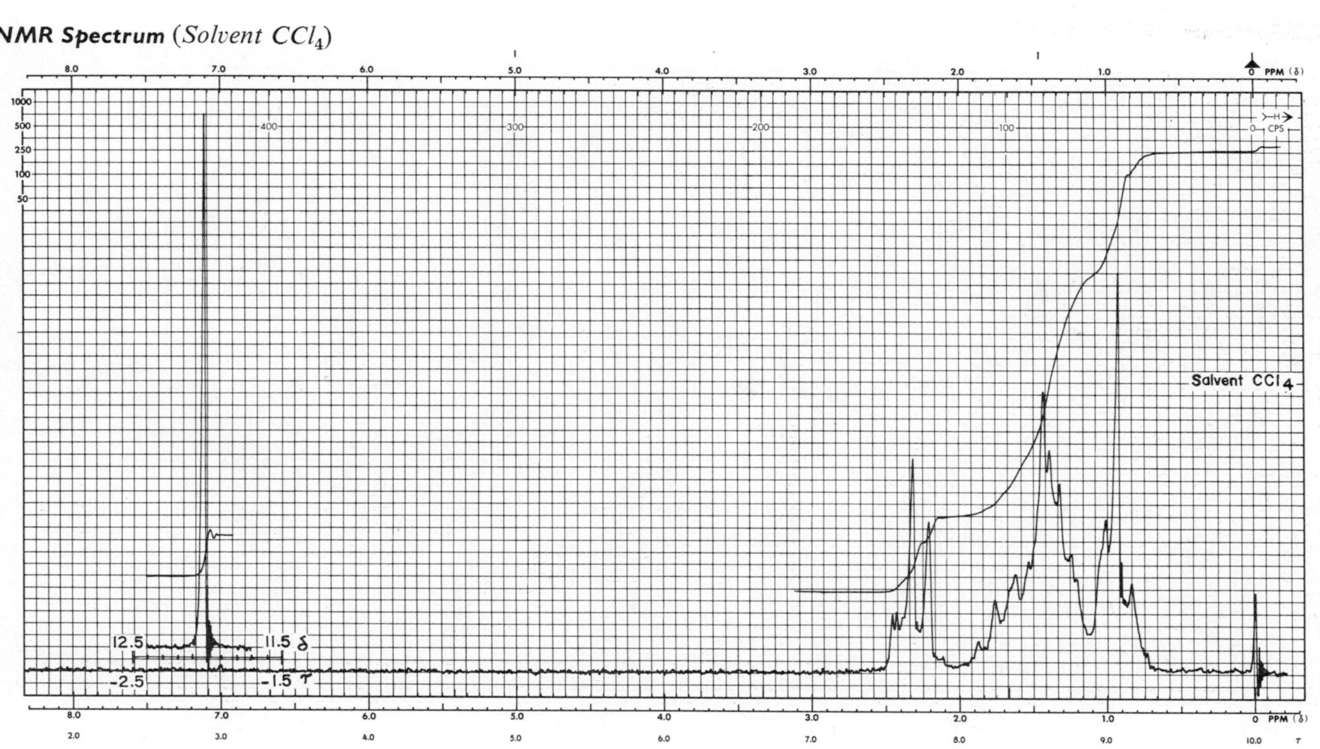

Infrared Spectrum

Compound No. 7-6
Beilstein Ref. **10,** 70

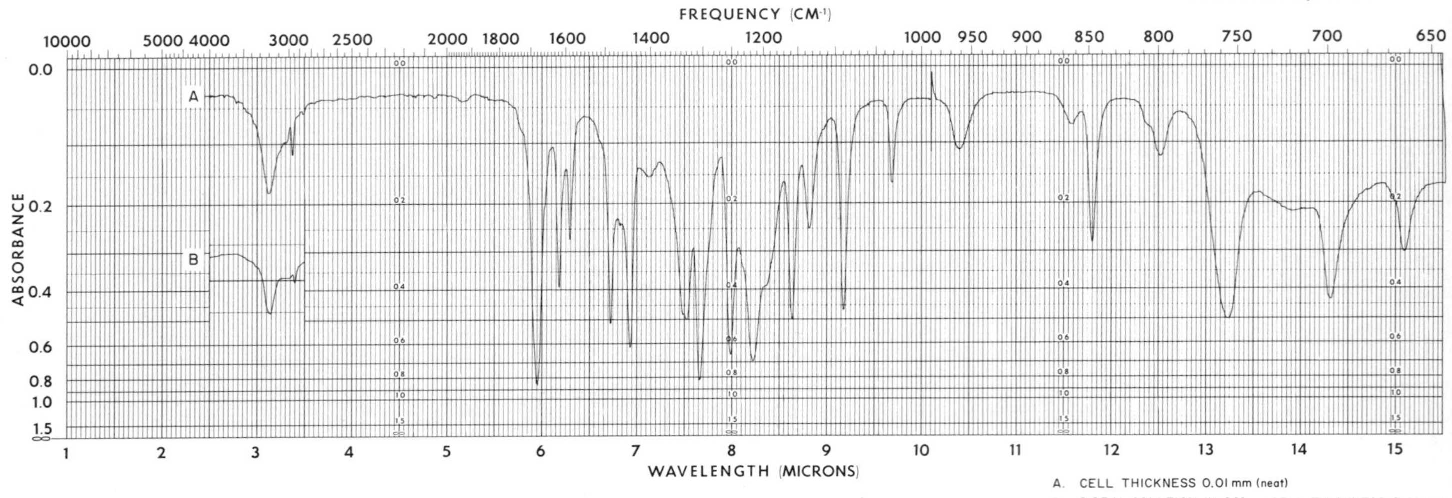

Mass Spectral Data (Relative Intensities)

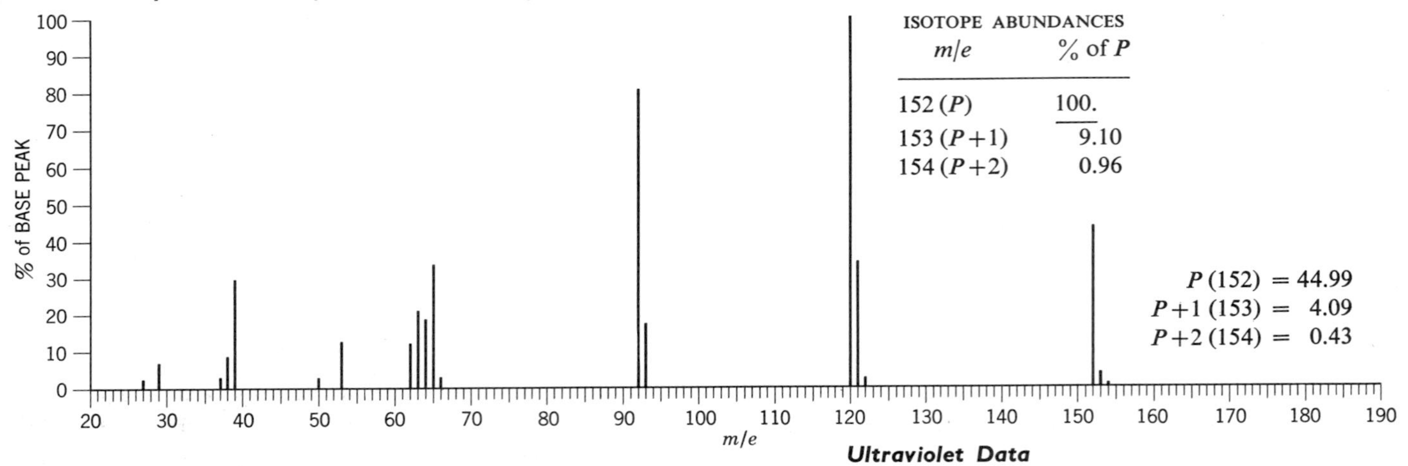

ISOTOPE ABUNDANCES

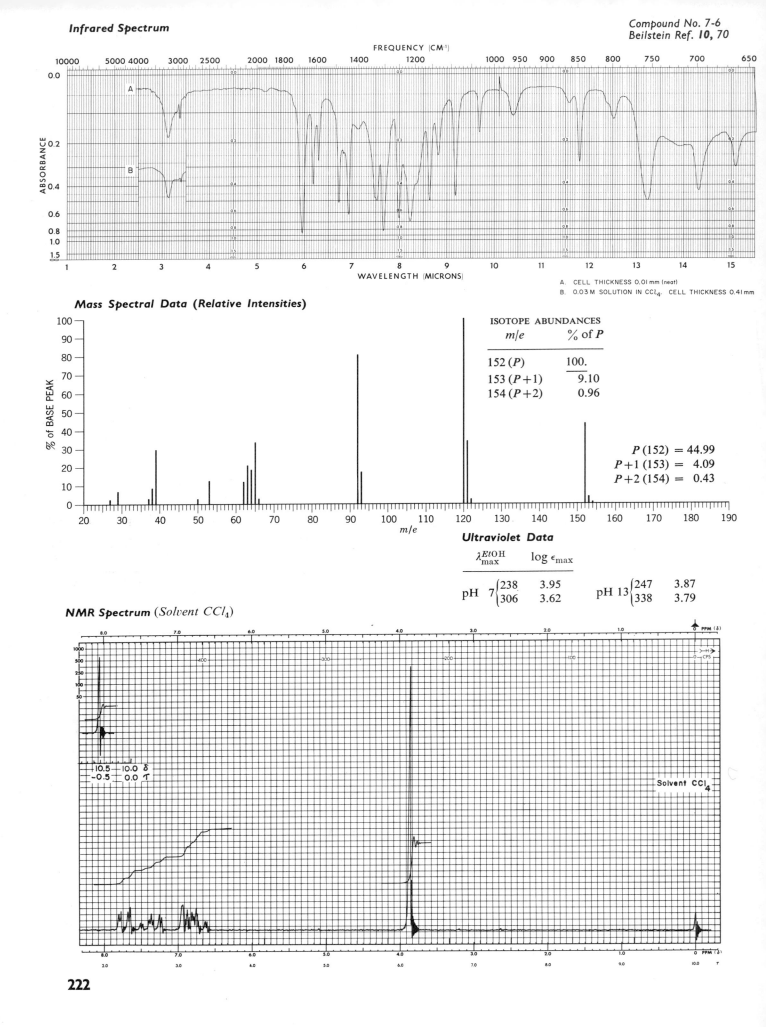

m/e	% of P
152 (P)	100.
153 (P+1)	9.10
154 (P+2)	0.96

P (152) = 44.99
P+1 (153) = 4.09
P+2 (154) = 0.43

Ultraviolet Data

	λ_{max}^{EtOH}	log ϵ_{max}
pH 7	238	3.95
	306	3.62
pH 13	247	3.87
	338	3.79

NMR Spectrum (*Solvent CCl_4*)

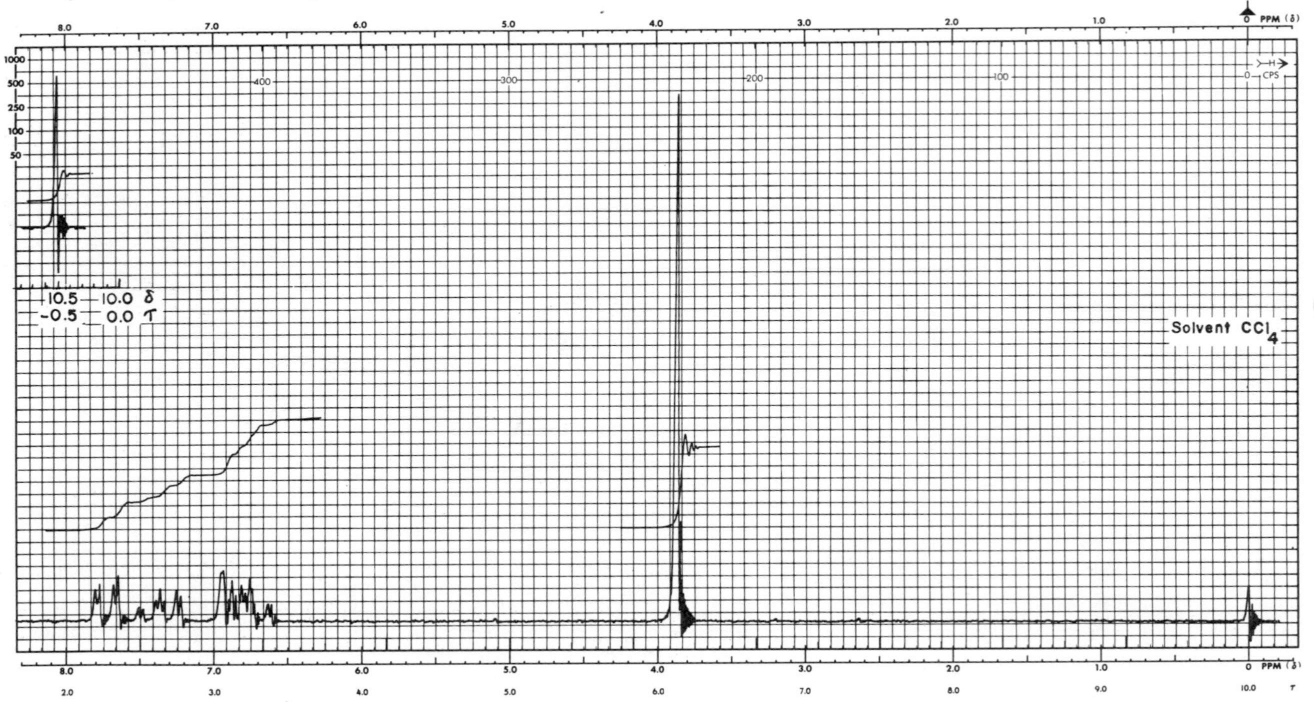

Infrared Spectrum

Compound No. 7-7
Beilstein Ref. **5**, 420

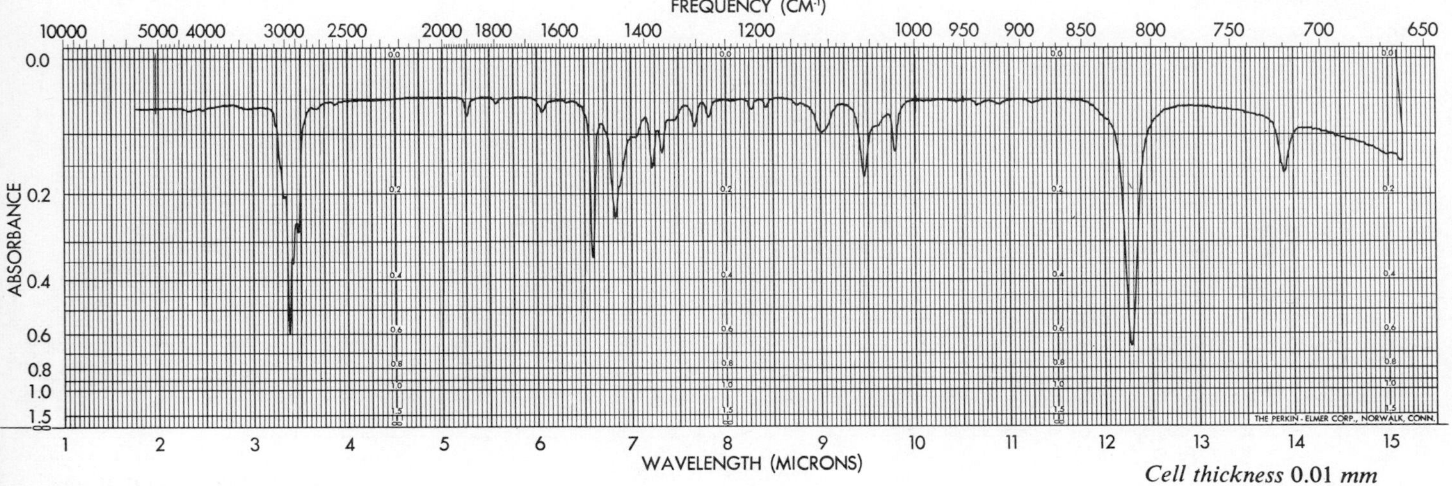

Cell thickness 0.01 *mm*

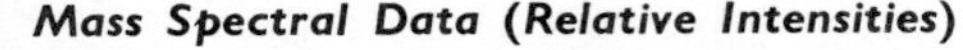

Mass Spectral Data (Relative Intensities)

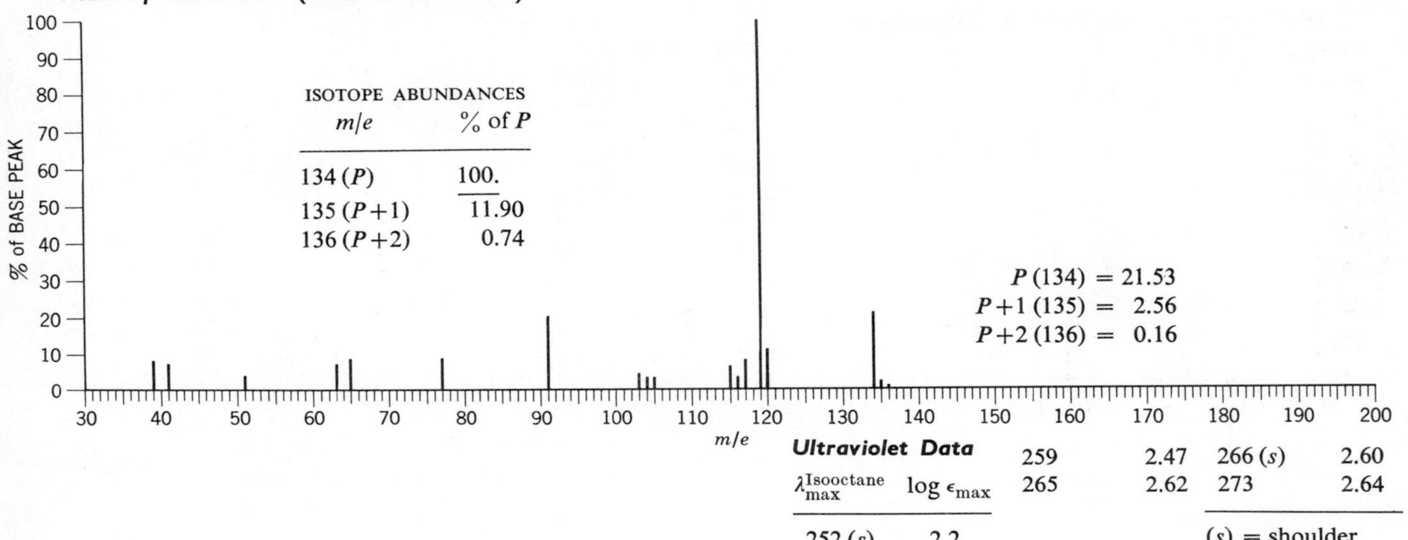

ISOTOPE ABUNDANCES

m/e	% of *P*
134 (*P*)	100.
135 (*P*+1)	11.90
136 (*P*+2)	0.74

P (134) = 21.53
P+1 (135) = 2.56
P+2 (136) = 0.16

Ultraviolet Data

$\lambda_{max}^{Isooctane}$	$\log \epsilon_{max}$
252 (*s*)	2.2
259	2.47
265	2.62
266 (*s*)	2.60
273	2.64

(*s*) = shoulder

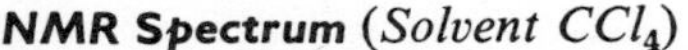

NMR Spectrum (*Solvent* CCl_4)

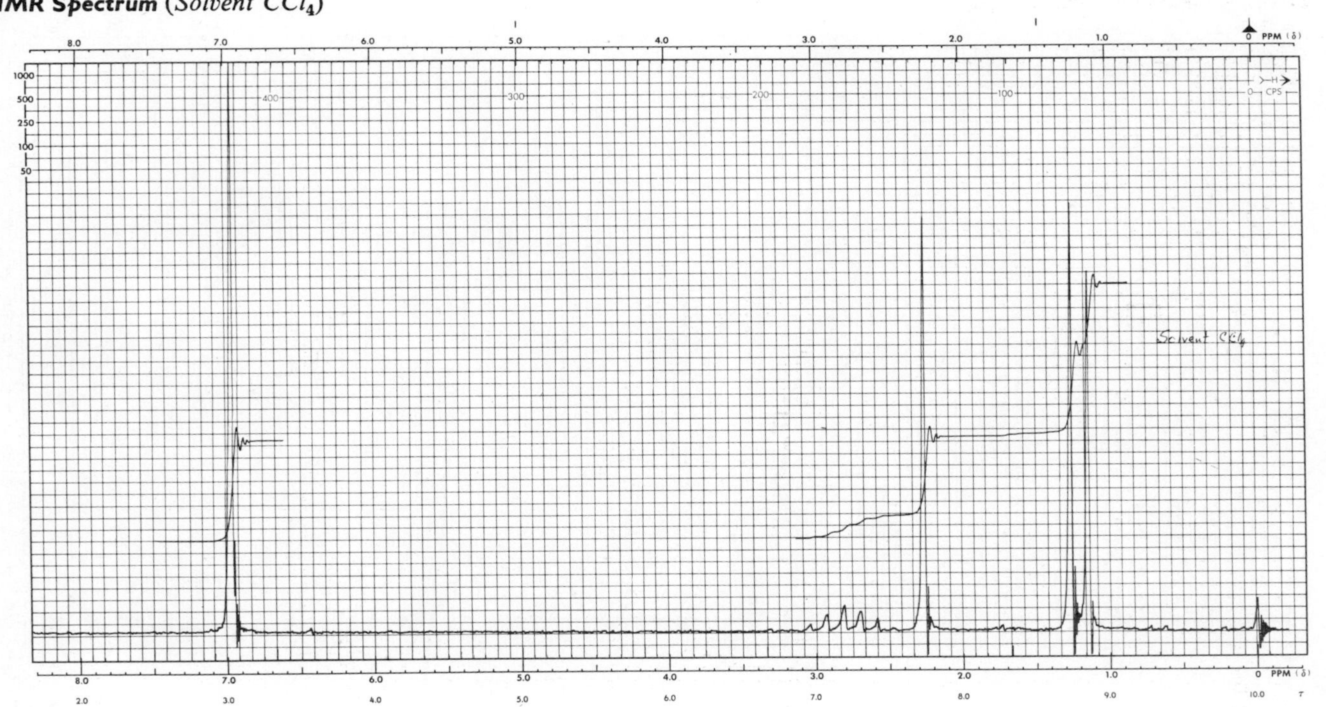

Infrared Spectrum

Compound No. 7-8
Beilstein Ref. **I**, (Supp. 3), 727

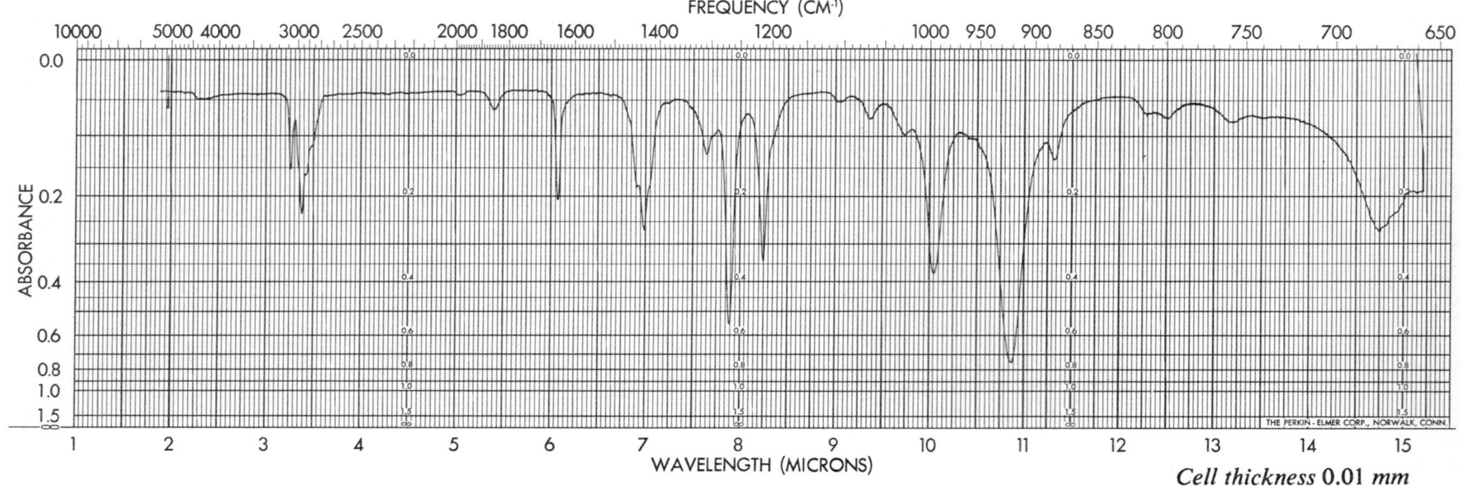

Cell thickness 0.01 mm

Mass Spectral Data (Relative Intensities)

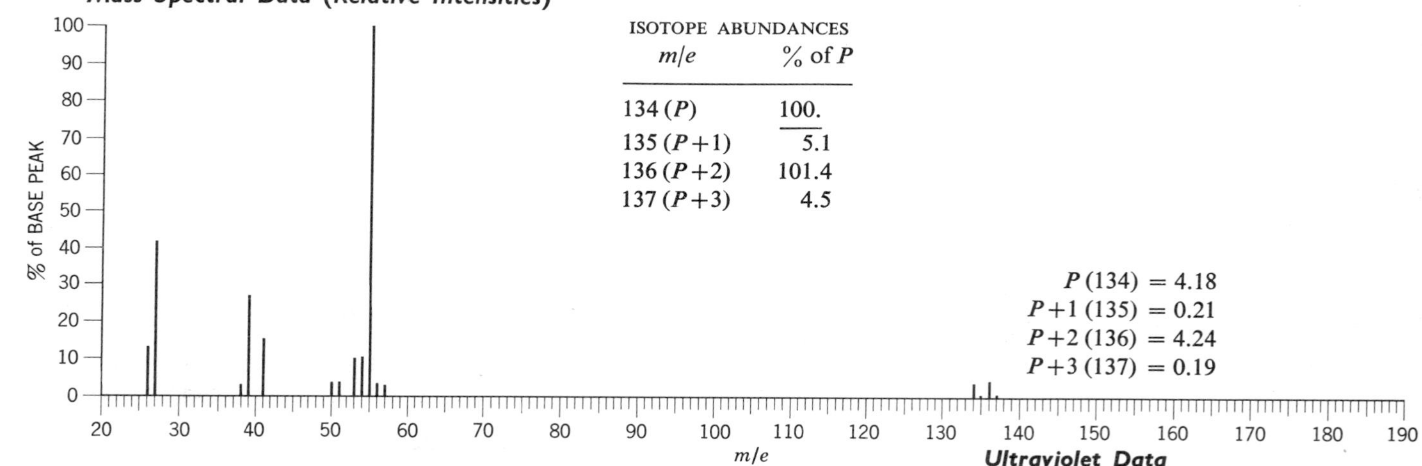

ISOTOPE ABUNDANCES	
m/e	% of *P*
134 (*P*)	100.
135 (*P*+1)	5.1
136 (*P*+2)	101.4
137 (*P*+3)	4.5

$P(134) = 4.18$
$P+1\ (135) = 0.21$
$P+2\ (136) = 4.24$
$P+3\ (137) = 0.19$

Ultraviolet Data

Featureless above 210 mμ.

NMR Spectrum (*Solvent* CCl_4)

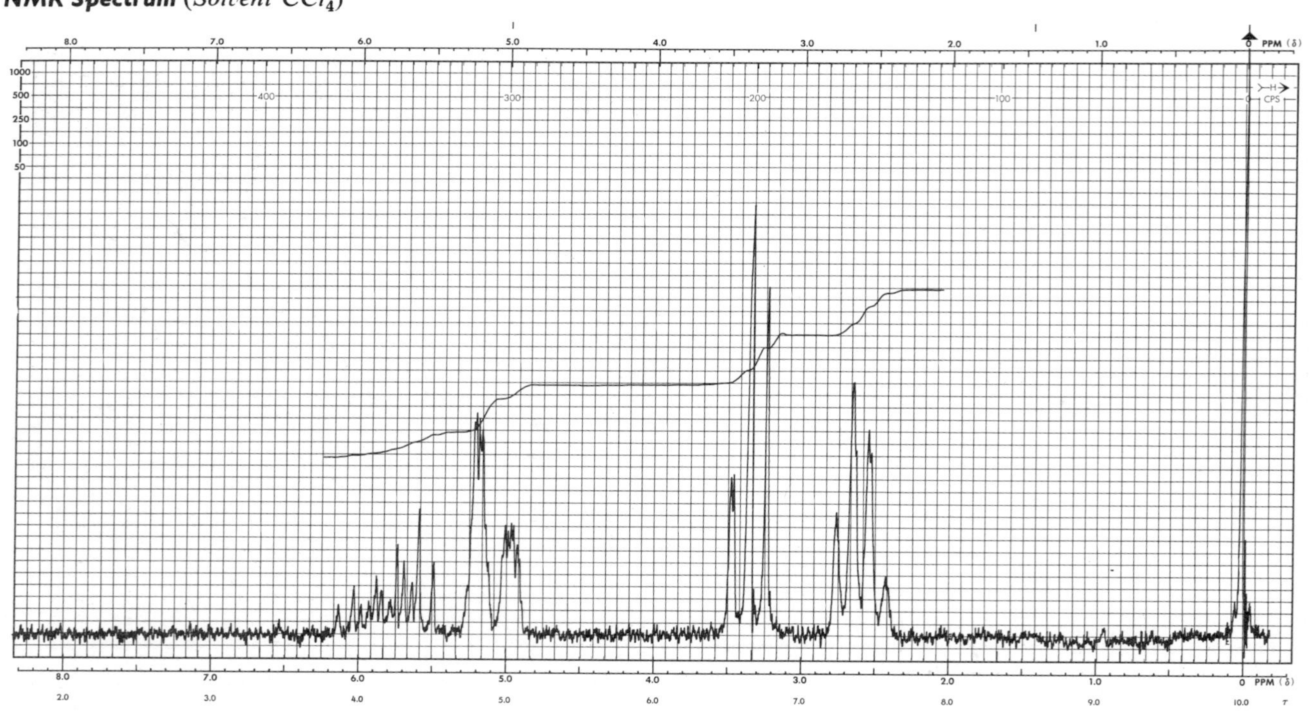

Infrared Spectrum

Compound No. 7-9
Beilstein Ref. **6**, 465

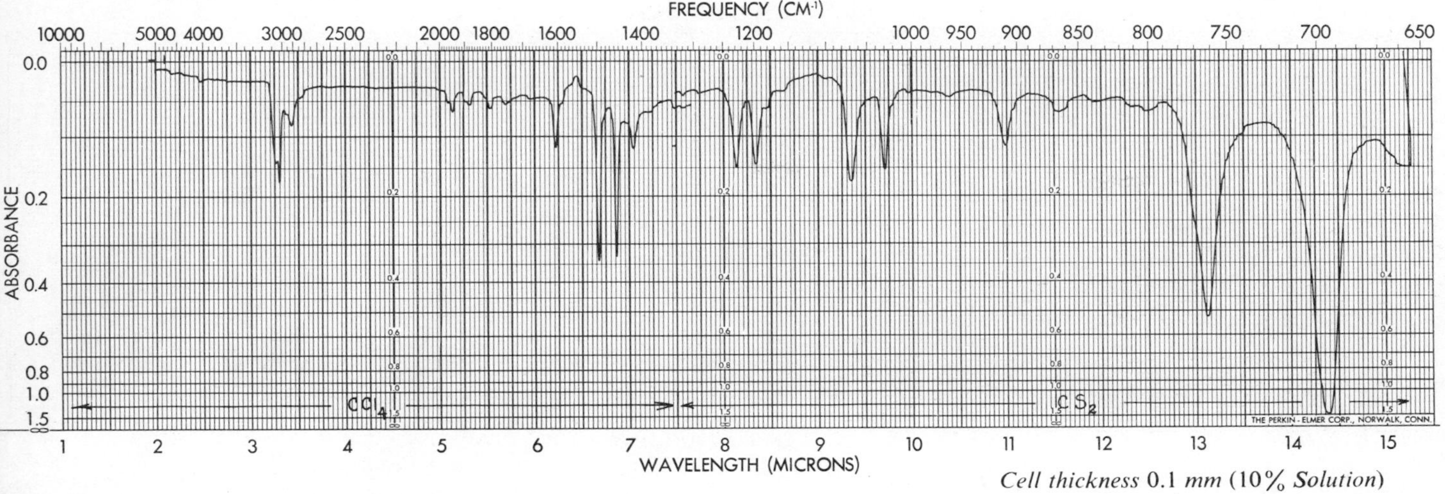

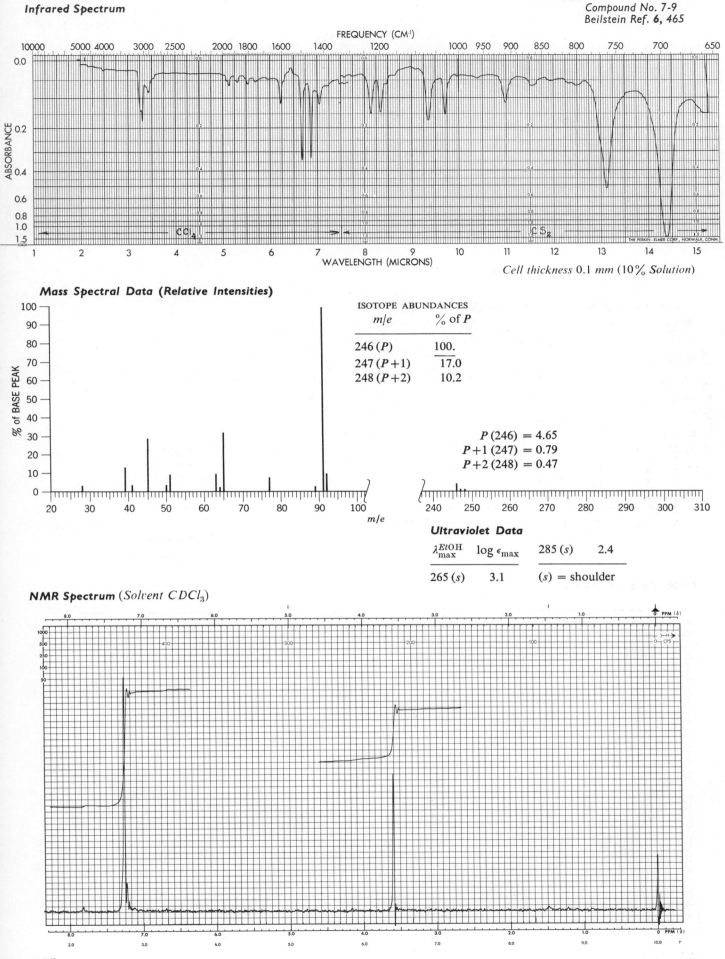

Cell thickness 0.1 *mm* (10% *Solution*)

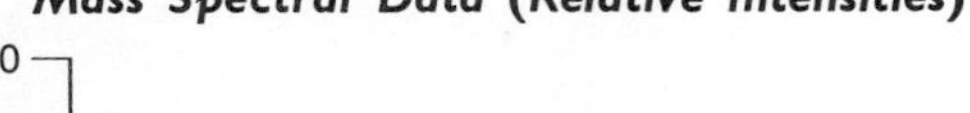

Mass Spectral Data (Relative Intensities)

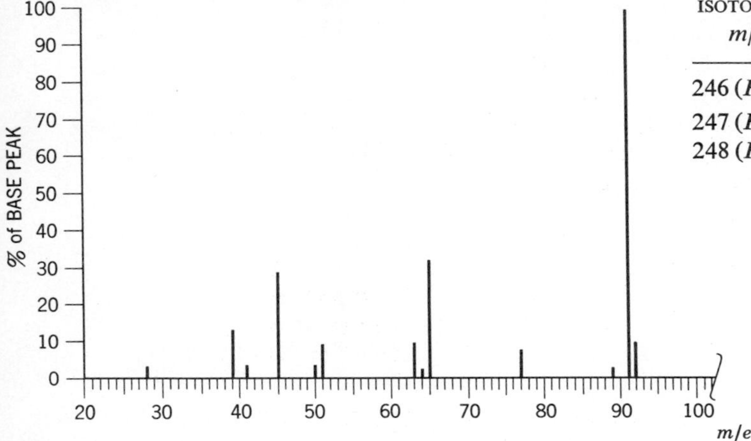

ISOTOPE ABUNDANCES

m/e	% of *P*
246 (*P*)	100.
247 (*P*+1)	17.0
248 (*P*+2)	10.2

P (246) = 4.65
$P+1$ (247) = 0.79
$P+2$ (248) = 0.47

Ultraviolet Data

λ_{max}^{EtOH}	log ϵ_{max}
265 (*s*)	3.1
285 (*s*)	2.4

(*s*) = shoulder

NMR Spectrum (*Solvent CDCl₃*)

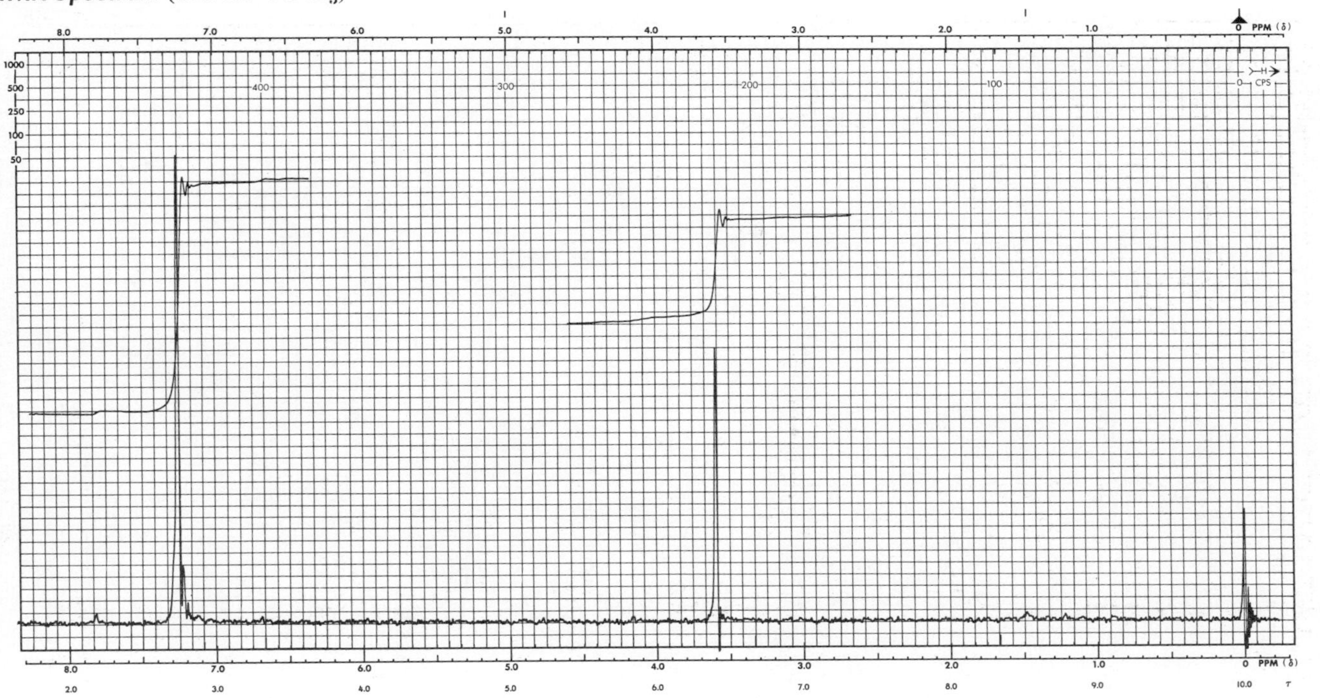

Infrared Spectrum

Compound No. 7-10
Beilstein Ref. **7,** 304

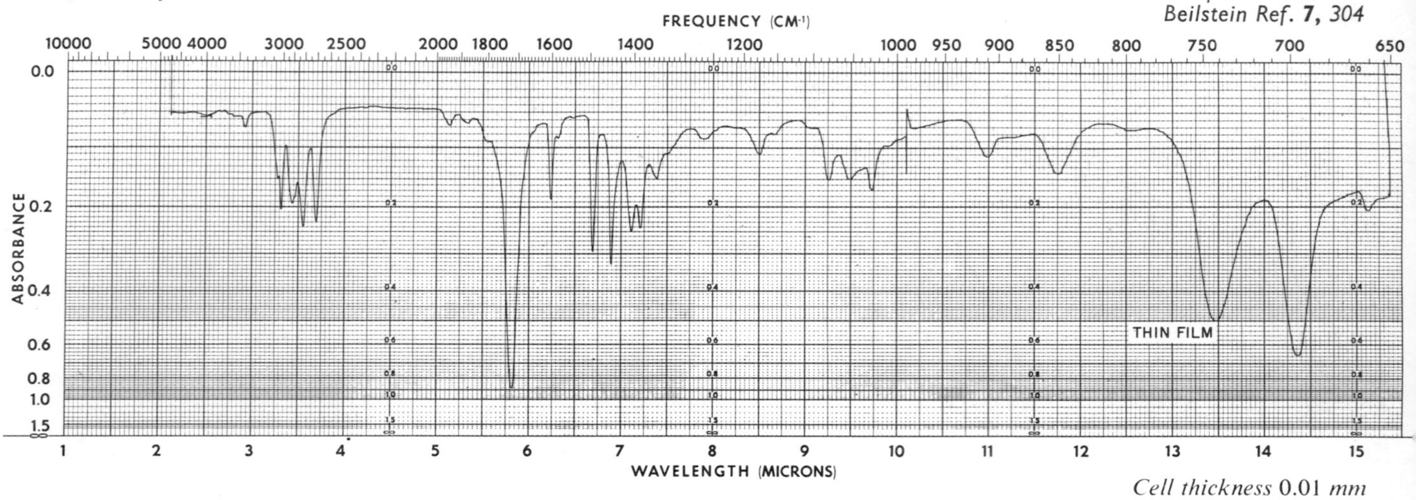
FREQUENCY (CM⁻¹)
ABSORBANCE
THIN FILM
WAVELENGTH (MICRONS)

Cell thickness 0.01 *mm*

Mass Spectral Data (Relative Intensities)

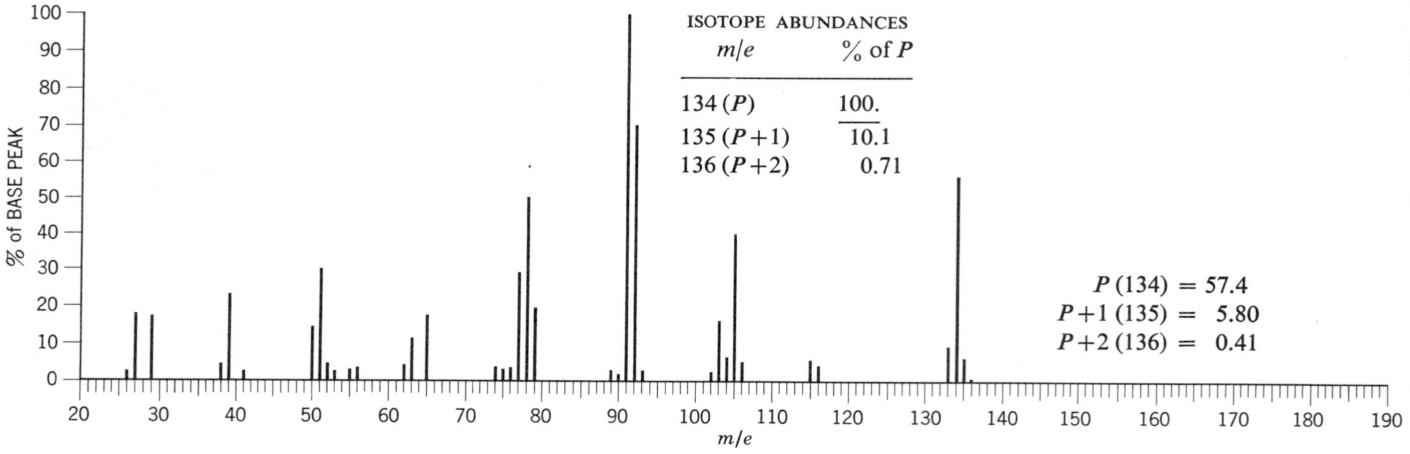
% of BASE PEAK
m/e

ISOTOPE ABUNDANCES

m/e	% of *P*
134 (*P*)	100.
135 (*P*+1)	10.1
136 (*P*+2)	0.71

P (134) = 57.4
P+1 (135) = 5.80
P+2 (136) = 0.41

Ultraviolet Data

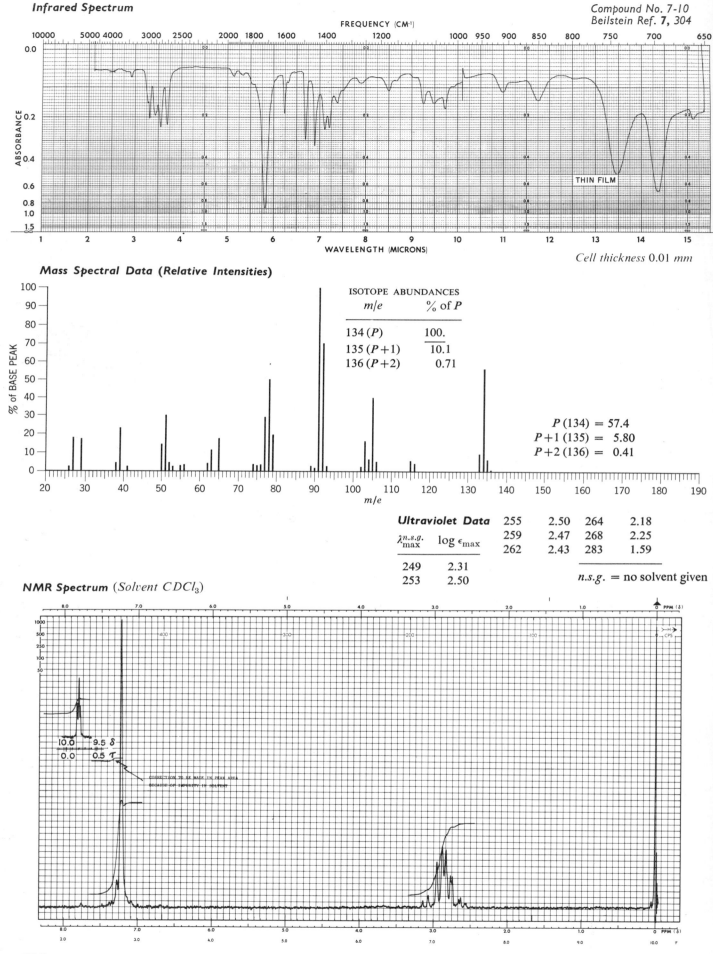

$\lambda_{max}^{n.s.g.}$	log ϵ_{max}
249	2.31
253	2.50
255	2.50
259	2.47
262	2.43
264	2.18
268	2.25
283	1.59

n.s.g. = no solvent given

NMR Spectrum (*Solvent* $CDCl_3$)

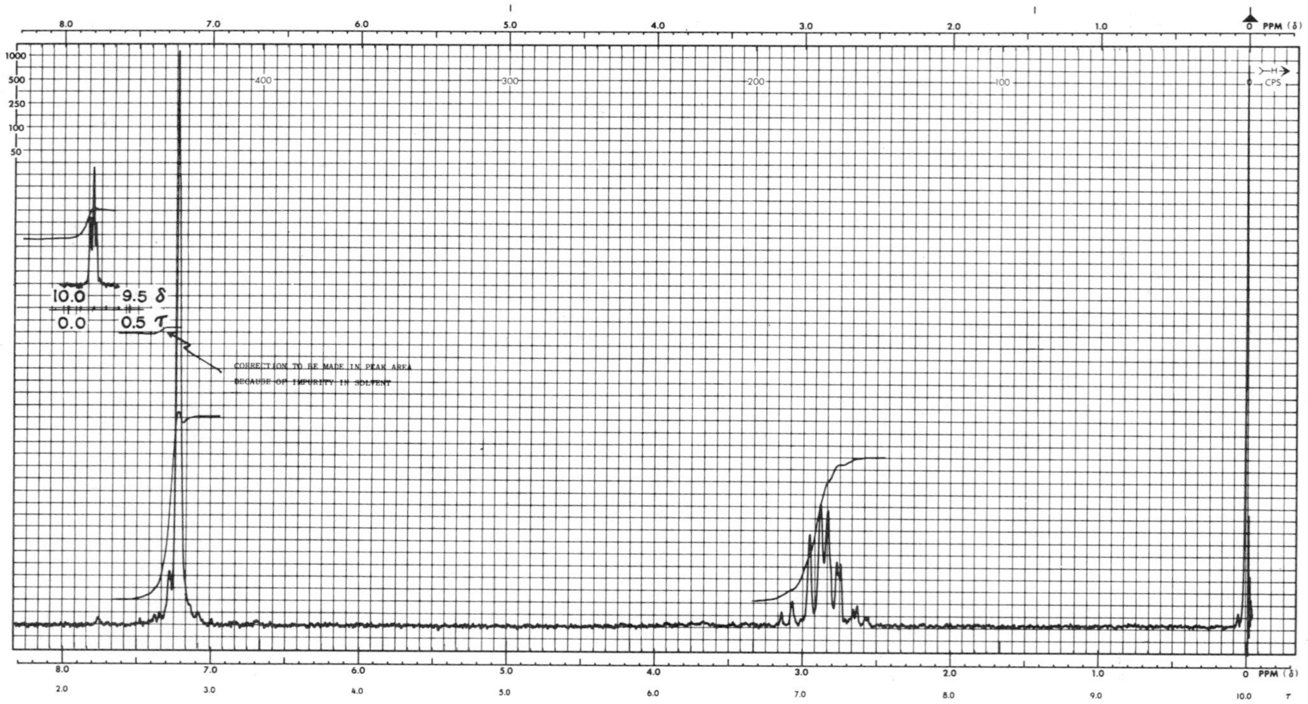
PPM (δ)
CPS
10.0 9.5 δ
0.0 0.5 τ
CORRECTION TO BE MADE IN PEAK AREA
BECAUSE OF IMPURITY IN SOLVENT

CHAPTER 8

Sets of Spectra, Unidentified

This chapter consists of twenty-one sets of spectra. These are presented without identification or reference.

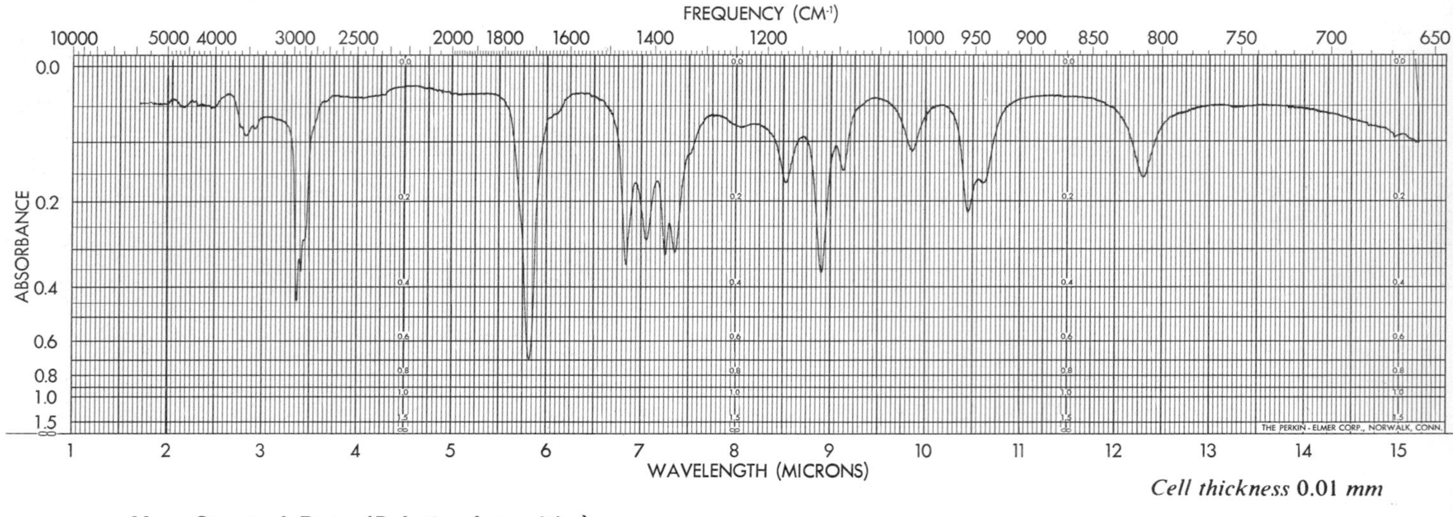

Cell thickness 0.01 *mm*

Mass Spectral Data (Relative Intensities)

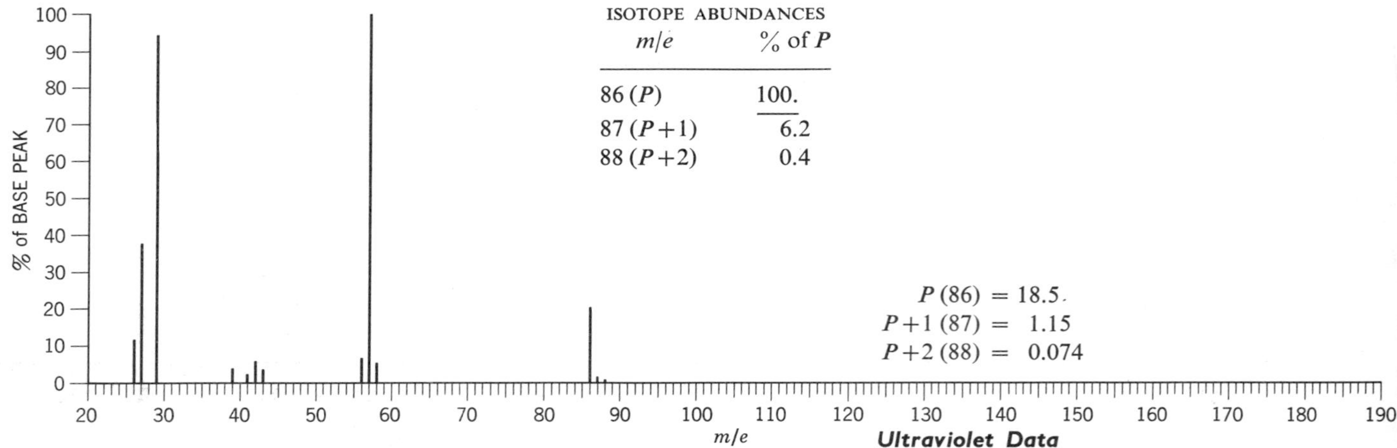

ISOTOPE ABUNDANCES

m/e	% of *P*
86 (*P*)	100.
87 (*P*+1)	6.2
88 (*P*+2)	0.4

P (86) = 18.5
$P+1$ (87) = 1.15
$P+2$ (88) = 0.074

Ultraviolet Data

λ_{max}^{EtOH}	$\log \epsilon_{max}$
273	1.31

NMR Spectrum *(Solvent $CDCl_3$)*

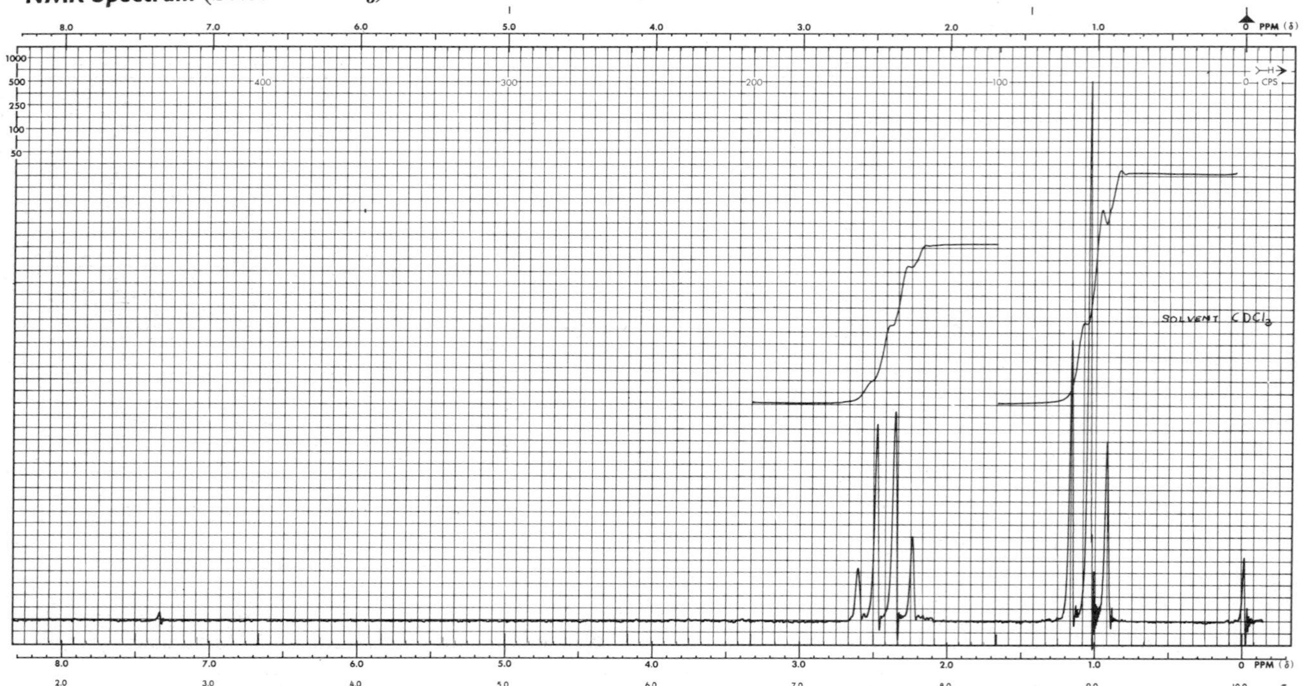

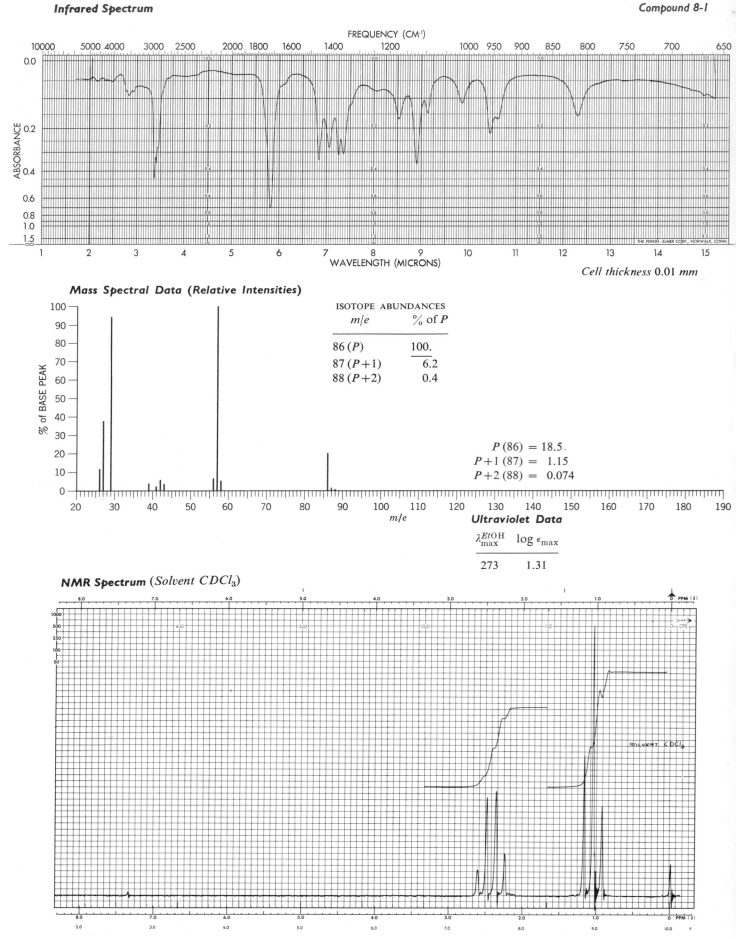

Infrared Spectrum *Compound 8-2*

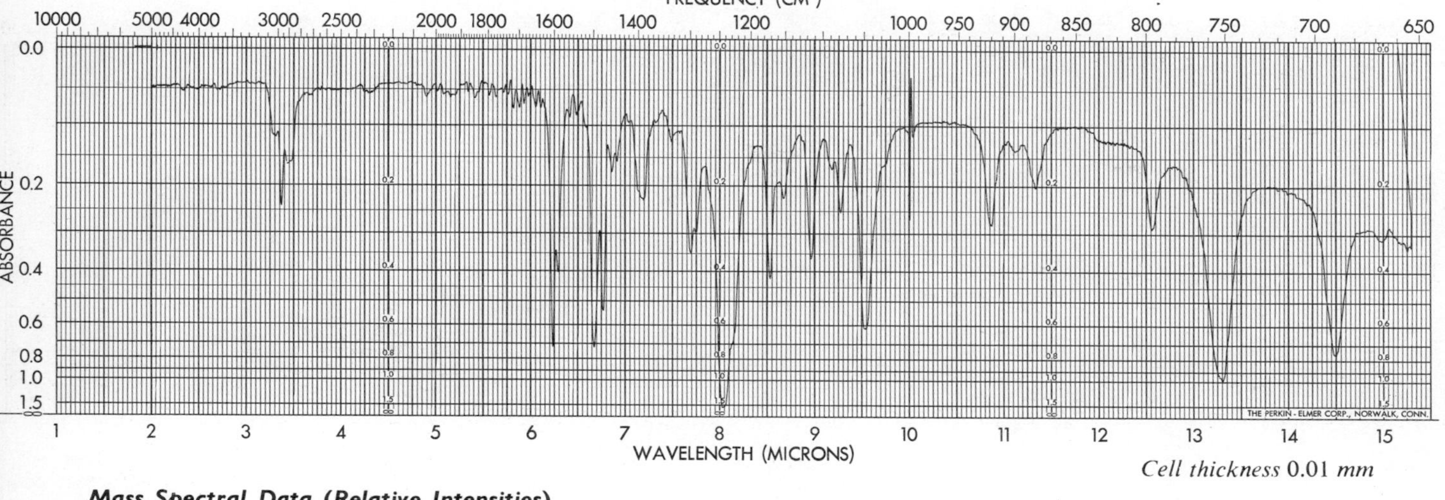

Cell thickness 0.01 *mm*

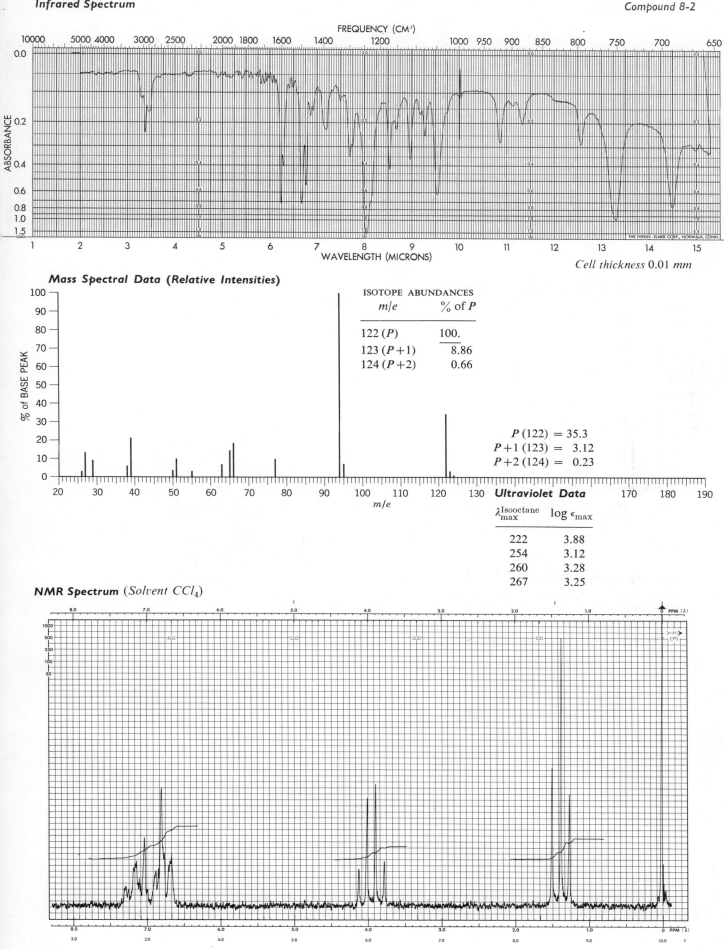

Mass Spectral Data (Relative Intensities)

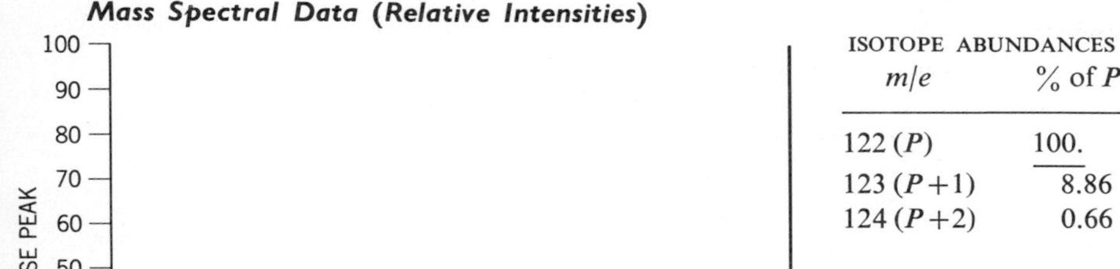

ISOTOPE ABUNDANCES

m/e	% of *P*
122 (*P*)	100.
123 (*P*+1)	8.86
124 (*P*+2)	0.66

P (122) = 35.3
P+1 (123) = 3.12
P+2 (124) = 0.23

Ultraviolet Data

$\lambda_{max}^{Isooctane}$	log ϵ_{max}
222	3.88
254	3.12
260	3.28
267	3.25

NMR Spectrum (*Solvent* CCl_4)

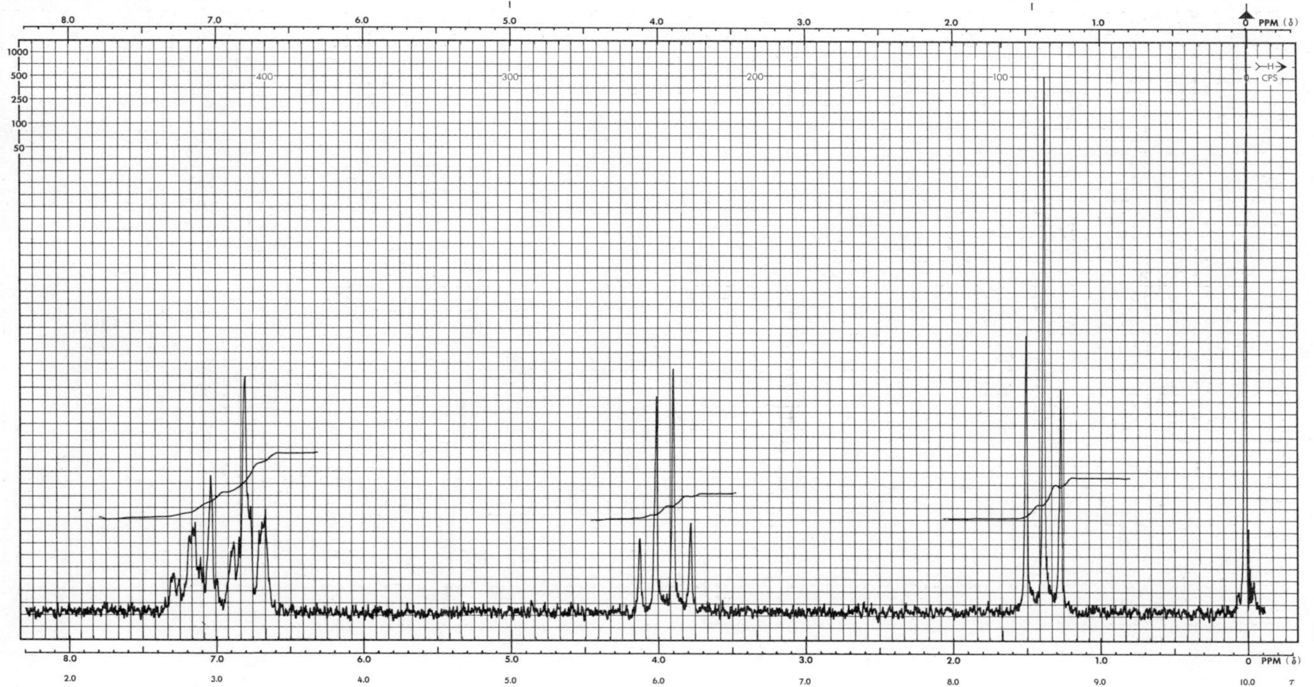

Infrared Spectrum

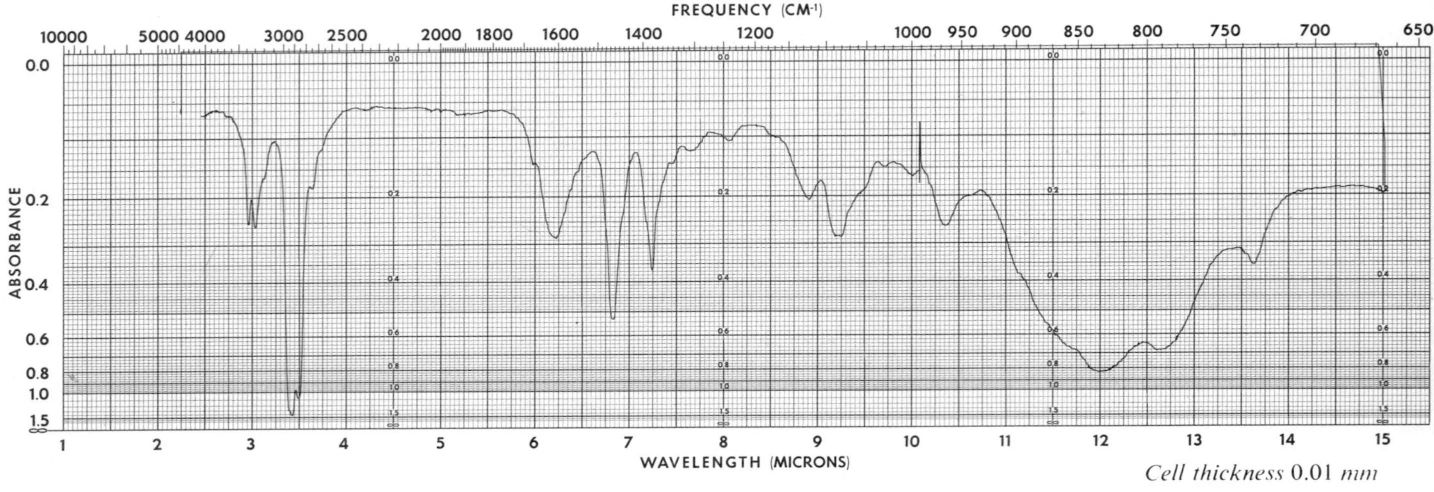

Cell thickness 0.01 *mm*

Mass Spectral Data (Relative Intensities)

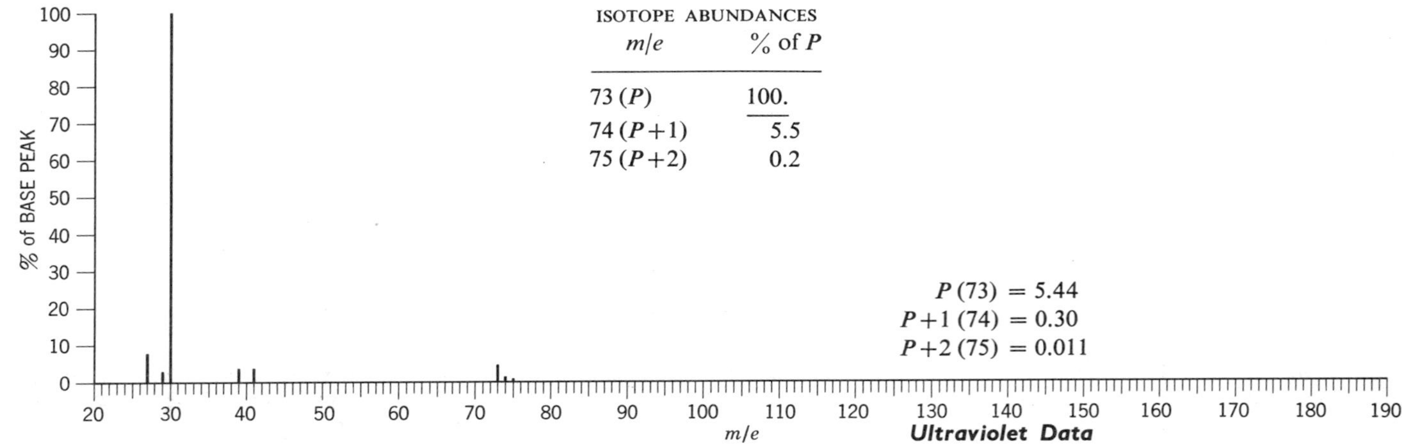

ISOTOPE ABUNDANCES

m/e	% of *P*
73 (*P*)	100.
74 (*P*+1)	5.5
75 (*P*+2)	0.2

$P\,(73) = 5.44$
$P+1\,(74) = 0.30$
$P+2\,(75) = 0.011$

Ultraviolet Data

λ_{max}^{EtOH}	ϵ_{max}
225 (*s*)	56

(*s*) = shoulder

NMR Spectrum (*Solvent* CCl_4)

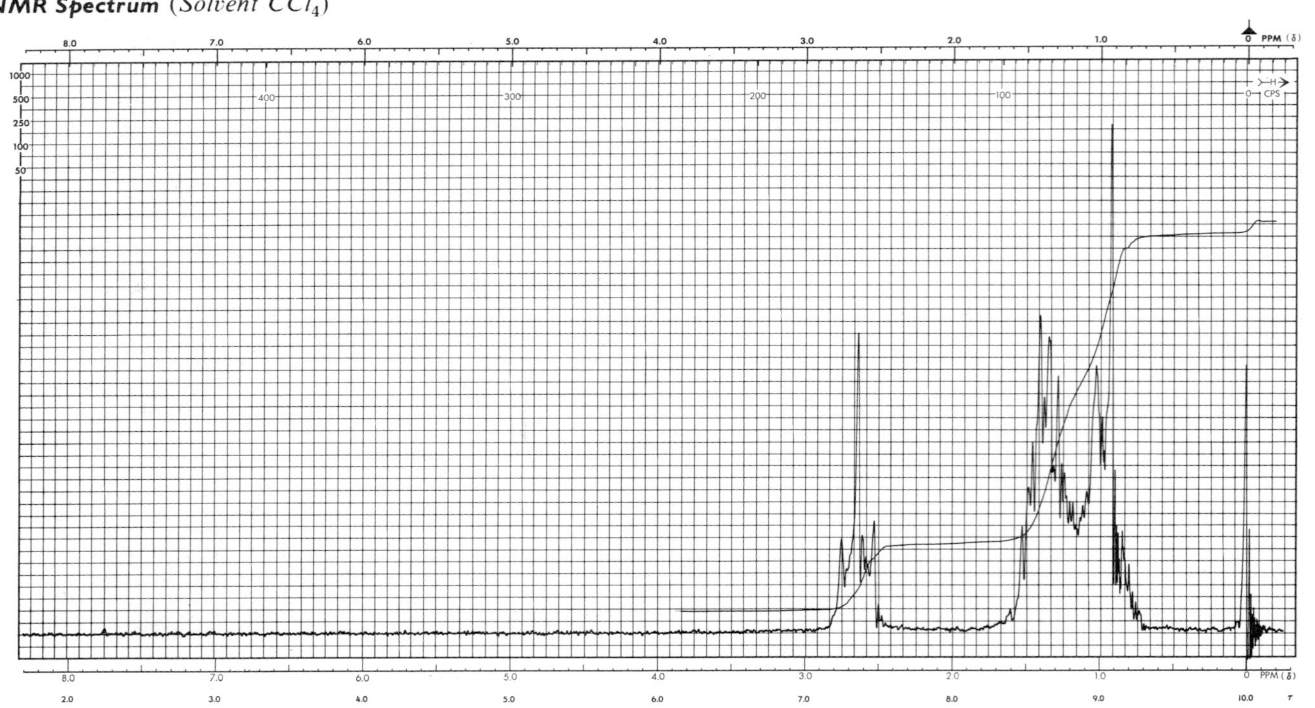

Infrared Spectrum

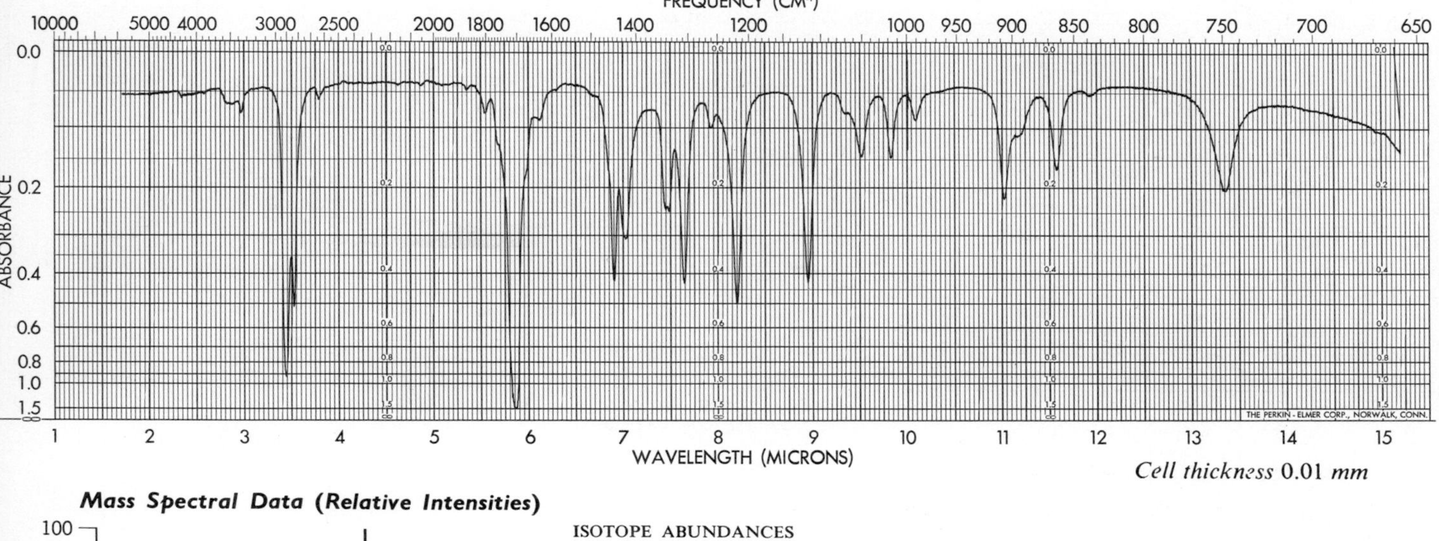

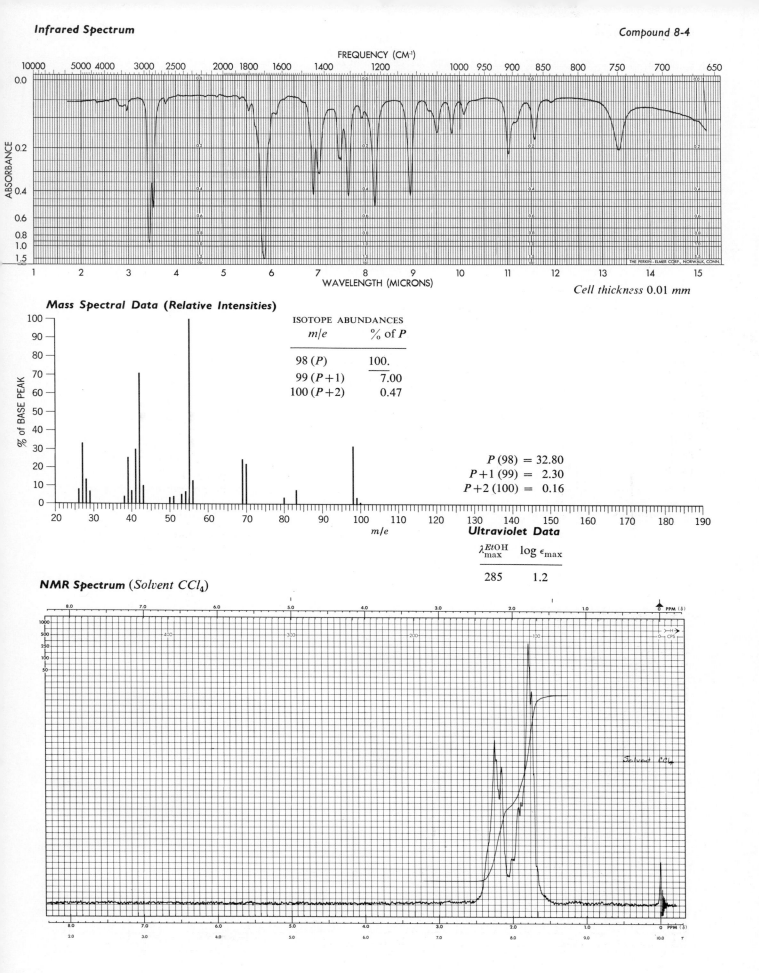

Cell thickness 0.01 *mm*

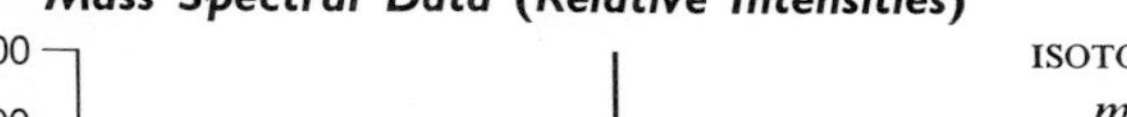

Mass Spectral Data (Relative Intensities)

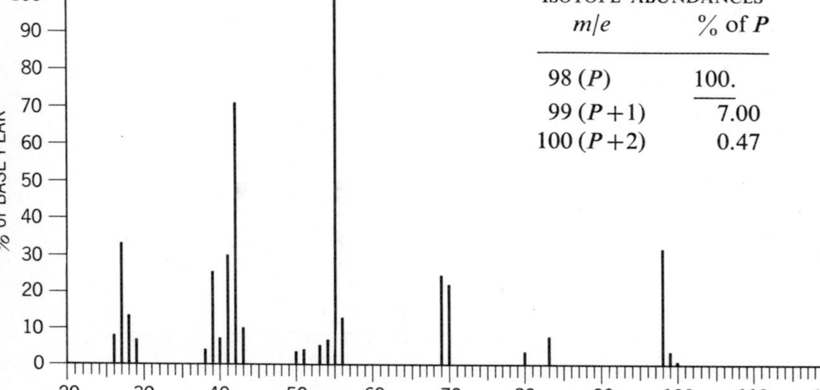

ISOTOPE ABUNDANCES

m/e	% of P
98 (P)	100.
99 ($P+1$)	7.00
100 ($P+2$)	0.47

P (98) = 32.80
$P+1$ (99) = 2.30
$P+2$ (100) = 0.16

Ultraviolet Data

λ_{max}^{EtOH}	$\log \epsilon_{max}$
285	1.2

NMR Spectrum (*Solvent* CCl_4)

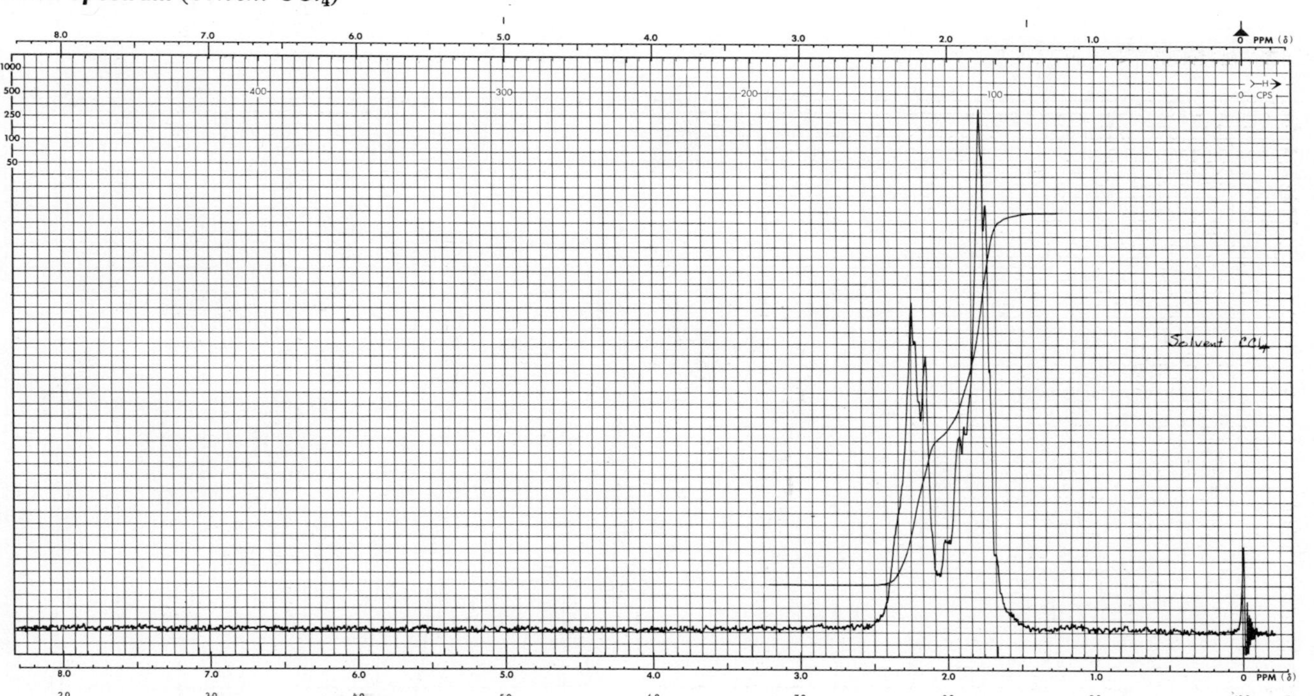

Compound 8-5

Infrared Spectrum

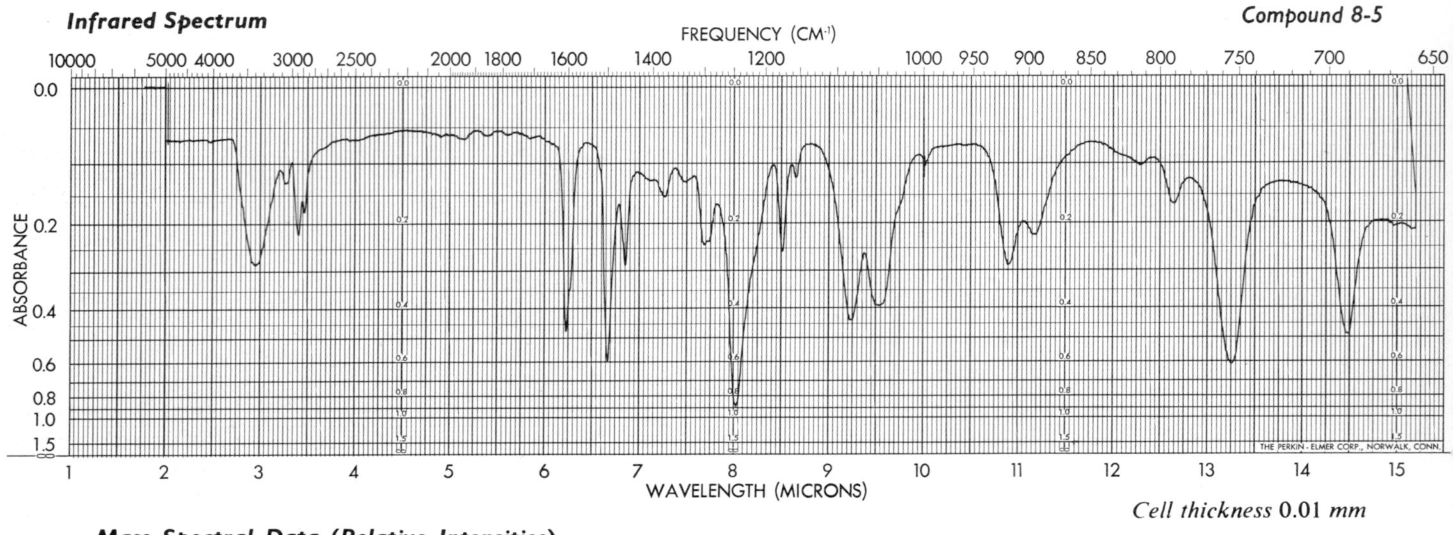

Cell thickness 0.01 *mm*

Mass Spectral Data (Relative Intensities)

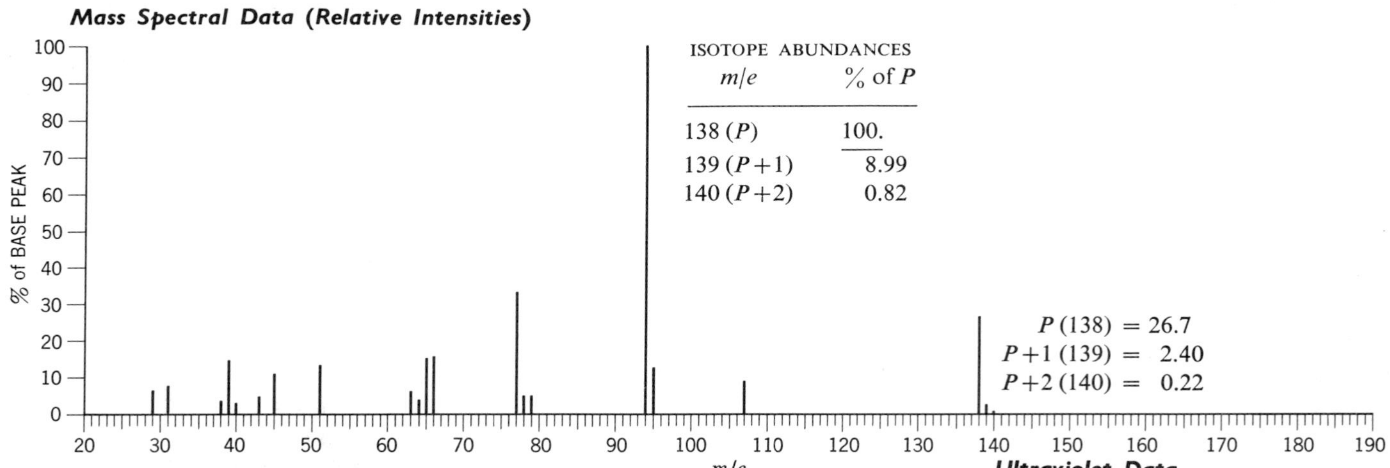

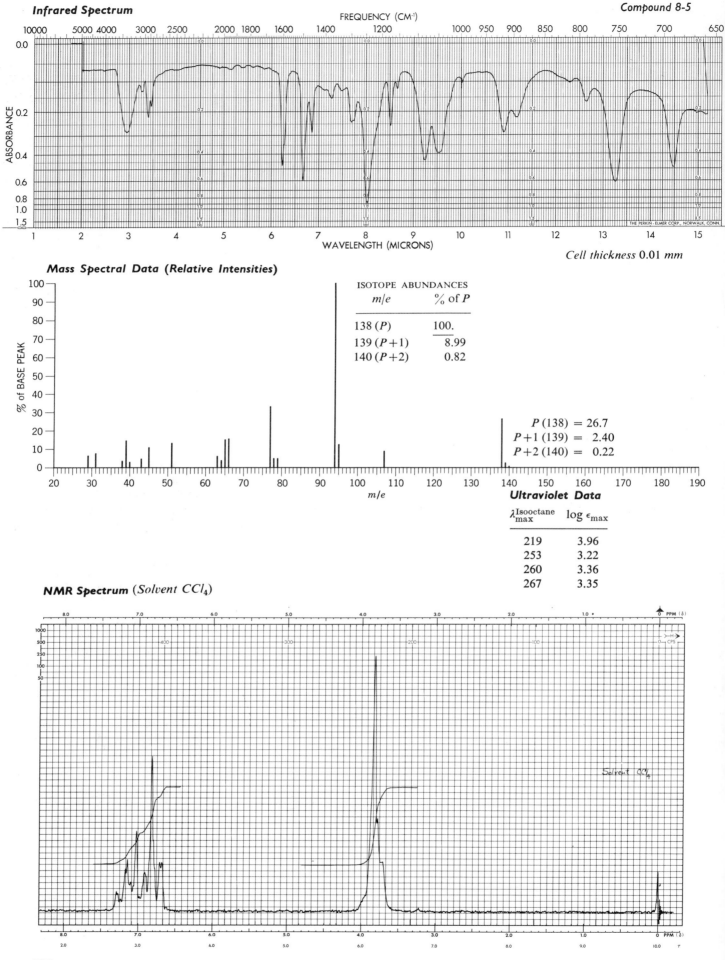

ISOTOPE ABUNDANCES

m/e	% of P
138 (P)	100.
139 ($P+1$)	8.99
140 ($P+2$)	0.82

P (138) = 26.7
$P+1$ (139) = 2.40
$P+2$ (140) = 0.22

Ultraviolet Data

$\lambda_{max}^{Isooctane}$	$\log \epsilon_{max}$
219	3.96
253	3.22
260	3.36
267	3.35

NMR Spectrum (*Solvent* CCl_4)

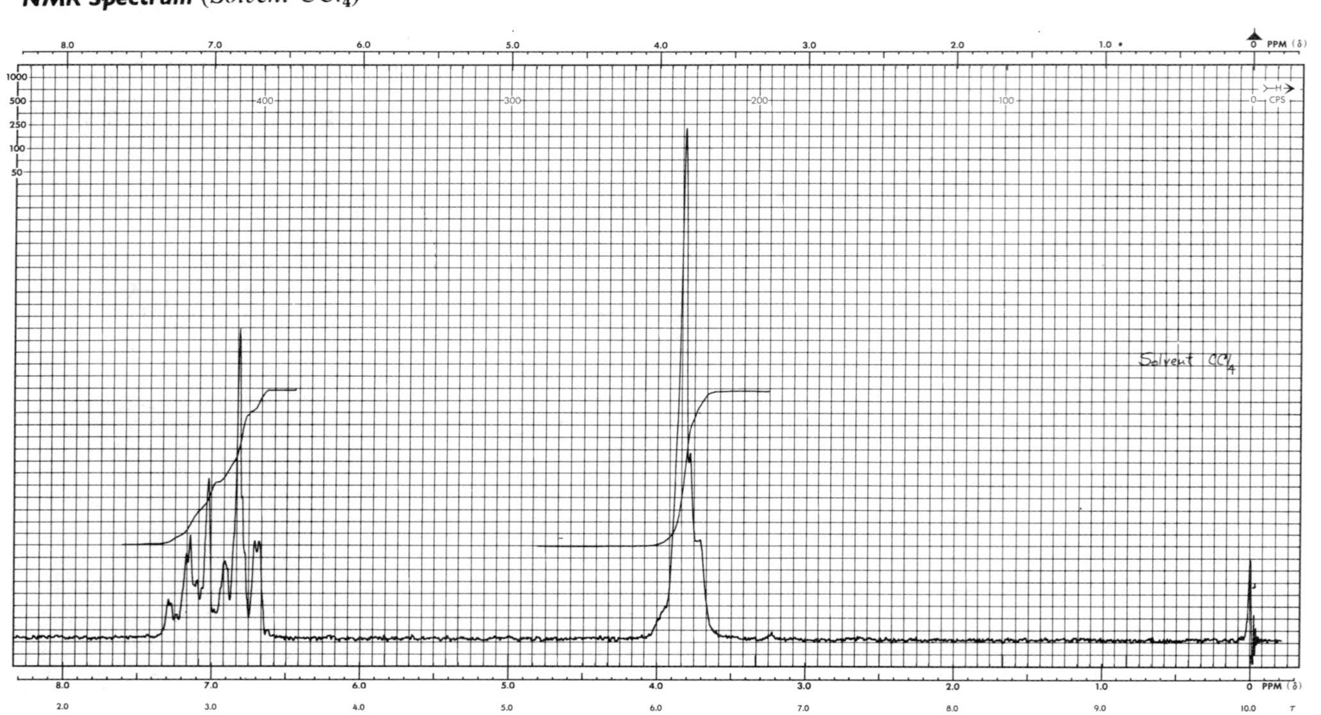

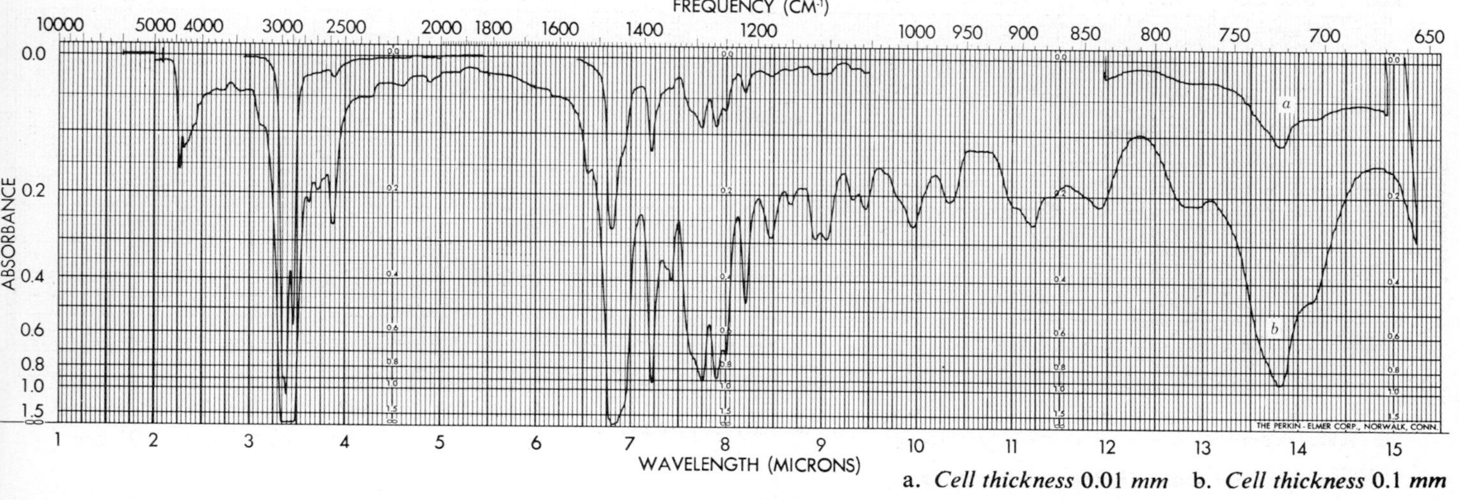

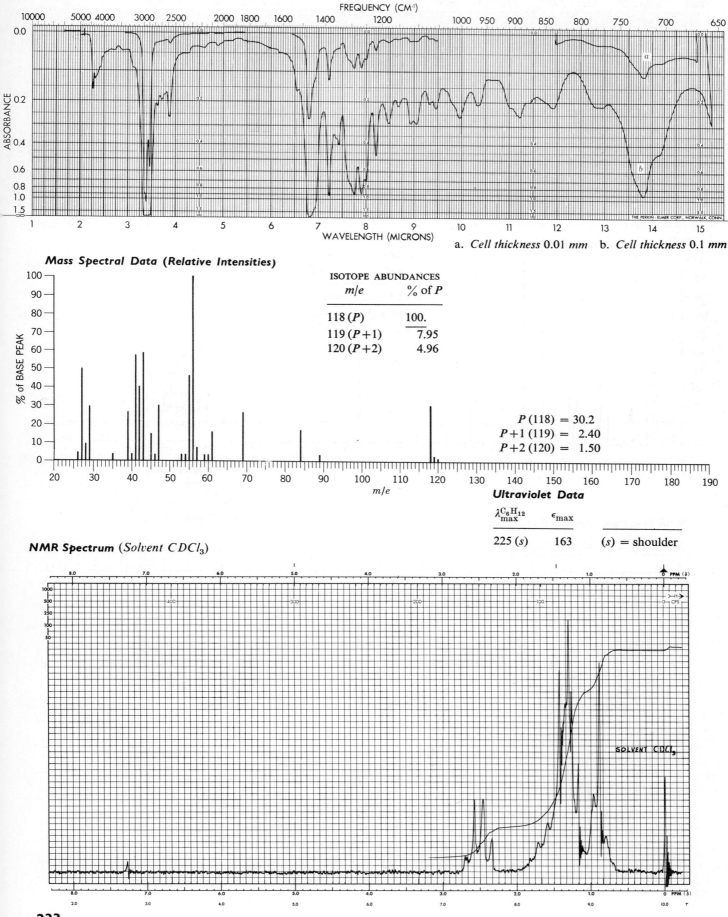

a. *Cell thickness* 0.01 *mm* b. *Cell thickness* 0.1 *mm*

Mass Spectral Data (Relative Intensities)

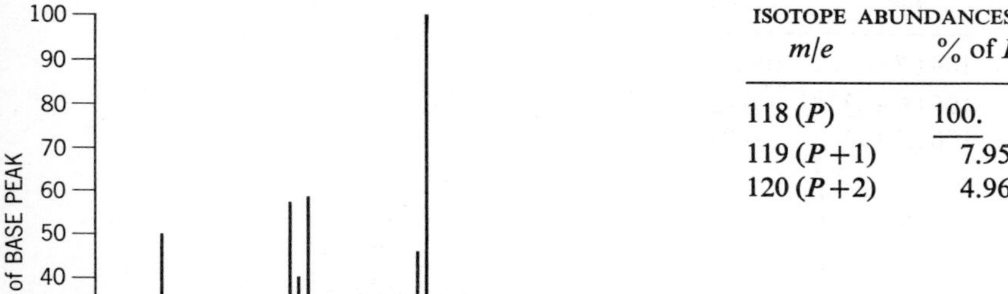

ISOTOPE ABUNDANCES

m/e	% of *P*
118 (*P*)	100.
119 (*P*+1)	7.95
120 (*P*+2)	4.96

P (118) = 30.2
P+1 (119) = 2.40
P+2 (120) = 1.50

Ultraviolet Data

$\lambda_{max}^{C_6H_{12}}$	ϵ_{max}
225 (*s*)	163

(*s*) = shoulder

NMR Spectrum (*Solvent CDCl₃*)

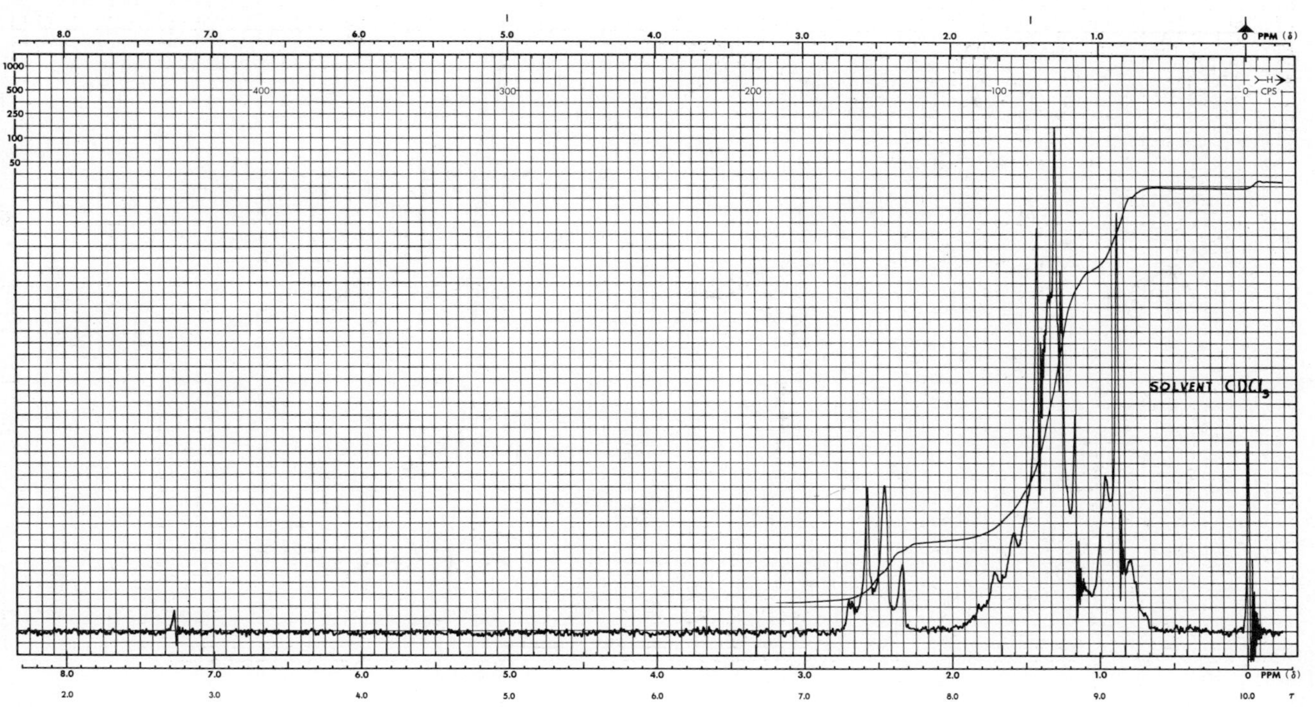

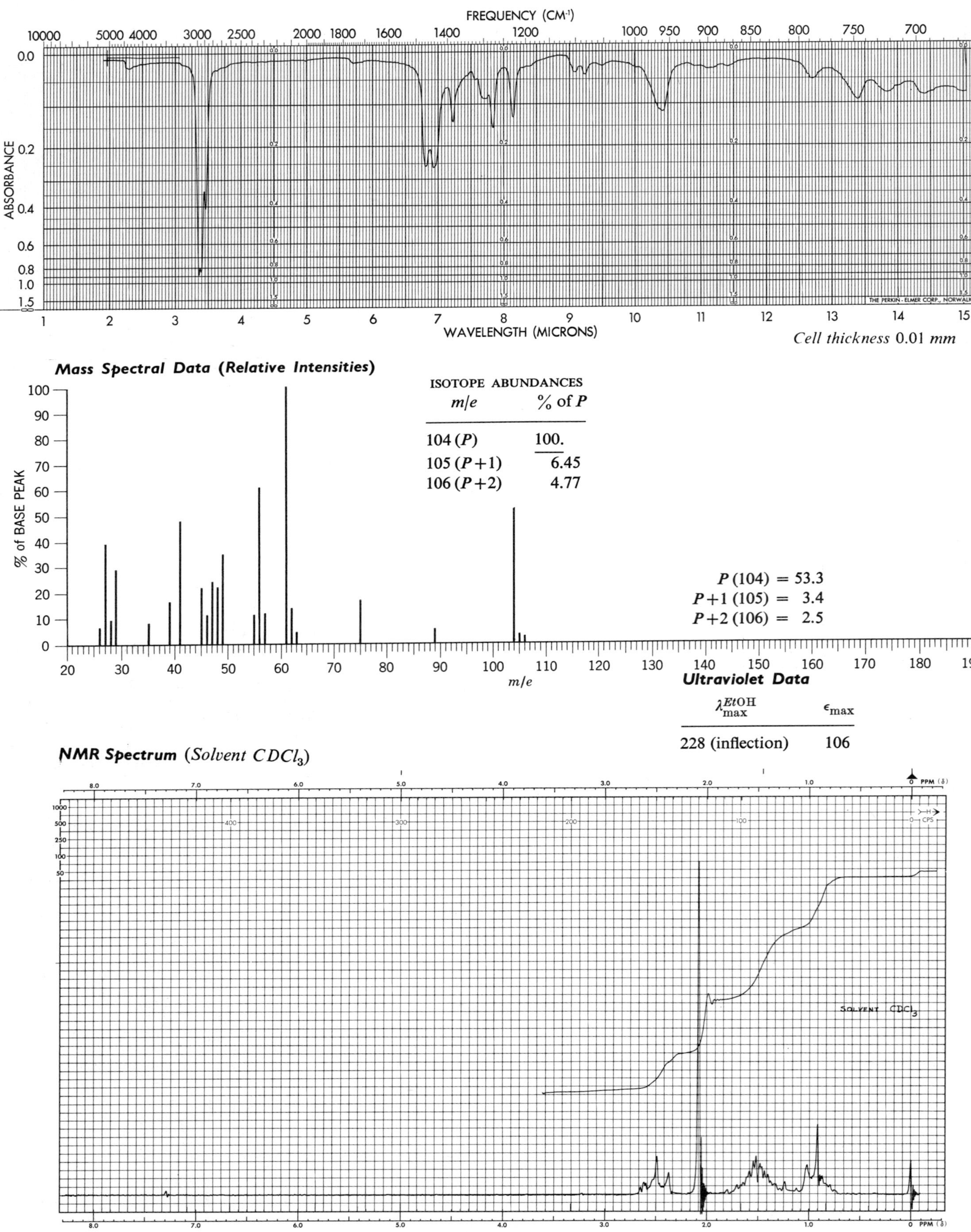

ISOTOPE ABUNDANCES m/e	% of P
104 (P)	100.
105 ($P+1$)	6.45
106 ($P+2$)	4.77

Ultraviolet Data

λ_{max}^{EtOH}	ϵ_{max}
228 (inflection)	106

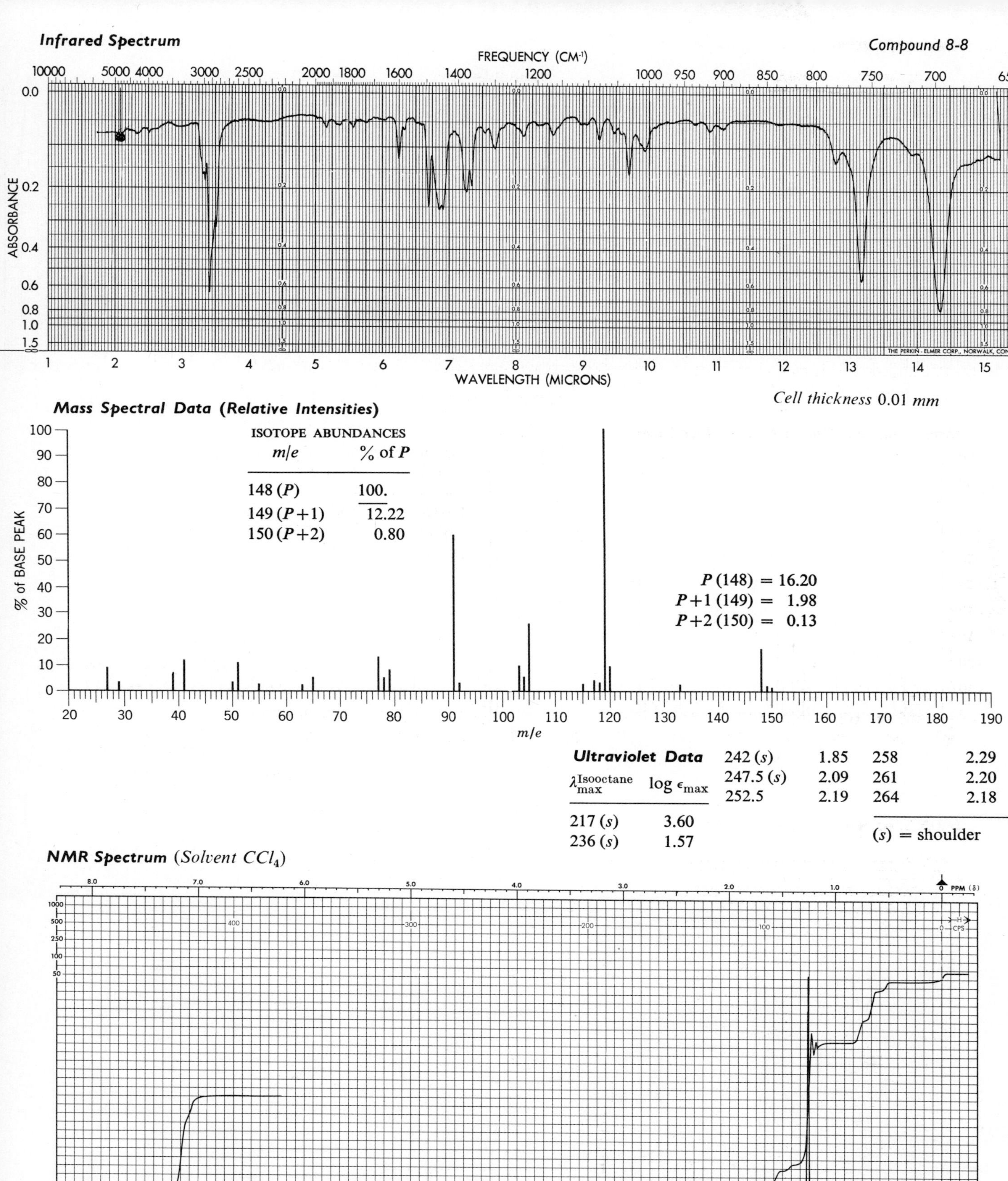

ISOTOPE ABUNDANCES

m/e	% of P
148 (P)	100.
149 ($P+1$)	12.22
150 ($P+2$)	0.80

Ultraviolet Data

$\lambda_{max}^{Isooctane}$	log ϵ_{max}
217 (*s*)	3.60
236 (*s*)	1.57
242 (*s*)	1.85
247.5 (*s*)	2.09
252.5	2.19
258	2.29
261	2.20
264	2.18

(*s*) = shoulder

Infrared Spectrum

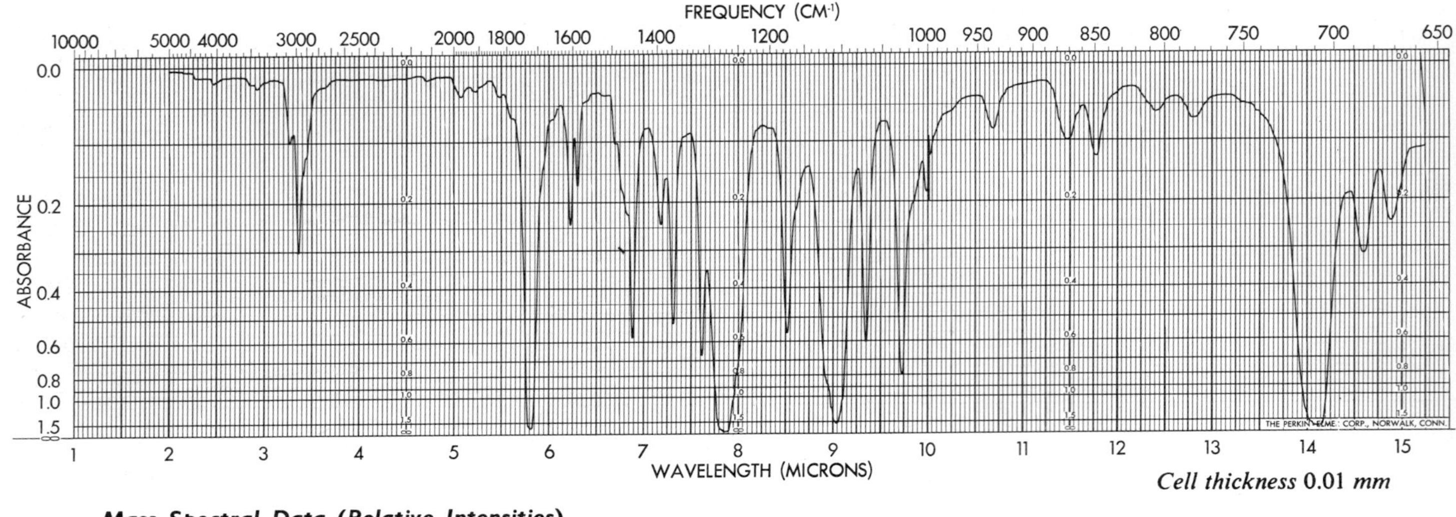

Cell thickness 0.01 *mm*

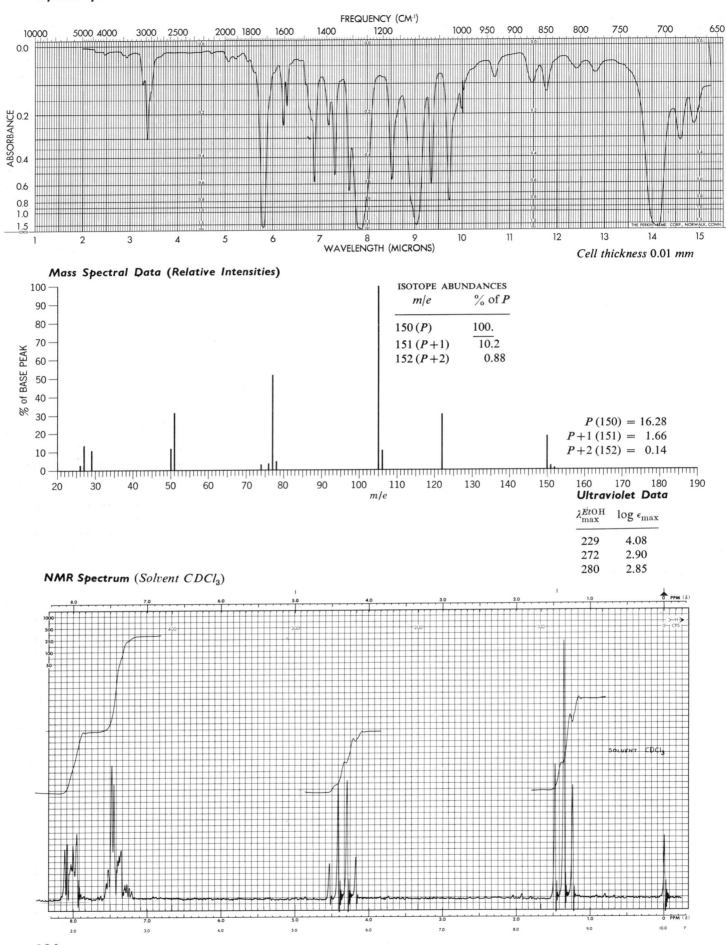

Mass Spectral Data (Relative Intensities)

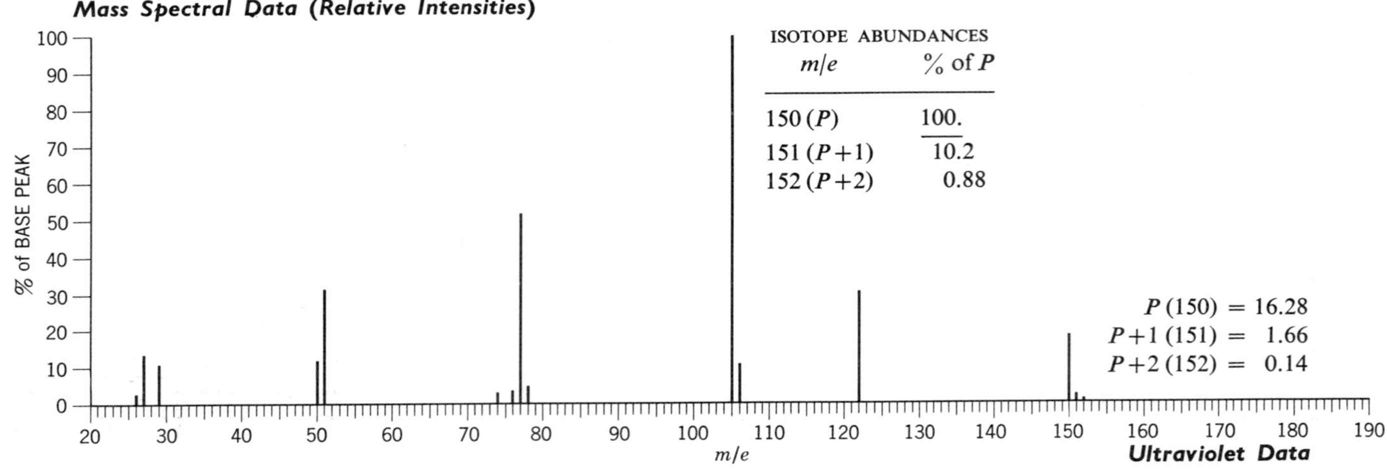

ISOTOPE ABUNDANCES

m/e	% of P
150 (P)	100.
151 ($P+1$)	10.2
152 ($P+2$)	0.88

P (150) = 16.28
$P+1$ (151) = 1.66
$P+2$ (152) = 0.14

Ultraviolet Data

λ_{max}^{EtOH}	$\log \epsilon_{max}$
229	4.08
272	2.90
280	2.85

NMR Spectrum (*Solvent* $CDCl_3$)

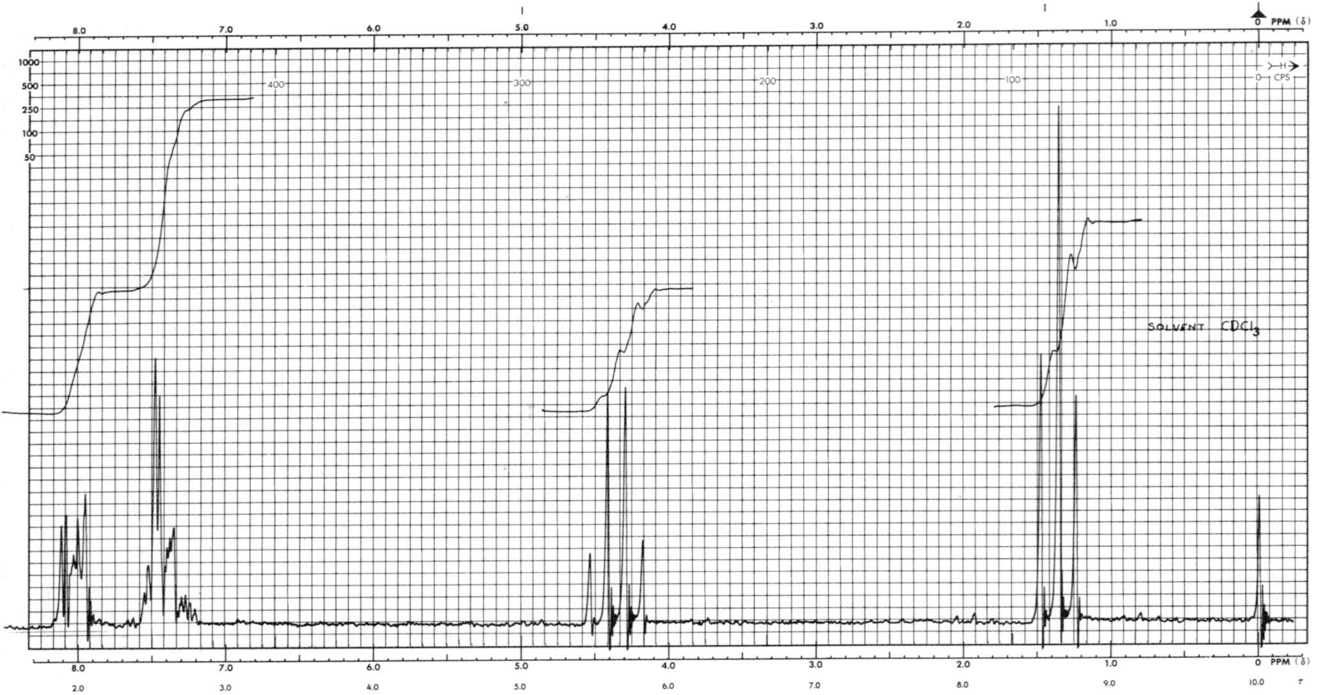

Infrared Spectrum **Compound 8-10**

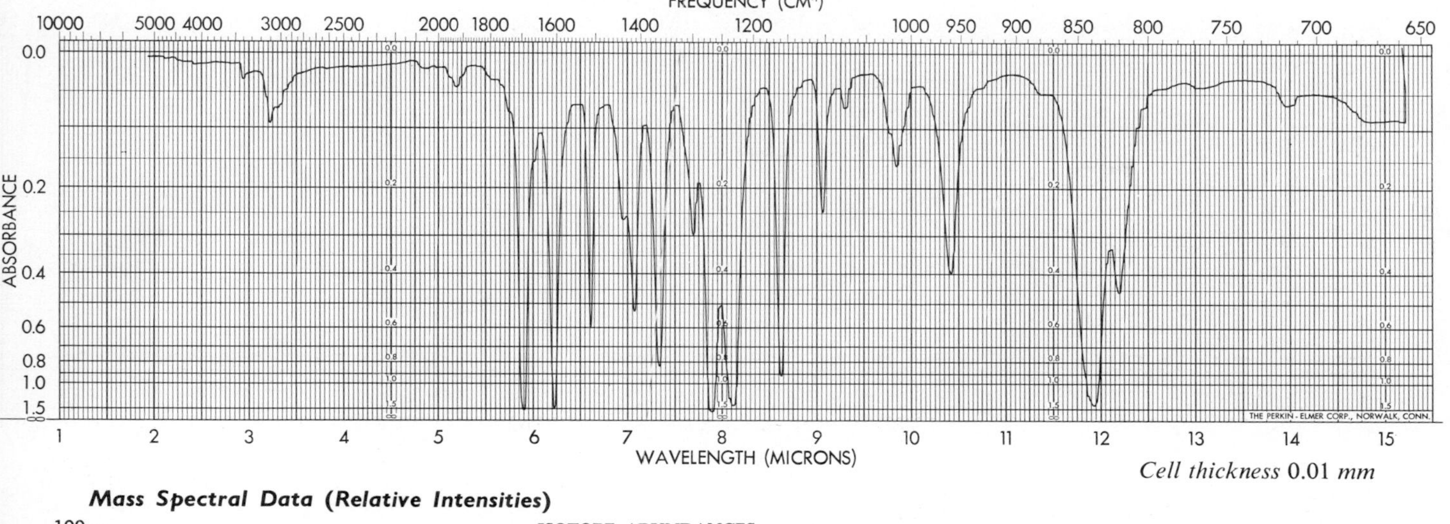

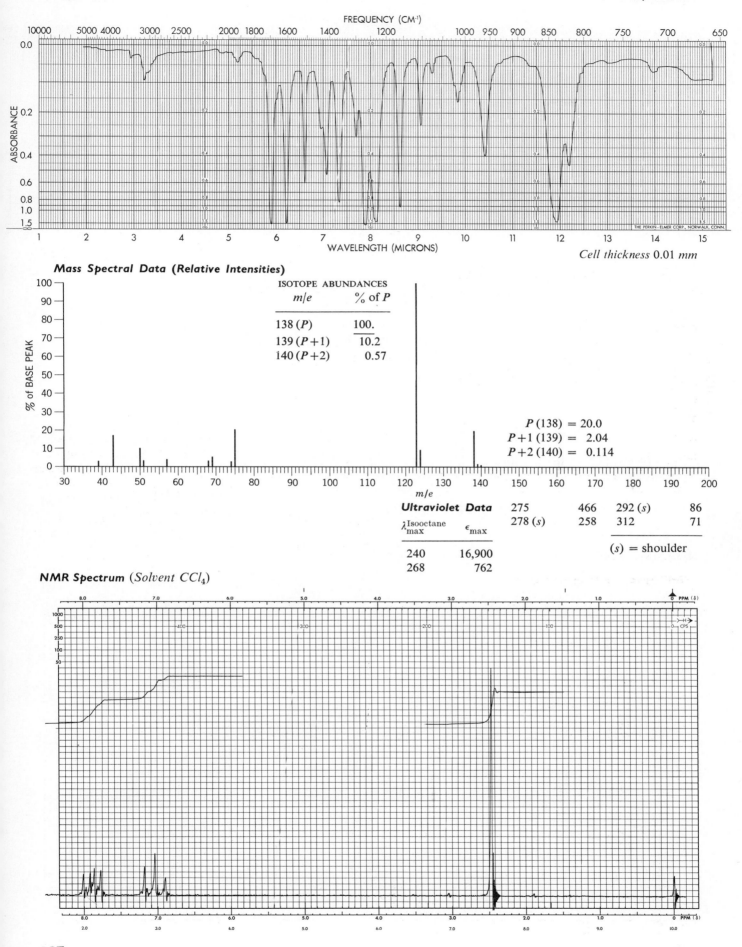

Cell thickness 0.01 *mm*

Mass Spectral Data (Relative Intensities)

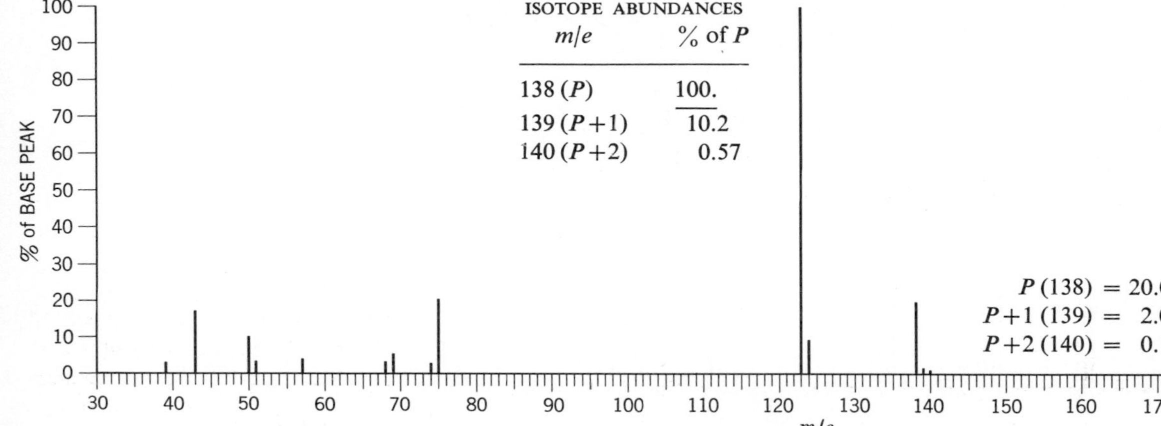

ISOTOPE ABUNDANCES

m/e	% of *P*
138 (*P*)	100.
139 (*P*+1)	10.2
140 (*P*+2)	0.57

P (138) = 20.0
P+1 (139) = 2.04
P+2 (140) = 0.114

Ultraviolet Data

$\lambda_{max}^{Isooctane}$	ϵ_{max}
240	16,900
268	762
275	466
278 (*s*)	258
292 (*s*)	86
312	71

(*s*) = shoulder

NMR Spectrum (*Solvent* CCl_4)

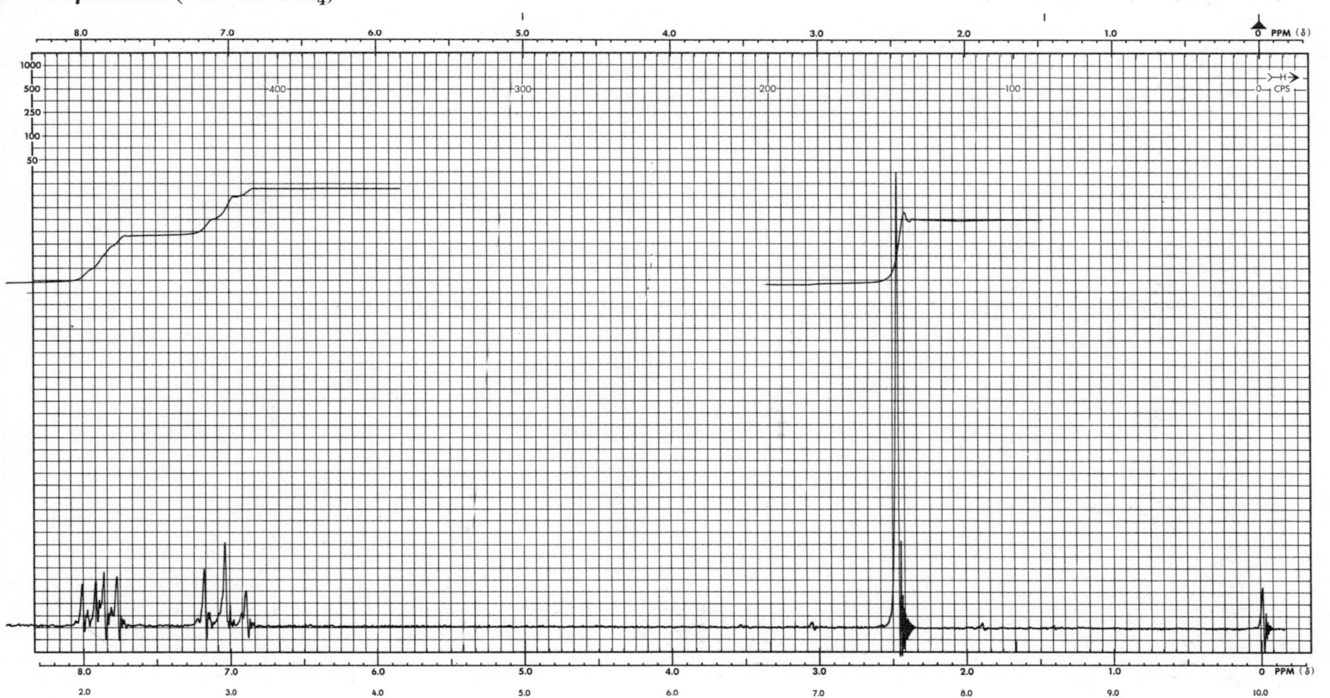

Infrared Spectrum **Compound 8-11**

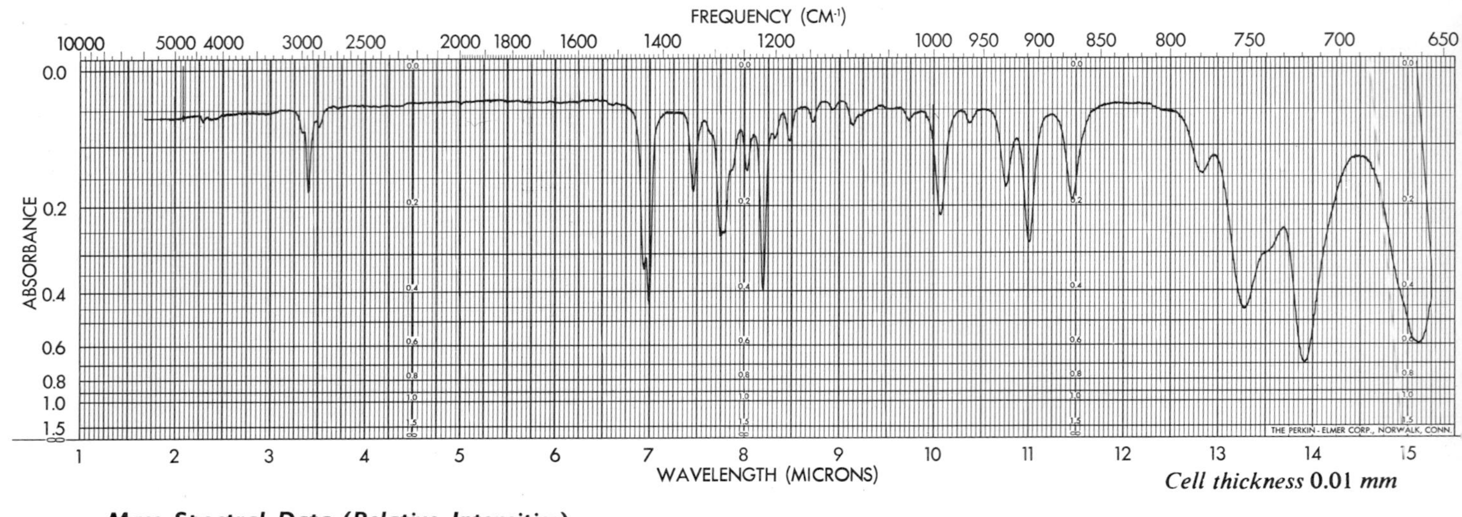

Cell thickness 0.01 *mm*

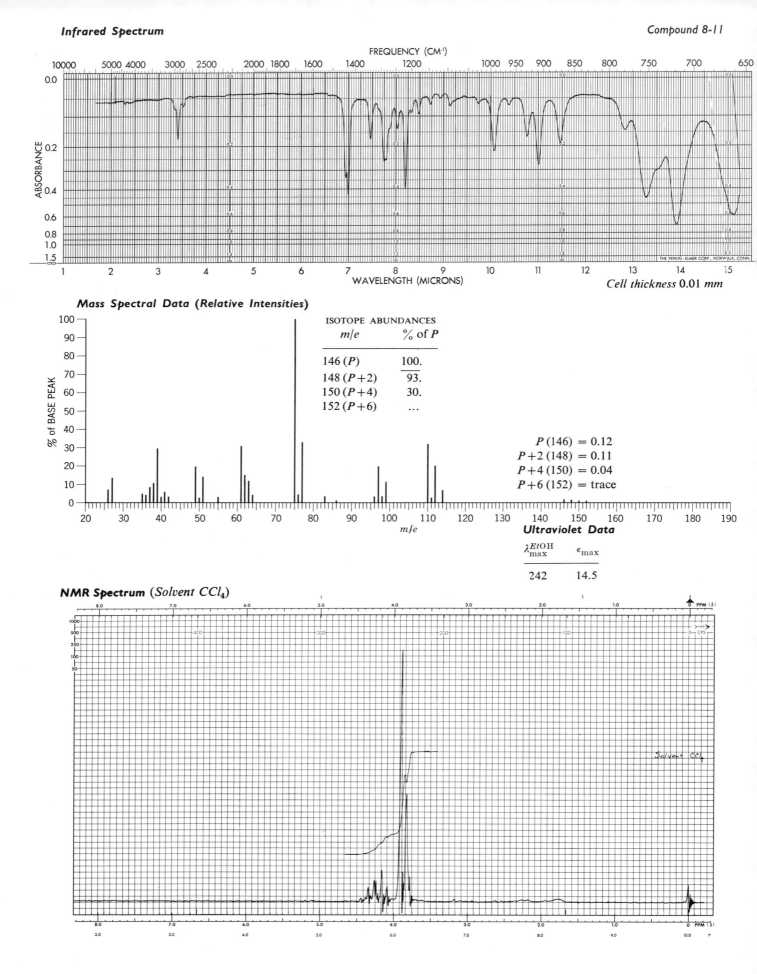

Mass Spectral Data (Relative Intensities)

ISOTOPE ABUNDANCES	
m/e	% of *P*
146 (*P*)	100.
148 (*P*+2)	93.
150 (*P*+4)	30.
152 (*P*+6)	...

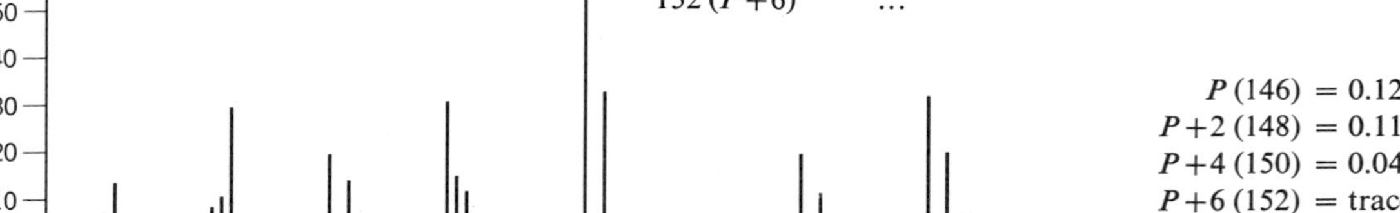

P (146) = 0.12
$P+2$ (148) = 0.11
$P+4$ (150) = 0.04
$P+6$ (152) = trace

Ultraviolet Data

λ_{max}^{EtOH}	ϵ_{max}
242	14.5

NMR Spectrum (*Solvent* CCl_4)

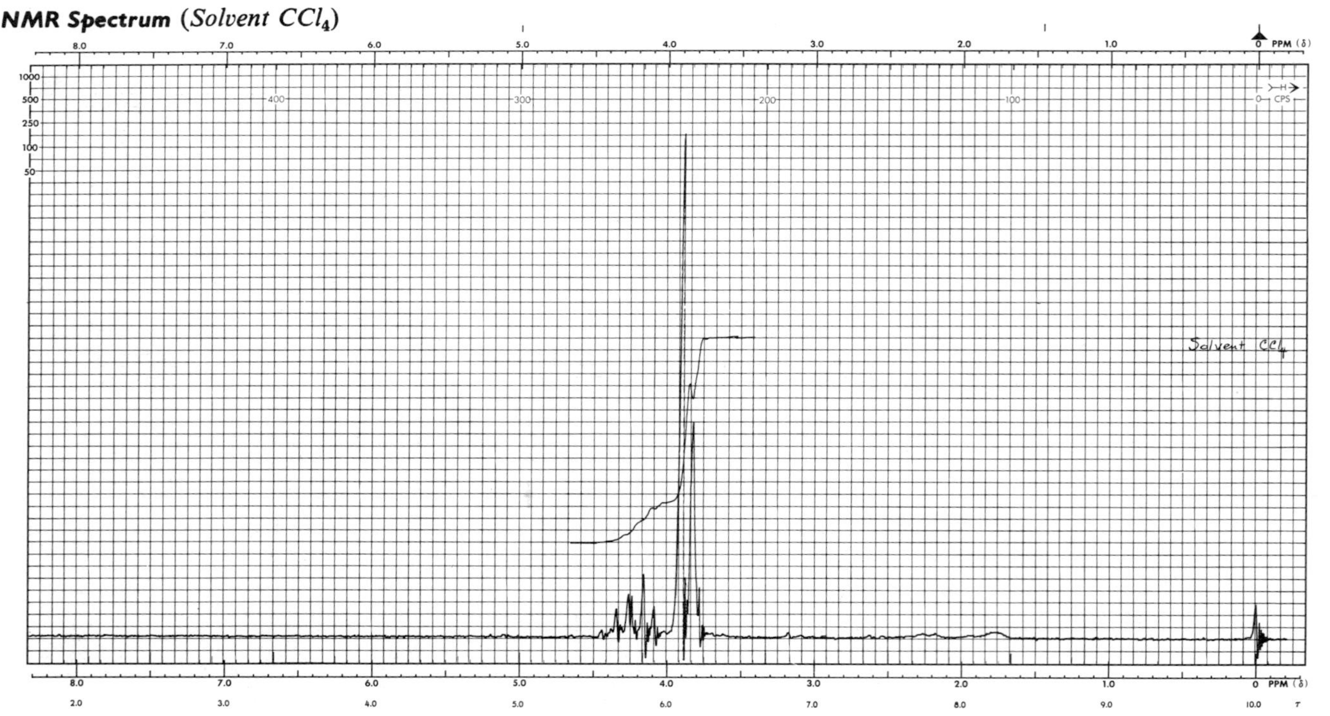

Infrared Spectrum

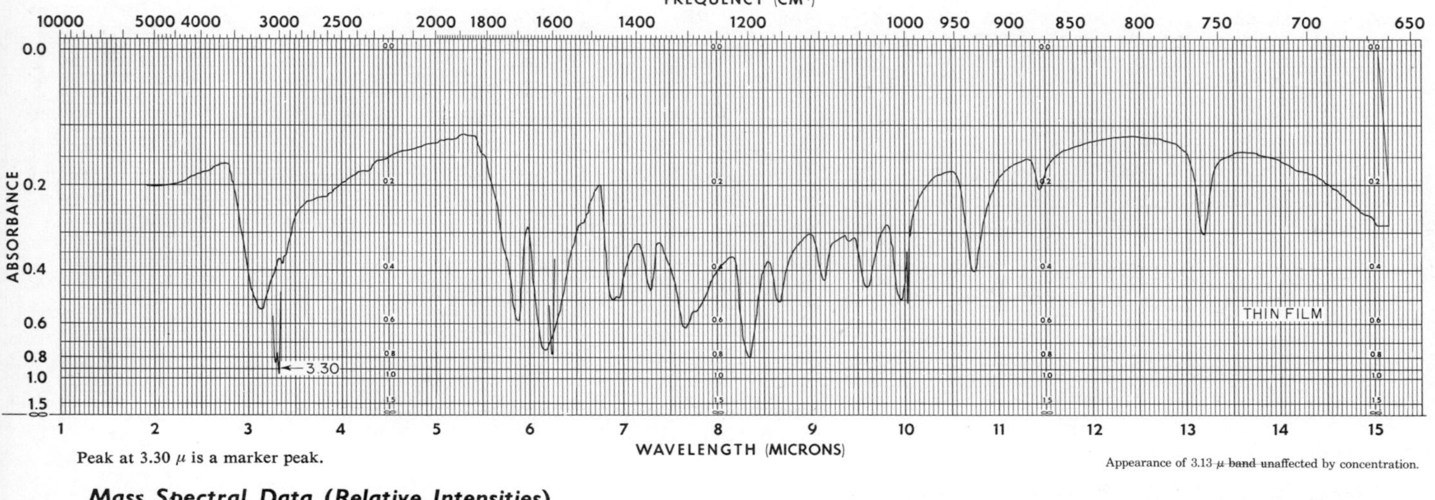

Peak at 3.30 μ is a marker peak.

Appearance of 3.13 μ band unaffected by concentration.

Mass Spectral Data (Relative Intensities)

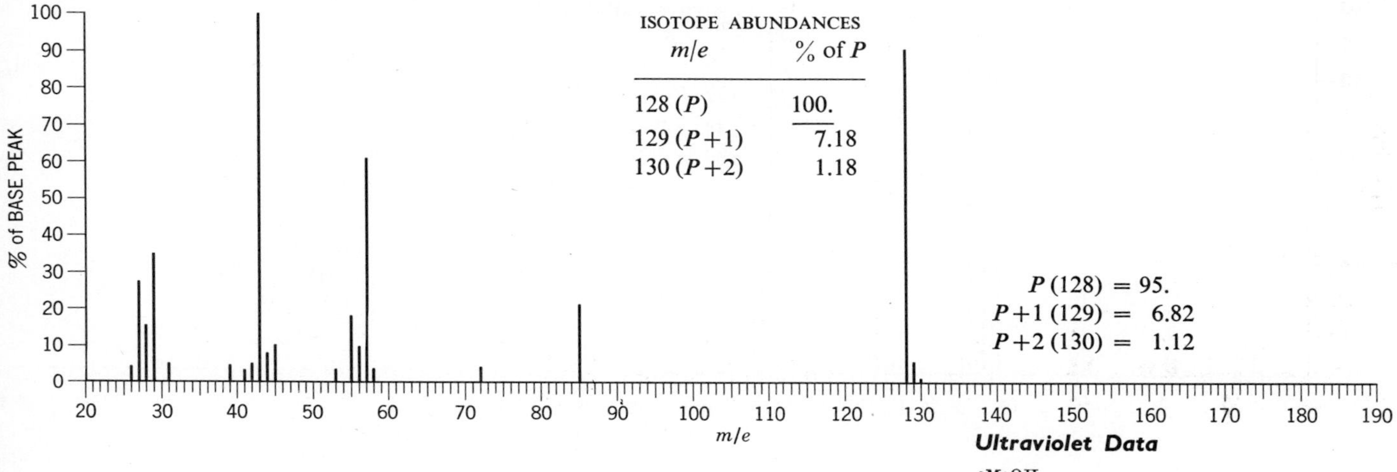

ISOTOPE ABUNDANCES

m/e	% of P
128 (P)	100.
129 (P+1)	7.18
130 (P+2)	1.18

P (128) = 95.
P+1 (129) = 6.82
P+2 (130) = 1.12

Ultraviolet Data

λ_{max}^{MeOH}	ϵ_{max}
291	8,700

NMR Spectrum

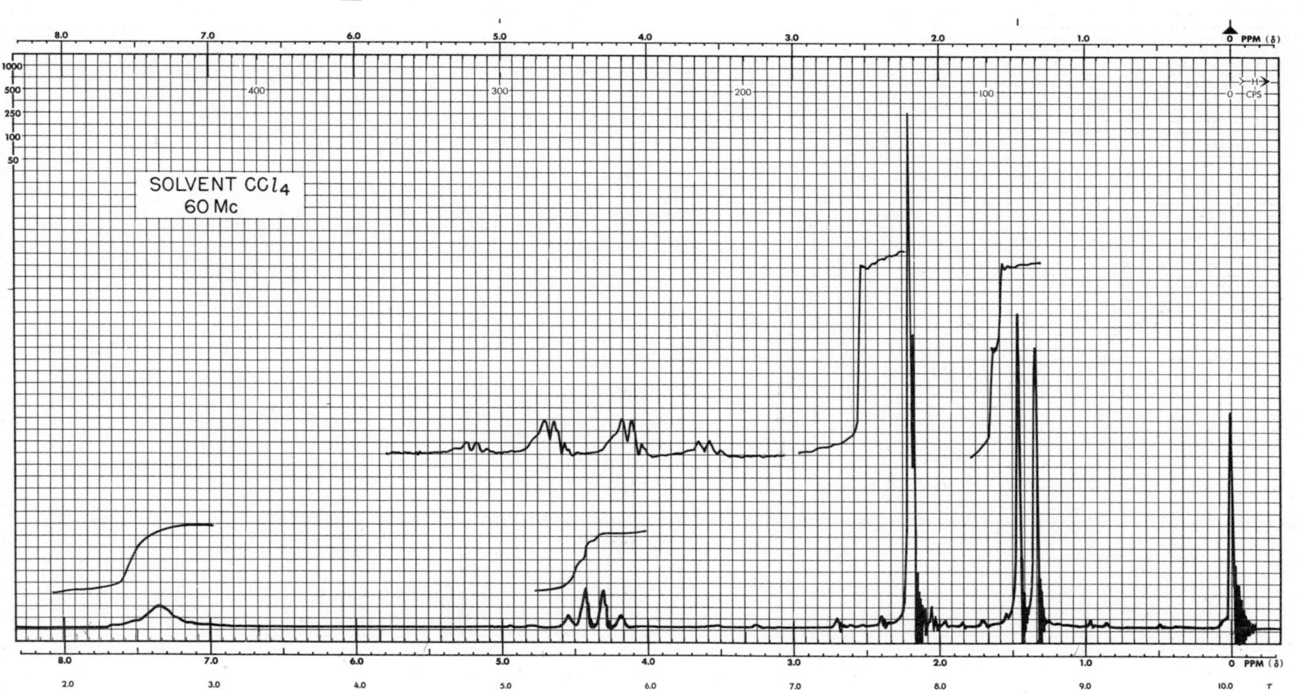

Infrared Spectrum

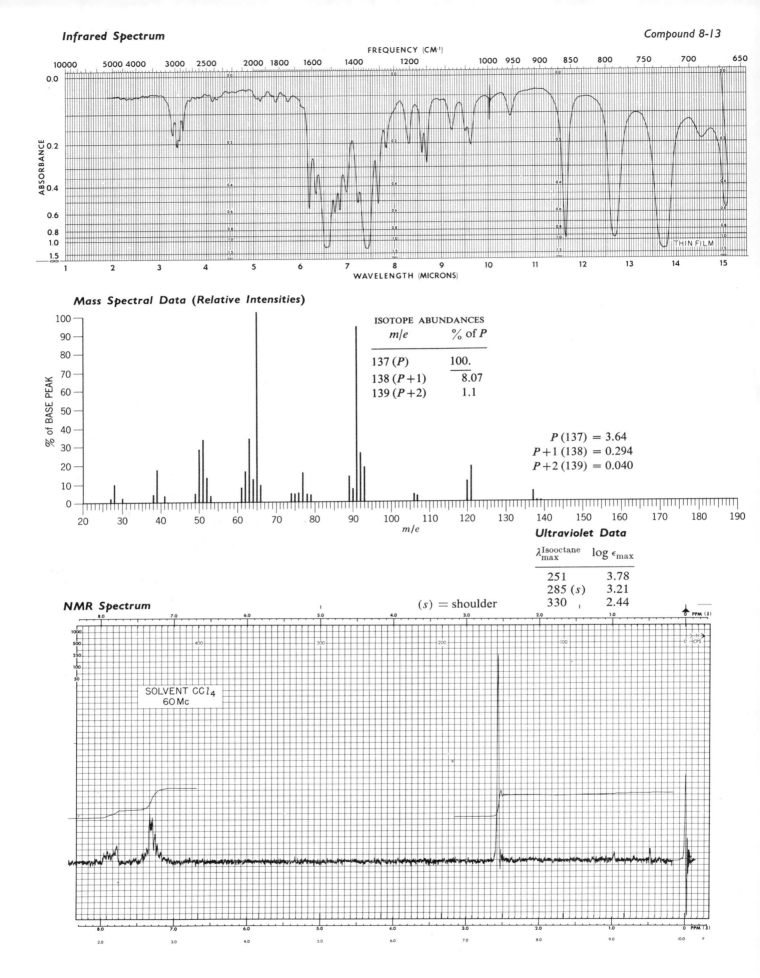

Compound 8-13

Mass Spectral Data (Relative Intensities)

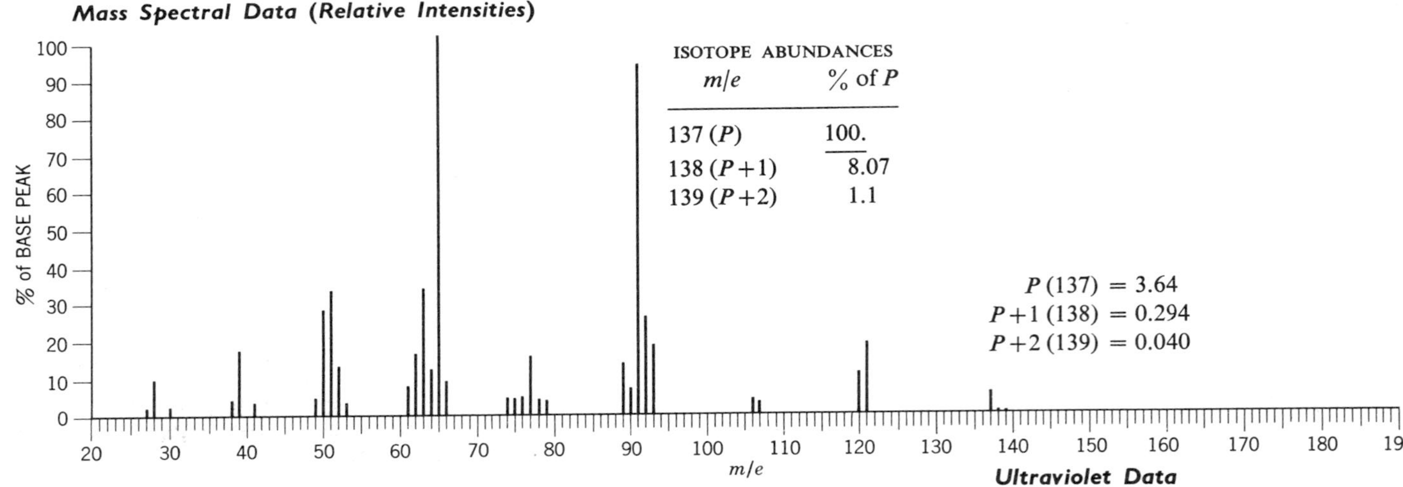

ISOTOPE ABUNDANCES

m/e	% of P
137 (P)	100.
138 ($P+1$)	8.07
139 ($P+2$)	1.1

P (137) = 3.64
$P+1$ (138) = 0.294
$P+2$ (139) = 0.040

Ultraviolet Data

$\lambda_{max}^{Isooctane}$	$\log \epsilon_{max}$
251	3.78
285 (s)	3.21
330	2.44

(s) = shoulder

NMR Spectrum

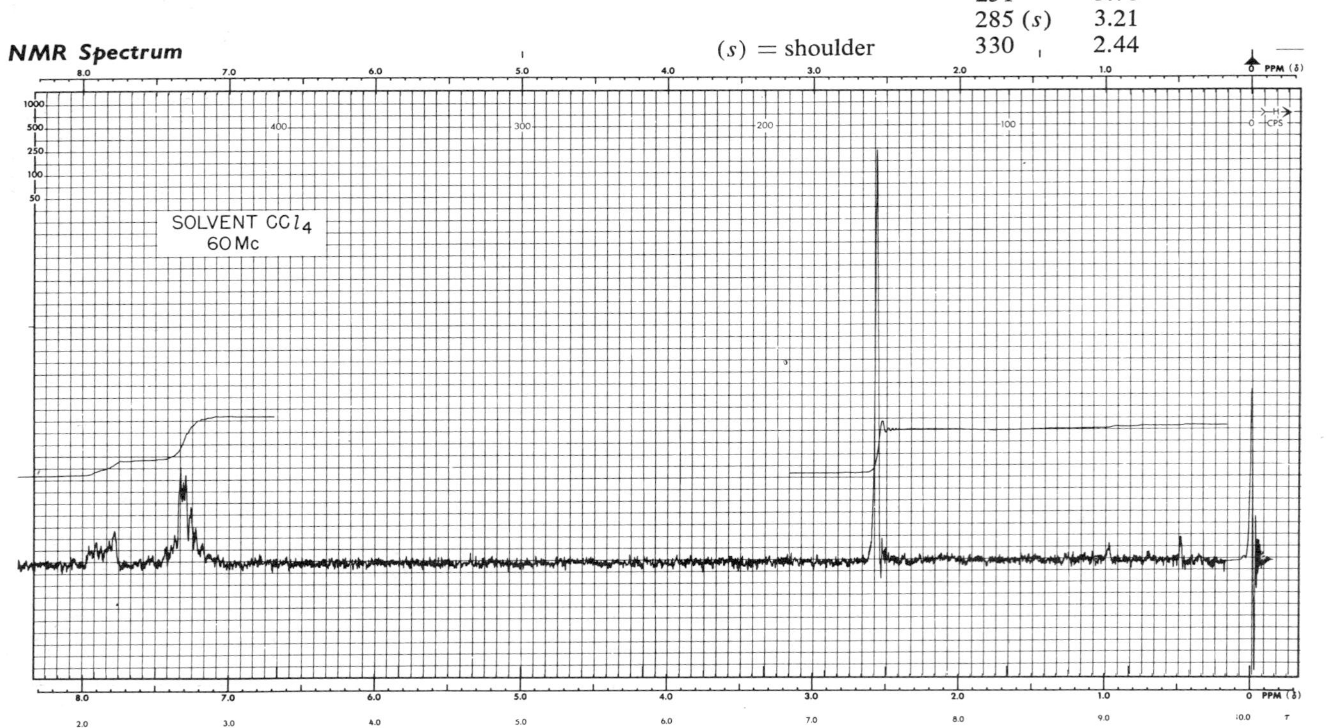

Infrared Spectrum

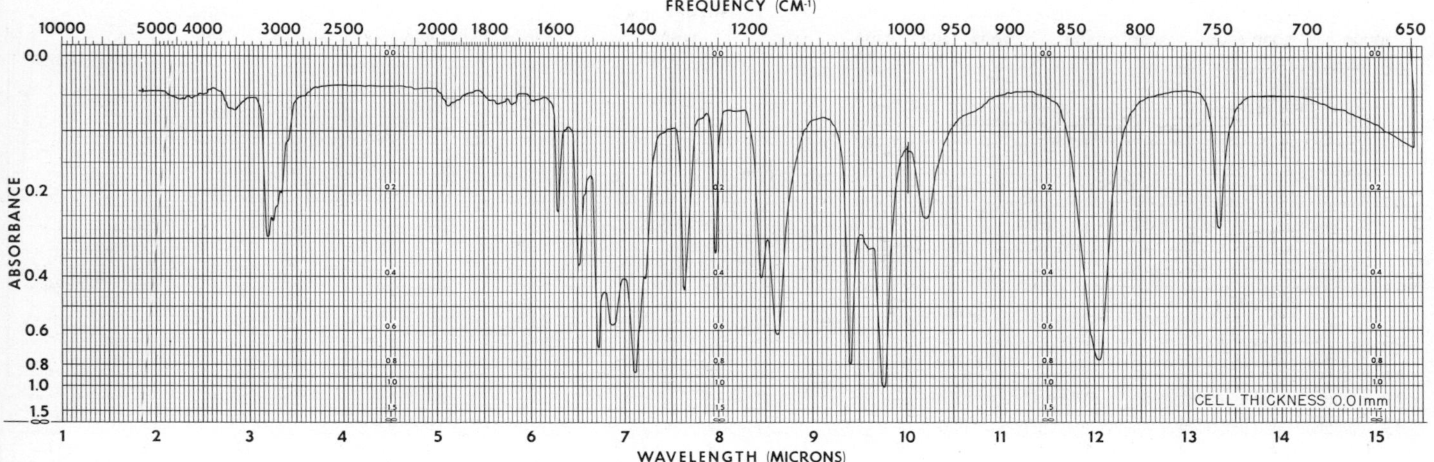

Mass Spectral Data (Relative Intensities)

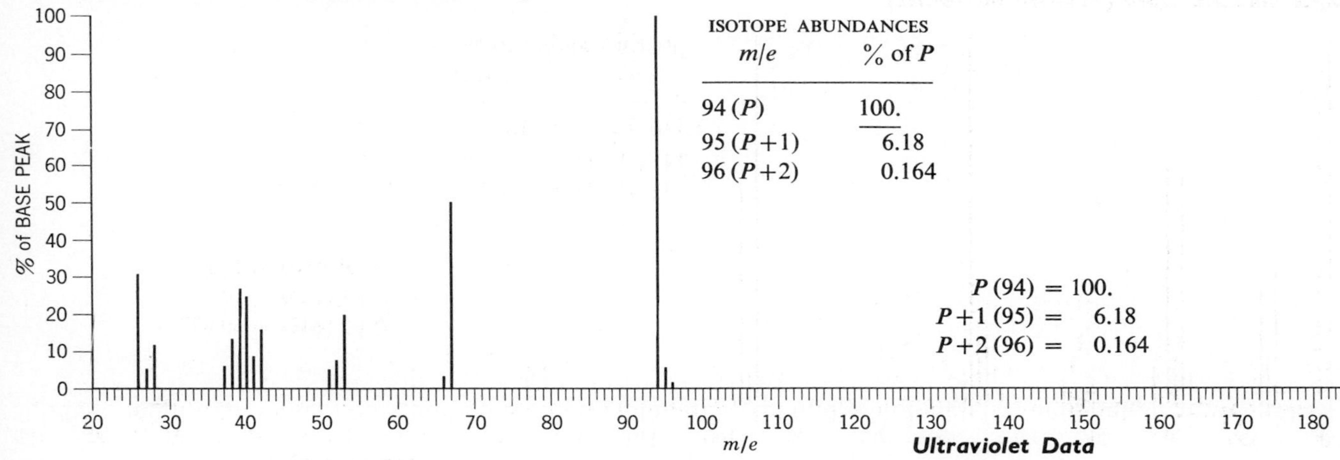

Ultraviolet Data

	λ_{max}^{EtOH}	ϵ_{max}
pH 7	266	6,600
	272.5	6,000
	305	900
pH 1	266	10,200
	273	9,700

NMR Spectrum

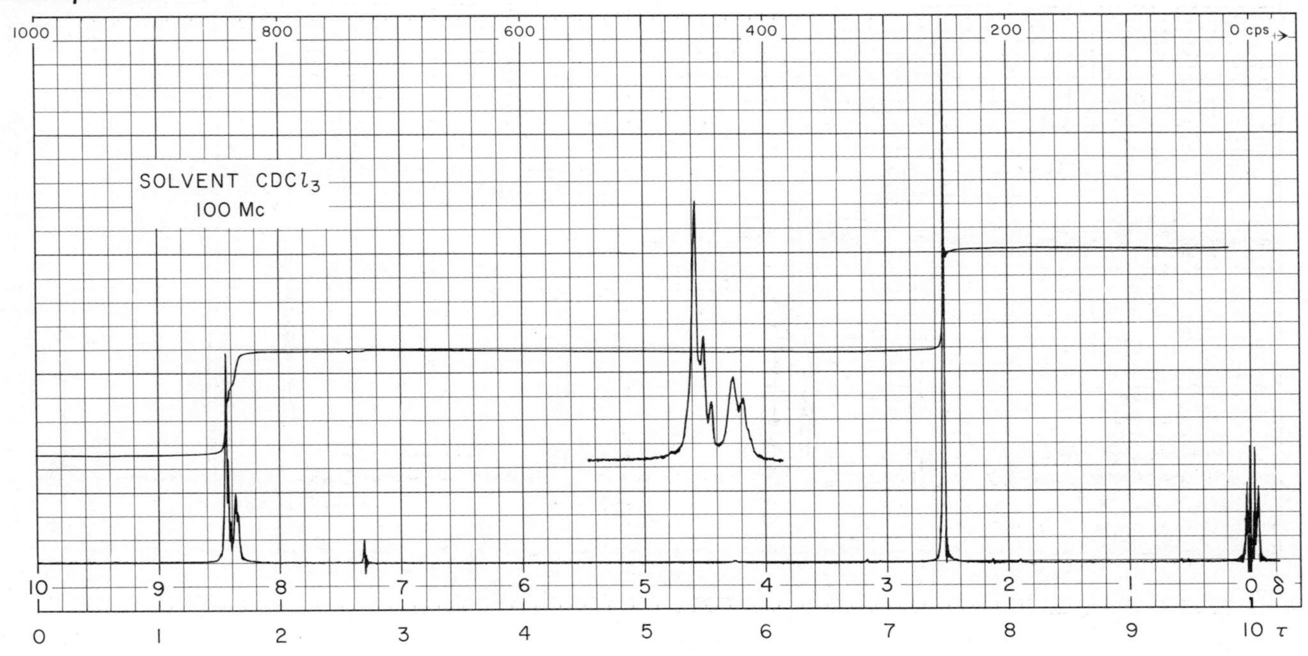

Infrared Spectrum

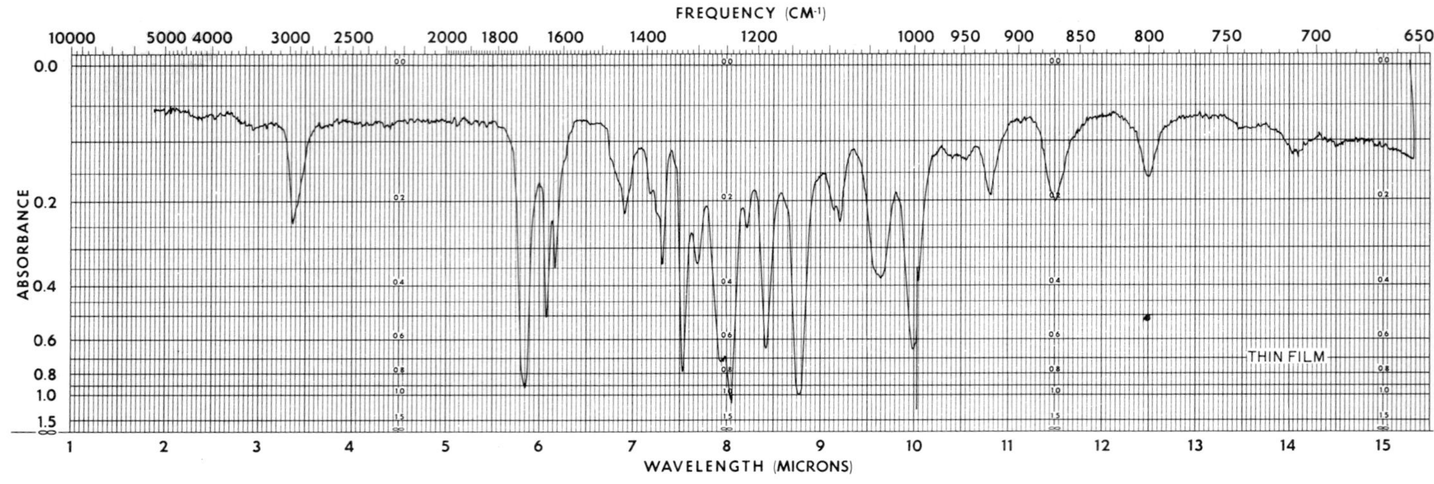

Mass Spectral Data (Relative Intensities)

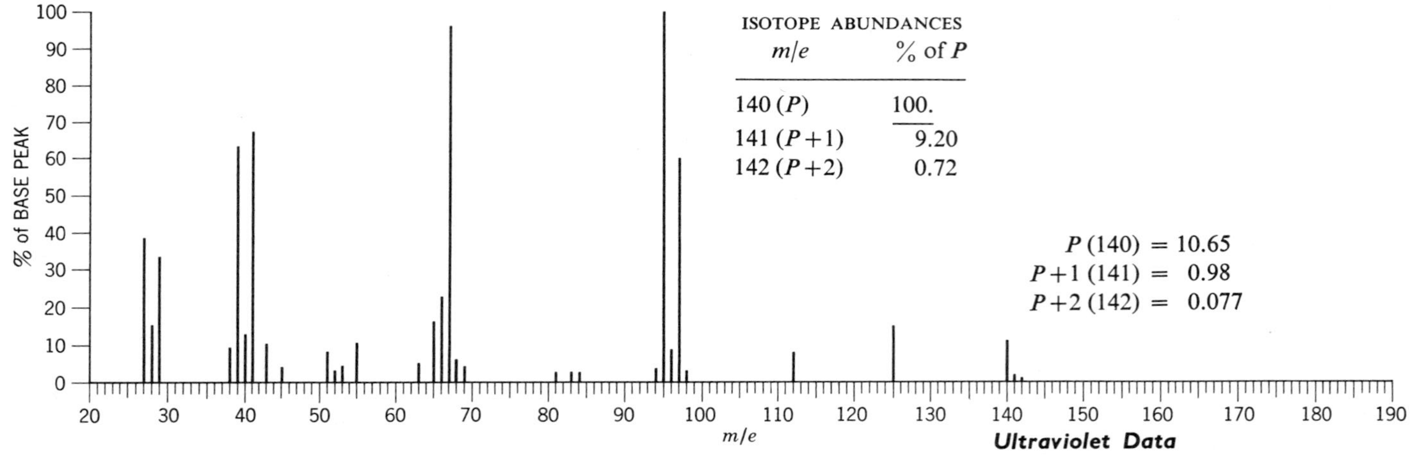

ISOTOPE ABUNDANCES

m/e	% of P
140 (P)	100.
141 ($P+1$)	9.20
142 ($P+2$)	0.72

P (140) = 10.65
$P+1$ (141) = 0.98
$P+2$ (142) = 0.077

Ultraviolet Data

λ_{max}^{EtOH}	$\log \epsilon_{max}$
259	4.4

NMR Spectrum

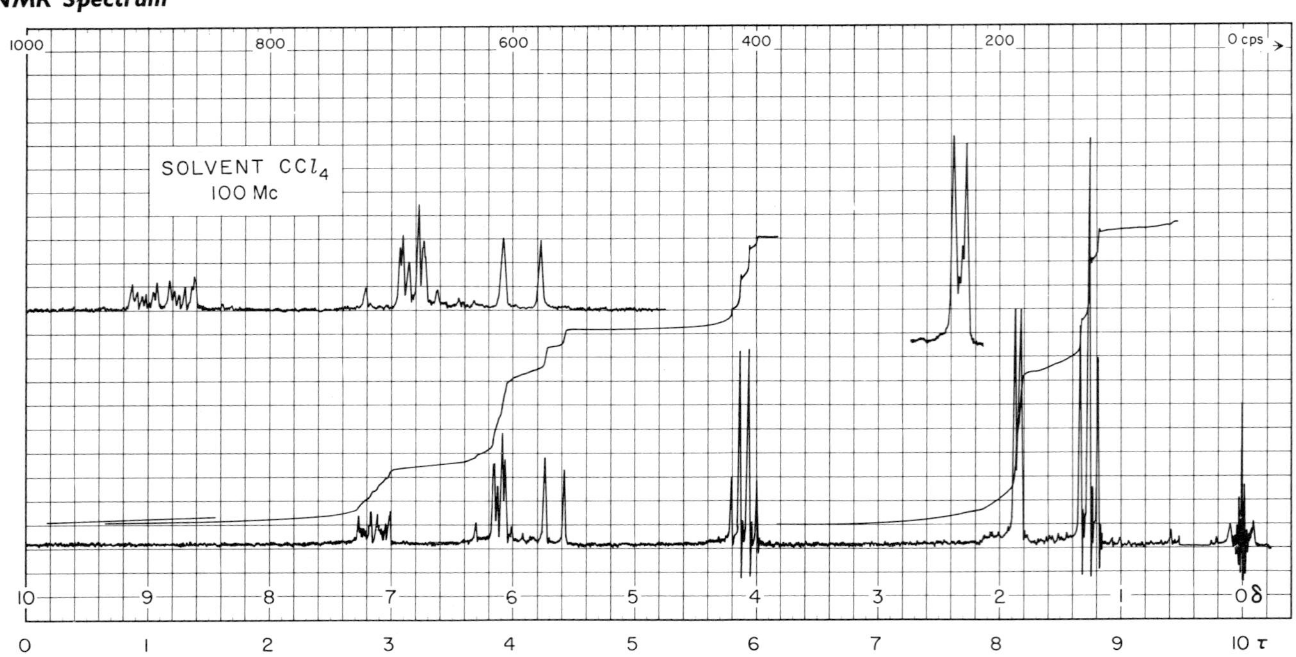

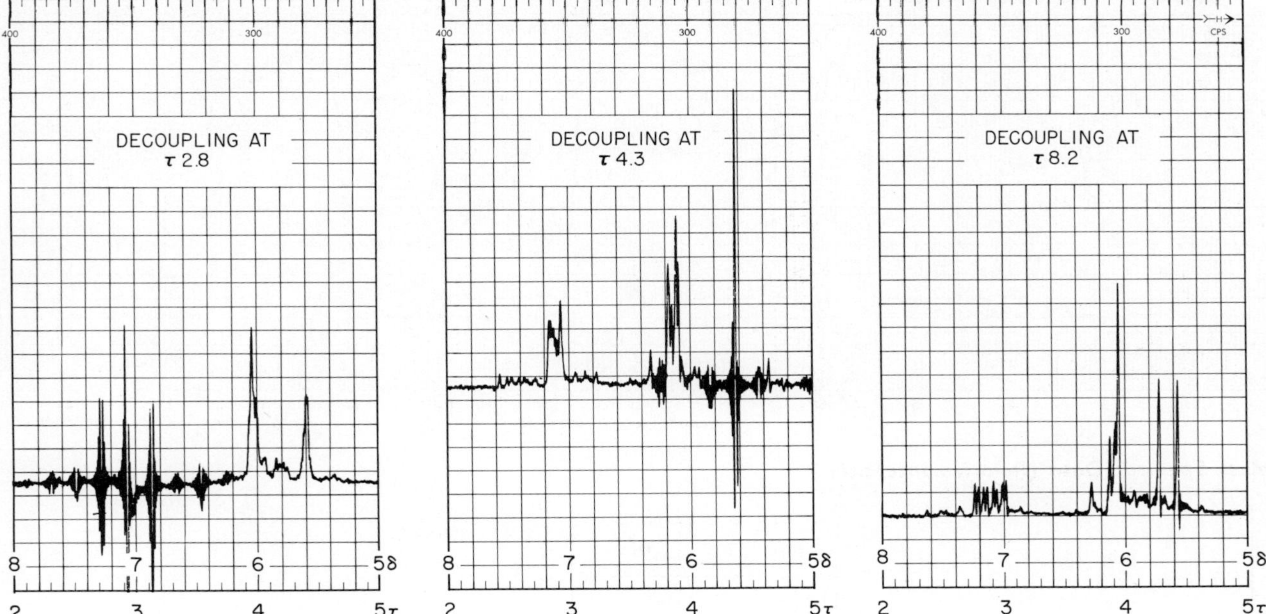
400
300
DECOUPLING AT
τ 2.8
8
7
6
5δ
2
3
4
5τ
400
300
DECOUPLING AT
τ 4.3
8
7
6
5δ
2
3
4
5τ
400
300
CPS
DECOUPLING AT
τ 8.2
8
7
6
5δ
2
3
4
5τ

Infrared Spectrum

Compound 8-16

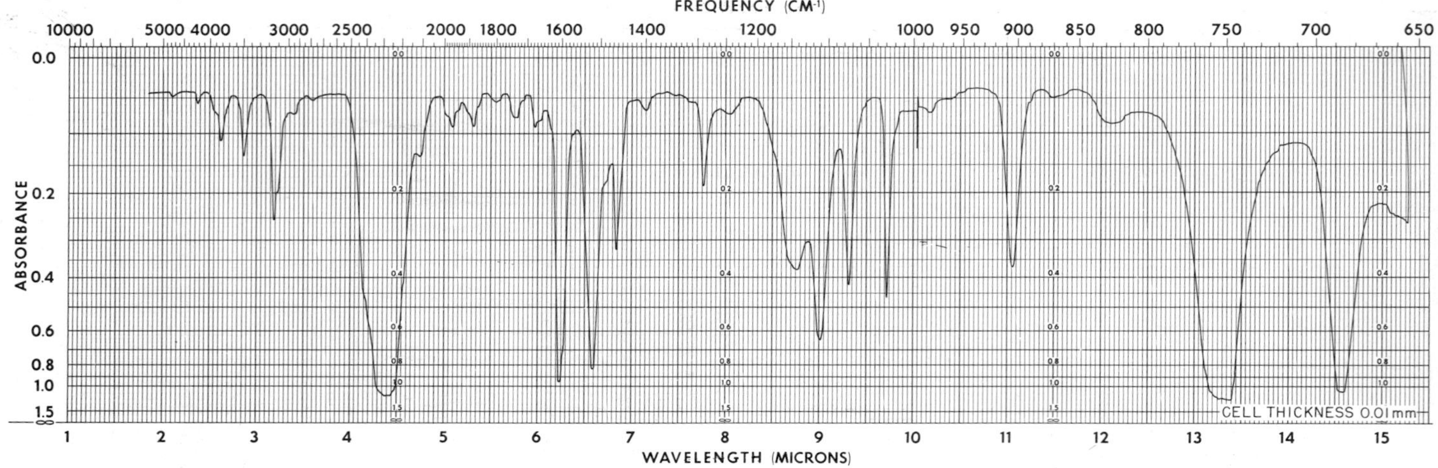

Mass Spectral Data (Relative Intensities)

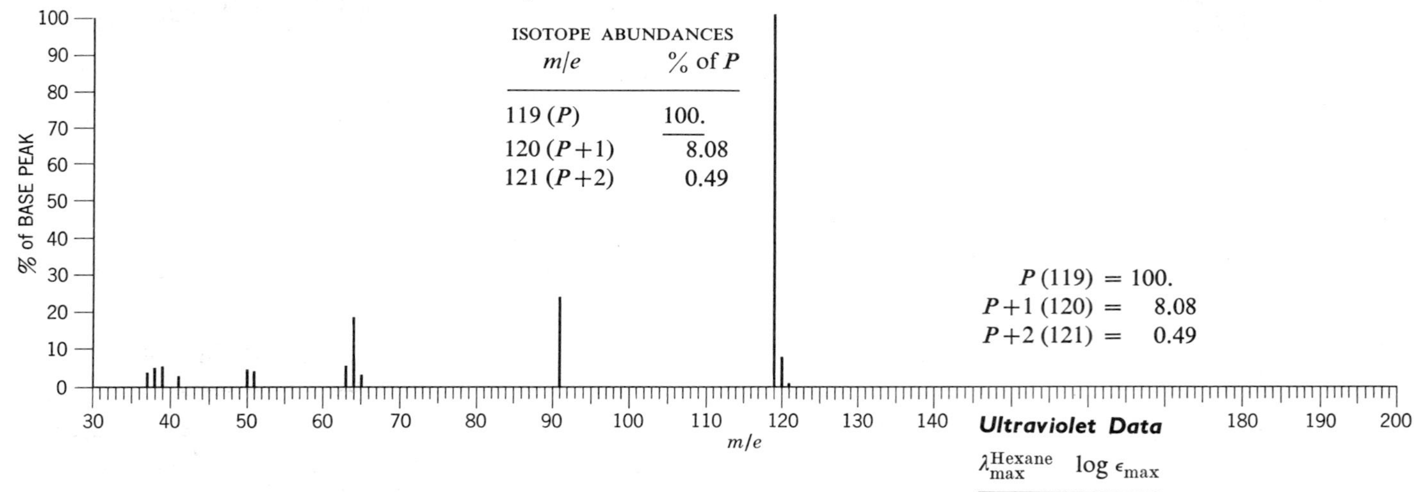

ISOTOPE ABUNDANCES

m/e	% of P
119 (P)	100.
120 ($P+1$)	8.08
121 ($P+2$)	0.49

P (119) = 100.
$P+1$ (120) = 8.08
$P+2$ (121) = 0.49

Ultraviolet Data

λ_{max}^{Hexane}	$\log \epsilon_{max}$		
226	4.04		
256	2.59	270	2.76
263	2.66	277	2.67

NMR Spectrum

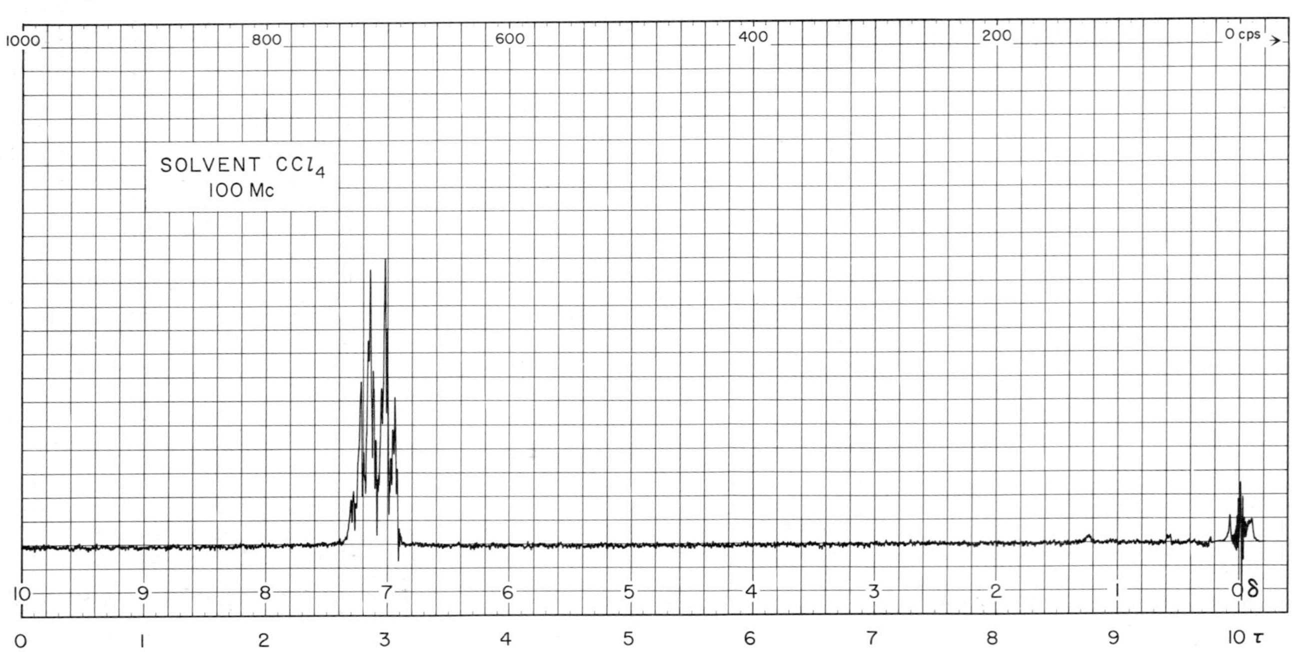

Compound isolated from ponderosa pine.

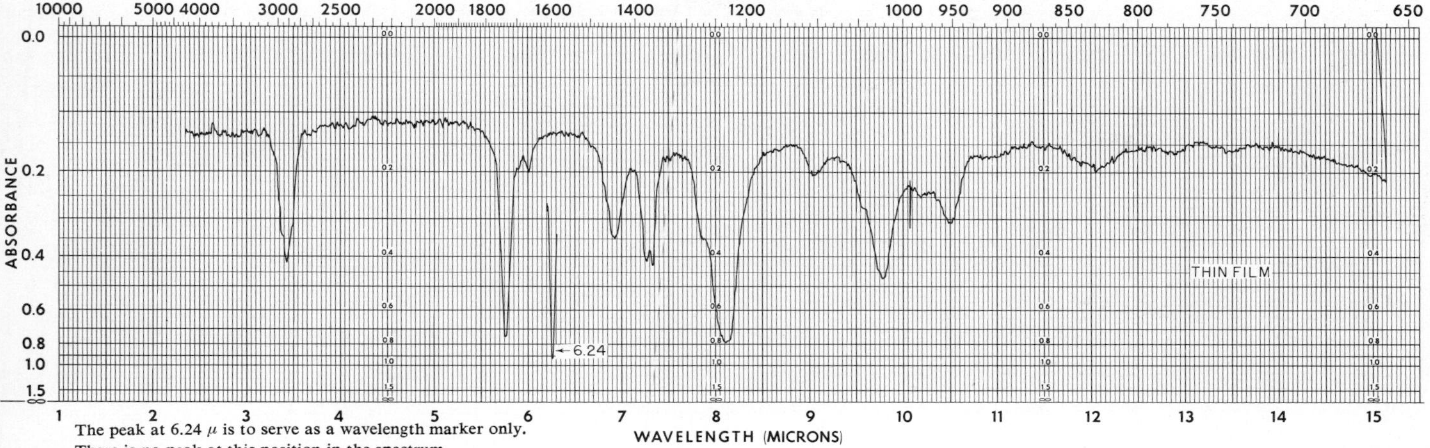

The peak at 6.24 μ is to serve as a wavelength marker only. There is no peak at this position in the spectrum.

Mass Spectral Data (Relative Intensities)

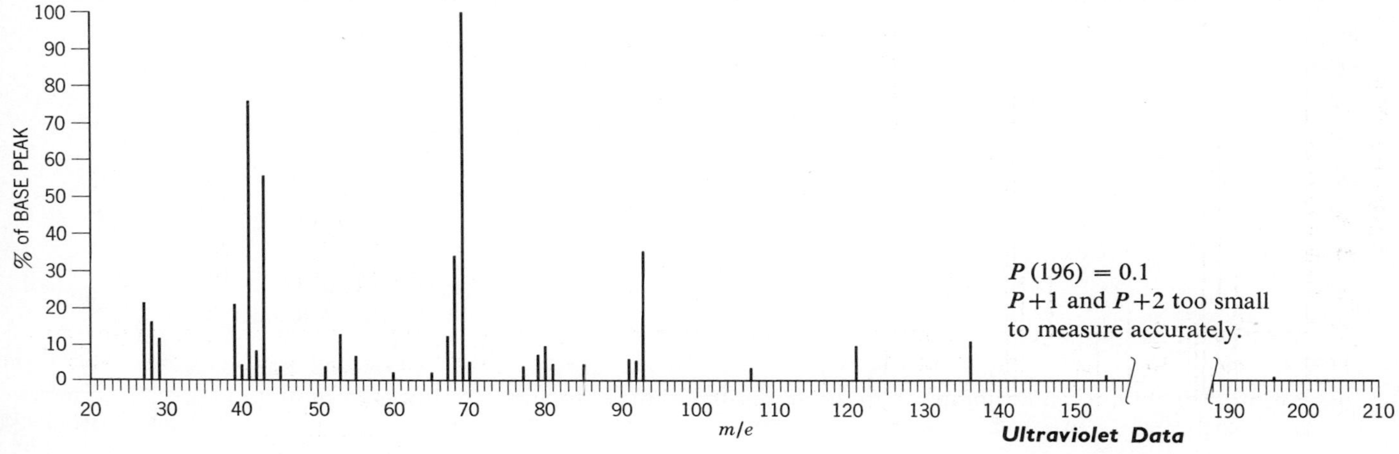

P (196) = 0.1
P+1 and *P*+2 too small to measure accurately.

Ultraviolet Data

Featureless beyond 210 mμ.

NMR Spectrum

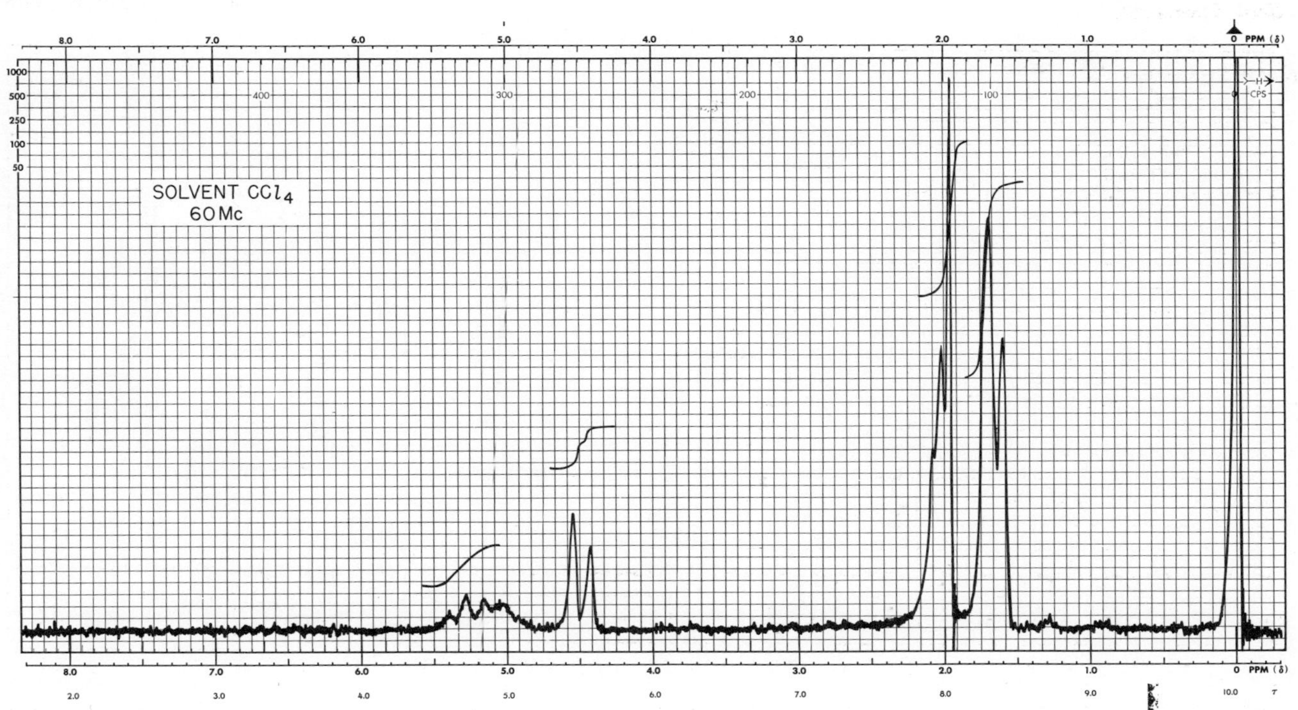

Compound isolated from ponderosa pine.
For derivative, see Compound 8-19.

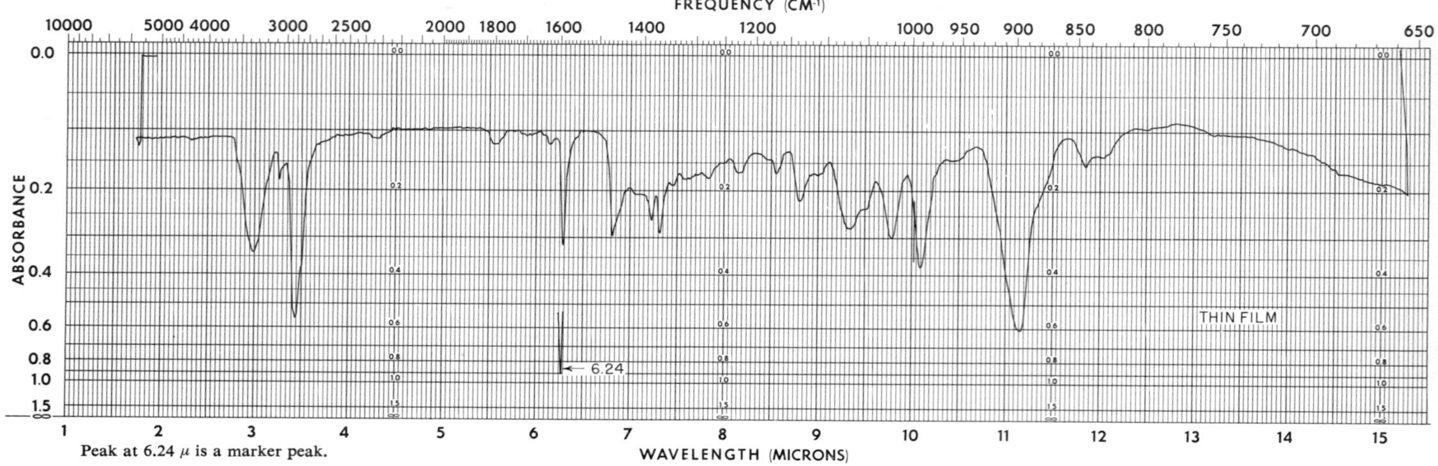

Peak at 6.24 μ is a marker peak.

Mass Spectral Data (Relative Intensities)

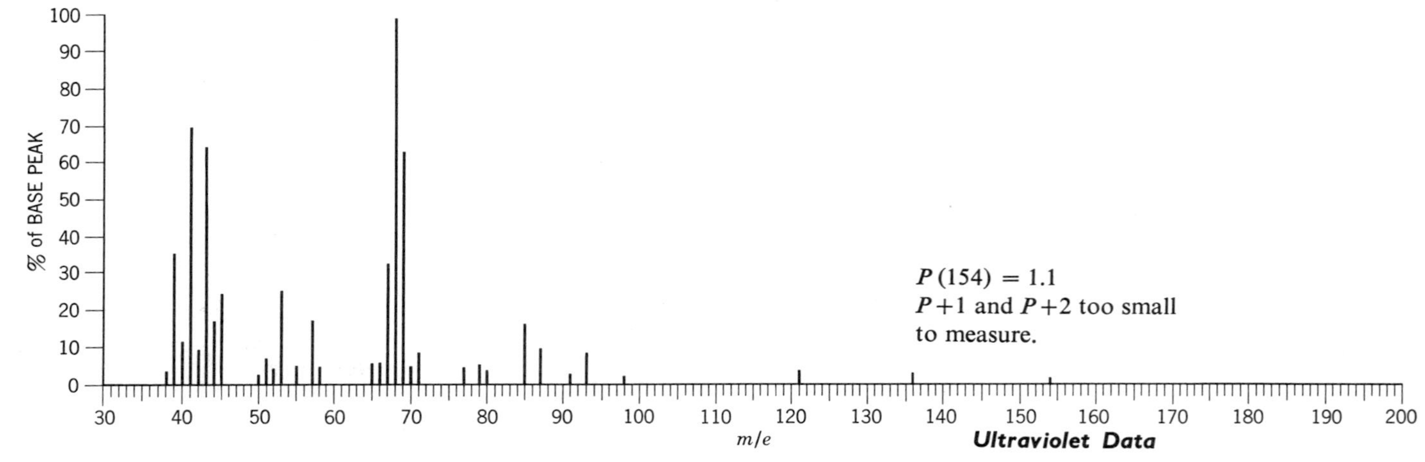

P (154) = 1.1
$P+1$ and $P+2$ too small to measure.

Ultraviolet Data

$\lambda_{max}^{C_6H_{12}}$	ϵ_{max}
226	20,000

NMR Spectrum

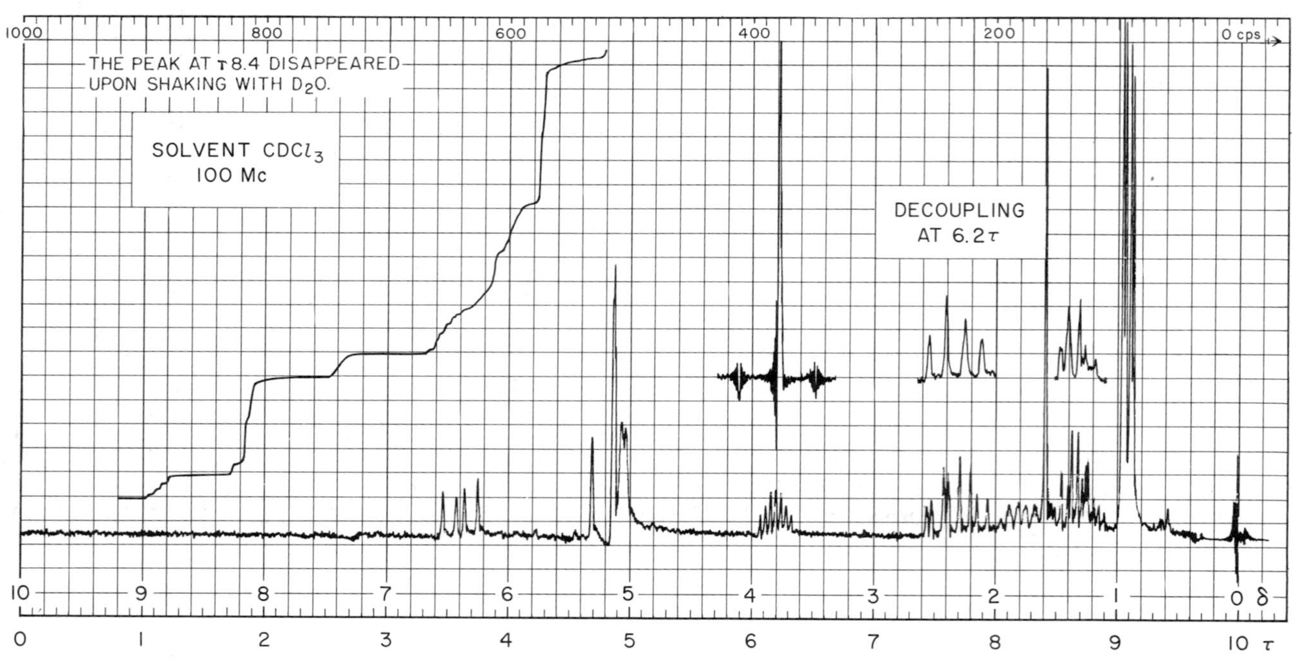

Infrared Spectrum *Derivative of Compound* 8-18 ***Compound 8-19***

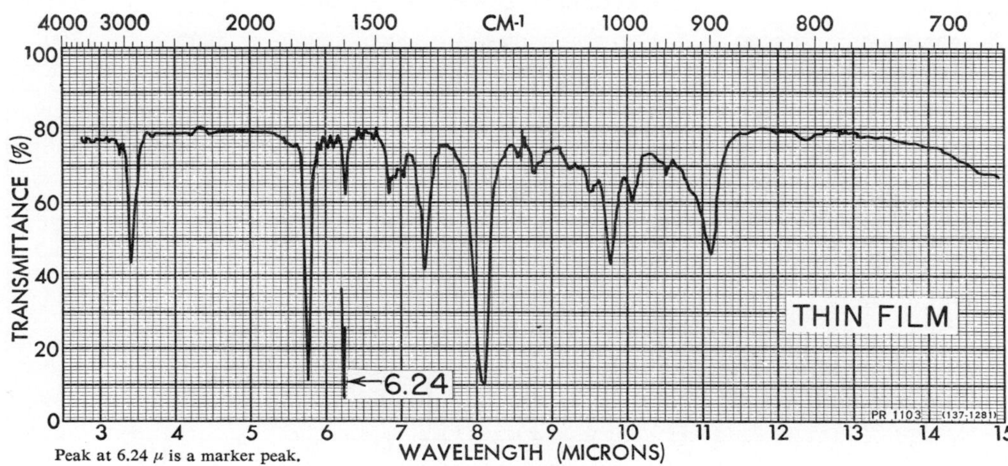

Peak at 6.24 μ is a marker peak.

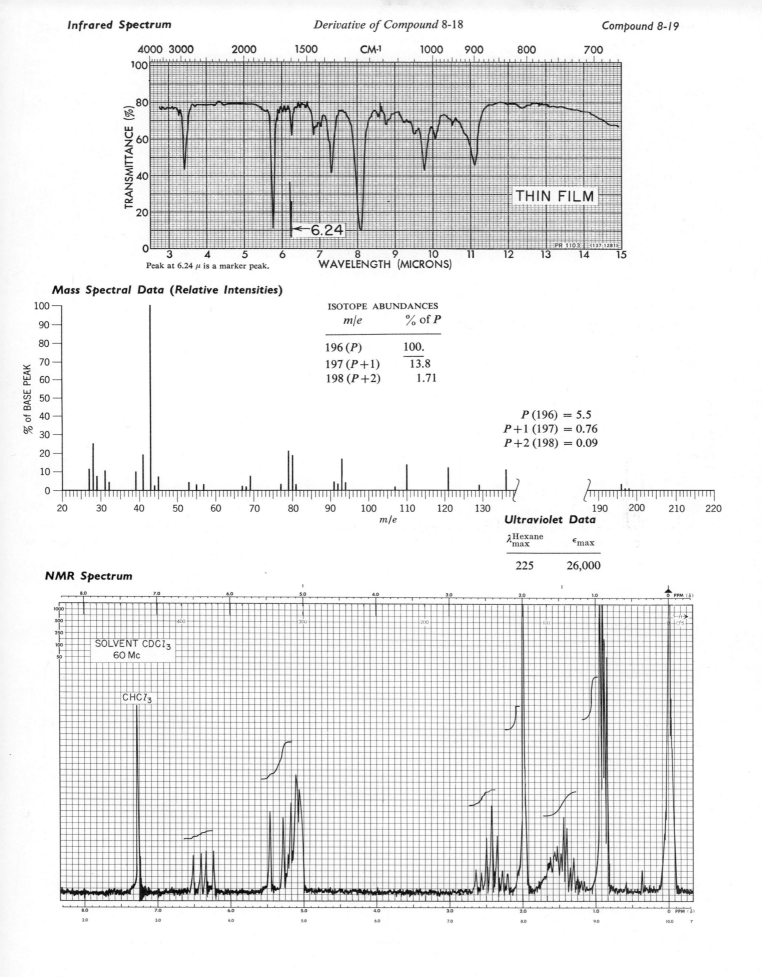

Mass Spectral Data (Relative Intensities)

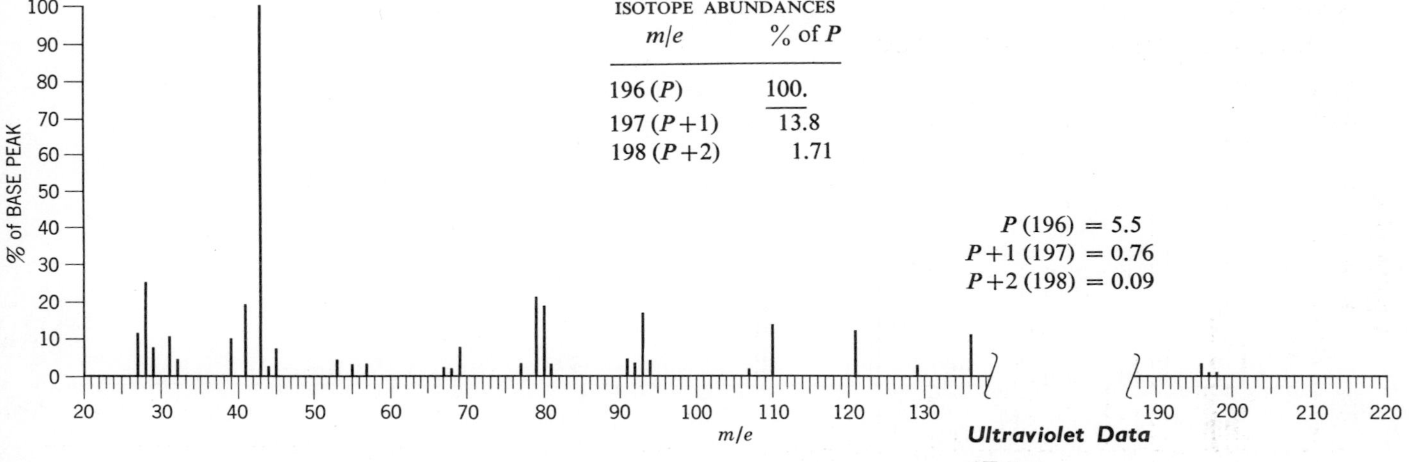

ISOTOPE ABUNDANCES

m/e	% of P
196 (P)	100.
197 ($P+1$)	13.8
198 ($P+2$)	1.71

$P\,(196) = 5.5$
$P+1\,(197) = 0.76$
$P+2\,(198) = 0.09$

Ultraviolet Data

λ_{max}^{Hexane}	ϵ_{max}
225	26,000

NMR Spectrum

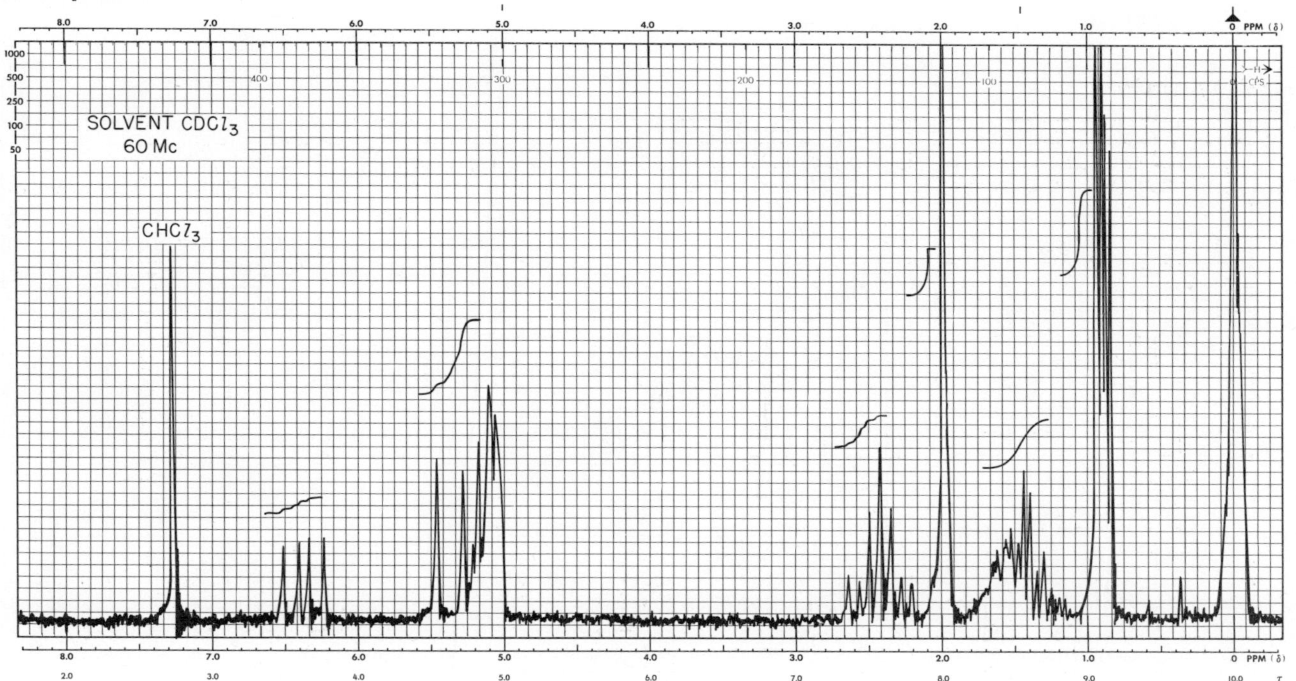

Infrared Spectrum *Compound isolated from ponderosa pine.* *Compound 8-20*

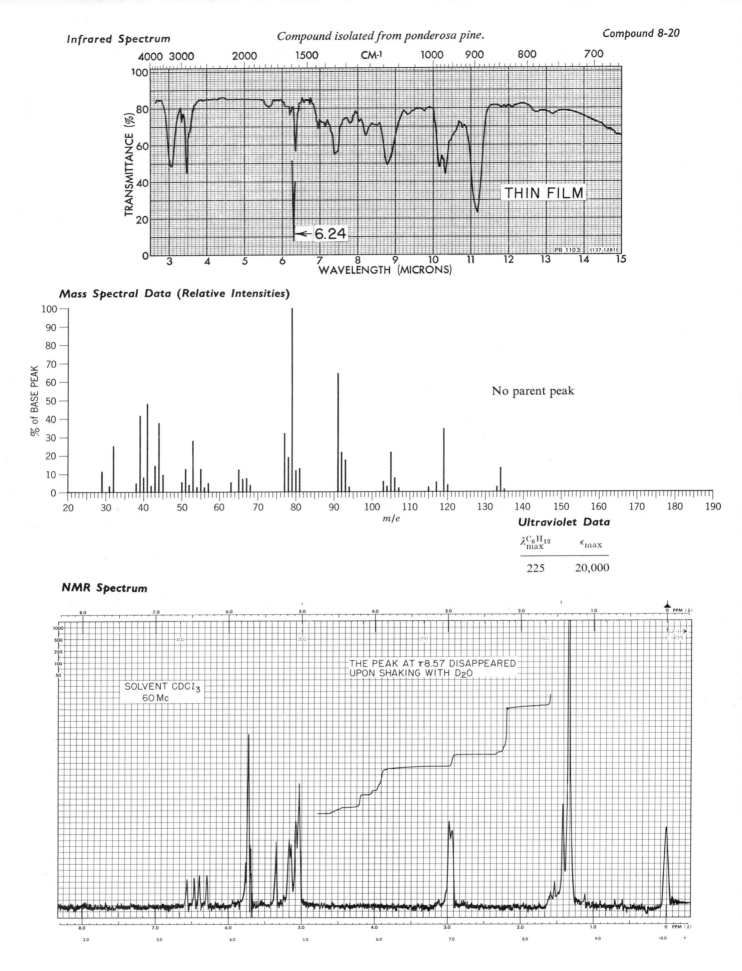

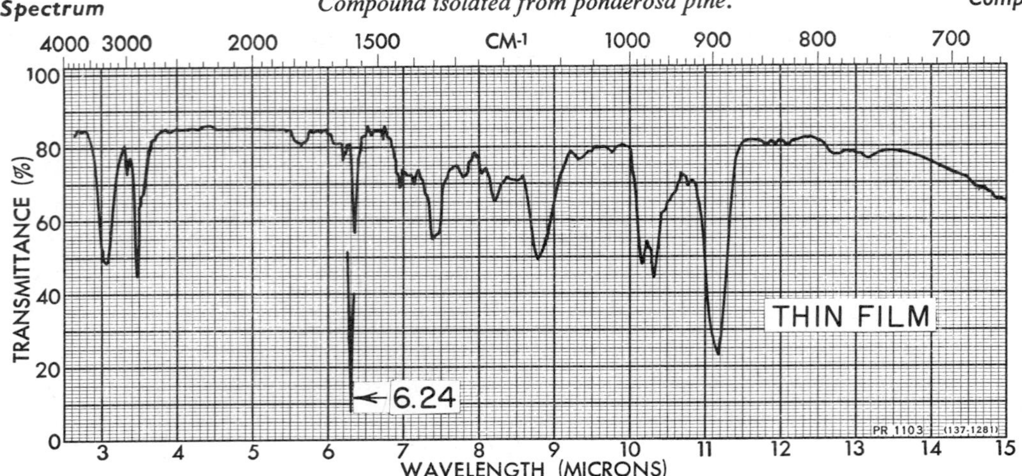

Mass Spectral Data (Relative Intensities)

% of BASE PEAK

No parent peak

m/e

Ultraviolet Data

$\lambda_{max}^{C_6H_{12}}$	ϵ_{max}
225	20,000

NMR Spectrum

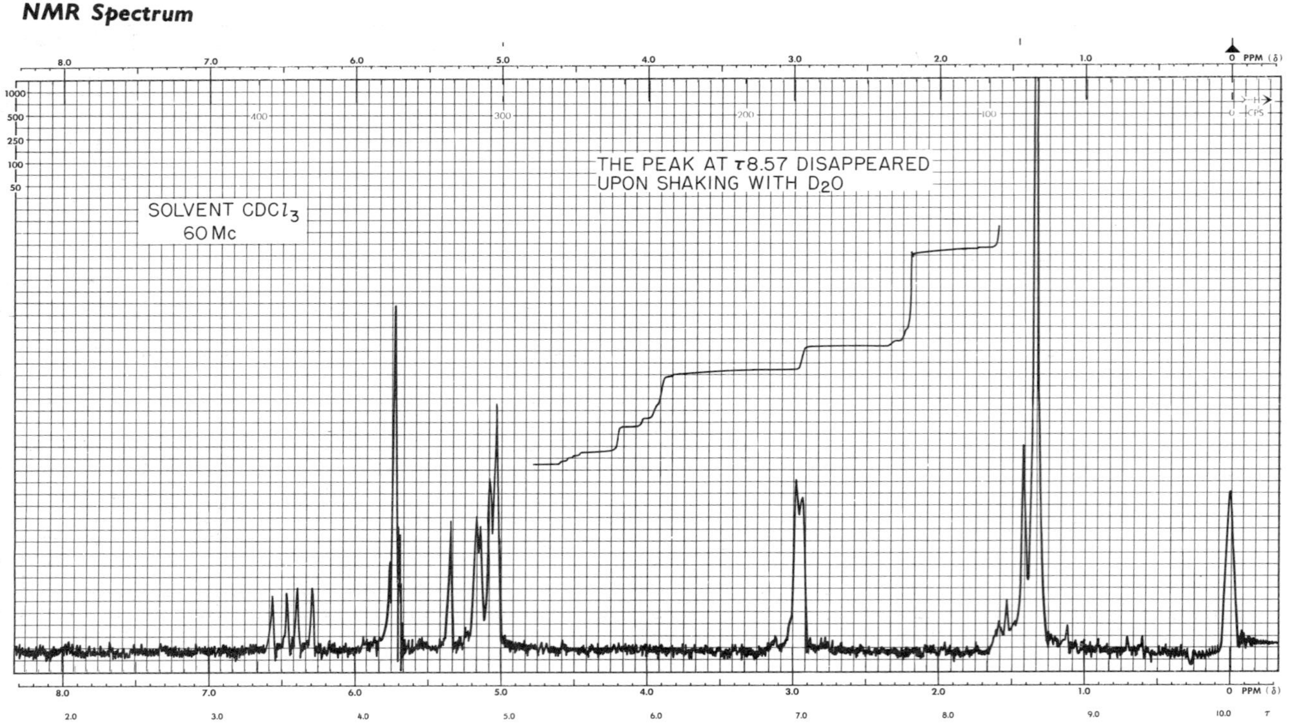

Infrared Spectrum

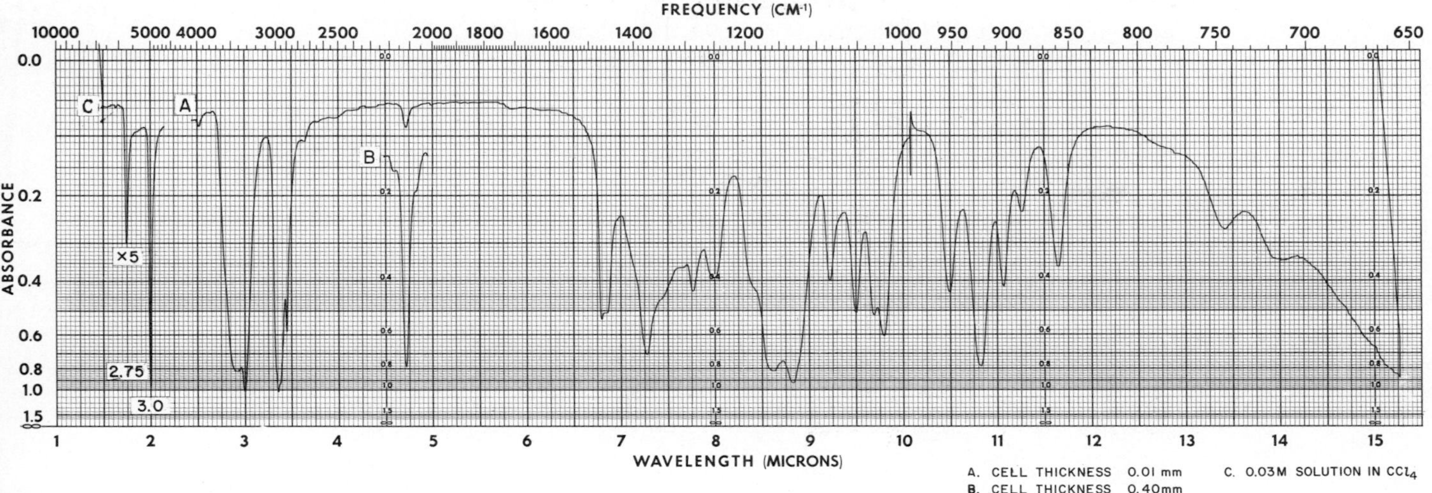

Mass Spectral Data (Relative Intensities)

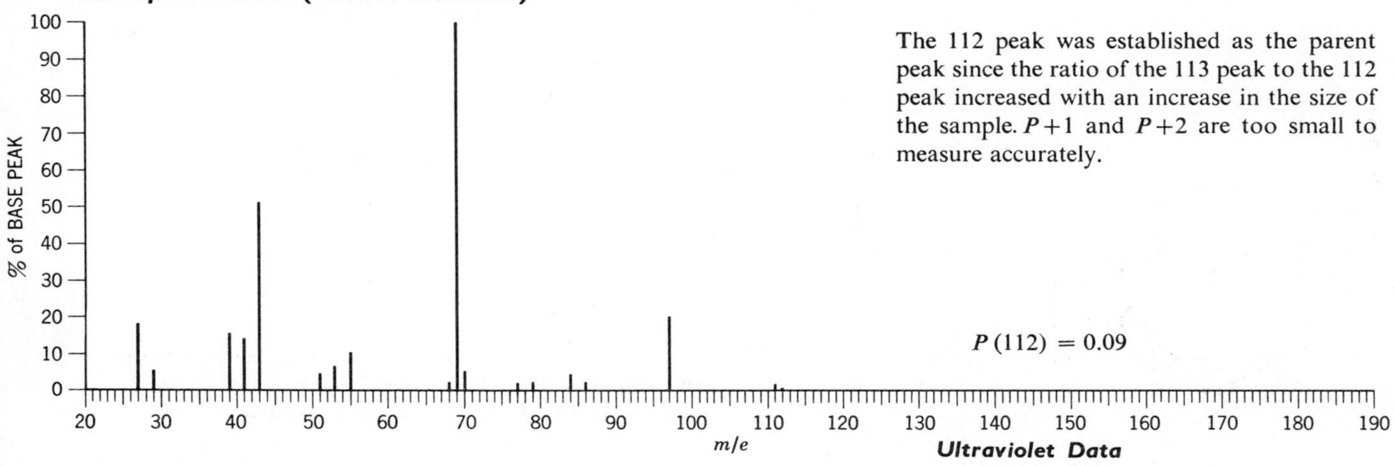

The 112 peak was established as the parent peak since the ratio of the 113 peak to the 112 peak increased with an increase in the size of the sample. $P+1$ and $P+2$ are too small to measure accurately.

$P(112) = 0.09$

Ultraviolet Data

Transparent beyond 200 mμ.

NMR Spectrum

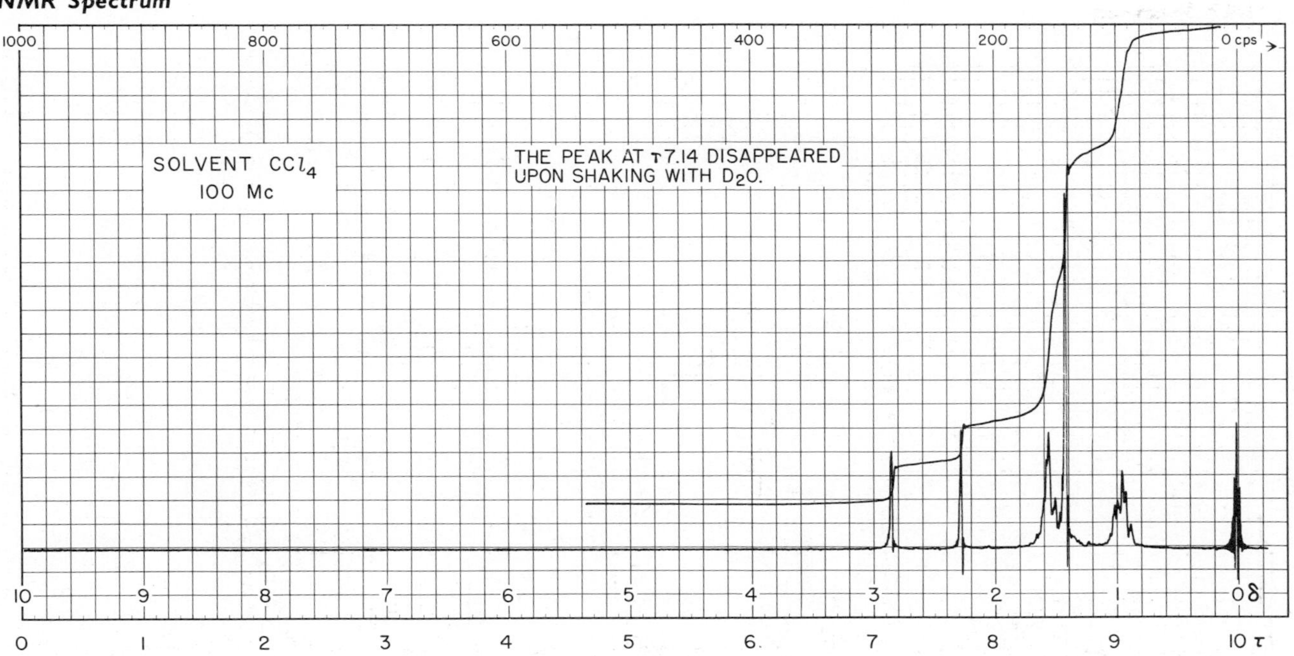

Index

Key: MS = Mass spectrometry
IR = Infrared spectrometry
NMR = Nuclear magnetic resonance spectrometry
UV = Ultraviolet spectrometry

The names of specific compounds appear in **bold** type.

Complete sets of spectra for the following compound classes appear in Chapter 6: